CHARITIES
DIGEST 2014

Selected Charities &
Voluntary Organisations

120th edition

© **Wilmington Business Intelligence 2014**
A division of Wilmington plc

Wilmington

Published by
Wilmington Business Intelligence
6-14 Underwood Street, London, N1 7JQ
Tel: 020 7490 0049   *Fax:* 020 7324 2343
DX: 122030 Finsbury 3

No amount of money can free Maddy from a lifetime on dialysis...

Only a successful transplant can do this.

In the meantime the British Kidney Patient Association strives to improve the quality of life for kidney patients and their families throughout the UK.

Please support us with our ongoing work.

BKPA Donation Appeal

To find out how you can help by making a donation please visit

www.britishkidney-pa.co.uk
or call us on **01420 541424**

BRITISH KIDNEY
Patient ASSOCIATION

improving life for kidney patients

British Kidney Patient Association • 3 The Windmills • St Mary's Close • Turk Street • Alton • GU34 1EF
Registered Charity No. 270288

CONTENTS

GIVING TO CHARITY vi
  Online donations; Gift Aid; Payroll giving; street collections; legacies

ABOUT CHARITIES DIGEST xxii

CHARITIES IN THE UK...xxiii
  Definitions; Registration; setting up a charity; fiscal benefits; Charity Commission;
  Scotland; Northern Ireland; Registry of Friendly Societies

GUIDE TO CODES USED IN THE MAIN ENTRIES...xxvii

NATIONAL AND REGIONAL CHARITIES..1
  Alphabetical List

LOCAL ORGANISATIONS

    Adoption Services 164
    Almshouses 166
    Citizens Advice Bureaux..167
    Community Foundations 189
    Councils for Voluntary Service, Rural Community Councils &
       Federations of Community Organisations 193
    Hospice Services...197
    Free Legal Advice...201
    Law Centres 203
    Voluntary Organisations for Blind & Partially Sighted People 206
    Voluntary Organisations & Residential Homes for Deaf People 213
    Local Associations of and for Disabled People 216
    Racial Equality Councils..222
    Volunteer Centres...225

OBJECT INDEX...243

ADVERTISERS' INDEX 262

Publishing Director
Paula McQuillan

Publisher
Tanya Noronha

Editor
Claudia Rios

Marketing Manager
Cheryl Bosher

Production Manager
Susan Sixtensson

Production Assistant
Annabelle Wood

Publishing Services
Louise Baynes
Jacqueline Hobbs
Stacey Perryment

Divisional Sales Manager
Julia Handley

Business Development Manager
Tatiana Der Avedissian

Senior Sales Executives
Steph Scanlon
Sophia Soltani

Editorial and Advertising:
Tel: 020 7490 0049 *DX:* 122030 Finsbury 3

Orders:
Marketing Department, Wilmington Business Intelligence
Tel: 020 7549 8672 *Fax:* 020 7608 1163

ISBN 978-1-85783-211-2

© Wilmington Business Intelligence 2014
6-14 Underwood Street, London N1 7JQ

Printed in the UK by Polestar Wheatons, Exeter, Devon, U.K.
Typesetting by Alpha Index, Brighton

Wilmington is a member of the Professional Publishers Association

GIVING TO CHARITY

Supporting charities online at www.charitychoice.co.uk

Donating to charities online is becoming an increasingly popular way of supporting your charity. To match the changing needs of charities and donors, the Charity Choice website has a range of features, giving people more ways to give.

Through Charity Choice you can choose how you give, whether that's through donating money, fundraising, volunteering, donating goods, or leaving a gift in your will. You can do all of this with confidence knowing that through our partnership with the Charity Commission, we now provide information on over 160,000 registered charities, including all charities registered in England and Wales, as well as many based in Northern Ireland and Scotland, so if you can't find the charity you're looking for in Charities Digest, rest assured that you'll be able to find it on www.charitychoice.co.uk.

Giving to charity online

Since our original online donations service launched in 2005, we have helped raise almost £7 million for over 3,000 charities. The new Charity Choice website makes it even easier to give money to charities and with our free integrated Gift Aid reclaim system, even more of your donation can reach your charity and support those who need it most.

But you can do more than just donate…

Fundraising events

Charities can use Charity Choice to add their upcoming events to our events calendar - a comprehensive listing of events organised by individual charities and major events which you can take part in and fundraise through.

If you would like to fundraise for your favourite charity and you have come up with your own event or you want to join an organised charity event, you can use Charity Choice to create an online fundraising page. You can personalise your fundraising page with photos and news, then link it to Facebook so you can keep all your family and friends up to date on your progress.

Gifts in wills

In conjunction with Smee & Ford, Charity Choice has been instrumental in securing legacies for charities across the country since its launch over 20 years ago. If you'd like to find out more about leaving a gift in your will to charity, visit www.charitychoice.co.uk/legacies.

Volunteering

Volunteers are the lifeblood of charities. 10 million people in the UK volunteer every year, and without them many would not be able to continue their good work. Using Charity Choice you can volunteer to gain new skills and useful life or work experience, and charities can post their own requests too.

Giving goods

At Charity Choice we understand that there is more than one way to give to charity, so created a platform where individuals and businesses can donate unwanted items, gifts, seconds and samples. It could be anything from an old TV or blankets through to past-season clothes – our charities really appreciate it. Charities can also post requests for items.

REMEMBER THE DONKEYS IN YOUR WILL

THE DONKEY SANCTUARY

PROVIDING A SANCTUARY FOR LIFE FOR DONKEYS AND MULES IN NEED OF REFUGE IN THE UK, IRELAND AND EUROPE

HELP US TO CARE FOR THEM IN THE FUTURE BY REMEMBERING US IN YOUR WILL.

Any donation, no matter how small, will be gratefully received and your name will be inscribed on a Memorial Wall at the Sanctuary in Sidmouth.

THE DONKEY SANCTUARY
Dept CD, Sidmouth,
Devon EX10 0NU

T 01395 578222 **F** 01395 579266
E enquiries@thedonkeysanctuary.org.uk
www.thedonkeysanctuary.org.uk

The Donkey Sanctuary (registered charity number 264818) and its sole corporate trustee, The Donkey Sanctuary Trustee Limited (Company number 07328588) both have their registered office at Slade House Farm, Sidmouth, EX10 0NU Incorporating: The Elisabeth Svendsen Trust for Children and Donkeys (EST); The International Donkey Protection Trust (IDPT).

FRSB
give with confidence

WORKING WORLDWIDE

0238_12_DS

PARTIALLY SIGHTED SOCIETY

Reg'd Charity 254052
Established since 1971

Supporting Partially Sighted People
Helping those with a visual impairment make the best possible use of their remaining sight

Activities
Providing advice and information, free of charge, by letter or phone on aspects of coping with im-paired vision. Supplies Aids to Daily Living such as large print stationary and calendars/diaries, easy to see/talking watches and clocks, easy to see phones and mobiles.

Funding
The Society does not recieve statutory funding, so relies heavily on voluntary donations, bequeasts and legacies.

To make a donation use the donate now facility via Charity Choice. To receive advice or a FREE copy of our Catalogue contact us at:

Partially Sighted Society (Ref: CD)
1 Bennetthorpe, Doncaster, DN2 6AA
Tel: 0844 477 4966   Fax: 0844 477 4969
Website: www.partsight.org.uk

News from The Passage

The Passage is about long term, lasting solutions and seeks to address the root causes that led to a person becoming homeless in the first place so that their cycle of homelessness can be broken for good. Recent achievements include:

- 92% of all new rough sleepers in South Westminster were either supported to return to their home area or linked into support services and accommodation off the streets within 2 contacts by The Passage Street Outreach team during 2011/12.

- The Passage helped 117 entrenched rough sleepers off the streets of South Westminster during the same period.

- For the 3rd year running every client moving on from The Passage's supported accommodation scheme and into their own tenancy has sustained that tenancy.

- Over the last 10 years The Passage has helped nearly 600 homeless people into full time employment.

The Passage has ninety staff and a volunteer to staff ratio of over 3:1. It costs nearly £4 million per year to run The Passage, and half of that income is dependent on voluntary donations. For every £1 donated in voluntary income, over 90% goes straight to our frontline services.

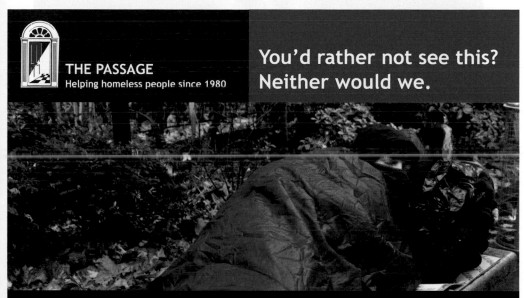

THE PASSAGE
Helping homeless people since 1980

You'd rather not see this? Neither would we.

At The Passage, we'd rather see vulnerable people with a roof over their head, and support at hand, than out and alone on the streets. To that end, our Day Centre opens its doors to up to 200 people every day, whilst our hostel, Passage House, has beds for 40 people and is open every night of the year.

In addition, Montfort House provides 16 studio flats preparing people for independent living. Our aim is to support individuals back into a settled way of life, as well as meeting basic needs.

If you're interested in being a volunteer, would like to make a donation or would simply like more information, we'd love to hear from you.

Give us a call on 0845 880 0689, email info@passage.org.uk or visit www.passage.org.uk

Alternatively, if you would like to make a postal donation, please make cheques payable to The Passage; and send to: St Vincent's Centre, Carlisle Place, London SW1P 1NL.

HELP NOW. Call us on 0845 800 0689

Reg. Charity No.1079764

Our brave faces deserve the *best* places

Birmingham Children's Hospital Charities

Please help us to give children like Mackenzie a world class Cancer Centre...

- **Make a donation;**
- **Take part in a fundraising event;**
- **Remember us in your will; or**
- **Ask your employer to create a partnership with us.** *Thank you*

Tel: 0300 323 1100 Email: bch.charities@bch.nhs.uk

www.bch.org.uk

safe and free

WHALE AND
DOLPHIN
CONSERVATION

Whale and Dolphin Conservation,
Brookfield House, 38 St Paul Street,
Chippenham, Wiltshire SN15 1LJ.
Registered Charity No 1014705
Contact: legacy@whales.org
whales.org

WDC

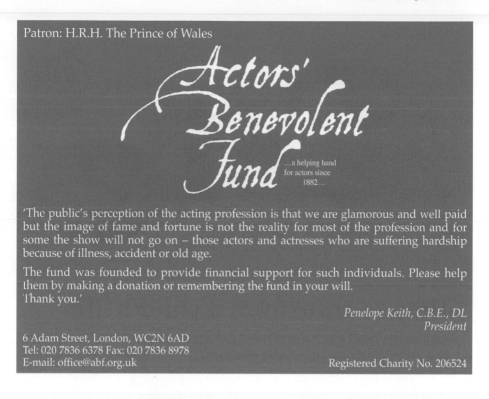

Help to transform a child's life

One man's legacy has been transforming children's lives for over 140 years. And now you can do the same.

When Thomas Bowman Stephenson arrived in London in 1869, he couldn't believe how many homeless children there were. Determined to help, he set up The Children's Home (later the National Children's Home, and then simply NCH) – a place where children would be safe from poverty and crime.

In 2008, we changed our name to one that better describes what we do and what we value – Action for Children.

Some things haven't changed with time

We're still committed to helping the most vulnerable and neglected children and young people break through injustice, deprivation and inequality, so they can achieve their full potential.

With over 650 children's projects we are at the heart of communities - where you live and work.

Our values of passion, equality and hope continue to drive our work in keeping children at the centre of everything we do

The world has moved on in so many ways since Stephenson's day. But some things haven't changed much at all. Our services are as vital now as they have ever been. By remembering Action for Children with a gift in your will, you can help us continue the amazing work Thomas Bowman Stephenson started all those years ago.

Please let us know if we can be of any further help

If you're interested in forming a partnership with your company and Action for Children, please contact corporate@actionforchildren.org.uk

For more information about remembering Action for Children in your will, please contact our Legacy Team.

Email legacies@actionforchildren.org.uk
actionforchildren.org.uk/legacies
Telephone 0300 123 2112

as long as it takes

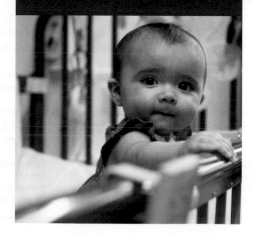

Pain Relief Foundation

RELIEVING CANCER AND OTHER PAIN THROUGH RESEARCH

Pain is a vital alarm bell to the brain, telling us that we have damaged ourselves and that something is wrong. So, when the damage is treated, the pain has normally done its job and usually goes away.

But then there is **chronic pain**, and that is very, very different. No matter how much treatment you give the painful area it doesn't go away; painkilling drugs often don't work; even opioids often don't kill the pain, it is relentless and sufferers are subject to a lifetime of agony!!

Here are just a few hard facts to consider:

FundRaising
Standards Board

- *1 in 7 people in the UK suffer from chronic pain – which does not go away.*
- *Chronic pain is a desperate debilitating pain bringing a life sentence of agony.*
- *Over half of sufferers endure chronic pain all day, every day of their lives.*
- *Many sufferers say they can't remember what it is like not to be in pain.*
- *1 in 5 chronic pain sufferers say their pain is so bad that they just want to die.*
- *Pain stops sufferers from enjoying simple activities like walking, shopping, sleeping, or just playing with their children.*
- *Many thousands of chronic pain sufferers lose their jobs because the pain is so bad that they cannot work.*
- *When a chronic pain sufferer lose their job, they are often on the downward spiral to poverty.*
- *A quarter of chronic pain sufferers are diagnosed with depression.*

We obviously pursue active research on Cancer Pain, because many cancer charities and research organisations are prevented from funding work on cancer pain. Their Trust Deeds specify *'research into the cause and cure of cancer'* and this, of course, **excludes pain**. Yet, for every £3.47p donated to cancer research, chronic pain research receives a donation of less than one (1p) penny.

The Pain Relief Foundation in Liverpool is a research charity working to find the causes of chronic pain; seeking new ways of improving the available treatments; educating all doctors and all other medical professionals on treatment methods to ease the pain; providing information packs for patients, sufferers and carers. If you need help, don't hesitate to contact us.

Research costs money, and there is always an urgent need for more and more research. The Pain Relief Foundation **DOES NOT** receive funding from the NHS or any other Government body. Instead, our vital work depends entirely on donations and the generosity of people like you. Will you please help?? – each and every £1 counts!!

Please help us to end the suffering!! There is a serious lack of funding for chronic pain research and you can help to change that!!

You can make a donation in many ways - making a subscription monthly, quarterly or yearly is usually the easiest way. Send a donation today!!

You can also help to defeat chronic pain by leaving a Legacy in your will. For help and advice on how to pledge a Legacy and what you need to do, just contact us we are here to help and advise you!!

Pain Relief Foundation
Clinical Sciences Centre
University Hospital Aintree
Liverpool L9 7AL

Telephone: 0151 529 5820   Fax: 0151 529 5821
Email   secretary@painrelieffoundation.org.uk
Website   www.painrelieffoundation.org.uk
Charity No   277732

REMEMBER THE DONKEYS IN YOUR WILL

THE DONKEY SANCTUARY

PROVIDING SANCTUARY FROM SUFFERING FOR WORKING DONKEYS IN DEVELOPING COUNTRIES. OUR MOBILE TEAMS PROVIDE VETERINARY TREATMENT, ADVICE AND TRAINING.

HELP US TO CARE FOR THEM IN THE FUTURE BY REMEMBERING US IN YOUR WILL.

Any donation, no matter how small, will be gratefully received and your name will be inscribed on a Memorial Wall at the Sanctuary in Sidmouth.

THE DONKEY SANCTUARY
Dept CDO, Sidmouth,
Devon EX10 0NU

T 01395 578222 **F** 01395 579266
E enquiries@thedonkeysanctuary.org.uk
www.thedonkeysanctuary.org.uk

The Donkey Sanctuary (registered charity number 264818) and its sole corporate trustee, The Donkey Sanctuary Trustee Limited (Company number 07328588) both have their registered office at Slade House Farm, Sidmouth, EX10 0NU Incorporating: The Elisabeth Svendsen Trust for Children and Donkeys (EST); The International Donkey Protection Trust (IDPT).

give with confidence

WORKING WORLDWIDE

0240_12_DS

ABOUT CHARITIES DIGEST

Charities Digest was first published in 1882 for the information and guidance of those concerned with charitable organisations, with the intention that its reference section should be updated and reprinted annually. Information included in the Digest is submitted to us by charities and is researched and updated each year.

Charities Digest is published by Wilmington Business Intelligence.

Registered Charities

There are over 160,000 registered charities in the UK. Charities Digest concentrates on national and regional charities. These charities appear in the alphabetical section, which forms the larger part of this book. Key local organisations are also listed. Most of them are registered charities, but we also include some charities which are excepted or exempt from registration under the Charities Act. Some Scottish and Northern Irish charities are also listed. A small number of organisations whose purposes are not exclusively charitable but whose addresses may be of assistance to users of the Digest also feature in the directory. We also include Object Codes to indicate charities prepared to offer grants and other financial services.

How the book works

Charities are listed in alphabetical order.

The basic information for each charity follows a standard format, which includes the name of the organisation; the date of foundation; the charity registration number or other information about charitable status; and their address and telephone number. Some charities also provide contact names, while other listings include bank details for donation purposes. Many entries will also feature additional text about their causes, aims, and history. The back of the book features an index which lists selected charities according to their main charitable objectives.

Wilmington Business Intelligence makes every effort to ensure that all organisations included are bona fide, but inclusion in or omission from Charities Digest does not indicate approval or otherwise by Wilmington Business Intelligence.

New entries are welcomed for consideration. For more information, please contact crios@wilmington.co.uk.

Other voluntary organisations

Charities Digest also contains updated directory listings of other relevant organisations that help people in need, including: Citizens Advice Bureaux, Community Foundations, Voluntary Organisations for Blind & Partially Sighted People, and Hospice Services. These listings are located in the second half of this publication and are arranged by region.

Acknowledgements

This book is produced with the assistance of many people, notably the Charity Commission, the Office of the Scottish Charity Regulator, and the Charity Commission for Northern Ireland.

We are also indebted to the co-ordinating organisations who annually assist in the updating of information in the listings of local organisations at the back of this volume, including: Action on Hearing Loss (previously known as RNID); Action with Communities in Rural England (ACRE); the Almshouse Association; the Community Foundation Network; Community Matters; DIAL UK (Scope); Disability Rights UK; the Equality & Human Rights Commission (EHRC); Help the Hospices; the Law Centres Federation; the National Association for Voluntary & Community Action (NAVCA); the National Association of Citizens Advice Bureaux; Northern Ireland Council for Voluntary Action (NICVA); the Royal National Institute for the Blind (RNIB); Volunteering England; and Wales Council for Voluntary Action (WCVA).

CHARITIES IN THE UK

Definitions

To qualify as a charity an organisation must exist for charitable purposes. The Charities Act 2006 lists purposes that can be defined as charitable, which include the relief of poverty, the advancement of education, the advancement of religion, or for other purposes beneficial to the community, such as community development or urban regeneration.

A full list can be viewed in the text of the Act itself or online at www.legislation.gov.uk.

The definitions themselves are at some times vague and have been the subject matter of extensive judicial interpretation, so legal advice is essential in the formation of any trust or organisation which intends to register as a charity.

The law governing registration applies to England and Wales only. Charities in Scotland are regulated by the Office of the Scottish Charity Regulator (OSCR) and Northern Irish charities are in the process of being registered by the new Charity Commission for Northern IReland.

ENGLAND AND WALES

Registration and exemptions

Section 3 of the Charities Act 2006 requires all charities to register with the Charity Commission, with specified exceptions. Charities excepted or exempt from registration are:

(a) any charity comprised in the second schedule to the 2006 Act referred to as an "exempt charity"
(b) any charity excepted by order or regulations
(c) any charity whose income from all sources does not exceed £5,000 in any year.

No charity is required to be registered in respect of any registered place of worship.

Charities exempt from the Commissioners' regulatory powers, although they may request the Commissions' advice or guidance, include certain universities and colleges, the British Museum, the Church Commissioners and certain institutions administered by them, and registered societies within the Industrial and Provident Societies Act 1965 or the Friendly Societies Act 1974. The Registry of Friendly Societies now falls under the remit of the Financial Services Authority. For more information contact them at 25 The North Colonnade, Canary Wharf, London E14 5HS Tel: 0845 606 1234 Website: www.fsa.gov.uk.

Setting up a charity: preliminary steps

In every case, before seeking registration and obtaining legal advice to that end, any founders of a would-be charity should consider the following guidance offered by the Charity Commission before consulting an expert adviser:

- Is a new charity the best way forward?
- Are there existing charities with the same purposes and activities as yours?
- Do you understand how a charity must operate?

After forming clear, positive ideas of the answers to these questions, founders should move forward.

Setting up a charity: secondary steps

Assuming it is decided to seek registration, the founders should consult the National Council for Voluntary Organisations (NCVO). The NCVO is based at Regent's Wharf, 8 All Saints Street, London N1 9RL, Tel: 020 7713 6161. Local voluntary councils can be found on the National Association for Voluntary and Community Action (NAVCA) website, www.navca.org.uk, while in Wales if would be best to use the Wales Council for Voluntary Action (WCVA), www.wcva.org.uk. It would be useful to consult the Charity Commission's official guidance, 'Registering as a Charity' (CC21) which sets out the legal requirements and procedure for registration.

It may also be necessary consult a qualified lawyer who has knowledge and experience of the workings of charity law and charities, or to engage a solicitor. Suitable legal advice can be found from Citizens Advice (www.citizensadvice.org.uk), or the Charity Law Association (CLA), who are online at www.charitylawassociation.org.uk).

Setting up a charity: governance

The would-be founders would also need to draft of a governing document for the charity in the form of a Constitution, deed, set of rules, or memorandum and articles of association.

In most cases this should be done by the founders' legal adviser.

Founders would also have to appoint trustees, who would form the charity's board. They would be recruited as per the process for standard job recruitment, although trustees are generally unpaid.

Potential charities are also required to prove that their existence would benefit the public. This means that they have to fit in to the Charities Act 2006 as having a charitable purpose. More guidance on this matter is available from the Charity Commission.

Before registering with the Commission, charities will also be required to choose a name, which will appear on the Register of Charities. It is advised that names are made as specific and unique as possible.

Setting up a charity: registration

Once these measures are all in place, founders can, if necessary, register with the Charity Commission. This can now be done free and quickly online, and the Commission hope to have most applications completed within 10 working days.

Charities with an income of under £5,000 per year are not required to register, and should instead apply for tax relief from Her Majesty's Revenue & Customs (HMRC).

Fiscal benefits

Charities, whether registered or not, may be entitled to certain fiscal benefits such as relief from income tax, corporation tax, capital gains tax and local council tax. Applications and enquiries regarding relief from income tax or capital gains tax should be addressed to HMRC at: St John's House, Merton Road, Bootle, Merseyside L69 9BB, Helpline: 0845 302 0203, or via email charities@hmrc.gov.uk.

Enquiries about all aspects of VAT as applied to charities should be addressed to the Collector of the local Customs and Excise VAT Office.

Fundraising from the public and from major sources of funds for voluntary organisations (e.g. charitable trusts and business firms) will be much easier if the organisation is a registered charity. In particular, many charitable trusts are prevented by their constitutions from making grants to other than registered charities.

THE CHARITY COMMISSION FOR ENGLAND & WALES

The Charity Commissioners have been in existence since 1853, and in 2013 now offer a large amount of their services via their website, www.charitycommission.gov.uk.

The Commission registers and regulates charities in England and Wales. It offers them advice and provide a wide range of services and guidance to help them run as effectively as possible. It also keeps the online Register of Charities, which provides information about each of the thousands of registered charities in England and Wales.

The Commission's particular functions include the maintenance of a central register of charities, the institution of inquiries, the protection of the endowments of charities, control of the taking of legal proceedings, the making of schemes and orders to modernise the purposes and administrative machinery of charities, and the giving of advice to trustees. The Commission acts as both a regulator and an enabler and stresses its support role in relation to charity trustees and encourages them to contact the Commission at an early stage if in doubt or difficulty. One of its stated objectives is to increase public trust and confidence in charities and it encourages charities to enhance their accountability and transparency in a range of ways. It does not provide funding and may not act in the administration of a charity.

The Charities Act 2006

The Charities Act 2006 was passed on the 8th November 2006 and its various provisions came into force from 2007 onwards.

The new income level for registration is £5,000, and all charities with a lower income are exempt. Previously, small charities with an income of £1,000 or less were required to register if they had a permanent endowment or the use or occupation of land. The Act underlined that all charities must exist for the public benefit, and the Commission has a new objective to promote understanding and awareness of the public benefit requirement.

The Act also ensured that both exempt and excepted charities are monitored for their compliance to charity law. Previously excepted charities such as some religious charities, armed forces charities and Boy Scout and Girl Guides, may also now have to register with the Commission if they have an annual income of £100,000 or more. Those with a lower income do not have to register but still come under the jurisdiction of the Commission.

The new Act liberalised and extended the powers for charities to make changes to their purposes, and allowed smaller charities to take certain actions without permission from the Commission. It also proposed the creation of a Register of Mergers to be held by the Commission to help ensure that legacies and donations left to charities which subsequently merged are transferred to the new charity. A new structure for charities was created by the Act, the Charitable Incorporated Organisation (CIO). This allows charities which want a corporate structure to have the benefits of incorporation without the burden of dual regulation with Companies House and the Commission.

The Act also created a new Charity Tribunal which allowed charities to appeal against decisions made by the Commission. The Charity Tribunal has since merged with HM Courts Service.

Contacting the Charity Commission

The Charity Commission prefers to receive communication via email, and have a form on their website that enables users to do so. The Commission is in the process of moving all of its services online, and while this will take quite some time, charities can also update their details and submit accounts through the website, www.charitycommission.gov.uk.

The Commission can be contacted by telephone on 0845 300 0218, or by textphone on 0845 300 0219. They can also be reached by post at Charity Commission Direct, PO Box 1227, Liverpool L69 3UG.

Guidance

The Commission offers its guidance in hard copy if you contact it directly. It also features an extensive guidance database on its website.

SCOTLAND

Only a body granted charitable status by the Office of the Scottish Charity Regulator (OSCR) or one recognised by the Charity Commission of England and Wales may represent itself as a charity in Scotland. OSCR is the body responsible for supervising and regulating charities in Scotland and they publish an index of recognised charities on their website, www.oscr.org.uk.

Under existing legislation, charities with an income of over £25,000 must complete as Annual Return form and a Supplementary Monitoring Return form. Charities must also complete and file an Annual Report to OSCR within 9 months of the end of their financial year. Charities that fail to comply with this measure are considered for removal from the Register. OSCR also perform a continuous review of their Register as per the Charities and Trustee Investment (Scotland) Act 2005, which allows them to confirm charities' details from time to time.

While OSCR doesn't publish listings of a charity's trustees as the Charity Commission does, trustees are responsible for keeping charity details up-to-date.

To make general enquiries, a complaint, or to set up a new charity, please contact OSCR at: 2nd Floor, Quadrant House, 9 Riverside Drive, Dundee DD1 4NY, Tel: 01382 220446, info@oscr.org.uk.

NORTHERN IRELAND

The Charities Act (NI) 2008 announced the creation of the Charity Commission for Northern Ireland (CCNI). It was launched as Northern Ireland's independent regulator in 2010. The Charity Commission for Northern Ireland has published a list of all Northern Irish charities falling within its power on its website, www.charitycommissionni.org.uk.

The CCNI has replaced the The Department for Social Development (DSD), which was previously the the main charity authority in Northern Ireland.

At the time of going to press, the CCNI itself is not yet fully operational and is still putting its organisational structures into place, but it does offer a range of services through its website. As a result, the resources it has made available to the public are not as detailed or in-depth as those available for the Charity Commission or OSCR.

The CCNI is based at: 257 Lough Road, Lurgan, Craigavon BT66 6NQ, and can be reached via email at admin@charitycommissionni.org.uk or by phone on 028 9051 5490.

GUIDE TO CODES USED IN THE MAIN ENTRIES

Objects

1A	Grants made to individuals
1B	Grantmaking organisation
2	Member organisation
3	Services Provider
A	Grants of money of varying amounts
B	Pensions, benefits or scholarships
C	Sheltered accommodation & hostels
D	Housing
E	Day Centres
F	Advice, counselling, information
G	Education, training
H	Publications and/or free literature
I	Crime prevention
J	Co-ordination, liaison
K	Workshops & other employment
L	Casework, welfare
M	Care equipment, practical services
N	Medical treatment, nursing
O	Rehabilitation, therapy
P	Social activities & relationships
Q	Adoption, fostering
R	Missionary & outreach work at home or abroad
S	Cultural pursuits
T	Reconciliation
U	Overseas aid or service
V	Holidays
W	Medical research
X	Protection against domestic violence
Y	Relief of poverty
Z	Social welfare and casework
W1	Animals and/or birds
W2	Conservation & environment
W3	Children, young people
W4	Older people
W5	Disabled people
W6	Blind people
W7	Deaf people
W8	Women
W9	Armed services & ex-services
W10	Ethnic minorities
W11	Ex professional or trade workers
W12	Museums, memorials
W13	Merchant Navy & Fishing Fleet
W14	Residential care
W15	Families
W16	Homeless people

Charity Registration

CR	Registered under the Charities Act 2006
Exempt	Excepted or exempt from registration
FS	Exempt under Friendly Societies Act/Provident Societies Act
SC	Scottish Charity
XN	Northern Irish Charity

Ensuring their good memories continue...

As people become older, their lives should continue to be fulfilling, but that's not always the case. At Abbeyfield we do everything we can to ensure our residents enjoy their lives, have choices, remain as independent as possible, but receive support when needed.

Founded in 1956, Abbeyfield is a leading UK charity providing housing and support for lonely and frail older people. A gift in your Will could make a lasting contribution to the future of many isolated older people.

For information on leaving a gift to Abbeyfield, please contact Val Langford on 01727 734125.

Abbeyfield

PLEASE THINK OF ABBEYFIELD IN YOUR WILL

Abbeyfield,
St Peter's House, 2 Bricket Road,
St Albans AL1 3JW
Email legacies@abbeyfield.com
www.abbeyfield.com
Registered charity number 200719

Numeric

21ST CENTURY LEARNING INITIATIVE (UK), THE
Founded: 1991 CR1003067
President: Mr John Abbott
Bridge House, 15 Argyle Street, Bath, Bath & North East Somerset BA2 4BQ
Tel: 01225 333376
Objects: W3,G,H

42ND STREET - WORKING WITH YOUNG PEOPLE UNDER STRESS
Founded: 1990 CR702687
Director: Ms Vera Martins
2nd Floor, Swan Buildings, 20 Swan Street, Manchester, Greater Manchester M4 5JW
Tel: .... 0161 832 0169; 0161 832 0170 Helpline
Fax: 0161 839 5424
Email: .... theteam@42ndstreet.org.uk
Objects: F,W6,W3,W7,W5,G,W10,O,3,P,W8

1989 WILAN CHARITABLE TRUST, THE
Founded: 1990 CR802749
Trustee: Mr Alexander Fettes
C/O The Community Foundation Serving Tyne & Wear & Northumberland, Cale Cross, 156 Pilgrim Street, Newcastle upon Tyne, Tyne & Wear NE1 6SU
Objects: W6,W3,F,W7,W5,G,W10,1B,W4,P,W8

A

ABBEYFIELD (BRISTOL) SOCIETY
CR257532
29 Alma Vale Road (CC), Clifton, Bristol BS8 2HL
Tel: 0117 973 6997
Fax: 0117 923 8863
Email: .... e-mail@abbeyfield-bristol.co.uk

ABBEYFIELD - ENHANCING THE QUALITY OF LIFE FOR OLDER PEOPLE
Founded: 1956 CR200719
St Peter's House, 2 Bricket Road, St Albans, Hertfordshire AL1 3JW
Tel: 01727 734125
Email: .... v.langford@abbeyfield.com
Object: W4
Abbeyfield exists to make older people's lives easier and more fulfilling. Since 1956 Abbeyfield has been providing housing, support and companionship to older people across the UK and internationally. Abbeyfield helps older people enjoy later life and offers a range of care and housing as well as supporting people in the wider community.
Legacy donations are vital to our work and help us build new houses, enhance existing ones and provide extra services that make a positive difference to the lives of older people now, and in the future.
See advert on this page

ABF THE SOLDIERS' CHARITY
Founded: 1944 CR1146420; SC039189
Controller: Major General M D Regan
Mountbarrow House, 6-20 Elizabeth Street, London SW1W 9RB

Tel: 0207 901 8908
Fax: 0845 241 4821
Email: . . . . enquiries@armybenfund.org
Objects: W9,A

ABILITYNET ADVICE AND INFORMATION - UK'S LEADING AUTHORITY ON DISABILITY AND COMPUTING
Founded: 1992 CR1067673
Chief Executive: Mr S Kennedy
PO Box 94, Warwick, Warwickshire CV34 5WS
Tel: 01926 312847
Fax: 01926 407425
Email: . . . . enquiries@abilitynet.org.uk
Objects: F,W6,W3,W7,W5,W4,3

THE ACADEMY OF THE SCIENCE OF ACTING AND DIRECTING
Founded: 1992 CR1014419
Trustee: Dr Helen Pierpoint BSc, phD
9-15 Elthorne Road, Archway, London N19 4AJ
Tel: 020 7272 0027
Objects: W3,G,3

ACOPS
See Advisory Committee on Protection of the Sea (ACOPS)

ACORNS CHILDREN'S HOSPICE, WEST MIDLANDS
Founded: 1986 CR700859
Chief Executive Officer: Mr John Overton
Acorns House, 4B Truemans Heath Lane,
Birmingham, West Midlands B47 5QB

Tel: 0121 248 4800
Fax: 0121 248 4816
Email: . . . . legacies@acorns.org.uk
Objects: F,W3,G,N,3

ACRE (ACTION WITH COMMUNITIES IN RURAL ENGLAND)
Founded: 1987 CR1061568
Chief Executive: Ms Sylvia Brown
Somerford Court, Somerford Road, Cirencester, Gloucestershire GL7 1TW
Tel: 01285 653477
Fax: 01285 654537
Email: . . . . acre@acre.org.uk
Objects: F,W3,J,G,D,2,W4,H,W8

ACTION AGAINST MEDICAL ACCIDENTS
Founded: 1982 CR299123
Chief Executive: Mr Peter Walsh
44 High Street, Croydon, London CRO 1YB
Tel: 0845 123 2352 Mon-Fri 10am-5pm; 020 8688 9555 admin line
Email: . . . . advice@avma.org.uk
Objects: F,W3,W5,G,W4,H,3

ACTION FOR BLIND PEOPLE - PART OF RNIB GROUP
Founded: 1857 CR205913
Chief Executive: Mr Stephen Remington
Director of Development: Mr Andy D. Taylor
14-16 Verney Road, London SE16 3DZ
Tel: 020 7635 4919
Fax: 020 7635 4892
Email: . . . . supportercare@afbp.org.uk
Objects: F,W6,W5,G,1A,A,V,D,B,H,3,C,K

ACTION FOR CHILDREN

CR1097940; SC038002

Chief Executive: Dame Clare Tickell

3 The Boulevard, Ascot Road, Watford,
Hertfordshire WD18 8AG

Tel: 01923 361500; 0300 123 2112
Email: .... ask.us@actionforchildren.org.uk
Web: .... http://www.actionforchildren.org.uk

Objects: Q,W3,E,3,P,Z

Action for Children supports the UK's most vulnerable and neglected children and young people for as long as it takes to transform their lives. With over 650 children's projects, 50 local fundraisers and volunteer coordinators, as well as a regional PR team, we are at the heart of communities – right where your staff and customers live and work.

To find out how we can tailor the ideal partnership for your company, to read more about partnerships with companies such as Barclays, E.ON and Dell, or meet the team, do have a look at our corporate pages http://www.actionforchildren.org.uk/get-involved/companies If you believe every child deserves a chance to achieve their potential then please support Action for Children. Get in touch with our Corporate Development team and help us transform lives.

ACTION FOR DYSPHASIC ADULTS

See Speakability (Action for Dysphasic Adults)

ACTION FOR KIDS CHARITABLE TRUST

Action For Kids
TOWARDS INDEPENDENCE

Founded: 1991 CR1068841
Ability House, 15a Tottenham Lane, Hornsey,
London N8 9DJ
Tel: 020 8347 8111
Fax, ... 020 8347 3482
Email: .... info@actionforkids.org
See advert on previous page

ACTION FOR SICK CHILDREN (NATIONAL ASSOCIATION FOR THE WELFARE OF CHILDREN IN HOSPITAL)

CR296295

Chairman: Mrs Pamela Barnes

3 Abbey Business Centre, Keats Lane, Earl Shilton, Leicestershire LE9 7DQ

Tel: 01455 845600

Objects: F,W3,J,G,2,H

ACTION MEDICAL RESEARCH

Founded: 1952 CR208701; SC039284
Chief Executive: Mr Simon Moore CB
Head of Communications: Mr Andrew Proctor
Vincent House, North Parade, Horsham, West Sussex RH12 2DP

Tel: 01403 210406
Fax: 01403 210541
Email: .... info@action.org.uk

Objects: W3,W5,1A,A,1B,N,W4,H,W8

ACTION ON ADDICTION

Founded: 2007 CR1117988
Chief Executive: Mrs Lesley King-Lewis
Clouds House, East Knoyle, Salisbury, Wiltshire SP3 6BE

Tel: 01747 832028
Email: .... action@aona.co.uk

Objects: F,W6,W3,G,W10,N,O,3

ACTION ON HEARING LOSS

Founded: 1911 CR207720; SC038926
Director of Fundraising: Mr Martin Bishop
Executive Director of Development: Ellie Gray
Director of Communications: Mr Brian Lamb OBE
19-23 Featherstone Street, London EC1Y 8SL

Tel: . 020 7296 8114; Textphone: 020 7296 8114
Fax: 020 7296 8129
Email: .... legacies@hearingloss.org.uk
Web: .... www.hearingloss.org.uk

Ten million people in the UK are affected by hearing loss and this is estimated to rise to 14.5 million by 2031. Hearing loss has a huge impact on people's lives. Struggling to communicate can affect confidence, opportunities and relationships. It can leave people feeling frustrated, humiliated, lonely and isolated. Action on Hearing Loss supports people with all levels of hearing loss including Tinnitus, from mild to profound. A donation or a gift in your will can help them stay connected to the world around them and to the people they love. We are committed to providing support, action and a cure.

Support:

• Offering independent information through leaflets, our website and freephone helplines.

• Developing and testing new technology.

• Giving face-to-face advice on how to get the best from hearing aids.

• Providing services such as sign language interpreters to help deaf and hearing people communicate with each other.

• Offering equipment to make life easier, such as flashing smoke alarms and doorbells.

• Providing care services for people who are deaf with additional needs such as blindness, physical disabilities or autism.

Action:

• Offering hearing checks by telephone, online, iPhone and in local communities.

• Lobbying for a national screening service for everyone over 55 so they can take early action if their hearing starts to deteriorate.

• Campaigning to challenge stigma, uphold rights and convince people of all ages to value and protect their hearing. Our Don't Lose The Music campaign reaches thousands of young people.

Cure:

• Funding biomedical research. Recent scientific breakthroughs we have funded could one day lead to treatments that restore natural hearing. A gift in your will could help us achieve our ultimate goal – a cure for deafness and tinnitus.

ACTION RESEARCH

See Action Medical Research

ACTION WITH COMMUNITIES IN RURAL ENGLAND

See ACRE (Action with Communities in Rural England)

ACTIONAID

Founded: 1972 CR274467
Director: Mr Salil Shetty
C.E.O: Mr Ramesh Singh
Hamlyn House, Macdonald Road, Archway,
London N19 5PG

Tel: 020 7561 7561
Fax: 020 7272 0899
Email: . . . . mail@actionaid.org.uk
Object: U

ACTORS' BENEVOLENT FUND
Founded: 1882 CR206524
General Secretary: Mr Willie Bicket Esq
6 Adam Street, London WC2N 6AD
Tel: 020 7836 6378
Fax: 020 7836 8978
Email: . . . . office@abf.org.uk
Web: . . . . www.actorsbenevolentfund.co.uk
Objects: F,W11,1A,A,2
The Actors' Benevolent Fund was founded as a national charity over 125 years ago by the distinguished actor Sir Henry Irving and a group of his friends. The Fund assists actors unable to work because of accidents, illness or old age and helps in a variety of ways, all of which are geared towards maintaining independence and improving quality of life. Beneficiaries include the very elderly, those with chronic conditions like arthritis or mental illness, and those suffering from all the major life threatening diseases like cancer, heart disease and AIDS.
Our support includes:
• Financial awards to assist people with basic living costs;
• Special purchases such as customised equipment to help with mobility and independence;
• Help with convalescent costs following serious illness or a spell in hospital;
Donations and Legacies are vital to continue our work. For more information please contact the General Secretary.

ADDICTION RECOVERY AGENCY
Founded: 1987 CR1002224
Business Manager: Mr David Page
61 Queen Charlotte Street, Bristol BS1 4HQ
Tel: 0117 930 0282
Fax: 0117 929 4810
Email: . . . . info@addictionrecovery.org.uk
Objects: F,E,D,O,3,C

ADJUTANT GENERAL'S CORPS REGIMENTAL ASSOCIATION
Founded: 1992 CR1035939
Regimental Headquarters, Gould House, Worthy Down, Winchester, Hampshire SO21 2RG
Tel: 01962 887254; 01962 887435
Fax: 01962 887690
Email: . . . . secretary@agcorps.org
Objects: W9,1A,A,V,2,P

ADOPTION UK - SUPPORTING ADOPTIVE FAMILIES BEFORE, DURING AND AFTER ADOPTION
CR326654
Linden House, 55 The Green, Banbury, Oxfordshire OX16 9AB
Tel: . . . 0844 848 7900 (Helpline); 01295 752240
Fax: 01295 752241
Email: . . . . enquiries@adoptionuk.org.uk
Objects: Q,2

ADREF LTD
Founded: 1990 CR703130
The Company Secretary
54-55 Bute Street, Aberdare, Rhondda Cynon Taff CF44 7LD
Tel: 01685 878755

ADVISORY COMMITTEE ON PROTECTION OF THE SEA (ACOPS)
Founded: 1952 CR290776
Assistant Executive Director: Mr Terry Jones
Executive Director: Dr Viktor Sebek
11 Dartmouth Street, London SW1H 9BN
Tel: 020 7799 3033
Fax: 020 7799 2933
Email: . . . . info@acops.org.uk
Objects: W2,G,H

ADVOCATES FOR ANIMALS / ST ANDREWS FUND FOR ANIMALS
SC041299
10 Queensferry Street, Edinburgh EH2 4PG
Tel: 0131 225 6039
Fax: 0131 220 6377
Email: . . . . info@advocatesforanimals.org

AECC CHIROPRACTIC COLLEGE
CR306289
13-15 Parkwood Road, Bournemouth BH5 2DF
Tel: 01202 436200
Fax: 01202 436312
Email: . . . . sachabillett@aecc.ac.uk

AFASIC - HELPING CHILDREN AND YOUNG PEOPLE WITH SPEECH, LANGUAGE & COMMUNICATION IMPAIRMENTS
CR1045617
Director, Fundraising and Support Services: Mr Mark Thompson
1st Floor, 20 Bowling Green Lane, London EC1R 0BD
Tel: . . . . 020 7490 9410; 0845 355 5577 Helpline
Fax: 020 7251 2834
Email: . . . . info@afasic.org.uk
Objects: F,M,W3,J,G,H,P,K

AFGHAN POVERTY RELIEF
CR1103876
Unit 100, 99-103 Lomond Grove, Camberwell, London SE5 7HN
Tel: 020 7701 7171
Email: . . . . info@afghanpoverty.org.uk

AFRICA INLAND MISSION INTERNATIONAL
See Aim International

AFRICAN CHILDREN'S EDUCATIONAL TRUST (A-CET)
CR1066869
PO Box 8390, Leicester, Leicestershire LE5 4YD
Tel: 0800 652 9475
Fax: 0800 652 9476
Email: . . . . dgs@a-cet.org

AFTAID - AID FOR THE AGED IN DISTRESS
CR299276
Administrator: Mrs Josick Harel-Green
Epworth House, 25 City Road, London EC1Y 1AA
Tel: 0870 803 1950
Fax: 0870 803 2128
Email: . . . . info@aftaid.org.uk
Object: W4

AFTER ADOPTION

Founded: 1990 CR1000888

Operations & Development Director: Mr Lynn Charlton

Chief Executive: Mrs Maureen Crank MBE

Unit 5 Citygate, 5 Blantyre Street, Manchester, Greater Manchester M15 4JJ

Tel: 0161 839 4932
Fax: 0161 832 2242
Email: . . . . : . . . information@afteradoption.org.uk

Objects: Q,F,W3,H,3,W8

AFTER ADOPTION, POST-ADOPTION SERVICES MANCHESTER

See After Adoption

AGE CONCERN MANCHESTER

CR1083242

Ms Nicola Mulholland

24 Mount Street (CD), Manchester, Greater Manchester M2 3NN

Tel: 0161 833 3944
Fax: 0161 833 3945
Email: . . . . enquiries@silverservice.org.uk

Objects: F,E,W4,B,3,P

Age Concern Manchester was formed 30 years ago to "promote relief of elderly people". Governed by a board of trustees, the charity is served by employees and volunteers providing a range of caring and supportive services. These include day care services for the mentally frail in three of the most deprived areas in England; advice and counselling, appointeeships and stewardship services for people in residential care and an Ageing Well project. "Age Concern Manchester also joins with other local charities in campaigning to improve the rights and financial circumstances of older people generally."

See advert on this page

AGE UK CALDERDALE & KIRKLEES

CR1102020

5-6 Park Road, Halifax, West Yorkshire HX1 2TS

Tel: 01422 252040
Fax: 01422 262000
Email: . . . jbarcoe@ageconcerncalderdale.org.uk
Objects: F,M,J,A,2,W4,B,H,3,P

AGE UK CORNWALL & THE ISLES OF SCILLY
Founded: 1990 CR900542
Director / Company Secretary
Boscawen House, Chapel Hill, Truro, Cornwall
TR1 3BN
Tel: 01872 266388
Email: . . . . email@ageukcornwall.org.uk
Objects: F,J,E,W5,W4,H

AGE UK EALING
Founded: 1990 CR1100474
The Chief Officer
135 Uxbridge Road, London W13 9AU
Tel: 020 8567 8017
Fax: 020 8566 5696
Email: . . . . reception@ageukealing.org.uk
Objects: F,J,W4,O,3

AGE UK ENFIELD

Founded: 1985 CR1063696
Mr Tony Seagroatt
Vincent House, 2E Nags Head Road, Enfield,
Middlesex EN3 7FN
Tel: 020 8375 4120
Fax: 020 8375 4138
Email: customerservices@ageukenfield.org.uk
Web: . . . . www.ageuk.org.uk/enfield
Objects: F,M,E,W4,H,P
Age UK Enfield is an independent charity responsible for raising its own funds and providing local activities, projects, and services for local people living in the London borough of Enfield. Age UK Enfield has been offering services to older people aged 50 and over in the London Borough of Enfield since 1985.

We provide activities, projects and services to promote independence and well-being in later life. Our mission is to ensure that people age well and enjoy later life making as many services and sources available to them in order to achieve this.

AGE UK GATESHEAD
Founded. 1990 CR702561
Chairman: Mr John Boyle
Chief Officer: Ms Anne Marshall
341-343 High Street, Gateshead, Tyne & Wear
NE8 1EQ
Tel: 0191 477 3559
Fax: 0191 478 5307
Email: . . . . admin@ageconcerngateshead.org.uk
Objects: F,J,E,W5,W4,3,P

AGE UK HARINGEY
Founded: 1991 CR1005145
Director: Mr Robert Edmonds
Tottenham Town Hall, Town Hall Approach Road,
Tottenham, London N15 4RY
Tel: 020 8801 2444
Fax: 020 8365 1732
Email: . . . . info@ageukharingey.org.uk
Objects: F,E,2,W4,3,P

AGE UK NEWHAM
Founded: 1990 CR802908
Chief Executive: Ms Sue McCarthy
655 Barking Road, Plaistow, London E13 9EX
Tel: 020 8503 4800
Fax: 020 8552 0718
Email: . . . . . . info@ageconcernnewham.org.uk
Objects: F,W10,1A,W4,H,3,P

AGE UK NORTH STAFFORDSHIRE
Founded: 1991 CR1087774
Chief Officer: Mrs Jane Emms
83-85 Trinity Street, Hanley, Stoke-on-Trent,
Staffordshire ST1 5NA
Tel: 01782 286209
Fax: 01782 209099
Email: . . . . info@ageuknorthstaffs.org.uk
Objects: F,J,W10,V,D,2,W4,B,H,O,3,P

AGE UK NORTH YORKSHIRE
CR1124567
9 North Park Road, Harrogate, North Yorkshire
HG1 5PD

AGE UK SUFFOLK
CR1085900
Head Office, 14 Hillview Business Park, Old
Ipswich Road, Claydon, Suffolk IP6 0AJ
Tel: 01473 359911
Fax: 01473 287955
Email: . . . . office@ageuksuffolk.org

AGE UK TEESSIDE
CR702714
190 Borough Road, Middlesbrough, North
Yorkshire TS1 2EH
Tel: 01642 805500
Email: . . . . admin@ageukteesside.org.uk
Objects: F,E,G,W10,2,W4,3,P

AGE UK WILTSHIRE
Founded: 1990 CR800912
Director: Mrs Liddy Davidson
13 Market Place, Devizes, Wiltshire SN10 1HT
Tel: 01380 727767
Fax: 01380 728797
Email: . . . . info@ageukwiltshire.org.uk
Objects: F,M,J,E,G,1A,A,1B,2,W4,B,H,O,3,P

AGECARE (THE ROYAL SURGICAL AID SOCIETY)
Founded: 1862 CR216613
Chief Executive: Mr Michael Corp
47 Great Russell Street, London WC1B 3PA
Tel: 020 7637 4577
Fax: 020 7323 6878
Email: . . . . enquiries@agecare.org.uk
Objects: G,W4,3,C

AHIMSA
Founded: 1990 CR328590
Chair of Trustees: Mr Martin Hunwick
Office Manager: Mrs Nicky Turner
Project Co-ordinator: Mr Paul Wolf-Light
6 Victoria Place, Millbay Road, Plymouth, Devon
PL1 3LP
Tel: 01752 213535
Fax: 01752 213520
Email: .... mail@ahimsa.org.uk
Objects: F,W3,G,O,3,W8

AHRTAG - APPROPRIATE HEALTH RESOURCES & TECHNOLOGIES ACTION GROUP
See Healthlink Worldwide

AID TO THE CHURCH IN NEED
Founded: 1947 CR1097984
Accounts Officer: Mrs Maureen Gillam
National Director: Mr Neville Kyrke-Smith
Press & Information Officer: Mr John Pontifex
1 Times Square, Sutton, Surrey SM1 1LF
Tel: 020 8642 8668
Fax: 020 8661 6293
Email: .... acn@acnuk.org
Object: R

AIDS EDUCATION & RESEARCH TRUST (AVERT)
See AVERT

AIM INTERNATIONAL
Founded: 1895 CR1096364
Halifax Place, Nottingham, Nottinghamshire
NG1 1QN
Tel: 0115 983 8120
Email: .... uk@aimeurope.net
Objects: R,3

AIR LEAGUE EDUCATIONAL TRUST - FOR BRITAIN'S YOUTH
CR1129969
Broadway House, Tothill Street, London
SW1H 9NS
Tel: 020 7222 8463
Fax: 020 7222 8462
Email: .... flying@airleague.co.uk
Objects: W3,G,1A,3

AIRBORNE FORCES SECURITY FUND
Founded: 1942 CR206552
Controller: Lieutenant Colonel T B Middleton
Flagstaff House, Napier Road, Colchester, Essex
CO2 7SW
Tel: 01206 541748; 01206 782342
Fax: 01206 541734
Email: .... abfsyfund@btopenworld.com
Objects: F,J,1A,A,V

AJEX CHARITABLE FOUNDATION
CR231442
General Secretary: Mr Jack Weisser
Shield House, Harmony Way, London NW4 2BZ
Tel: 020 8202 2323
Fax: 020 8202 9900
Objects: F,A,D

ALABARÉ CHRISTIAN CARE AND SUPPORT
Founded: 1991 CR1006504
Chief Executive: Mr Andrew Lord
Chairman: Reverend John Proctor
33 Brown Street, Salisbury, Wiltshire SP1 2AS
Tel: 01722 322882
Fax: 01722 341657
Email: .... enquiries@alabare.co.uk
Objects: F,W9,W3,W5,G,D,W4,3,C,W8,K

ALBRIGHTON TRUST
Founded: 1990 CR1000402
Chief Executive / Trustee: Mr William ('Bill') G Jukes
Blue House Lane, Albrighton, Wolverhampton, West Midlands WV7 3FL
Tel: 01902 372441
Fax: 01902 374117
Objects: W6,W3,W2,E,W7,W5,G,W4

ALCOHOL AND DRUG SERVICE
Founded: 1973 CR702559
Chief Executive: Lady Rhona Bradley
87 Oldham Street, Manchester, Greater Manchester M4 1LW
Tel: 0161 834 9777
Fax: 0161 214 6407
Objects: F,W3,E,G,W10,W4,O,3,C,W8

ALCOHOL RESEARCH UK
Founded: 1982 CR284748
Director: Professor Ray Hodgson
Willow House (EH1.4), 4th Floor, 17-23 Willow Place, London SW1P 1JH
Tel: 020 7821 7880
Email: .... andrea.tilouche@aerc.org.uk
Objects: 1A,A,1B,B

ALDER HEY CHILDREN'S CHARITY

CR1049275
Head of Charity Operations: Ms Madeleine Fletcher
Alder Hey Children's Hospital, Eaton Road, Liverpool, Merseyside L12 2AP
Tel: **0151 252 5716**
Email: .... **info@alderheycharity.com**
Objects: W3,N

ALDERMAN TOM F SPENCE CHARITY, THE
Founded: 1991 CR1002235
Chairman: The Right Worshipful The Mayor
Working Party Chairman: Mr D W Parnaby
Solicitor: Mr H J Wilson
c/o Rippon City Council, Town Hall, Ripon, North Yorkshire HG4 1PA
Tel: 01765 604097
Objects: W3,W2,3

alzheimers.org.uk

Leading the fight against dementia

Alzheimer's Society

At the time he said he'd never forget it.
Now he can't remember it.

With the number of older people in the UK on the increase, dementia will become a problem for many more of us. By the year 2021, it is estimated that one million people in the UK will be affected. Regardless of this, research into Alzheimer's disease and dementia is severely underfunded. With over 100,000 people developing dementia every year, our resources are stretched to the limit and the legacy donations we receive are vital to meet the ever increasing demands for help.

Helping people with Alzheimer's and their families cope with the problems that dementia can bring is a crucial part of our work. By remembering the Society in your Will, you will be offering a lifeline of support through our network of services across England, Wales and Northern Ireland.

Our free legacy booklet will tell you more about leaving a gift in your Will; please call 0870 011 0290 to speak to someone or email legacies@alzheimers.org.uk (please quote CD012)

Alzheimer's Society is the UK's leading care and research charity for people with dementia, their families and carers.
Alzheimer's Society, Devon House, 58 St Katharine's Way, London E1W 1LB
Registered charity no. 296645

FRSB
FundRaising
Standards Board

ALL NATIONS CHRISTIAN COLLEGE
CR311028
Finance Manager: Mrs Rowena Biddlecombe
Executive Director: Mr Mike Wall MBA
Easneye, Ware, Hertfordshire SG12 8LX
Tel: 01920 443500
Fax: 01920 462997
Email: .... info@allnations.ac.uk
Objects: G,R,3

ALL SAINTS EDUCATIONAL TRUST
Founded: 1979 CR312934
Clerk to the Trust: Mr S.P. Harrow
Suite 8c, First Floor, Royal London House, 22-25
Finsbury Square, London EC2A 1DX
Tel: 020 7920 6465
Email: .... aset@aset.org.uk
Objects: G,1A,1B

ALMOND TRUST, THE
Founded: 1990 CR328583
Trustee: Lady Cooke
Trustee: Sir Jeremy Cooke
19 West Square, London SE11 4SN
Objects: 1A,A,1B,R

ALONE IN LONDON
Founded: 1972 CR1107432
188 King's Cross Road, London WC1X 9DE
Tel: ..... 020 7278 4486 Admin; 020 7278 4224
Advice
Fax: 020 7837 7943
Email: .... enquiries@als.org.uk
Objects: F,W3,D,T,3,C

ALTERNATIVE FUTURES LTD
Founded: 1992 CR1008587
Chief Executive: Mr M Clarke
Anita Samuels Centre, 4 Ellison Grove, Liverpool,
Merseyside L36 9GA
Tel: 0151 489 5501
Email: .... mail@alternativefutures.co.uk

ALZHEIMER'S - BRACE
Founded: 1987 CR297965
Chief Executive: Mr Mark Poarch
The Brace Appeal Office (CD), Frenchay Hospital,
Manor Road, Bristol BS16 1LE
Tel: 0117 340 4831
Fax: 0117 975 4831
Email: .... admin@alzheimers-brace.org
Object: W4

ALZHEIMER'S RESEARCH UK
CR1077089; SC042474
3 Riverside, Granta Park, Cambridge,
Cambridgeshire CB21 6AD
Tel: 0300 111 5555
Fax: 01223 843325
Email: .... enquiries@alzheimersresearchuk.org
Objects: W6,W7,W5,W10,W11,1B,W4,W8

ALZHEIMER'S SOCIETY

Founded: 1979 CR296645
Legacy Marketing & Recognition Giving
Manager: Mr Mike Hilder
Chief Executive: Mr Jeremy Hughes
Devon House, 58 St Katharine's Way,
London E1W 1LB
Tel: Customer Care 0845 306 0898; National
Helpline: 0300 222 1122
Fax: 020 7423 3501
Email: .... legacies@alzheimers.org.uk
Web: .... alzheimers.org.uk/legacies
Objects: F,G,W10,2,W4,H,3,W
Our vision

A world without dementia.

Our mission

We will

• change the face of dementia research
• demonstrate best practice in dementia care and
support
• provide the best advice and support to anyone
dealing with dementia
• use our influence so that the state and society
enables those affected by dementia to live as
they wish to live

By pursuing these four goals we will reduce the
impact of dementia on lives today and create a
world without dementia tomorrow.

See advert on previous page

AMELIA METHODIST TRUST FARM
Founded: 1991 CR1001546
Honorary Secretary & Trustee: Mr George H
Stokes
Five Mile Lane, Barry, Vale of Glamorgan
CF62 3AS
Tel: 01446 781427
Email: .... andrew@ameliatrust.org.uk
Objects: W3,W2,G,V,O,3,P,K

AMNESTY INTERNATIONAL (UK SECTION) CHARITABLE TRUST (AIUKSCT)
Founded: 1986 CR1051681
Supporter Development Manager: Ms Nina Botting
Mr David Bull
Direct Marketing Co-ordinator: Mr Charles
Mugenyi
Marketing Director: Mr Simon Stanley
The Human Rights Action Centre, 17-25 New Inn
Yard, London EC2A 3EA
Tel: . 020 7033 1500; 020 7033 1664 (textphone)
Fax: 020 7033 1503
Email: .... legacy@amnesty.org.uk
Objects: G,U

ANCIENT MONUMENTS SOCIETY
Founded: 1924 CR209605
Secretary: Mr Matthew Saunders MBE, MA, FSA
St Ann's Vestry Hall, 2 Church Entry, London
EC4V 5HB

Tel: 020 7236 3934
Email: . office@ancientmonumentssociety.org.uk
Objects: F,W2,G,2,H

ANGLO-RUSSIAN OPERA AND BALLET TRUST / THE MARIINSKY THEATRE TRUST
Founded: 1992 CR1010450
Company Secretary: Mr Garry Glover
Chief Executive: Mrs Caroline Gonzalez-Pintado
Third Floor, 33 Bedford Street, London
WC2E 9ED
Tel: 020 7836 7033
Email: . . . . mail@mariinskyfriends.co.uk
Objects: S,G,A,2

ANIMAL CARE (LM&D)
CR508819
Ms Linda Hunter
Blea Tarn Road, Scotforth, Lancaster, Lancashire
LA2 0RD
Tel: 01524 65495 (11AM-3PM)
Fax: 01524 841819
Email: . . . . . . admin@animalcare-lancaster.co.uk

ANIMAL CARE TRUST
CR281571
The Royal Veterinary College Animal Care Trust,
Room CC1A, Hawkshead Lane, North Mymms,
Hatfield, Hertfordshire AL9 7TA
Tel: 01707 666039
Fax: 01707 666382
Email: . . . . legacy@rvc.ac.uk
Objects: W1,G

ANIMAL CONCERN ADVICE LINE (ACAL)
Founded: 2000SC030982
Secretary: Mr John F. Robins
c/o Animal Concern, PO Box 5178, Dumbarton,
West Dunbartonshire G82 5YJ
Tel: 01389 841111
Fax: 0870 706 0327
Email: . . . . acal@jfrobins.force9.co.uk
Web: . . . . www.adviceaboutanimals.info
Objects: F,W1,W2
Animal Concern Advice Line is a stand alone organisation created to conduct the charitable work formerly carried out by Animal Concern (founded in 1876 as the Scottish Anti-Vivisection Society). Through our telephone and website service we endeavour to help people help animals 24/7.

ANIMAL HEALTH TRUST

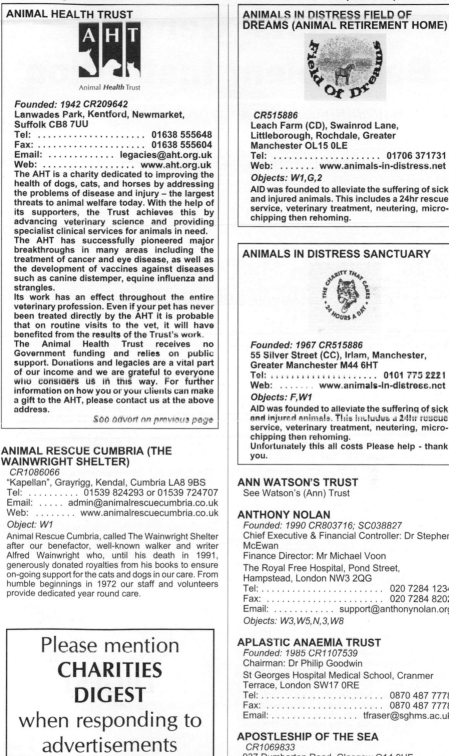

Animal *Health* Trust

Founded: 1942 CR209642
Lanwades Park, Kentford, Newmarket, Suffolk CB8 7UU
Tel: 01638 555648
Fax: 01638 555604
Email: .... legacies@aht.org.uk
Web: .... www.aht.org.uk
The AHT is a charity dedicated to improving the health of dogs, cats, and horses by addressing the problems of disease and injury – the largest threats to animal welfare today. With the help of its supporters, the Trust achieves this by advancing veterinary science and providing specialist clinical services for animals in need.
The AHT has successfully pioneered major breakthroughs in many areas including the treatment of cancer and eye disease, as well as the development of vaccines against diseases such as canine distemper, equine influenza and strangles.
Its work has an effect throughout the entire veterinary profession. Even if your pet has never been treated directly by the AHT it is probable that on routine visits to the vet, it will have benefited from the results of the Trust's work.
The Animal Health Trust receives no Government funding and relies on public support. Donations and legacies are a vital part of our income and we are grateful to everyone who considers us in this way. For further information on how you or your clients can make a gift to the AHT, please contact us at the above address.

See advert on previous page

ANIMAL RESCUE CUMBRIA (THE WAINWRIGHT SHELTER)

CR1086066
"Kapellan", Grayrigg, Kendal, Cumbria LA8 9BS
Tel: .... 01539 824293 or 01539 724707
Email: ..... admin@animalrescuecumbria.co.uk
Web: .... www.animalrescuecumbria.co.uk
Object: W1
Animal Rescue Cumbria, called The Wainwright Shelter after our benefactor, well-known walker and writer Alfred Wainwright who, until his death in 1991, generously donated royalties from his books to ensure on-going support for the cats and dogs in our care. From humble beginnings in 1972 our staff and volunteers provide dedicated year round care.

Please mention
CHARITIES
DIGEST
when responding to advertisements

ANIMALS IN DISTRESS FIELD OF DREAMS (ANIMAL RETIREMENT HOME)

CR515886
Leach Farm (CD), Swainrod Lane, Littleborough, Rochdale, Greater Manchester OL15 0LE
Tel: 01706 371731
Web: .... www.animals-in-distress.net
Objects: W1,G,2
AID was founded to alleviate the suffering of sick and injured animals. This includes a 24hr rescue service, veterinary treatment, neutering, micro-chipping then rehoming.

ANIMALS IN DISTRESS SANCTUARY

Founded: 1967 CR515886
55 Silver Street (CC), Irlam, Manchester, Greater Manchester M44 6HT
Tel: 0101 775 2221
Web: .... www.animals-in-distress.net
Objects: F,W1
AID was founded to alleviate the suffering of sick and injured animals. This includes a 24hr rescue service, veterinary treatment, neutering, micro-chipping then rehoming.
Unfortunately this all costs Please help - thank you.

ANN WATSON'S TRUST
See Watson's (Ann) Trust

ANTHONY NOLAN
Founded: 1990 CR803716; SC038827
Chief Executive & Financial Controller: Dr Stephen McEwan
Finance Director: Mr Michael Voon
The Royal Free Hospital, Pond Street, Hampstead, London NW3 2QG
Tel: 020 7284 1234
Fax: 020 7284 8202
Email: .... support@anthonynolan.org
Objects: W3,W5,N,3,W8

APLASTIC ANAEMIA TRUST
Founded: 1985 CR1107539
Chairman: Dr Philip Goodwin
St Georges Hospital Medical School, Cranmer Terrace, London SW17 0RE
Tel: 0870 487 7778
Fax: 0870 487 7778
Email: .... tfraser@sghms.ac.uk

APOSTLESHIP OF THE SEA
CR1069833
937 Dumbarton Road, Glasgow G14 9UF

Tel: 0141 339 6657
Email: . . . . info@apostleshipofthesea.org.uk
Objects: 1B,2,R,P

APULDRAM CENTRE, THE
Founded: 1990 CR801169
Company Secretary: Mr Trevor Charles Allen
Common Farm, Apuldram Lane, Chichester, West
Sussex PO20 7PE
Tel: 01725 512147

THE ARCHITECTURAL HERITAGE FUND

THE ARCHITECTURAL HERITAGE FUND

Founded: 1976 CR266780; SC043840
15 Whitehall, London SW1A 2DD
Tel: 020 7925 0199
Email: . . . . ahf@ahfund.org.uk
Objects: W2,S,A,1B,3
Promotes the conservation of historic buildings
in the UK by providing advice, information and
financial assistance in the form of grants and
competitive loans for projects undertaken by
eligible charities and not-for-profit
organisations.

ARDIS
Founded: 1986 CR297811
Company Secretary / Honorary Treasurer: Major
Peter Carr
Chairman of the Board: Dr A J Whitehead
14 Gundreda Road, Lewes, East Sussex
BN7 1PX
Tel: 01273 472049
Fax: 01273 887595
Objects: E,1B,2,W4,C

ARMED FORCES' CHRISTIAN UNION
Founded: 1851 CR249636
Office Manager: Major (Retd) L R Smith
Havelock House, Barrack Road, Aldershot,
Hampshire GU11 3NP
Tel: 01252 311221
Fax: 01252 350722
Email: . . . . office@afcu.org.uk
Objects: W9,2,R

ARMS AROUND THE CHILD
CR1123038
Communications House, 26 York Street, London
W1U 6PZ
Tel: 0845 094 9491
Email: . . . . ukinfo@keepachildalive.org

ARROWE PARK HOSPITAL POSTGRADUATE EDUCATION CENTRE TRUST
Founded: 1990 CR703069
Deputy Chairman: Doctor Martin Greaney
Chairman: Doctor Hani D Zakhour
Arrowe Park Road, Upton, Wirral, Merseyside
CH49 5PE
Tel: 0151 604 7196
Objects: G,N,3

ART FUND, THE
Founded: 1903 CR209174
Director: Mr David Barrie
Membership & Legacy Manager: Ms Claire Longrigg
Deputy Director: Andrew MacDonald
Millais House, 7 Cromwell Place, South Kensington, London SW7 2JN
Tel: 020 7225 4800
Fax: 020 7225 4848
Email: . . . . info@artfund.org
Objects: S,A,1B,2,W12,3

ART IN HEALTHCARE
Founded: 2005SC036222
Director: Mr Roger Jones
The Drill Hall, 32-36 Dalmeny Street, Edinburgh
EH6 8RG
Tel: 0131 555 7638
Fax: 0131 555 7639
Email: . . . . admin@artinhealthcare.org.uk
Objects: W3,W2,S,W7,W5,W10,W4,O,3,W8

ARTHUR RANK HOSPICE CHARITY
CR1133354
Chief Executive: Dr Lynn Morgan
351 Mill Road, Cambridge, Cambridgeshire
CB1 3DF
Tel: 01223 723115, 01223 723117
Email: . . . . fundraising@arhc.org.uk
Web: . . . . www.arhc.org.uk
Objects: F,E,W5,G,W15,N,W4,O,3
Arthur Rank Hospice Charity supports people in Cambridgeshire by providing end of life care, counselling and support for adult patients with life limiting illness. Each year, the Charity must fundraise over £1.5 million to meet their financial commitments at the Hospice and to continue to provide all services free of charge to those who benefit from them.

ARTHUR TOWNROW PENSIONS FUND
See Townrow (Arthur) Pensions Fund

ARTISTS' GENERAL BENEVOLENT INSTITUTION
Founded: 1814 CR212667
Secretary: Mr Brad Feltham
Burlington House, Piccadilly, London W1J 0BB
Tel: 020 7734 1193
Fax: 020 7734 9966
Email: . . . . agbi1@btconnect.com
Web: . . . . http://www.agbi.org.uk
Object: 1A
Relief of professional artists, sculptors, designers, and other creative artists who cannot work due to accident, illness or old age. Admission: By application supported by two referees. New applications must be accompanied by examples of work. Management: Council. Also at the same address is The Artists' Orphan Fund (CR219356) - to assist with education and maintenance of the children of deceased artists.
See advert on previous page

ARTLINK WEST YORKSHIRE
Founded: 1990 CR702492
Director: Ms Sylvie Fourcin
Community Arts Centre, 191 Belle Vue Road, Leeds, West Yorkshire LS3 1HG
Tel: 0113 243 1005
Objects: F,W3,S,W5,G,W10,W4,3,K

ASH - ACTION ON SMOKING & HEALTH
Founded: 1971 CR262067
Business Manager: Mr Phil Rimmer
First Floor, 144-145 Shoreditch High Street, London E1 6JE
Tel: 020 7739 5902
Fax: 020 7729 4732
Email: . . . . enquiries@ash.org.uk
Objects: F,W3,W4,H

ASIAN PEOPLE'S DISABILITY ALLIANCE
Founded: 1990 CR803283
Chairperson: Mr A K Ghose
Director: Mr Michael Jeewa
Daycare and Development Centre, Alric Avenue, Harlesden, London NW10 8RA
Tel: 020 8961 6773
Fax: 020 8838 0594
Email: . . . . apdmcha@aol.com
Objects: F,W6,S,E,W7,W5,G,W10,W4,3,P

ASSESSMENT AND QUALIFICATIONS ALLIANCE
Founded: 1992 CR1073334
Chief Executive: Mr Andrew Hall
Stag Hill House, Guildford, Surrey GU2 7XJ
Tel: 0161 853 1180
Objects: G,3

ASSISI ANIMAL CHARITIES FOUNDATION
CR1102985
Fundraiser: Ms Lucy Warnes
Assisi, Home Close Farm, Shilton Road, Burford, Oxfordshire OX18 4PF
Tel: 0870 609 2810
Fax: 01993 823083
Email: . . . . enquiries@assisi.org.uk
Objects: W1,2

ASSOCIATION FOR LANGUAGE LEARNING, THE
Founded: 1991 CR1001826
President: Helen Myers
Director: Linda Parker
University of Leicester, University Road, Leicester, Leicestershire LE1 7RH
Tel: 0116 229 7453
Email: . . . . info@all-languages.org.uk
Objects: G,2,H

ASSOCIATION FOR PEOPLE WITH LOWER LIMB ABNORMALITIES - STEPS
See STEPS Charity Worldwide

ASSOCIATION FOR REAL CHANGE
Founded: 1976 CR285575
Acting Chief Executive: Ms Jane Livingstone
ARC House, Marsden Street, Chesterfield, Derbyshire S40 1JY

THE ATHLONE TRUST

(Registered Charity No 277065)
FINANCIAL ASSISTANCE FOR ADOPTED CHILDREN WITH SPECIAL NEEDS

Chairman and Correspondent:
David King-Farlow
Thomas Eggar LLP incorporating
Pritchard Englefield
14 New Street
London
EC2M 4HE

Tel: 020 7650 3947
Fax: 020 7972 9722
Email: david.king-farlow@thomaseggar.com
www.athlonetrust.com

Tel: 01246 555043
Fax: 01246 555045
Email: . . . . contact.us@arcuk.org.uk
Objects: F,W3,J,E,W5,G,2,W4,H,3,C

ASSOCIATION FOR STAMMERERS
See British Stammering Association

ASSOCIATION OF JEWISH REFUGEES CHARITABLE TRUST (AJR)
CR211239
Jubilee House, Merrion Avenue, Stanmore,
Middlesex HA7 4RL
Tel: 020 8385 3070
Fax: 020 8385 3080
Email: . . . . enquiries@ajr.org.uk

ASSOCIATION OF TAXATION TECHNICIANS
Founded: 1990 CR803480
Secretary: Mr Andrew R Pickering
12 Upper Belgrave Street, London SW1X 8BB
Tel: 020 7235 2544
Fax: 020 7235 4571
Email: . . . . info@att.org.uk
Objects: G,2

ASTHMA UK

Founded: 1990 CR802364; SC039322
Chief Executive: Kay Boycott
Summit House (CD14), 70 Wilson Street, London EC2A 2DB
Tel: . . . . **020 7786 4900; 0800 121 6244 (AdviceLine)**
Fax: **020 7256 6075**
Email: . . . . **info@asthma.org.uk**
Web: . . . . **www.asthma.org.uk**
Objects: F,W3,J,G,1B,V,2,H,3
Asthma UK is dedicated to improving the health and well-being of over 5 million children and adults affected by asthma across the UK. Asthma is an underestimated condition. Every seven hours someone dies from a severe asthma attack in the UK, yet 90% of these deaths are preventable.
It is only through the generosity of our supporters that we can continue to fund vital research into the root causes and triggers of asthma, so we can improve our understanding and potentially develop new treatments that will alleviate the symptoms or ultimately lead to a cure in the future.
Gifts in Wills contribute over a third of Asthma UK's voluntary income and play a critical role in helping us to achieve our vision of gaining control over asthma today and freedom from asthma tomorrow.

ASYLUM AID
Founded: 1990 CR328729
Co-ordinator: Mr Maurice Wren
Club Union House, 253-254 Upper Street, London
N1 1RY
Tel: 020 7354 9631
Fax: 020 7354 5620
Email: .... info@asylumaid.org.uk
Objects: F,W3,W5,W10,2,W4,3,W8

AT HOME IN THE COMMUNITY LTD
Founded: 1990 CR803280
Chairman: Mr Donald Curry
Company Secretary: Mr G V Goulty
391 West Road, Newcastle upon Tyne, Tyne &
Wear NE15 7PY
Tel: 0191 228 8300
Fax: 0191 228 8301
Email: .... athomeoffice@line1.net
Objects: W5,3

THE ATHLONE TRUST
CR277065
c/o Thomas Eggar LLP incorporating Pritchard
Englefield, 14 New Street, London EC2M 4HE
Tel: 020 7650 3947
Fax: 020 7972 9722
Email: .... david.king-farlow@thomaseggar.com
See advert on previous page

ATLANTIC FOUNDATION, THE
Founded: 1990 CR328499
Administrator to Trustees: Mr B L Thomas
Atlantic House, Cardiff Gate Business Park,
Greenwood Wharf, Cardiff CF23 8RD
Tel: 029 2054 5680

ATS & WRAC ASSOCIATION BENEVOLENT FUND
Founded: 1964 CR206184
Case Secretary: Mrs Margaret Wroot
AGC Centre, Worthy Down, Winchester,
Hampshire SO21 2RG
Tel: 01962 887612
Fax: 01962 887478
Email: benfund.wracassociation@googlemail.com
Objects: F,W9,1A,A,B,W8

ATTEND
Founded: 1949 CR1113067
Communications Officer: Ms Rebecca Rendle
11-13 Cavendish Square, London W1G 0AN
Tel: 0845 450 0285
Fax: 020 7307 2571
Email: .... info@attend.org.uk
Objects: F,W3,J,W5,G,W10,A,1B,2,W4,W8,K

AUTISM ANGLIA
CR1063717
Century House, Riverside Office Centre, North
Station Road, Colchester, Essex CO1 1RE
Tel: 01206 577678
Fax: 01206 578581
Email: .... info@autism-anglia.org.uk
Objects: F,W5,G

AUTISM LONDON
Founded: 1992 CR1009720
Finance Manager: Mr V G Dunham
Service Development Officer: Ms Gill Lea-Wilson
1 Floral Place, London N1 2FS
Tel: 020 7704 0501
Fax: 020 7704 2306
Email: .... info@autismlondon.org.uk
Objects: F,W5,2,3,C

AVERT
Founded: 1986 CR1074849
Director: Ms Annabel Kanabus BSc
4 Brighton Road, Horsham, West Sussex
RH13 5BA
Tel: 01403 210202
Email: .... info@avert.org
Objects: F,W3,G,1B,U,3

AVIATION ENVIRONMENT TRUST
Founded: 1978 CR276987
Secretary: Mr T M Johnson
Broken Wharf House, 2 Broken Wharf, London
EC4V 3DT
Tel: 020 7248 2223
Fax: 020 7329 8160
Email: .... info@aet.org.uk
Objects: F,J,W2,G,H,3

AVOCET TRUST
Founded: 1991 CR1004537
Secretary: Ms S M Devereux
Head Office, Clarence House, 60-62 Clarence
Street, Hull, Kingston upon Hull HU9 1DN
Tel: 01482 329226
Email: .... chris@avocet-trust.co.uk

AXIS WEB
Founded: 1991 CR1002841
Chief Executive: Ms Kate Hainsworth
Round Foundry Media Centre, Foundry Street,
Leeds, West Yorkshire LS11 5QP
Tel: 0870 443 0701
Fax: 0870 443 0703
Email: .... info@axisweb.org
Objects: F,W6,W3,J,W9,8,W7,W5,C,W10,W12,
W4,H,3,W8,K

B

BABY LIFELINE LTD
Founded: 1991 CR1006457
Company Secretary: Mr T A Ledger
Empathy Enterprise Building, Bramston Crescent,
Tile Hill Lane, Tile Hill, Coventry, West Midlands
CV4 9SW
Tel: 024 7642 2135
Objects: W3,G,A,W8

BACON'S CITY TECHNOLOGY COLLEGE
Founded: 1990 CR803396
Clerk to the Trustees: Mrs Linda Borthwick
Timber Pond Road, Rotherhithe, London
SE16 6AT
Tel: 020 7237 1928
Object: G

BACUP
See Cancerbackup

BAKERS' BENEVOLENT SOCIETY
Founded: 1832 CR211307
Clerk to the Society: Mr Graham Allen
Clerk to the Society: Mrs Suzanne Pitts
The Mill House, 23 Bakers Lane, Epping, Essex
CM16 5DQ

Tel: 01992 575951
Fax: 01992 561163
Objects: W5,1A,A,D,W4,B,3

BAKEWELL & EYAM COMMUNITY TRANSPORT
Founded: 1996 CR1049389
Chief Executive: Edwina Edwards
Treasurer: Mr M J Taylor
South Lodge Newholme Hospital, 3 Baslow Road,
Bakewell, Derbyshire DE45 1AD
Tel: 01629 814889
Fax: 01629 815233
Objects: W6,M,W3,W7,W5,2,W4,3,W8

THE BARCLAY FOUNDATION
Founded: 1990 CR803696
Trustees Accountant: Mr Michael Seal FCA
3rd Floor, 20 St James's Street, London
SW1A 1ES
Tel: 020 7915 0915
Objects: W3,1B

BARNARDO'S - BELIEVE IN CHILDREN

Believe in children

Barnardo's

Founded: 1866 CR216250; SC037605
Gift in Wills (CC), Room 113, Barnardo's,
Tanners Lane, Barkingside, Ilford, Essex
IG6 1QG
Tel: 020 8498 7880
Email: ..... giftsinwills@barnardos.org.uk
Web: .. www.barnardos.org.uk/giftsinwills
Objects: Q,F,M,W3,E,G,D,H,3,C,P,K

Barnardo's transforms the lives of the most vulnerable children through the work of our projects, campaigning and research expertise. As one of the UK's leading children's charities we work directly with over 200,000 children, young people and their families each year, running over 800 projects across the UK.
Barnardo's aim is always the same; to bring out the best in any child, no matter what they have done, or what they have been through, as well as reaching and helping those children and young people whose voices are unheard.
Our work includes helping children without families find loving homes through fostering and adoption, supporting children who have been victims of abuse or sexual exploitation and offering vocational training for young people no longer in mainstream education or employment.
Our vision is that the lives of all children and young people should be free from poverty, abuse and discrimination and we depend heavily on the generosity and support of the public to continue to expand this vital work. By leaving a gift in your Will to Barnardo's – however large or small – you will help us to give the most vulnerable children a chance of a happier childhood and a brighter future.

BARNSTONDALE CENTRE
Founded: 1990 CR1087502
Manager: Mr George Jones
Dawstone Road, Wirral, Merseyside CH60 8NP

Tel: 0151 342 3807
Fax: 0151 648 1412
Objects: W6,W3,W7,W5,G,V,3,P

BAROW HILLS SCHOOL WITLEY
Founded: 1990 CR1000190
Roke Lane, Witley, Godalming, Surrey GU8 5NY
Tel: 01428 683639
Email: .... barhills@netcomuk.co.uk

BARRISTERS' BENEVOLENT ASSOCIATION

Founded: 1873 CR1106768
Secretary: Mrs Susan Eldridge
14 Gray's Inn Square, London WC1R 5JP
Tel: 020 7242 4761
Fax: 020 7831 5366
Email: .... susan@the-bba.com
Web: .... www.the-bba.com
Objects: F,M,W15,1A

The object of the Association is to help needy and deserving members of the English Bar who are, or have been, in practice in England or Wales, their husbands or wives, widows or widowers, children and, in exceptional circumstances, dependants. Application to Secretary.

See advert on next page

BARRY GREEN MEMORIAL FUND
CR1000492
Trustee: Mr M E Fitzgerald-Hart
Mr Alan L Ware
Claro Chambers, Bridge Street, Boroughbridge,
York, North Yorkshire YO51 9LD
Email: .... info@fitz-law.co.uk
Objects: W1,A,1B

BASINGSTOKE DIAL-A-RIDE
Founded: 1990 CR900594
Company Secretary: Mr R M Bale
Whiteditch Playing Field, Sherbourne Road,
Basingstoke, Hampshire RG21 5UT
Tel: 01256 816069
Objects: M,W4,3

BASPCAN (BRITISH ASSOCIATION FOR THE STUDY AND PREVENTION OF CHILD ABUSE AND NEGLECT)
Founded: 1979 CR279119
Administration Officer: Maureen Gordon
National Office Manager: Judy Sanderson
17 Priory Street, York, North Yorkshire YO1 6ET
Tel: 01904 613605
Fax: 01904 642239
Email: .... baspcan@baspcan.org.uk
Objects: W3,J,G,2,H,P

BAT CONSERVATION TRUST
Founded: 1990 CR1012361
Joint Chief Executive: Ms Amy Coyte
Deputy Chief Executive: Ms Julia Hanmer
15 Cloisters House, Cloister Business Centre, 8
Battersea Park Road, Battersea, London
SW8 4BG

THE BARRISTERS' BENEVOLENT ASSOCIATION

BBA

14 Gray's Inn Square, London, WC1R 5JP
Tel. 0207 242 4761
Email: susan@the-bba.com

The BBA exists to help to past and present practising members of the bar in England and Wales, including the judiciary, and their families and dependants. The Criteria are that the applicant is needy and worthy. The aim is, wherever possible, to overcome the problem and rebuild the applicant's life and career. There is a wide range of reasons for needing help ... there can be serious long-term or terminal illness, shorter health scares or accidents affecting income for weeks or months, unexpected financial problems due to circumstances beyond the beneficiary's control problems of old age...

Although we cannot offer specific advice our staff can point people towards those who can particularly in cases of financial need. They are also happy to be a contact on the phone, someone to call for a reassuring chat.

In appropriate cases we are able to offer financial help, - as a grant or a secured or unsecured loan. If all else fails we can help with IVA's and bankruptcies. Some beneficiaries receive regular "disregard" grants as well as other specific occasional help.

Single parents have been helped with given with funding a much-needed holiday break, providing a computer, paying telephone bills, mending or replacing home equipment.
Every case is unique and every application is considered on it's own merits and circumstances.

Tel: 020 7627 2629; 0845 130 0228
Fax: 020 7627 2628
Email: . . . . enquiries@bats.org.uk
Objects: F,W1,W3,W2,G,2,H

BATTERSEA DOGS & CATS HOME
Founded: 1860 CR206394
Chief Executive: Ms Claire Horton
Director of Fundraising: Ms Liz Tait
4 Battersea Park Road (LCD2012), London
SW8 4AA
Tel: 020 7627 9247
Fax: 020 7622 6451
Email: . . . . fundraising@battersea.org.uk; info@
battersea.org.uk
Objects: Q,F,W1,G,O

BATTLE OF BRITAIN MEMORIAL TRUST
Founded: 1990 CR803258
Honorary Secretary & Trustee: Group.Captain
P S E Tootal OBE, RAF (Ret'd)
PO Box 337, West Malling, Kent ME6 9AA
Tel: 01732 870809
Fax: 01732 870809
Email: . . . . battleofbritain@btinternet.com
Objects: W9,G,2,W12
Maintains the national Memorial to all those who fought, flew and died in the Battle of Britain.

BCASS - BARNET CARE AND SUPPORT SERVICES
Founded: 1990 CR1000630
Director: Mrs Karen Whitaker
Avenue House, East End Road, Finchley, London N3 3QE
Tel: 020 8346 0003/0055
Object: 3

BCPC
Founded: 1992 CR1075620
Administrator: Mrs Vicky McCamley
1 Walcot Terrace, London Road, Bath, Bath & North East Somerset BA1 6AB
Tel: 01225 429720
Fax: 01225 429720
Objects: F,G,2,3

BEACON CENTRE FOR THE BLIND
Founded: 1875 CR216092
Chief Executive: Mr Ian Ferguson BSc (Hons)
Wolverhampton Road East, Wolverhampton, West Midlands WV4 6AZ
Tel: 01902 880111
Fax: 01902 886795
Email: . . . . enquiries@beacon4blind.co.uk
Objects: F,W6,M,W3,E,W5,G,V,W4,O,3,C,P,K

BEAUMONT ANIMALS' HOSPITAL
See Animal Care Trust

BEDFORDSHIRE AND HERTFORDSHIRE HISTORIC CHURCHES TRUST

Founded: *1991 CR1005697*
The Black Swan, 64 Blanche Lane, South Mimms, Potters Bar, Hertfordshire EN6 3PD
Tel: **01707 644180**
Email: ...... **wmarsterson@yahoo.co.uk**
Web: .... **www.bedshertshct.org.uk**
Objects: W2,A
Aims:
• To assist with the care of places of worship of all denominations in the two counties;
• To grant funds for their restoration, maintenance, preservation, repair and reconstruction.

Objectives:
• To generate income from members to fund the Trust's activities;
• To raise substantial income through the annual Bike 'n Hike event, and also via legacies;
• To co-operate with other bodies making funds available for the purposes above;
• To foster the appreciation of the history and architecture of these places of worship.

BEIS AHARON
Founded: 1992 CR1010420
Company Secretary: Mr J Lipschitz
86 Darenth Road, London N16 6ED

BELL MEMORIAL HOME (INC)
Founded: 1890 CR206244
164 South Street, Lancing, West Sussex
BN15 8AU
Tel: 01903 752020
Fax: 01903 766064
Objects: W5,G,W4,3

BEN - THE AUTOMOTIVE INDUSTRY CHARITY
Founded: 1905 CR297877; SC039842
Marketing & Communications Manager: Ms Kirsten Galvin
Chief Executive: Mr David Main
Lynwood, Sunninghill, Ascot, Windsor & Maidenhead SL5 0AJ
Tel: 01344 620191
Fax: 01344 622042
Email: .... info@ben.org.uk
Objects: F,E,W11,1A,A,D,N,B,3,C

BERKSHIRE, BUCKINGHAMSHIRE & OXFORDSHIRE WILDLIFE TRUST
Founded: 1960 CR204330
Chief Executive: Ms Phillippa Lyons
Director: Mr Martin Spray
Media & Campaigns: Ms Wendy Tobitt
The Lodge, 1 Armstrong Road, Littlemore, Oxford, Oxfordshire OX4 4XT
Tel: 01865 775476
Fax: 01865 711301
Email: .... info@bbowt.org.uk
Objects: W2,2

BESO (BRITISH EXECUTIVE SERVICE OVERSEAS)
Founded: 1972 CR268094
Mr Ian Ford
164 Vauxhall Bridge Road, London SW1V 2RA
Tel: 020 7630 0644
Fax: 020 7630 0624
Email: .... team@beso.org
Object: U

BETHESDA HOSPICE, STORNOWAY

Bethesda Care Home & Hospice

Founded: 1987 CR44253; SC015783
Springfield Road, Stornoway, Western Isles HS1 2PS
Tel: 01851 706222
Fax: 01851 706285
Email: .... bethesdahospice@hotmail.com
Web: .... http://shop.bethesdahospice.co.uk
Objects: W5,N,W4,W14

BIRCHINGTON CONVALESCENT BENEFIT FUND
CR249574
Finance Assistant: Mr Michael Locke
Gen. Secretary: Rev David Phillips
Dean Wace House, 16 Rosslyn Road, Watford, Hertfordshire WD18 0NY
Tel: 01923 235111
Fax: 01923 800362
Email: .... finance@churchsociety.org
Objects: W3,1A,A,1B,V

BIRMINGHAM BIBLE INSTITUTE MINISTRIES, THE
See Birmingham Christian College

BIRMINGHAM BROOK ADVISORY CENTRE
Founded: 1966 CR702584
Chief Executive: Ms Penny Barber
59-65 John Bright Street, Birmingham, West Midlands B1 1BL
Tel: ... 0121 248 2500; 0121 643 5341 Services
Fax: 0121 248 2552
Objects: F,W3,G,3,W8

Birmingham Children's Hospital Charities

Our brave faces deserve the *best* places

Please help us to give children like Abigail a world class Cancer Centre. Support our **Cancer Centre Appeal** by:

- Making a donation;
- Taking part in a fundraising event;
- Remembering us in your will; or
- Asking your employer to create a partnership with us.

Thank you

Tel: **0121 333 8598**
Email: **bch.charities@bch.nhs.uk**
Web: **www.bchcharity.org**

Birmingham Children's Hospital Charities

BIRMINGHAM CHILDREN'S HOSPITAL CHARITIES

Founded: 1862 CR1074850
PO Box 12008, Birmingham Children's
Hospital, Birmingham, West Midlands B4 6WZ
Tel: 0121 333 8598
Fax: 0121 333 8597
Email: .... bch.charities@bch.nhs.uk
Objects: W3,W

Providing the extras for children in hospital that make their stay more comfortable; investing in child health research; and purchasing advanced equipment to improve children's health.

See advert on previous page

BIRMINGHAM CHRISTIAN COLLEGE
Founded: 1953 CR1002205
Chief Executive Officer: Patrick Rush
Finance Officer: Briony Seymour
Hamilton Drive, Selly Oak, Birmingham, West Midlands B29 6AJ
Tel: 0121 472 0726
Fax: 0121 471 1132
Email: .... info@bhxc.ac.uk
Objects: G,R,3

BIRMINGHAM CONTEMPORARY MUSIC GROUP
Founded: 1991 CR1001474
General Manager: Ms Jackie Newbould
CBSO Centre, Berkley Street, Birmingham, West Midlands B1 2LF
Tel: 0121 616 2616
Fax: 0121 616 2622
Email: .... info@bcmg.org.uk
Objects: S,G,3

BIRMINGHAM DOGS' HOME, THE
CR222436
Ms Alayna Warner
New Bartholomew Street (CC), Digbeth, Birmingham, West Midlands B5 5QS
Tel: 0121 643 5211
Email: ...... info@birminghamdogshome.org.uk
Object: W1

BIRMINGHAM MIND
Founded: 1991 CR1003906
Director: Ms Fiona Taylor
17 Graham Street, Birmingham, West Midlands B1 3JR
Tel: 0121 608 8001
Fax: 0121 608 8006
Email: .... info@birminghammind.org
Objects: F,E,3,C

BIRMINGHAM REPERTORY THEATRE LTD
Founded: 1991 CR223660
Chairman: Mr John Gunn
Business Development & Sponsorship Manager: Ms Joanne Swatkins
Birmingham Repertory Theatre, Centenary Square, Broad Street, Birmingham, West Midlands B1 2EP
Tel: 0121 245 2000
Fax: 0121 245 2182
Email: .. yvonne.stevens@birmingham-rep.co.uk
Objects: S,G

BIRTH DEFECTS FOUNDATION
Founded: 1991 CR1001817
Chief Executive Officer: Mrs Sheila A Brown
Hemlock Way, Cannock, Staffordshire WS11 7GF
Tel: 01543 468888
Objects: F,G,A,1B,3

BLACK WOMEN'S HEALTH & FAMILY SUPPORT
Founded: 1991 CR1083654
Co-ordinator: Mrs S Dirir
1st Floor, 82 Russia Lane, London E2 9LU
Tel: 020 8980 3503
Email: .... bwhafs@btconnect.com

BLACKBURN GROUNDWORK TRUST
Founded: 1990 CR702800
Company Secretary: Mr Brian Woodhouse
Groundwork Environment Centre, Bob Watts Building, Nova Scotia Wharf, Bolton Road, Blackburn, Lancashire BB2 3GE
Tel: 01254 265163
Objects: F,W1,W3,W2,W5,G,W10,W4,3,W8

BLACKWOOD
Founded: 1972SC007658
Craigievar House, 77 Craigmount Brae, Edinburgh EH12 8XF
Tel: 0131 317 7227
Fax: 0131 317 7294
Email: .... info@mbha.org.uk
Web: .... www.mbha.org.uk
Provides specially designed housing for disabled people and their families in mixed-community developments throughout Scotland. Blackwood also specialises in individually tailored care and support packages.

BLANDFORD MUSEUM OF FASHION
CR1052471
Lime Tree House, The Plocks, Church Lane, Blandford Forum, Dorset DT11 7AA
Tel: 01258 453006
Objects: W3,S,G,W4,3

BLESMA - THE LIMBLESS VETERANS
Founded: 1932 CR1084189
Frankland Moore House (CC), 185-187 High Road, Chadwell Heath, Essex RM6 6NA
Tel: 020 8590 1124
Fax: 020 8599 2932
Email: .... fundraising@blesma.org
Objects: F,W9,M,W5,1A,A,1B,V,2,B,H,O,3,C,P

A voluntary organisation for limbless serving and ex-Service men and women.
Objectives: To enable limbless veterans to lead independent and fulfilling lives. Assists with matters of pensions, allowances, welfare, prosthetics and employment. Provides Wellbeing programmes and operates a residential home in Blackpool. Operates a

When a bullet took out my eye, someone from BLESMA helped me to see that I had a future.

Losing an eye is traumatic. But then imagine if you also lose your job, your sense of purpose, your whole way of life. That's tough. Sometimes, when you lose sight of an eye, an arm or a leg, the only thing that helps is talking to someone who understands. Someone who has been in your situation before.

BLESMA is an organisation that has been helping ex-service men and women in this way for 75 years. One way that you could help BLESMA is to leave a legacy in your will. Making a will need not be about death. It can be about life. And by remembering BLESMA you will be making life better for those who have done so much for the future of our country.

To find out more about leaving a legacy, please call 020 8590 1124 or write to us at the address below.

British Limbless Ex-Service Men's Association
185-187 High Road, Chadwell Heath, Romford, Essex RM6 6NA
Tel: 0208 590 1124   Fax: 0208 599 2932   Email: headquarters@blesma.org
www.blesma.org

regular visiting service to members and widows. Supports research and development around limb loss and the training of prosthetists.

See advert on previous page

BLINDAID

Founded: 1834 CR262119
Lantern House, 102 Bermondsey Street,
London SE1 3UB
Tel: 020 7403 6184
Fax: 020 7234 0708
Email: .... enquiries@blindaid.org.uk
Web: .... http://www.blindaid.org.uk
BlindAid has over 175 years of experience.
Working in the 12 Inner London Boroughs, we provide vital home visits to over 600 isolated blind and visually impaired people offering friendship, company and conversation.

BLISS
Founded: 1979 CR1002973; SC040006
Head of Income: Ms Caley Eldred
9 Holyrood Street, London SE1 2EL
Tel: ... 020 7378 1122; 0500 618140 Freephone
Familly Support Helpline
Fax: 020 7403 0673
Email: .... information@bliss.org.uk
Objects: F,W3,G,1A,N,H

BLUE BADGE NETWORK, THE
Founded: 1986 CR1018535
Chairman: Mr W Bowdler
Director / Secretary: Doctor M J Weatherly
198 Wolverhampton Street, Dudley, West
Midlands DY1 1DZ
Tel: 01384 257001
Objects: W5,2

BLUE CROSS
Founded: 1897 CR224392; SC040154
Chief Executive: Ms Kim Hamilton
Ms Carole A. Bankes
Mrs Emma Miller
Registered Office, Shilton Road, Burford,
Oxfordshire OX18 4PF
Tel: 0300 777 1897
Fax: 0300 777 1601
Email: .... info@bluecross.org.uk
Objects: W1,E,G,H,3

BLUEBELL RAILWAY TRUST
CR292497
The Bluebell Railway, Sheffield Park Station,
Uckfield, East Sussex TN22 3QL
Tel: 01825 720800
Fax: 01825 720804
Email: .... roger.kelly@bluebell-railway.co.uk
Web: .... www.bluebell-railway.co.uk
Objects: W2,S,G,1A,A,1B,W12
Established for all charitable purposes connected with railways. The principal objects are the provision of facilities for recreation and leisure time activities connected with railways, particularly by organising voluntary work on the restoration and maintenance of railway items of historic interest with special regard to matters connected with operating the "Bluebell Railway" as a preserved steam railway in Sussex. Other objects include research to improve railway and safety equipment, support of museums and institutions devoted to the preservation and public display of railway equipment and assistance to railway apprentices and dependent employees.

BLYTHSWOOD CARE
SC021848
Highland Deephaven Industrial Estate, Evanton,
Highland IV16 9XJ
Tel: 01349 830777
Fax: 01349 830477
Email: .... info@blythswood.org
Objects: W3,W10,R,U,H,K

BMA CHARITIES
Founded: 1792 CR219102
Director: Ms Marian Flint
Chairman: Dr M Wilks
BMA House, Tavistock Square, London
WC1H 9JP
Tel: 020 7383 6142
Email: .... info.bmacharities@bma.org.uk
Objects: W11,1A,A
Helps doctors and their dependants and medical students in times of financial crisis.

BMS WORLD MISSION
Founded: 1792 CR233782
PO Box 49, 129 Broadway, Didcot, Oxfordshire
OX11 8XA
Tel: 01235 517700
Fax: 01235 517601
Email: .... mail@bmsworldmission.org
Objects: W3,W7,G,W10,W15,A,1B,W16,2,R,W4,
U,B,H,Y,P,W8,L

BODY POSITIVE NORTH EAST LIMITED
Founded: 1990 CR1000714
Chair of the Board of Directors: Mr David Fawcett
Client Services: Ms Dorothy Foster
Finance Manager: Ms Diane Taylor
12 Princess Square, Newcastle upon Tyne, Tyne
& Wear NE1 8ER
Tel: 0191 232 2855
Email: .... bpne@btinternet.com
Objects: F,W6,M,W3,J,E,W7,W5,G,W10,W4,H,3,
P,W8

BOLENOWE ANIMAL SANCTUARY
CR296673
Bonaventure Farm, Ruan Minor, Helston, Cornwall
TR12 7LW
Tel: 01326 573545
Email: .... info@bolenowe.co.uk

BOLTON COMMUNITY & VOLUNTARY SERVICE
Founded: 1991 CR1003123
Chief Officer: Ms Alison Hill
Bridge House, Pool Street South, Bolton, Greater
Manchester BL1 2BA
Tel: 01204 546010
Fax: 01204 373694
Email: .... shafiqa@boltoncvs.org.uk
Objects: F,2,H

Books change lives

Book Aid International
www.bookaid.org

Poverty and illiteracy go hand in hand. But in sub-Saharan Africa, books are a luxury few can afford. Many children leave school functionally illiterate, and adults often fall back into illiteracy in later life due to a lack of available reading material.

Book Aid International knows that books change lives

Books can bring hope to some of the poorest readers in the world, giving people of all ages the chance to make opportunities for themselves. Books are urgently needed in sub-Saharan Africa, where 153 million people remain functionally illiterate.

Every year we send over half a million books to our partners in 12 countries in sub-Saharan Africa, to stock libraries in schools, refugee camps, prisons, universities and communities. Literally millions of readers have access to books and information that could teach them new skills. Many more will know the pleasure of losing themselves in a novel.

Illustration © Chitra Merchant

Our supporters make it possible for us to continue our work

Each donation or legacy that we receive has the potential to make a long-lasting impact on education for hundreds, if not thousands of readers. Please contact us on 020 7733 3577 for further information, or go to our website at www.bookaid.org.

Book Aid International is a charity and a limited company registered in England and Wales.
Charity No. 313869 Company No. 880754 39-41 Coldharbour Lane, Camberwell, London SE5 9NR
T + (0)20 7733 3577   F + (0)20 7978 8006   E info@bookaid.org   www.bookaid.org

---

BOLTON YMCA
Founded: 1991 CR1001884
Chairman: Mr D Howell
General Secretary: Mr J Finch Sutherland
125 Deansgate, Bolton, Greater Manchester
BL1 1HA
Tel: 01204 522855
Fax: 01204 522855
Objects: W3,E,A,2,3,P

BOOK AID INTERNATIONAL
Founded: 1954 CR313869
Director: Alison Hubert
39-41 Coldharbour Lane, Camberwell, London
SE5 9NR
Tel: 020 7733 3577
Fax: 020 7978 8006
Email: . . . . info@bookaid.org
Objects: G,U,3

See advert on this page

BOOTSTRAP COMPANY (BLACKBURN) LIMITED
Founded: 1990 CR702427
Company Secretary: Mr Graham Jones
35 Railway Road, Blackburn, Lancashire BB1 1EZ
Tel: 01254 680367
Objects: G,3

BORDER COLLIE TRUST GB
CR1053585
Heathway, Colton, Rugeley, Staffordshire
WS15 3LY
Tel: 0871 560 2282
Fax: 01889 574517
Email: . . . . info@bordercollietrustgb.org.uk

BOSCO SOCIETY
Founded: 1991 CR1129588
59/61 Merton Road, Bootle, Liverpool, Merseyside
L20 7AP
Tel: 0151 944 1818
Objects: G,2,O,C

BOWEL & CANCER RESEARCH
CR1119105
Secretary to the Trustees: Mr David Carlton
National Centre for Bowel Research and Surgical
Innovation, Barts & the London School of
Medicine and Dentistry, 1st Floor, Abernethy
Building, 2 Newark Street, London E1 2AT
Tel: 020 7882 8749
Email: . . . . mail@bowelcancerresearch.org
Objects: W3,W5,W10,W4,W8

BOWEL CANCER UK
CR1071038; SC040914
Wilcox House, 14-148 Borough High Street,
London SE1 1LB
Tel: . . . . . 020 7381 9711; 0800 840 3540 Bowel
Cancer Advisory Service
Fax: 020 7381 5752
Email: . . . . legacy@bowelcanceruk.org.uk
Objects: F,N

THE BOYS' BRIGADE (NATIONAL OFFICE)

>the adventure begins here

Founded: 1883 CR305969
Headquarters, Felden Lodge, Hemel Hempstead, Hertfordshire HP3 0BL
Tel: 01442 231681
Fax: 01442 235391
Email: ...... enquiries@boys-brigade.org.uk
Web: .... www.boys-brigade.org.uk
Objects: W3,J,S,G,2,R,H,3
The BB seeks to care for and challenge young people for life through a programme of informal education underpinned by the Christian faith. Currently there are 70,000 members sharing activities in 1500 churches throughout the British Isles. You can help by giving of your time to your local Company, offering financial support or remembering us in your will.

BRADFIELD FOUNDATION, THE
Founded: 1990 CR900457
Director of Development: Miss Elizabeth Atkinson
Bradfield College, Bradfield, Reading RG7 6AU
Tel: 0118 964 4840
Email: .... development@bradfieldcollege.org.uk
Objects: W3,S,G,A,D,B

BRADFORD COMMUNITY FOR VOLUNTARY SERVICE
Founded: 1991 CR1090036
Secretary to the Trustees: Mr A Clipsom
Information Officer: Mr Gavin Massingham
19-25 Sunbridge Road, Bradford, West Yorkshire BD1 2AY
Tel: 01274 722772
Fax: 01274 393938
Email: .... cvs@bradfordcvs.org.uk
Objects: F,J,2,H,3

BRAIN INJURY REHABILITATION TRUST
CR800797
Director: Mrs Lynn Turley
60 Queen Street, Normanton, West Yorkshire WF6 2BU
Tel: 01924 896100
Fax: 01924 899264
Objects: W5,O,3,C

BRAIN RESEARCH TRUST
Founded: 1971 CR1137560
Dutch House, 307-308 High Holborn, London WC1V 7LL
Tel: 020 7404 9982
Fax: 020 7404 9983
Email: .... info@brt.org.uk
Object: W

BRAMBLEY HEDGE CHILDRENS CENTRE CHARITY LIMITED
Founded: 1979 CR278497
Treasurer: Mrs Teresa Brown
Chairperson: Ms Lyn Davies
Manager: Ms Twigs Redman
Brambley Hedge Childrens Centre, Tower Street, Dover, Kent CT17 0AW
Tel: 01304 211811
Objects: W3,E,3

BREAK: HIGH QUALITY SUPPORT FOR VULNERABLE CHILDREN AND FAMILIES
Founded: 1968 CR286650
Chris Hoddy
Chief Executive
Davison House, 1 Montague Road, Sheringham, Norfolk NR26 8WN
Tel: 01263 822161
Fax: 01263 822181
Email: .... office@break-charity.org
Objects: W3,E,W5,V,W4,3

BREAKTHROUGH BREAST CANCER

BREAKTHROUGH CANCER

CR1062636; SC039058
Weston House, 246 High Holborn, London WC1V 7EX
Tel: 08080 100 200
Fax: 020 7025 2401
Email: .... legacies@breakthrough.org.uk
Breakthrough Breast Cancer is the UK's leading charity dedicated to stopping women dying from breast cancer. Our mission is to save lives through improving early diagnosis, developing new treatments and preventing all types of breast cancer. Our breakthroughs are made by funding 25% of the breast cancer research in the UK, campaigning to ensure survival rates are among the best in the world and educating all women to recognise the signs and symptoms of the disease.

BREAST CANCER CAMPAIGN
Founded: 1988 CR299758
Chief Executive: Baroness Delyth Morgan
Clifton Centre, 110 Clifton Street CC, London EC2A 4HT
Tel: 020 7749 4114
Fax: 020 7749 3701
Email: .... info@bcc-uk.org
Objects: W5,W10,W15,1B,W4,W8,W

BRENDONCARE FOUNDATION
CR326508
The Old Malthouse, Victoria Road, Winchester, Hampshire SO23 7DU
Tel: 01962 852133
Fax: 01962 851506
Email: .... enquiries@brendoncare.org.uk

BRISTOL ASSOCIATION FOR NEIGHBOURHOOD DAYCARE LTD (BAND LTD)
Founded: 1978 CR1017307
Chief Executive Officer: Mr Paul Dielhenn
The Proving House, Sevier Street, St. Werburghs, Bristol BS2 9LB
Tel: 0117 954 2128
Fax: 0117 954 1694
Email: . . . . admin@bandltd.org.uk
Objects: F,W3,G,W15,2,3

BRISTOL CANCER HELP CENTRE
See Penny Brohn Cancer Care

BRISTOL OLD VIC THEATRE SCHOOL LTD
Founded: 1990 CR900280
Secretary to the Company: Mr D M W Simpson
2 Downside Road, Bristol BS8 2XF
Tel: 0117 973 3535
Email: . . . . enquiries@oldvic.drama.ac.uk
Objects: G,3

BRITAIN NEPAL MEDICAL TRUST
Founded: 1968 CR255249
Company Secretary/Administrator: Mrs A G Peck
Export House (CD 2014), 130 Vale Road, Tonbridge, Kent TN9 1SP
Tel: 01732 360284
Fax: 01732 363876
Email: . . . . . info@britainnepalmedicaltrust.org.uk
Since 1968 BNMT has been assisting the people of Nepal to improve their health by working in partnership with the Ministry of Health, international and local NGOs, local committees and communities to prevent disease and establish and maintain sustainable basic health services.
See advert on this page

BRITISH AMERICAN SECURITY INFORMATION COUNCIL (BASIC)
Founded: 1990 CR1001081
The Secretary to the Trustees
3 Whitehall Court, London SW1A 2EL
Tel: 020 7766 3461
Email: . . . . basicuk@basicint.org
Objects: G,3

BRITISH AND FOREIGN SCHOOL SOCIETY
Founded: 1808 CR314286
Director: Mr Charles M C Crawford
Maybrook House, Godstone Road, Caterham, Surrey CR3 6RE
Tel: 01883 331177
Objects: W3,G,1A,A,1B,2

BRITISH & INTERNATIONAL SAILORS' SOCIETY
See Sailors' Society

BRITISH ASSOCIATION FOR IMMEDIATE CARE - BASICS
Founded: 1977 CR276054
Chief Executive: Mrs Ruth Lloyd
Chairman: Mr Richard Steyn
Turret House, Turret Lane, Ipswich, Suffolk IP4 1DL

Tel: 01473 218407
Fax: 01473 280585
Email: .... cx@basics.org.uk
Objects: J,G,N,2,H,3

BRITISH ASSOCIATION OF PLASTIC RECONSTRUCTIVE AND AESTHETIC SURGERY (BAPRAS)
Founded: 1946 CR1005353
Senior Administrator: Mrs H C Roberts
The Royal College of Surgeons, 35-43 Lincolns Inn Fields, London WC2A 3PN
Tel: 020 7831 5161
Fax: 020 7831 4041
Email: .... secretariat@bapras.org.uk
Objects: W9,W3,W5,G,1A,A,2,W4

BRITISH COUNCIL FOR PREVENTION OF BLINDNESS
CR270941
Chairman: Professor Andrew Elkington CBE, FRCS, FRCOphth
Mr Steve Silverton
4 Bloomsbury Square, London WC1A 2RP
Tel: 020 7404 7114
Email: .... info@bcpb.org
Objects: W6,1B,U

BRITISH DEAF ASSOCIATION
Founded: 1890 CR1031687
Chief Executive: Mr Jeff McWhinney
1-3 Worship Street, London EC2A 2AB
Tel: . 020 7588 3520 Voice; 020 7588 2529 Text; 0800 652 2965 Helpline Text; 0870 770 3300 Voice
Fax: 020 7588 3527
Email: .... info@bda.org.uk
Objects: F,J,S,W7,G,V,2,U,H,3,P

BRITISH DENTAL ASSOCIATION BENEVOLENT FUND
CR208146
64 Wimpole Street, London W1G 8YS
Tel: 020 7486 4995
Objects: W11,1A,A

BRITISH DENTAL HEALTH FOUNDATION
CR263198
Chief Executive: Doctor Nigel Carter
Smile House, 2 East Union Street, Rugby, Warwickshire CV22 6AJ
Tel: 0870 770 4000
Fax: 0870 770 4010
Email: .... mail@dentalhealth.org
Objects: F,W2,W7,W5,W10,2,W4,H,3,W8

BRITISH DISABLED WATER SKI ASSOCIATION, THE
Founded: 1979 CR1063678
The Tony Edge National Centre, Heron Lake, Hythe End, Staines, Middlesex TW19 6HW
Tel: 01784 483664
Fax: 01784 482747
Objects: W6,W7,W5,G,3,P

BRITISH DIVERS MARINE LIFE RESCUE
CR803438; SC039304
Chairman: Mr Alan Knight
Lime House, Regency Close, Uckfield, East Sussex TN22 1DS
Tel: 01825 765546
Fax: 01825 768012
Email: .... info@bdmlr.org.uk

BRITISH DYSLEXIA ASSOCIATION
Founded: 1972 CR289243
CEO: Mrs Judith Stewart
Unit 8, Bracknell Beeches, Old Bracknell Lane, Bracknell, Bracknell Forest RG12 7BW
Tel: .... 0845 251 9003 (Office); 0845 251 9002 (Helpline)
Fax: 0845 251 9005
Email: .... admin@bdadyslexia.org.uk
Objects: F,J,W5,G,2,H,3

BRITISH EMUNAH (IN AID OF CHILD RESETTLEMENT FUND)
See Emunah (in Aid of Child Resettlement Fund)

THE BRITISH HEART FOUNDATION (BHF)

Founded: 1961 CR225971; SC039426
Greater London House, 180 Hampstead Road, London NW1 7AW
Tel: 020 7554 0226; 020 7554 0000
Fax: 020 7554 0100
Email: .... partners@bhf.org.uk
Web: .... http://www.bhf.org.uk
Coronary heart disease is still the UK's single biggest killer, claiming more than 74,000 lives every year. We believe that one day we can help to create a world where people no longer die prematurely from heart disease. The British Heart Foundation is dedicated to keeping vulnerable hearts beating through our pioneering research, vital prevention work and quality care and support. We also run numerous campaigns to deliver essential information to help people understand and care for their own heart health. As the nation's heart charity, we rely on your support and your donations of time and money to continue our life saving work. Only by working together can we fight for every heartbeat.

THE BRITISH HOME - CARING FOR SEVERELY DISABLED PEOPLE
Founded: 1861 CR206222
The House Governor: Mrs Noelle Kelly
Crown Lane, Streatham, London SW16 3JB
Tel: 020 8670 8261
Fax: 020 8766 6084
Email: .... info@britishhome.org.uk
Objects: M,N,B,C

BRITISH HORSE SOCIETY
Founded: 1947 CR210504; SC038516
Chief Executive: Mr Graham Cory
Abbey Park (CC), Stareton, Kenilworth, Warwickshire CV8 2XZ
Tel: 02476 840 500
Email: .... enquiry@bhs.org.uk
Objects: W1,W2,G,2

BRITISH-ITALIAN SOCIETY
Founded: 1941 CR253386
Chairman: Mr Charles de Chassiron
Honorary Director: Mrs Susan Kikoler
Hurlingham Studios (Unit 4), Ranelagh Gardens, London SW6 3PA

Tel: . . . . 020 8150 9167 (Membership); 020 7371 7111 (Events)
Email: jj@british-italian.org (Membership); reiko@british-italian.org (Events)
Objects: S,A,P

BRITISH KIDNEY PATIENT ASSOCIATION (BKPA)

BRITISH KIDNEY
Patient **ASSOCIATION**

improving life for kidney patients

Founded: 1975 CR270288
Ms Suzan Yianni
3 The Windmills, St Mary's Close, Turk Street, Alton, Hampshire GU34 1EF
Tel: 01420 541424
Fax: 01420 89438
Objects: W3,W5,A

The British Kidney Patient Association is a well established charity working to improve the quality of life for all kidney patients living with the mental and physical demands of kidney disease. The funds we raise are used to help provide valuable advice, information and much needed financial aid to patients and their families during difficult times, as well as supporting the development of quality facilities within kidney units around the UK.

BRITISH MIGRAINE ASSOCIATION
See Migraine Action Association

BRITISH OCCUPATIONAL HEALTH RESEARCH FOUNDATION
Founded: 1991 CR1077273
Chief Executive: Mr Brian Kazer
6 St Andrew's Place, London NW1 4LB
Tel: 020 7317 5898
Fax: 020 7317 5899
Email: . . . . admin@bohrf.org.uk
Objects: A,1B,2

BRITISH ORNITHOLOGISTS' UNION
Founded: 1858 CR249877
Honorary Treasurer: Mr R Clarke
Administrator: Mr Steve Dudley
President: Mr Ian Newton
Dept of Zoology, South Parks Road, Oxford, Oxfordshire OX1 3PS
Tel: 01865 281842
Email: . . . . bou@bou.org.uk
Objects: 1A,A,2,H

BRITISH PLUMBING EMPLOYERS COUNCIL (TRAINING) LIMITED
Founded: 1992 CR1012890
Chief Executive: Mr Paul Johnson
2 Mallard Way, Pride Park, Derby, Derbyshire DE24 8GX
Tel: 0845 644 6558
Fax: 0845 121 1931
Email: . . . . info@bpec.org.uk
Objects: G,H,3

BRITISH RECORD INDUSTRY TRUST
Founded: 1990 CR1000413
Company Secretary: Ms Roz Groome
Riverside Building, County Hall, Westminster Bridge Road, London SE1 7JA
Tel: 020 7803 1300
Fax: 020 7803 1340
Email: . . . . roz.groome@bpi.co.uk
Objects: W3,G,1B

BRITISH RED CROSS
CR220949; SC037738
44 Moorfields, London EC2Y 9AL
Tel: 0844 87 100 87
Fax: 020 7562 2039
Email: . . . . legacy@redcross.org.uk

BRITISH SKIN FOUNDATION
CR313865
Office Manager: Ms Sarah Battersby
4 Fitzroy Square, London W1T 5HQ
Tel: 020 7391 6341
Fax: 020 7391 6099
Email: . . . . . admin@britishskinfoundation.org.uk
Objects: W9,W6,W3,W7,W5,W10,W11,W15,1A, W16,W4,W8,W

BRITISH SOCIETY FOR HAEMATOLOGY, THE
Founded: 1960 CR1005735
Secretary: Doctor J T Reilly
2 Carlton House Terrace, London SW1Y 5AF
Tel: 020 8643 7305
Fax: 020 8770 0933
Email: . . . . jtr@bshhya.demon.co.uk
Objects: G,1A

BRITISH SPORTS ASSOCIATION FOR THE DISABLED
See Disability Sport England

BRITISH STAMMERING ASSOCIATION
Founded: 1978 CR1089967
15 Old Ford Road, Bethnal Green, London E2 9PJ
Tel: . . . . 020 8983 1003; 0845 603 2001 Helpline
Fax: 020 8983 3591
Email: . . . . mail@stammering.org
Objects: F,W3,J,W5,G,2,H,O

BRITISH TRUST FOR THE MYELIN PROJECT
See Myelin Project

BRITISH WIRELESS FOR THE BLIND FUND (BWBF)
CR1078287
10 Albion Place, Maidstone, Kent ME14 5DZ
Tel: 01622 754757
Fax: 01622 751725
Email: . . . . Info@blind.org.uk
Object: W6

BRITTLE BONE SOCIETY
Founded: 1972 CR272100
Administrator: Mr Raymond Lawrie
30 Guthrie Street, Dundee DD1 5BS
Tel: 01382 204446
Fax: 01382 206771
Email: . . . . bbs@brittlebone.org
Objects: F,M,W3,W5,A,2,H,P

BROGDALE HORTICULTURAL TRUST, THE
Founded: 1990 CR328674
Chief Executive: Ms Jane Garrett
Chief Guide: Mr Ted Hobday
Brogdale Road, Faversham, Kent ME13 8XZ
Tel: 01795 535286
Fax: 01795 535170
Email: .... info@brogdale.org.uk
Objects: W2,G,2,W12

BROMLEY & SHEPPARD'S COLLEGES
Founded: 1666 CR210337
Chaplain & Clerk to Trustees: Revd George Bailey
c/o Chaplain's House, Bromley College, London Road, Bromley, Kent BR1 1PE
Tel: 020 8460 4712
Fax: 020 8464 3558
Objects: D,W4,C

BROMLEY AUTISTIC TRUST
CR1002032
Chief Executive: Mr Richard Lane
129 Southlands Road, Bromley, Kent BR2 9QT
Tel: 020 8464 2897
Fax: 020 8464 2994
Email: .... info@bromleyautistictrust.co.uk
Objects: W3,E,W5,D,W4,3,P

BROOK ADVISORY CENTRE (AVON)
Founded: 1990 CR900431
Chair of Executive Committee: Mr David Crawford
Centre Manager: Ms Anna Hutley
Finance Officer: Mr John Jameson
1 Unity Street, Bristol BS1 5HH
Tel: 0117 929 1191
Fax: 0117 922 1293
Objects: F,W3,W5,G,N,3,W8

BT BENEVOLENT FUND
Founded: 1853 CR212565
Manager: Mrs Debbie Terry
Room 323 (CD), Reading Central TE, 41 Minster Street, Reading RG1 2JB
Tel: 0208 726 2145
Email: .... benevolent@bt.com
Web: .... http://www.benevolent.bt.com
Objects: W11,1A,A,2
The Fund assists current and former BT employees and their dependents who are experiencing financial hardship as well as running a pro-active Pensioner Contact Scheme.
Bank: Santander. Account Number: 28014005. Sort Code: 09-01-55.

THE BUCKINGHAMSHIRE ASSOCIATION FOR MENTAL HEALTH
See Buckinghamshire Mind

BUCKINGHAMSHIRE MIND
CR1103063
4 Temple Street, Aylesbury, Buckinghamshire HP20 2RQ
Tel: 01494 533163
Fax: 01296 437328
Email: .... carolyn.smyth@bucksmind.org.uk
Objects: F,J,E,W5,G,D,2,W4,H,3,P

BUCKS COUNTY AGRICULTURAL ASSOCIATION
Founded: 1990 CR1000652
Secretary: Mrs Diana Amies
The Old Barn, Wingbury Courtyard Business Village, Leighton Road, Wingrave, Buckinghamshire HP22 4LW
Tel: 01296 680400
Fax: 01296 680445
Email: .... alison@buckscountyshow.co.uk

BUPA FOUNDATION, THE
CR277598
Bupa House, 15-19 Bloomsbury Way, London WC1A 2BA
Tel: 020 7656 2591
Fax: 020 7656 2708
Email: .... bupafoundation@bupa.com
Object: 1B

BURTON CONSTABLE FOUNDATION, THE
Founded: 1992 CR1010121
Director to the Foundation: Dr David Connell
Burton Constable Hall, Burton Constable, Skirlaugh, East Riding of Yorkshire HU11 4LN
Tel: 01964 562400
Objects: W3,W2,S,G,W12,W4,3

BUSINESS IN THE COMMUNITY
CR297716
Company Secretary: Ms Lesley Bader
Executive Director: Mr Graham Bann
137 Shepherdess Walk, London N1 7RQ
Tel: 0870 600 2482
Email: .... lesley.bader@bitc.org.uk
Objects: W3,J,G,W10,2,H,W8

BUSINESSDYNAMICS TRUST
Founded: 1991 CR1004426
Chief Executive: Mr David Millar
Company Secretary: Mr J W C Wren
Enterprise House, 59-65 Upper Ground, London SE1 9PQ
Tel: 020 7620 0735
Fax: 020 7928 0578
Objects: W6,W3,W7,G,3

BUTTERFLY CONSERVATION
CR254937
Fundraising Manager: Mr David Bridges
Chairman: Mr Dudley Cheesman
Chief Executive: Dr Martin Warren
Manor Yard, East Lulworth, Wareham, Dorset BH20 5QP
Tel: 01929 400209
Fax: 01929 400210
Email: .... info@butterfly-conservation.org
Objects: W2,2,H

C

C.H.A.T.
See Celia Hammond Animal Trust

CABRINI CHILDREN'S SOCIETY
Founded: 1887 CR233296
Chief Executive: Mr Jonathan Pearce
49 Russell Hill Road, Purley, Surrey CR8 2XB

Tel: 020 8668 2181
Fax: 020 8703 2274
Email: .... info@cabrini.org.uk
Web: .... http://www.cabrini.org.uk
Objects: Q,F,W3,E,V,O,3,P
We support vulnerable children and families of all backgrounds who need protection. Visit our website for more information. Thank you.

CALDECOTT FOUNDATION
Founded: 1911 CR307889
Finance Officer: Ms Sylvia Crouch
Director: Mr Clive Lee
Caldcott House, Smeeth, Ashford, Kent TN25 6SP
Tel: 01303 815678
Fax: 01303 815677
Objects: W3,G,O

CALDERDALE MENCAP
Founded: 1991 CR1002398
Company Secretary: Mrs Sue Anderson
162 King Cross Road, Halifax, West Yorkshire HX1 3LN
Tel: 01422 322552
Fax: 01422 381835
Email: .... marklacey001@supanet.com
Objects: F,W3,J,W5,G,1A,A,1B,V,D,2,R,3,C,P,K

CALIBRE AUDIO LIBRARY
Founded: 1974 CR286614
Liz Clarke
Director: Mr M Lewington
New Road, Weston Turville, Aylesbury, Buckinghamshire HP22 5XQ
Tel: 01296 432339
Fax: 01296 392599
Email: .... enquiries@calibre.org.uk
Objects: W6,W3,S,W5,G,2,W4,H,O,3

THE CALVERT TRUST
CR1042423
Kielder Water & Forest Park, Hexham, Northumberland NE48 1BS
Tel: 01434 250232
Fax: 01434 250015
Email: .... enquiries@calvert-kielder.com

CALVERT TRUST EXMOOR
Founded: 1991 CR1005776
Ms Fiona Sim
Wistlandpound, Kentisbury, Barnstaple, Devon EX31 4SJ
Tel: 01598 763221
Email: .... exmoor@calvert-trust.org.uk
Objects: W6,W3,W7,W5,V,3,P

CAM SIGHT (THE CAMBRIDGESHIRE SOCIETY FOR THE BLIND & PARTIALLY SIGHTED)
Founded: 1912 CR201640
Chief Executive: Mrs Anne Streather
167 Green End Road, Cambridge, Cambridgeshire CB4 1RW
Tel: 01223 420033
Fax: 01223 501829
Email: .... info@camsight.org.uk
Objects: F,W6,M,W3,J,S,W5,G,W10,W4,O,3,P,K

CAMDEN COMMUNITY NURSERIES LIMITED
Founded: 1991 CR1002534
Co-ordinator: Ms Carol Berger
99 Leighton Road, Kentish Town, London NW5 2RB
Tel: 020 7485 2105

CAMPAIGN FOR NATIONAL PARKS
CR295336
6/7 Barnard Mews, London SW11 1QU
Tel: 020 7924 4077
Fax: 020 7924 5761
Email: .... info@cnp.org.uk
Objects: F,J,W2,2

CAMPAIGN TO PROTECT RURAL ENGLAND - CPRE
Founded: 1926 CR1089685
Director: Mr Shaun Spiers
5-11 Lavington Street, London SE1 0NZ
Tel: 020 7981 2855
Email: .... info@cpre.org.uk
Objects: F,W1,J,W2,S,2,H

CAMPDEN CHARITIES
CR1104616
Clerk to the Trustees: Mr A E Cornick
27A Pembridge Villas, London W11 3EP
Tel: 020 7243 0551
Fax: 020 7229 4920
Objects: F,M,W3,J,E,W5,G,W10,1A,A,1B,V,D,2,W4,B,O,C,P,W8,K

CAMPHILL VILLAGE TRUST
Founded: 1954 CR232402
The Fundraising Manager
Camphill Family Appeals Office, Botton Village, Danby, Whitby, North Yorkshire YO21 2NJ
Tel: 01287 661294
Fax: 01287 660888
Email: .... family@camphill.org.uk
Objects: W2,S,W5,D,W4,W14,3,K
We are a leading, long established and progressive UK charity supporting adults with learning disabilities, mental health problems and other special needs. We support people in their home life, work, social and cultural activities through our 9 urban and rural communities in England.

CAN - DRUGS, ALCOHOL & HOMELESSNESS

CR1025395
Denmark House, 8 Billing Road, Northampton, Northamptonshire NN1 5AW
Tel: 01604 824777
Fax: 01604 635679
Email: .... administration@can.org.uk
Web: .... www.can.org.uk
Objects: F,W3,G,W15,D,W8
Services available throughout Northamptonshire and Bedfordshire for anyone who is affected by alcohol,

drugs and homelessness. We also offer support to families and carers.

CANBURY SCHOOL LIMITED
Founded: 1990 CR803766
Headmaster: Mr Robin F Metters
Trustees Solicitor: Mr J N Stapleton
Kingston Hill, Kingston upon Thames, Surrey
KT2 7LN
Tel: 020 8549 8622
Objects: W3,G,3

CANCER FOCUS NORTHERN IRELAND
XN48265
40-44 Eglantine Avenue, Belfast BT9 6DX
Tel: . 028 9066 3281; 0800 783 3339 (Freephone Information Helpline)
Fax: 028 9066 8715
Email: . . . . hello@cancerfocusni.org

CANCER HELP CENTRE
See Penny Brohn Cancer Care

CANCER PREVENTION RESEARCH TRUST

CR265985
231 Roehampton Lane, London SW15 4LB
Tel: 020 8785 7786
Fax: 020 8785 6466
Email: . . . . cprt@talk21.com
Web: . www.cancerpreventionresearch.co. uk

Objects: F,A,H,3
The Cancer Prevention Research Trust is the leading cancer prevention research organisation in the world. Through a programme of research grants and education it has created awareness that cancer is a preventable disease. Since its inception in 1973 it has supported pioneering cancer prevention research and developed a programme of cancer education to help men, women and children reduce their cancer risk. With increasing information about lifestyle and diet which can reduce the risk of cancer the Trust will pass on the results through its monthly newsletter, *Cancer Prevention and Health News* and awareness initiatives.
See advert on next page

CANCER RELIEF MACMILLAN FUND (SEE MACMILLAN CANCER RELIEF)
See Macmillan Cancer Support

CANCER RESEARCH FUND, WORLD
See World Cancer Research Fund (WCRF UK)

CANCER RESEARCH WALES
CR248767
Velindre Hospital (CD), Whitechurch, Cardiff
CF14 2TL
Tel: 029 2031 6976
Fax: . . . . 029 2052 1609 (24 Hour Line)
Email: . . . . crw@wales.nhs.uk

CANCERBACKUP
See Macmillan Cancer Support

CANCERBACKUP
Founded: 1984 CR1019719
3 Bath Place, Rivington Street, London EC2A 3JR
Tel: 020 7696 9003
Fax: 020 7696 9002
Email: . . . . info@cancerbackup.org.uk
Objects: F,G,H,3

CANCERWISE
Founded: 1982 CR290574
Chairman: Mrs Marnie Duval
Secretary: Mr James Fergusson
Tavern House, 4 City Business Centre, Basin Road, Chichester, West Sussex PO19 8DU
Tel: 01243 778516
Fax: 01243 778516
Email: . . . . enquiries@cancerwise.org.uk
Objects: F,J,G,H,O,3

CANTERBURY DAY NURSERY, HOLIDAY PLAYSCHEME AND AFTER SCHOOL CLUB
Founded: 1991 CR1001989
Accountant: Mr F Whitten
29 High Street, Bridge, Canterbury, Kent CT4 5JZ
Tel: 01227 831076
Object: G

CANTERBURY DISTRICT C.A.B
Founded: 1990 CR803115
Honorary Secretary: Mr Brian Collins
3 Westgate Hall Road, Canterbury, Kent CT1 2BT
Tel: 01227 452762
Objects: F,W9,W6,W7,W5,W10,W11,2,W4,3,W8

CANTERBURY OAST TRUST & SOUTH OF ENGLAND RARE BREEDS CENTRE
Founded: 1985 CR291662
Chief Executive: Mr David Jackson
Ms Angela Phibbs
Highlands Farm, Woodchurch, Ashford, Kent TN26 3RJ
Tel: 01233 861493
Fax: 01233 860433
Email: . . . . enquiries@canterburyoasttrust.org.uk
Objects: W2,W5,G,D,3

CANTERBURY UMBRELLA
Founded: 1988 CR298480
Chair: Dr Edwina Bell
Canterbury Umbrella Centre, St Peters Place, Canterbury, Kent CT1 2DB
Tel: 01227 767660
Objects: F,W6,E,W7,W5,W10,W4,3,P,W8

CAPITB TRUST
Founded: 1990 CR1000290
Group Accountant: Mr H Smith
PO Box 91, Brighouse, West Yorkshire HD6 2WB
Tel: 0113 227 3345
Objects: G,3

CARAVAN, THE CHARITY FOR GROCERY PEOPLE
Founded: 1964 CR1095897; SC039255
Director General: Mrs Gillian M Barker
Honorary Treasurer: Mr Tony Paine
2 Lakeside Business Park, Swan Lane, Sandhurst, Slough GU47 9DN
Tel: 01252 875925
Fax: 01252 890562
Email: . . . . info@caravan-charity.org.uk
Objects: F,W11,1A,A,W4,B,3

CARAVAN, THE TRADING NAME OF THE NATIONAL GROCERS BENEVOLENT FUND
See Caravan, the Charity for Grocery People

CARDIAC RESEARCH AND DEVELOPMENT FUND
Founded: 1990 CR328613
Treasurer: Mr Simon Strong
PricewaterhouseCoopers, One Kingsway, Cardiff CF10 3PW
Email: . . . . simon.r.strong@uk.pwc.com

CARDIFF CHINESE CHRISTIAN CHURCH
Founded: 1991 CR1004056
Chairman: Doctor Alan NG
65 Llandaff Road, Canton, Cardiff CF11 9NG
Tel: 029 2038 8724

CARE FOR THE WILD INTERNATIONAL

Founded: 1984 CR288802
72 Brighton Road, Horsham, West Sussex RH13 5BQ
Tel: 01403 249832
Fax: 01403246950
Email: . . . . info@careforthewild.com
Web: . . . . www.careforthewild.org
Objects: Q,W1,W2,1B
Care for the Wild is a small charity dedicated to the protection of wildlife in the UK and around the globe. We have been around for almost 30 years and we operate under three key areas: - Rescue - Protect - Defend
See advert on this page

CARERS RELIEF SERVICE
Founded: 1983 CR1051841
Office Manager: Mrs T O'Brien
Lingley House, Rooms 2 & 3, Commissioners Road, Strood, Rochester, Kent ME2 4EE
Tel: 01634 715995
Objects: M,W5,3,P

CARERS UK
Founded: 1988 CR246329
20 Great Dover Street, London SE1 4LX

Cat Welfare Trust

The Cat Fancy's own Charity, established 1988

Making a lasting difference to all cats' lives

Registered Charity No. 800719

The Cat Welfare Trust helps fund research projects into feline disease that are unlikely to attract commercial funding in their initial stages. The current project is a study being conducted by Bristol University in conjunction with Manchester University and the University of California-Davis into the genes that play a pivotal role in the control of infectious diseases in cats—vital research that will benefit all felines. Every penny you donate is spent on the work of the Trust, nothing is spent on administration or salaries, making your valuable support extremely cost effective.

To make a donation, including leaving a legacy in your will, or for further information about the work of the Trust, contact The Treasurer, Mrs. Eileen Fryer at:

Governing Council of the Cat Fancy
5 King's Castle Business Park, The Drove, Bridgwater   TA6 4AG
tel: 01278 427575   email: info@catwelfaretrust.org   www.catwelfaretrust.org

---

Tel: 020 7378 4952
Fax: 020 7378 9781
Email: . . . . info@carersuk.org
Objects: F,W3,J,G,2,W4,H,3

CAT SURVIVAL TRUST
CR272187
The Centre, 46-52 Codicote Road, Welwyn,
Hertfordshire AL6 9TU
Tel: 01438 716873
Fax: 01438 717535
Email: . . . . cattrust@aol.com
Web: . . . . www.catsurvivaltrust.org
Objects: W1,W2,G
Formed in 1976 for the captive breeding and preservation in the wild of the 37 endangered species of wild cat and their habitat. Also research the effect of climate change on all life including humans!

CAT WELFARE TRUST
CR800719
GCCF, 5 Kings Castle Business Park, The Drove, Bridgwater, Somerset TA6 4AG
Tel: 01278 427575
Fax: 01278 446627
Email: . . . . info@catwelfaretrust.org
The Cat Welfare Trust helps fund research projects into feline disease. The current project, a collaboration between three major Universities, is researching into the genes that play a pivotal role in the control of infectious diseases in cats. All donations are spent on the work of the Trust, not administration or salaries.
See advert on this page

CATASTROPHES CAT RESCUE

CR1017304
Half Moon Cottage, Bakers Lane, Dallington, Heathfield, East Sussex TN21 9JS
Tel: 01435 830212
Fax: 01825 768012
Email: . . . . lizzie@catastrophescats.org
Object: W1
Catastrophes Cat Rescue in East Sussex provides a safe haven for unwanted cats in the UK. Many of the cats we rescue have been abandoned or need a new home because of a change in their owners' circumstances. Some have been ill treated. They are all in need of love and care. Catastrophes' aim is to help any cat in need, regardless of age, temperament or behavioural problems. Consequently we often receive calls for help with elderly or feral cats, or animals that are difficult to rehome. We do not believe in putting animals to sleep unnecessarily and we actively encourage spaying and neutering as a vital part of responsible pet ownership. Please remember us in your will. Your donation or legacy will help us continue to provide a vital lifeline and a bright future for cats in desperate need.

CATHOLIC DEAF ASSOCIATION UK
CR262362
Secretary: Rev Peter McDonough
Hollywood House, Sudell Street, Collyhurst,
Manchester, Greater Manchester M4 4JF
Tel: .... 0161 834 8828; 0161 835 1767 Minicom
Fax: 0161 833 3674
Objects: F,S,W7,2,R,P

CATHOLIC FUND FOR HOMELESS & DESTITUTE PEOPLE
See The Catholic Fund for the Homeless and
Destitute

CATHOLIC INSTITUTE FOR INTERNATIONAL RELATIONS (CIIR)
See Progressio

CATS PROTECTION (CP)
Founded: 1927 CR203644; SC037711
Chief Executive: Mr Derek Conway
Head of Finance: Mr Anthony Hall
Chariman of Trustees: Heather McCann
National Cat Centre, Chelwood Gate, Haywards
Heath, West Sussex RH17 7TT
Tel: 01825 741271
Fax: 01825 741004
Email: .... giftsinwills@cats.org.uk
Objects: F,W1,H

THE CAUDWELL CHARITY
CR1079770
Minton Hollins Building, Shelton Old Road, Stoke-
on-Trent, Staffordshire ST4 7RY
Tel: 01782 600437; 08453 001348
Email: . communityaffairs@caudwellchildren.com

A CAUSE FOR CONCERN
See Prospects for People with Learning
Disabilities

CAVALCADE OF COSTUME MUSEUM
See Blandford Museum of Fashion

CBF (CENTRAL BRITISH FUND FOR WORLD JEWISH RELIEF)
See Central British Fund for World Jewish Relief

CBM
Founded: 1996 CR1058162; SC041101
Mr Stephen Butler
Assistant Director: Mr Martin Carter
National Director: Doctor William McAllister
Vision House, 7/8 Oakington Business Park,
Oakington, Cambridge, Cambridgeshire
CB24 3DQ
Tel: 01223 484700
Fax: 01223 484701
Email: .... info@cbmuk.org.uk
Objects: W6,W3,W7,W5,G,N,U,O,3

CCHF ALL ABOUT KIDS
Founded: 1884 CR206958
42-43 Lower Marsh, London SE1 7RG
Tel: 020 7928 6522
Fax: 020 7401 3961
Email: .... cchf@dircon.co.uk
Objects: W3,V,3

CELIA HAMMOND ANIMAL TRUST
Founded: 1986 CR293787
Administrator: Ms Sarah Le Fevre
High Street, Wadhurst, East Sussex TN5 6AG
Tel: .... 01892 783820 / 01892 783367
Fax: 01892 784882
Email: .... headoffice@celiahammond.org
Objects: F,W1,3

CENTRAL AFRICA'S RIGHTS & AIDS (CARA) SOCIETY
CR1135610
Unit 4, 2nd Floor, The Printhouse, 18-22 Ashwin
Street, Dalston, London E8 3DL
Tel: 020 7254 6415
Fax: 0872 115 8436
Email: .... info@cara-online.org

CENTRAL & CECIL HOUSING TRUST
Founded: 1926FS27693R
Chief Executive: Mrs Dorry Mclaughlin
Cecil House, 266 Waterloo Road, London
SE1 8RQ
Tel: 020 7922 5300
Fax: 020 7922 5301
Objects: F,M,E,W5,G,D,W4,3,C,P,W8

CENTRAL BRITISH FUND FOR WORLD JEWISH RELIEF
Founded: 1990 CR290767
Director: Mr Daniel A Casson
c/o World Jewish Relief, Oscar Joseph House, 54
Crewys Road, London NW2 2AD
Tel: 020 8736 1250
Fax: 020 8736 1259
Email: .... info@wjr.org.uk
Objects: F,W3,W10,W4,U,3

CENTRAL BRITISH FUND FOR WORLD JEWISH RELIEF
Founded: 1990 CR290767
Director: Mr Daniel A Casson
c/o World Jewish Relief, Oscar Joseph House, 54
Crewys Road, London NW2 2AD
Tel: 020 8736 1250
Fax: 020 8736 1259
Email: .... info@wjr.org.uk
Objects: F,W3,W10,W4,U,3

CENTRAL MANCHESTER UNIVERSITY HOSPITALS NHS FOUNDATION TRUST CHARITY

Central Manchester University Hospitals NHS Foundation Trust **Charity**
supporting excellence in treatment, care and research

CR1049274
**The Lodge, Oxford Road, Manchester, Greater
Manchester M13 9WL**
Tel: 0161 276 4522
Fax: 0161 276 4241
Email: .... charity.office@cmft.nhs.uk
Objects: W3,N,W4

See advert on next page

Your Legacy - Creating a Brighter Future

From our comprehensive state-of-the-art facilities in central Manchester we serve over one million people every year. Clinical research is the cornerstone of first-class healthcare but much of the development of innovative care lies outside the core funding provided to the NHS.

That's why we need your help. A legacy can help us to explore new research areas, then translate them into real solutions to the problems that affect the lives of so many of our population - of every age.

If you would like to receive a copy of our free guide to making a Will, please contact our charities department on **0161 276 4522** or email **charity.office@cmft.nhs.uk**.

To learn more about the work of the charity, please visit **www.cmftcharity.org.uk**

Central Manchester University Hospitals NHS Foundation Trust **Charity**

supporting excellence in treatment, care and research

Registered charity number 1049274

Registered charity number 1049274

CENTRAL YOUNG MEN'S CHRISTIAN ASSOCIATION LIMITED, THE
Founded: 1844 CR213121
General Secretary: Ms Rosi J Prescott
112 Great Russell Street, London WC1B 3NQ
Tel: 020 7343 1844
Objects: W3,G,H,P

CENTRE FOR ACCESSIBLE ENVIRONMENTS
CR1050820
Chief Executive: Ms Sarah Langton-Lockton
70 South Lambeth Road, London SW8 1RL
Tel: 020 7840 0125
Fax: 020 7840 5811
Email: . . . . info@cae.org.uk
Objects: F,W6,W3,W2,W7,W5,G,2,W4,H,3

CENTRE FOR LOCAL ECONOMIC STRATEGIES
Founded: 1990 CR1089503
Director Secretary to the Trustees: Mr Neil McInroy
Express Networks, 1 George Leigh Street, Manchester, Greater Manchester M4 5DL
Tel: 0161 236 7036
Fax: 0161 236 1891
Objects: W3,W7,W5,G,W10,2,W4,H,3,W8

CENTREPOINT
Founded: 1969 CR292411
Central House, 25 Camperdown Street, London E1 8DZ
Tel: 0845 466 3400; 020 7426 6809
Fax: 0845 466 3500
Email: . . . . yoursupport@centrepoint.org
Objects: F,W3,J,G,D,H,3,C,P

CEREBRA, THE FOUNDATION FOR BRAIN INJURED INFANTS AND YOUNG PEOPLE
Founded: 1991 CR1089812
Chief Executive: Mr C Jones
Second Floor Offices, The Lyric Building, King Street, Carmarthen, Carmarthenshire SA31 1BD
Tel: 01267 244200
Fax: 01267 244201
Email: . . . . info@cerebra.org.uk
Objects: F,W3,1B,H

CEREBRAL PALSY MIDLANDS
Founded: 1947 CR529464
Executive Officer: Mr Robert Nutt
Chairman: Mr A W Wall
17 Victoria Road, Harborne, Birmingham, West Midlands B17 0AQ
Tel: 0121 427 3182
Fax: 0121 426 5934
Email: . . . . info@cpmids.free-online.co.uk
Objects: F,W6,M,W3,J,S,E,W7,W5,G,W10,1A,A, V,D,H,O,3,C,P,K

CGD SOCIETY
Founded: 1991 CR1143049
Chairman: Mr David Barlow
Vice-Chairman: Mrs J. Fullerton
CGD Office, Manor Farm, Wimborne St Giles, Dorset BH21 5NL
Tel: 01725 517977
Fax: 01725 517977
Email: . . hayley.banyard@geneticdisordersuk.org
Objects: F,W3,A,1B,N,2,W4,H,3

CHAI CANCER CARE
CR1078956
Chief Executive: Mrs Elaine Kerr
142-146 Great North Way, London NW4 1EH
Tel: 020 8202 2211
Fax: 020 8202 2111
Email: . . . . info@chaicancercare.org
Objects: F,M,W3,J,G,W4,H,O,3,P

CHALLOCK VILLAGE FUND
Founded: 1990 CR802634
Treasurer & Trustee: Mr R G Wilkinson
Brambles, Church Lane, Challock, Ashford, Kent TN25 4BU
Objects: W3,W2,A,1B,W4,P

CHANGING FACES - SUPPORTING PEOPLE WITH DISFIGUREMENTS
Founded: 1992 CR1011222
Public Fundraising Officer: Miss Sophie Erskine
Chief Executive: Mr James Partridge
Changing Faces Centre, 33-37 University Street, London WC1E 6JN
Tel: 0845 450 0275
Fax: 0845 450 0276
Email: . . . . info@changingfaces.org.uk
Objects: F,W3,W5,G,H,O,3,W8

THE CHARITY FOR CIVIL SERVANTS (FORMERLY THE CIVIL SERVICE BENEVOLENT FUND)
CR1136870
Fund House, 5 Anne Boleyn's Walk, Cheam, Sutton SM3 8DY
Tel: 020 8240 2400; 0800 056 2424 (Freephone); 020 8770 0572 (Minicom)
Fax: 020 8240 2401
Email: . . . . info@foryoubyyou.org.uk
Objects: F,J

THE CHARITY FOR CIVIL SERVANTS (FORMERLY THE CIVIL SERVICE BENEVOLENT FUND)
CR1136870
Fund House, 5 Anne Boleyn's Walk, Cheam, Sutton SM3 8DY
Tel: . . 020 8240 2400 (Administration); 0800 056 2424 (Freephone Helpline)
Fax: 020 8240 2401
Email: . . . . info@foryoubyyou.org.uk
Objects: F,W6,M,W3,W7,W5,1A,A,W4,H,3,W8

CHARITY SEARCH - FREE ADVICE FOR OLDER PEOPLE
Founded: 1987 CR296999
25 Portview Road, Avonmouth, Bristol BS11 9LD
Tel: 0117 982 4060
Fax: 0117 982 7070
Objects: F,W4,3

THE CHARITY SERVICE LTD
Founded: 1992 CR1011293
CEO: Mr Michael Colin FCA
6 Great Jackson Street, Manchester, Greater Manchester M15 4AX
Tel: 0161 839 3291
Fax: 0161 839 3298
Email: . . . . . michael.colin@charityservice.org.uk
Objects: A,1B,3

CHARTERED INSTITUTE OF ARBITRATORS
Founded: 1990 CR803725
Secretary General: Mr K R K Harding
Head of Administration & Finance: Mr Michael Keogh
International Arbitration and Mediation Centre, 12 Bloomsbury Square, London WC1A 2LP
Tel: 020 7421 7444
Email: .... info@arbitrators.org
Object: 2

CHARTERED INSTITUTE OF BUILDING BENEVOLENT FUND LTD
Founded: 1992 CR1013292
Secretary: Mr Franklin MacDonald
Chairman: Mr Christopher Thorpe
Englemere, King's Ride, Ascot, Windsor & Maidenhead SL5 7TB
Tel: 01344 630700
Fax: 01344 630777
Email: .... fjmacdonald@ciob.org.uk
Objects: F,A

CHARTERED INSTITUTE OF JOURNALISTS
Founded: 1894 CR208176
General Secretary: Mr Christopher J Underwood FCIJ
2 Dock Offices, Surrey Quays Road, London SE16 2XU
Tel: 020 7252 1187
Fax: 020 7232 2302
Objects: A,B

CHARTERED INSTITUTE OF LIBRARY AND INFORMATION PROFESSIONALS (CILIP)
Founded: 1898 CR313014
Ms Annie Mauger
7 Ridgmount Street, London WC1E 7AE
Tel: 020 7255 0500
Email: .... info@cilip.org.uk
Objects: G,2

CHARTERED INSTITUTE OF LOGISTICS AND TRANSPORT (UK), THE
Founded: 1991 CR1004963
Marketing Executive: Miss Alexandra Lethvillier
Logistics and Transport Centre, Earlstrees Court, Earlstrees Road, Corby, Northamptonshire NN17 4AX
Tel: 01536 740100
Fax: 01536 740101; 01536 740102/3
Email: .... membership@ciltuk.org.uk
Objects: G,W11,1B,2,B,H,3

CHARTERED INSTITUTION OF CIVIL ENGINEERING SURVEYORS
Founded: 1972 CR1131469
Executive Director: Mr Chris Deighton
Dominion House, Sibson Road, Sale, Greater Manchester M33 7PP
Tel: 0161 972 3100
Fax: 0161 972 3118
Email: .... admin@cices.org
Objects: G,2,H

CHARTERED SOCIETY OF PHYSIOTHERAPY'S MEMBERS' BENEVOLENT FUND

CHARTERED SOCIETY OF PHYSIOTHERAPY

Founded: 1894 CR279882
14 Bedford Row, London WC1R 4ED
Tel: 020 7306 6666
Fax: 020 7306 6623
Email: .... enquiries@csp.org.uk
Web: .... http://www.csp.org.uk
Objects: F,J,G,1A,A,2,H,O
The Chartered Society of Physiotherapy (CSP) is the professional, educational and trade union body for the UK's 51,000 chartered physiotherapists, physiotherapy students and support workers. The CSP's Members' Benevolent Fund (MBF) makes financial awards to members, support workers and students (including retired members) who need help. Whether as a result of illness or injury, job loss or bereavement, the MBF exists to support CSP members.

CHASE HOSPICE CARE FOR CHILDREN
CR1042495
Loseley Park, Guildford, Surrey GU3 1HS
Tel: 01483 454213
Fax: 01483 454214
Email: .... info@chasecare.org.uk

THE CHASELEY TRUST - CARING FOR PEOPLE WITH SEVERE DISABILITIES
CR1090579
Chaseley Bungalows (CC), South Cliff, 9 The Sidings, Eastbourne, East Sussex BN20 7JH
Tel: 01323 744200
Fax: 01323 744208
Email: .... info@chaseleytrust.org
Objects: W9,W5,N,O,3

CHATHAM HISTORIC DOCKYARD TRUST
Founded: 1984 CR292101
Chairman: Admiral Sir Ian Garnett KCB
The Historic Dockyard, Chatham, Kent ME4 4TZ
Tel: 01634 823800
Fax: 01634 823801
Email: .... info@chdt.org.uk
Objects: W2,G,W12,3,K

CHEMICAL ENGINEERS BENEVOLENT FUND
Founded: 1934 CR221601
Chairman: Mr Kenneth Sutherland
Secretary: Miss Joanne Downham
165-189 Railway Terrace, Rugby, Warwickshire CV21 3HQ
Tel: 01788 578214
Fax: 01788 560833
Email: .... jdownham@icheme.org
Objects: W11,1A,A

CHERNOBYL CHILDREN LIFE LINE
Founded: 1992 CR1014274; SC040136
Chairman Trustee Administrator: Mr V E Mizzi
Courts, 61 Petworth Road, Haslemere, Surrey GU27 3AX
Tel: 01428 642523
Email: .... vicmizzi@nildram.co.uk
Objects: W3,V,U,3

CHESTNUT TREE HOUSE CHILDREN'S HOSPICE
CR256789
Dover Lane, Arundel, West Sussex BN18 9PX
Tel: 01903 871800
Fax: 01903 871828
Email: ...... admin@chestnut-tree-house.org.uk
Web: .... www.chestnut-tree-house.org.uk

CHILD ACCIDENT PREVENTION TRUST
CR1053549
4th Floor, Cloister Court, 22-26 Farringdon Lane, London EC1R 3AJ
Tel: 020 7608 3828
Fax: 020 7608 3674
Email: .... safe@capt.org.uk
Objects: F,W3,J,G,H,3

CHILD HEALTH RESEARCH APPEAL TRUST
Founded: 1976 CR271834
Accounts / Charitable Trust Assistant: Ms Dolly Rob
Institute of Child Health, University College London, 30 Guilford Street, London WC1N 1EH
Tel: 020 7905 2681
Fax: 020 7829 8689
Email: .... d.rob@ich.ucl.ac.uk
Object: W3

CHILDHOOD FIRST
Founded: 1973 CR286909
Chief Executive: Mr Stephen Blunden
210 Borough High Street, London SE1 1JX
Tel: 020 7928 7388
Fax: 020 7261 1307
Email: .... enquiries@childhoodfirst.org.uk
Objects: Q,F,W3,J,G,O,3

CHILDREN 1ST - ROYAL SCOTTISH SOCIETY FOR PREVENTION OF CRUELTY TO CHILDREN
SC016092
83 Whitehouse Loan, Edinburgh EH9 1AT
Tel: ... 0131 446 2300; 0845 108 0111 (Donation Line)
Fax: 0131 446 2339
Email: .... info@children1st.org.uk
Objects: F,W3,H,O,3,W8

CHILDREN & YOUTH COMMITTEE FOR GREAT BRITAIN AND EIRE
See Youth Aliyah - Child Rescue

CHILDREN IN CRISIS
Founded: 1993 CR1020488
Chief Executive: Mr Mark O McKeown
206-208 Stewarts Road, London SW8 4UB
Tel: 020 7627 1040
Email: .... info@childrenincrisis.org
Objects: W3,U

CHILDREN IN DISTRESS

Founded: 1990 CR1001327; SC039383
Suite 30, Ladywell Business Centre, 94 Duke Street, Glasgow G4 0UW

Tel: 0141 559 5690
Fax: 0141 559 5694
Email: .... admin2@childrenindistress.org.uk
Objects: W3,W5,G,N,U,Y
To cure, sometimes; To help, often; To comfort, always. Offering help, hope and hospice care as well as child development and therapies for infants and children with autism or disabilities.

See advert on next page

CHILDREN IN WALES - PLANT YNG NGHYMRU
Founded: 1993 CR1020313
Chief Executive: Ms Catriona Williams
25 Windsor Place, Cardiff CF10 3BZ
Tel: 029 2034 2434
Fax: 029 2034 3134
Email: ...... info@childreninwales.org.uk
Web: .... www.childreninwales.org.uk
Children in Wales is the national umbrella organisation for professionals and individuals who work with children, young people and families in Wales. We are a membership body and offer practical information and support; we organise conferences and events on topical issues; can organise a range of training events in Welsh and English; develop new courses to meet commissioners' needs and offer consultancy services. We co-ordinate specialist forums and networks across Wales where participants can exchange information and share good practice. All our contacts are able to raise issues of concern relating to a range of policy areas which Children in Wales can channel through to policy makers.

CHILDREN NATIONWIDE MEDICAL RESEARCH FUND
See WellChild

CHILDREN'S CANCER AND LEUKAEMIA GROUP (CCLG)

Founded: 1977 CR286669
University of Leicester (CC, Hearts of Oak House), 3rd Floor, Hearts of Oak House, 9 Princess Road West, Leicester, Leicestershire LE1 6TH
Tel: 0116 249 4461
Fax: 0116 249 4470
Email: .... info@cclg.org.uk
Web: .... www.cclg.org.uk
Objects: W3,N,2,H,3,W
31 children are diagnosed with cancer and leukaemia each WEEK in the UK. Through a network of treatment centres, CCLG members aim to provide the best possible treatment for all children with cancer, and today over 70% are cured. However until every child can be cured without serious side effects, further carefully conducted research is essential. CCLG is the only UK charity supporting research and those looking after children with cancer and leukaemia. We are also a leading producer of award-winning, free information booklets for patients and their families. Support for CCLG is always gratefully received.

Children in Distress

We are a UK registered charity which provides respite, palliative and end of life care for the "forgotten" children of the Balkans. These children are terminally or incurably ill as a result of accident, infection, genetic or birth defect and HIV/AIDS.

It also offers hope through education and therapy to those with autistic spectrum disorders and the severest physical handicap and disability. Our work is made possible only by individual gifts and legacy donations.

Children in Distress, Suite 30 Ladywell Business Centre, 94 Duke Street, Glasgow G4 0UW. **Tel:** 0141 559 5690
Web: www.childrenindistress.org.uk **E-mail:** info@childrenindistress.org.uk
Registered Charity Number: 1001327. Scottish Registered Charity Number: SCO 39383

CHILDREN'S FAMILY TRUST
Founded: 1945 CR208607
MKA House, 4-6 St Andrew's Road, Droitwich, Worcestershire WR9 8DN
Tel: 01905 798229
Fax: 01905 798230
Email: .... carolyn@thecft.org.uk
Objects: Q,W3,3

CHILDREN'S HEART FEDERATION
CR1120557
2-4 Great Eastern Street, London EC2A 3NW
Tel: 020 7422 0630
Email: .... info@chfed.org.uk
Objects: F,M,W3,W5,1A,A,V,H,3

CHILDREN'S HEART SURGERY FUND
CR1148359
Room 001 (Dept CC), Ground Floor, Old Nurses Home, Leeds, West Yorkshire LS1 3EX
Tel: 0113 392 5742
Email: .... info@chsf.org.uk

Please mention
CHARITIES DIGEST
when responding to
advertisements

CHILDREN'S HOSPICE SOUTH WEST
Founded: 1991 CR1003314
Head Office, Little Bridge House, Redlands Road, Fremington, Barnstaple, Devon EX31 2PZ
Tel: **01271 325270**
Fax: **01271 328640**
Email: .... donna.jones@chsw.org.uk
Objects: W3,N,3
Children's Hospice South West provides the only hospice care in the South West for children with life-limiting conditions. Our three hospices, Little Bridge House in Devon, Charlton Farm in North Somerset, and Little Harbour in Cornwall provide respite and emergency care and support for in excess of 400 families. Of these some come to us for planned respite and a rare opportunity for a break. Others will also be supported through our bereavement team after the loss of their child.
Children's Hospice South West is the only organisation in the region offering this vital service in a home from home environment and is almost entirely funded by the generosity of people in the South West.

CHILDREN'S RIGHTS ALLIANCE FOR ENGLAND
CR1005135
Director: Ms Carolyne Willow
94 White Lion Street, London N1 9PF
Tel: 020 7278 8222
Fax: 020 7278 9552
Email: .... info@crae.org.uk
Objects: W3,2,H

THE CHILDREN'S SOCIETY
Founded: 1881 CR221124
Head of Media: Mr Richard Johnson
Chief Executive: Mr Bob Reitemeier
Edward Rudolf House, Margery Street, London WC1X 0JL
Tel: 020 7841 4400
Fax: 020 7841 4500
Email: .... legacies@childrenssociety.org.uk
Objects: Q,F,W3,J,E,H,3

CHINA INLAND MISSION
See OMF International (UK)

CHOLMONDELEYS, THE
Founded: 1991 CR1001606
General Manager: Miss Catherine Willmore
LF1.1 Lafone House, The Leathermarket, 11-13 Leathermarket Street, London SE1 3HN
Tel: 020 7378 8800
Objects: S,G,3

CHRIST'S HOSPITAL
Founded: 1552 CR306975
Partnership Director: Mr Mark Curtis
Clerk / Chief Executive: Mr Michael Simpkin
The Counting House, Christ's Hospital, Horsham, West Sussex RH13 0YP
Tel: 01403 211293
Fax: 01403 211580
Email: .... enquiries@christs-hospital.org.uk
Objects: W3,G,3

CHRISTIAN AID
CR1105851
Director of Finance: Mr Martin Birch
Head of Marketing: Mr Jeff Dale
Director: Dr Daleep Mukarji
PO Box 100, London SE1 7RT
Tel: 020 7620 4444
Fax: 020 7620 0719
Email: .... ckemp@christian-aid.org
Objects: W6,M,W3,W2,W7,W5,G,W10,A,1B,W4, U,H,T,O,W8

CHRISTIAN ALLIANCE
See KeyChange Charity

CHRISTIAN CHILD CARE FORUM
CR1049477
Chair of Trustees: Dr. David Evans
UK Honorary Executive: Dr. Keith J. White
10 Crescent Road, South Woodford, London E18 2JB
Tel: 020 8504 2702
Email: ...... info@christianchildcareforum.co.uk
Objects: F,W3,J,2

CHRISTIAN CONCERN FOR THE MENTALLY HANDICAPPED
See Prospects for People with Learning Disabilities

CHRISTIAN EDUCATION MOVEMENT
Founded: 1882 CR1086990
Chief Executive: Mr Peter Fishpool
1020 Bristol Road, Selly Oak, Birmingham, West Midlands B29 6LB
Tel: 0121 472 4242
Fax: 0121 472 7575
Email: ..... enquiries@christianeducation.org.uk
Objects: W3,G,1B,W4,H,P

CHRISTIAN WITNESS TO ISRAEL
CR271323
Oke Ekakitie
166 Main Road, Sundridge, Sevenoaks, Kent TN14 6EL
Tel: 01959 565955
Fax: 01959 565966
Email: .... cwi@cwi.org.uk
Objects: G,W10,R,H,3

CHRISTINA NOBLE CHILDREN'S FOUNDATION

Founded: 1992 CR1007484
11-15 Lillie Road, West Brompton, London SW6 1TX
Tel: 020 7381 8550
Fax: 020 7385 9228
Email: .... uk@cncf.org
Web: .... www.cncf.org
Objects: W6,M,W3,S,E,W7,W5,G,W10,D,N,U,O, 3,C,W8
Primary objective to care for disadvantaged and street children in Vietnam and Mongolia.

CHRISTOPHER PLACE
Founded: 1991 CR1002463
Director: Mrs Angela Harding
1-5 Christopher Place, Chalton Street, London NW1 1JF
Tel: 020 7383 3834
Fax: 020 7383 3099
Email: .... info@speech-lang.org.uk
Objects: W3,G,O,3,K

CHRONIC GRANULOMATOUS DISORDER RESEARCH TRUST
See CGD Society

CHRYSALIS AIDS FOUNDATION CHARITABLE TRUST
Founded: 1991 CR1001550
Secretary to the Trust: Prof A.J. Pinching
c/o Professor Pinching, Peninsula Medical School, Royal Cornwall Hospital, Truro, Cornwall TR1 3HD
Tel: 01872 256402
Object: 1B

CHURCH ACTION ON POVERTY
Founded: 1990 CR1079986
National Co-ordinator: Mr Niall Cooper
Chairperson: Mr Lewis Rose
Central Buildings, Oldham Street, Manchester, Greater Manchester M1 1JQ
Tel: 0161 236 9321
Fax: 0161 237 5359
Email: .... info@church-poverty.org.uk
Objects: G,2,H

CHURCH ARMY
Founded: 1882 CR226226
Chief Executive Officer: Mr Mark Russell
Marlowe House, 109 Station Road, Sidcup, Kent DA15 7AD

Tel: 020 8309 3519
Email: . . . . info@churcharmy.org.uk
Objects: W9, W3, E, G, R, W4, 3, C, P, W8

CHURCH LADS' & CHURCH GIRLS' BRIGADE
CR276821
Brigade Secretary: Mr Alan J Millward
2 Barnsley Road, Wath upon Dearne, Rotherham, South Yorkshire S63 6PY
Tel: 01709 876535
Fax: 01709 878089
Email: . . . . brigadesecretary@clcgb.org.uk
Objects: W3, G, 2

THE CHURCH OF ENGLAND PENSIONS BOARD – RETIREMENT HOUSING FOR CLERGY PENSIONERS
Founded: 1926 CR236627
Secretary & Chief Executive: Ms B Kenny
29 Great Smith Street (CC), Westminster, London SW1P 3PS
Tel: 020 7898 1808
Email: . . . . . cepbappeals@churchofengland.org
Web: . . . . http://www.cepb.org.uk
Objects: 1A, D, N, W4, B, 3, C

Running supported housing and also a nursing and dementia care home, the Board is able to offer specialised care needed by its more elderly pensioners, including clergy widows or widowers.
We rely on support from gifts and legacies to continue this much needed work for those who have given their lives towards helping others in the name of Christ. Please help us in any way you can.

CHURCH OF ENGLAND SOLDIERS', SAILORS' AND AIRMEN'S HOUSING ASSOCIATION LIMITED
Founded: 1972FS21222R
Chief Executive: Mr Martin Marks OBE
1 Shakespeare Terrace, 126 High Street, Portsmouth, Hampshire PO1 2RH
Tel: 023 9282 9319
Objects: W9, D, W4, 3, C

CHURCH OF SCOTLAND HOUSING & LOAN FUND FOR RETIRED MINISTERS & WIDOWS AND WIDOWERS OF MINISTERS
SC011353
121 George Street, Edinburgh EH2 4YN
Tel: 0131 225 5722
Email: . . . . lmacmillan@cofscotland.org.uk
Web: . . . . . . www.churchofscotland.org.uk
Objects: W11, W4, Y

The Fund endeavours, wherever possible, to assist Ministers and Widow(er)s of Ministers with their retirement housing, by way of a house to rent or a house purchase loan. The Trustees may grant the tenancy, on advantageous terms, of a house. Alternatively the Trustees may grant a loan up to 70% of a house purchase price at favourable rates of interest. House prices are capped for both rentals and loans. The Trustees are also prepared to consider assisting those who are already housed, but are seeking to move to more suitable accommodation. Further information may be obtained from The Secretary; Miss L.J.Macmillan, MA, at the above address.

CHURCHES COMMUNITY WORK ALLIANCE
CR1004053
UK Co-ordinator: Revd Nils Chittenden
CCWA, St Chads College, North Bailey, Durham, Co. Durham DH1 3RH
Email: . . . . info@ccwa.org.uk
Objects: F,J,G,2,H,3

CHURCHES TOGETHER IN ENGLAND
Founded: 1991 CR1110782
General Secretary: Rev Dr David Cornick
27 Tavistock Square, London WC1H 9HH
Tel: 020 7529 8133
Fax: 020 7529 8134
Objects: 1B,2,T

CINEMA & TELEVISION BENEVOLENT FUND (CTBF)
Founded: 1924 CR1099660
Head of Welfare: Mrs Eunice Boomasty
Secretary: Mr Peter Meunier
Head of Events & Marketing: Ms Sophie Pacellini
Chief Executive: Mr Brian Robertson
Providing Care Behind The Scenes, 22 Golden Square, London W1F 9AD
Tel: 020 7437 6567
Fax: 020 7437 7186
Email: . . . . charity@ctbf.co.uk
Objects: W11,1A,3

CIRCULATION FOUNDATION
Founded: 1992 CR1102769
Fundraising & Research Manager: Ms Rebecca Wilkinson
35-43 Lincoln's Inn Fields, London WC2A 3PE
Tel: 020 7869 6937
Email: . . . . info@circulationfoundation.org.uk
Objects: F,W10,A,1B,N,W4,H,3,W8,W
Vascular disease attacks your veins and arteries. Every part of the body to which blood flows can be affected, which is why we're committed to saving lives and limbs. The Foundation raises funds for research into the causes, treatments and prevention of vascular disease and provides information and on-going support for sufferers and those who care for them.
See advert on previous page

CIRCUS SPACE, THE
Founded: 1991 CR1001839
Coronet Street, Hackney, London N1 6HD
Tel: 020 7613 4141
Fax: 020 7729 9422
Email: . . . . robhardy@thecircusspace.co.uk
Objects: W3,S,G,3

CIRDAN SAILING TRUST
CR1091598
Mr C Anderson
Chief Executive: Mr N Back
Mr D Cole
Rev ACC Courtauld
Trustee: Mr J Douglas-Hughes
Chairman: Mr Jonathan Douglas-Hughes
Mr R Hodgkinson
Mrs A King
Mr D Lee
Mr D Richards
Mr B Sainsbury
Fullbridge Wharf, 3 Chandlers Quay, Maldon, Essex CM9 4LF
Email: . . . . info@cirdan-faramir.co.uk
Objects: W3,W5,G,W10,2,3,P

CITY LITERARY INSTITUTE
Founded: 1990 CR803007
The Company Secretary
1-10 Keeley Street, London WC2B 4BA
Tel: 020 7242 9872
Email: . . . . denise.gill@citylit.ac.uk
Objects: G,3

CITY OF BRADFORD FUND FOR THE DISABLED
Founded: 1968 CR254783
Honorary Secretary: Mrs A Sugden
1st Floor, Jacobs Well, Manchester Road, Bradford, West Yorkshire BD1 5RW
Tel: 01274 757796
Objects: W5,A

CITY OF EXETER Y M C A
Founded: 1990 CR803226
Secretary: Mr Mike Brooking
39-41 St Davids Hill, Exeter, Devon EX4 4DA
Tel: 01392 410530
Objects: W3,D,3,C

CITY SOLICITORS EDUCATIONAL TRUST, THE
Founded: 2007 CR1121091
Treasurer: Mr Neil Cameron
4 College Hill, London EC4R 2RB
Tel: 020 7329 2173
Email: . . . . mail@citysolicitors.org.uk
Objects: G,1B

CLAIRE HOUSE CHILDREN'S HOSPICE
Founded: 1991 CR1004058
Head of Fundraising: Ms Pat Faragher
Chairman: Mr Gerald Martin QC
Fundraising Centre, Clatterbridge Road, Bebington, Merseyside CH63 4JD
Tel: 0151 343 0883
Fax: 0151 343 1004
Email: . . . . appeals@claire-house.org.uk
Objects: F,W3,N,3

CLARENDON TRUST LTD
CR1069942
Company Secretary: Mr Kevin Rose
21-23 Clarendon Villas, Hove, Brighton & Hove BN3 3RE
Tel: 01273 747687
Fax: 01273 889394
Email: . . . . office@cck.org.uk
Objects: G,1A,2,R,U

CLEFT LIP & PALATE ASSOCIATION (CLAPA)
CR1108160
1st Floor, Green Man Tower, 332B Goswell Road, London EC1V 7LQ
Tel: 020 7833 4883
Fax: 020 7833 5999
Email: . . . . info@clapa.com
Objects: F,M,W3,W5,N,W4,H,3,P

CLIC SARGENT (SCOTLAND)
CR1107328; SC009057
Room 13, 5th Floor (SCC), Mercantile Chambers,
53 Bothwell Street, Glasgow G2 6TS
Tel: 0141 572 5700
Fax: 0141 572 5701
Email: .... legacies@clicsargent.org.uk
Objects: F,W3,1A,A,V,H

CLIFF COLLEGE
Founded: 1883 CR529386
Financial Registrar: Mr John Newton
Principal: Reverend Christopher Blake MA
(Cantab), BSc, PhD (Surrey)
Calver, Hope, Derbyshire S32 3XG
Tel: 01246 584200
Email: .... admin@cliffcollege.ac.uk
Web: .... http://www.cliffcollege.ac.uk
Objects: G,3
Methodist College offering vocational training for
Christian Leadership to those of all denominations. BA
and MA courses available and research degrees. All
courses validated by University of Manchester.
Conference centre facilities for up to 280.

CLOWNE AND DISTRICT COMMUNITY TRANSPORT
Founded: 1990 CR1055035
Vice Chair of MC: Mr Jim Clifton
Manager: Ms Jill Meeds
Chair of Management Committee: Mr Tom
Pettinger
Unit 10, 10 Creswell Road, Clowne, Chesterfield,
Derbyshire S43 4PW
Tel: 01246 573010
Fax: 01246 573033
Objects: M,W3,W5,W4,3,W8

CLUBS FOR YOUNG PEOPLE (CYP)
Founded: 1925 CR306065
Chief Executive: Mr Tony Bennett
Headquarters, 371 Kennington Lane, London
SE11 5QY
Tel: 020 7793 0787
Fax: 020 7820 9815
Email: ...... office@clubsforyoungpeople.org.uk
Objects: M,W3,J,S,G,2,H,3,P

CODA INTERNATIONAL TRAINING
Founded: 1990 CR1000717
129 Seven Sisters Road, London N7 7QG
Tel: 020 7281 0020
Fax: 020 7263 8847
Email: ..... enquiries@coda-international.org.uk
Objects: W3,J,W2,W5,G,W10,1B,W4,U,W8

COED CYMRU
CR702443
The Old Sawmill, Tregynon, Newtown, Powys
SY16 3PL
Tel: 01686 650777
Fax: 01686 650696
Email: .... coedcymru@coedcymru.org.uk
Objects: F,J,W2,G,A,3,K

COELIAC UK
Founded: 1968 CR1048167
Suites A-D, Octagon Court, High Wycombe,
Buckinghamshire HP11 2HS
Tel: 01494 437278
Fax: 01494 474349
Email: .... info@coeliac.co.uk
Objects: F,W9,W6,W3,J,W7,W5,W10,W11,1B,2,
W4,H,W8

COLCHESTER COMMUNITY VOLUNTARY SERVICES
CR1092567
Winsley's House, High Street, Colchester, Essex
CO1 1UG
Tel: 01206 505250
Fax: 01206 500367
Email: .... information@ccvs.org
Objects: W6,W3,J,W7,W5,W10,W15,W16,W4,3,
W8

COLLEGE FOR HIGHER RABBINICAL STUDIES TCHABE KOLLEL
Founded: 1990 CR803466
Sugarwhite Halle Davis & Co
4-6 Windus Mews, Windus Road, London
N16 6UP
Tel: 020 8880 8910
Fax: 020 8442 8762

COLLEGE FOR HIGHER RABBINICAL STUDIES TIFERETH SHOLOM
See College for Higher Rabbinical Studies Tchabe
Kollel

COMMUNITY ACTION HALFWAY HOME LTD
Founded: 1991 CR1005379
Company Secretary: Ms Anna Kalopsidiotis
23 Filey Street, Sheffield, South Yorkshire
S10 2FG
Tel: 0114 279 6777
Fax: 0114 279 6555
Objects: D,R,3,C,P

COMMUNITY HOUSING AND THERAPY
Founded: 1994 CR1040713
Chief Executive: Mr John Gale
Bishop Creighton House, 378 Lillie Road, London
SW6 7PH
Tel: 020 7381 5888
Fax: 020 7610 0608
Email: .... chtcharity@yahoo.co.uk
Objects: F,C

COMMUNITY MATTERS (NATIONAL FEDERATION OF COMMUNITY ORGANISATIONS)
Founded: 1991 CR1002383
Co-Secretary & National Director: Mr David Tyler
12 - 20 Baron Street, London N1 9LL
Tel: 020 7837 7887
Fax: 020 7278 9253
Email: .. communitymatters@communitymatters.
org.uk
Objects: F,W3,J,G,W10,2,W4,H,3

COMMUNITY NETWORK
CR1000011
Chief Executive: Ms Pat Fitzsimons
Ground Floor, 12-20 Baron Street, London N1 9LL

Tel: 020 7923 5250
Fax: 020 7713 8163
Objects: W5,W10,W4,3,P

COMMUNITY SECURITY TRUST (CST)
CR1042391
Freepost 12303, London NW1 0YY
Tel: 020 8457 9999
Fax: 020 7935 7257
Email: . . . . enquiries@thecst.org.uk

COMMUNITY TRANSPORT ASSOCIATION UK
Founded: 1991 CR1002222
Director: Mr Keith Halstead
Company Secretary: Mr Stephen Sears
Highbank, Halton Street, Hyde, Greater
Manchester SK14 2NY
Tel: 0870 774 3586
Fax: 0870 774 3581
Email: . . . . ctauk@communitytransport.com
Objects: F,W6,W3,W7,W5,G,W10,2,W4,H,3,W8

COMPASSION IN WORLD FARMING
CR1095050
River Court, Mill Lane, Godalming, Surrey
GU7 1EZ
Tel: 01483 521953
Fax: 01483 861639
Email: . . . . legacy@ciwf.org.uk
Objects: W1,W2

COMPTON HOSPICE
CR512387
Head of Fundraising, Trading & PR: Ms Susan
Chance
39, Compton Road West, Wolverhampton, West
Midlands WV3 9DW
Tel: 0845 225 5497
Fax: 01902 774 504
Email: . . . . fundraising@compton-hospice.org.uk
Objects: W3,N,W4,3,W8

CONNECTION AT ST MARTIN'S, THE
Founded: 1990 CR1078201
Chief Executive: Ms Helen Garry
Chief Executive: Mr Colin Glover
Head of Appeals: Ms Debbie Lyne
12 Adelaide Street, London WC2N 4HW
Tel: 020 7766 5555
Fax: 020 7839 6277
Email: . . . . info@cstm.org.uk
Objects: F,M,W3,E,G,W4,3,P,K

CONSTRUCTION INDUSTRY TRUST FOR YOUTH
See Construction Youth Trust

CONSTRUCTION YOUTH TRUST
CR1094323
The Building Centre, 26 Store Street, London
WC1E 7BT
Tel: 020 7467 9540
Fax: 020 7631 3760
Email: . . . . cyt@cytrust.org.uk
Objects: W3,G,1A,1B,3

CONTACT A FAMILY
Founded: 1979 CR284912; SC039169
Chief Executive: Ms Francine Bates
Information & Publications Officer: Ms Yvonne
McGahren
209-211 City Road, London EC1V 1JN
Tel: . . . . . 020 7608 8700 Admin; 0808 808 3556
Textphone; 0808 808 3555 Mon - Fri, 10-4pm;
Mon 5:30-7:30pm
Fax: 020 7608 8701
Email: . . . . fundraising@cafamily.org.uk
Objects: F,W3,W10,H,3

CORNERSTONE TRUST
Founded: 1991 CR1003948
Manager: Mr Clive Olive
Trustee: Mr E. Taylor
12 Cornwall Avenue, Bolton, Greater Manchester
BL5 1DZ
Tel: 01204 405015
Objects: F,W5

CORNWALL BLIND (AND PARTIALLY SIGHTED) ASSOCIATION
Founded: 1856 CR1108761
General Manager: Mrs Lyn Preston
Chairman: Dr Graham Stephens
The Sight Centre, Newham Road, Truro, Cornwall
TR1 2DP
Tel: 01872 261110
Fax: 01872 222349
Email: . . . . info@cornwallblind.org.uk
Objects: F,W6,M,W3,S,G,1A,A,1B,V,2,W4,H,O,3,
P

CORONA WORLDWIDE
Founded: 1950 CR204802
President: Mrs Pam Cowan
Chairman: Mrs Kathy Cracknell
Southbank House, Black Prince Road, London
SE1 7SJ
Tel: 020 7793 4020
Email: . . . . corona@coronaworldwide.org
Objects: F,J,G,2,U,H,3,P,W8

CORONARY PREVENTION GROUP
Founded: 1979 CR277243
2 Taviton Street, London WC1H 0BT
Tel: 020 7927 2125
Fax: 020 7927 2127
Email: . . . . cpg@lshtm.ac.uk
Objects: J,W4,H

CORONARY RESEARCH FUND, THE
Founded: 1990 CR1000783
Chairman: Mr Graham Jackson
Certified Accountants: Dr McCarthy Palmer
49a South End, Croydon, Surrey CR9 1LT
Tel: 020 7407 5887
Objects: G,1A,N,H,O

CORPORATION OF THE SONS OF THE CLERGY
Founded: 1655 CR207736
Registrar: Mr Robert Welsford
1 Dean Trench Street, Westminster, London
SW1P 3HB

Tel: 020 7799 3696
Fax: 020 7222 3468
Email: .... enquiries@sonsoftheclergy.org.uk
Objects: W11,Y

COTSWOLD ARCHAEOLOGY LIMITED
Founded: 1991 CR1001653
Managing Director: Mr Neil Holbrook
Unit 4, Cromwell Business Centre, Howard Way,
Newport Pagnell, Milton Keynes, Buckinghamshire
MK16 9QS
Tel: 01908 218320
Email: .. enquiries@cotswoldarchaeology.org.uk
Objects: S,G,H,3

COUNCIL FOR BRITISH ARCHAEOLOGY
CR287815; SC041971
St Mary's House, 66 Bootham, York, North
Yorkshire YO30 7BZ
Tel: 01904 671417
Fax: 01904 671384
Email: .... admin@archaeologyUK.org
Web: .... http://new.archaeologyuk.org/
Objects: W3,W2,G,1B,2,H

Exists to advance the knowledge and work of
archaeology throughout Great Britain on behalf of
archaeologists and the general public alike. In fulfilling
this role the Council draws upon the regional and
national expertise of its network of professional and
amateur members in order to unite views, foster
education at all levels, exert influence on government
and the media, give advice to the public, business and
industry, and the environmental conservation
movement, shape opinion among legislators and
administrators as well as the archaeological
community, and promote action designed to improve
the protection and understanding of the historic
heritage. Donations and support would be very
gratefully received.

COUNCIL FOR DEPENDENCY PROBLEMS
Founded: 1991 CR1002636
Company Secretary: Mrs M N Quinn
6 Wright Street, Kingston upon Hull, East Riding of
Yorkshire HU2 8HU
Tel: 01482 225868
Objects: F,W3,W10,W4,O,3,P,W8

COUNCIL FOR NATIONAL PARKS
See Campaign for National Parks

COUNCIL FOR WORLD MISSION
Founded: 1977 CR1097842
Secretary for Finance & Stewardship: Miss Gillian
Palmer
General Secretary: Revd Dr Des Vander Water
32-34 Great Peter Street, London SW1P 2DB
Tel: 020 7222 4214
Fax: 020 7233 1747
Email: .... council@cwmission.org
Objects: 2,R

COUNSEL AND CARE
Founded: 1954 CR203429
Senoir Policy & Communications Officer: Mrs
Anna Passingham
Twyman House, 16 Bonny Street, London
NW1 9PG

Tel: . 020 7241 8555; 0845 300 7585 Advice Line
(Mon-Fri 10-4, Wed 10-1)
Fax: 020 7267 6877
Email: .... advice@counselandcare.org.uk
Objects: F,1A,2,W4,B,H,3,P

COVENANT MINISTRIES INTERNATIONAL
Founded: 1990 CR328513
Administrator: Miss Caroline Okell
Nettle Hill, Brinklow Road, Ansty, Coventry, West
Midlands CV7 9JL
Tel: 024 7660 2777
Objects: G,R,U,H

CRESWELL GROUNDWORK TRUST
Founded: 1991 CR1004253
Executive Director: Mr P Bromley
96 Creswell Road, Clowne, Chesterfield,
Derbyshire S43 4NA
Tel: 01246 570977

CREWE/NANTWICH BOROUGH AND CONGLETON BOROUGH DIAL-A-RIDE ASSOCIATION
Founded: 1990 CR702629
Co-ordinator: Mrs M L Dale
Units 12 & 15, Brierley Business Centre, Mirion
Street, Crewe, Cheshire CW1 2AZ
Tel: 01270 251662
Fax: 01270 215493

CROFT CARE TRUST
Founded: 1990 CR703194
Finance Manager: Mrs Julie Marklew
Honorary Secretary: Mr Phillip Heath
The Croft, Hawcoat Lane, Barrow-in-Furness,
Cumbria LA14 4HE
Tel: 01229 820090
Objects: W5,3

CROHN'S AND COLITIS UK
Founded: 1979 CR1117148; SC038632
Chair: Mr Keith Stewart
Chief Executive: Mr David Barker
4 Beaumont House, Sutton Road, St Albans,
Hertfordshire AL1 5HH
Tel: 01727 830038 (Admin & Membership); 0845
130 2233 (Information & Support)
Fax: 01727 862550
Email: .... enquiry@crohnsandcolitis.org.uk
Web: .... http://www.crohnsandcolitis.org.uk
Objects: F,W3,W5,1A,2,W4,H,3,P,W

Crohn's and Colitis UK supports patients and families
affected by these devastating bowel conditions and also
funds research. Services include helplines, information,
web forum, local Groups, personal grants and
resources for health professionals.
See advert on previous page

CROSSROADS GREENWICH & LEWISHAM LTD
Founded: 1997 CR1062951
Director: Mrs Jane Haines
2a Wildfell Road, London SE6 4HU
Tel: 020 8690 8554
Fax: 020 8690 1808
Objects: M,W3,W5,W10,W4,3

CROSSWAYS COMMUNITY
Founded: 1991 CR1007156
General Manager: Mr Martin Granger
8 Culverden Park Road, Tunbridge Wells, Kent
TN4 9QX

Tel: 01892 529321
Fax: 01892 540043
Email: . . . . info@crosswayscommunity.org.uk
Objects: W5,O,3,C

CRUSADERS
See Urban Saints

CRUSADERS IN IRELAND
See Urban Saints

CRUSAID
Founded: 1986 CR1011718
Chief Executive: Mr Robin Brady
1-5 Curtain Road, London EC2A 3JX
Tel: 020 7539 3880
Fax: 020 7539 3890
Email: . . . . office@crusaid.org.uk
Objects: W5,1A,A,1B

CSHS
Founded: 1990 CR328742
Marketing & Research Manager: Mr Stephen Bell
Director: Mrs Christine Walker
1st Floor, Elgar House, Shrub Hill Road,
Worcester, Worcestershire WR4 9EE
Tel: 01905 21155
Fax: 01905 22330
Email: . . . . cshs@cornwall.co.uk
Objects: J,G,W10,D,W4,H,3,K

THE CTBI - THE SALESPEOPLES CHARITY
Founded: 1849 CR216538
Secretary: Mrs Mandi Leonard
2 Fletcher Road, Ottershaw, Chertsey, Surrey
KT16 0JT
Tel: 01932 429636
Fax: 01932 429636
Email: . . . . sec.ctbi@ntlworld.com
Objects: W11,1A,A

Supporting around 300 beneficiaries annually with
regular grants, one off payments and gifts in kind. The
Institution incorporates the London Commercial
Travellers' Benevolent Society and is the national
charity for sales professionals, their spouses, widows
and dependants.

CUMBERLAND AND WESTMORLAND CONVALESCENT INSTITUTION
Founded: 1862 CR223946
Matron: Mrs E A Blair RGN
Chairman: Mr I W Brown
Nursing and Residential Care, Silloth, Wigton,
Cumbria CA7 4JH
Tel: 01697 331493
Objects: W5,N,W4,3

THE CURE PARKINSON'S TRUST
CR1111816
St Botolph's, Aldgate High Street, London
EC3N 1AB
Tel: . . . . Office: 0207 929 7656
Mobile: 07867 978662
Email: . . . . cptinfo@cureparkinsons.org.uk

CWMNI THEATR ARAD GOCH
Founded: 1990 CR702506
Administrator: Miss Nia Williams
Stryd Y Baddon, Aberystwyth, Ceredigion
SY23 2NN
Tel: 01970 617998
Fax: 01970 611223
Objects: W3,G,3

CYSTIC FIBROSIS TRUST
Founded: 1964 CR1079049; SC040196
Chief Executive: Mrs Rosie Barnes
Deputy Chief Executive: Mr Alan Larsen
11 London Road, Bromley, Kent BR1 1BY
Tel: 0300 373 1100
Email: . . . . legacies@cysticfibrosis.org.uk
Objects: F,H

D

DAIN FUND, THE
Founded: 1940 CR313108
Chairman: Dr Mike Downes
Director: Ms Marian Flint
BMA Charities, BMA House, Tavistock Square,
London WC1H 9JP
Tel: 020 7383 6142
Email: . . . . info.bmacharities@bma.org.uk
Objects: G,W11,1A

Helps with the education costs of doctors' children in
times of financial crisis.

THE DAME VERA LYNN TRUST FOR CHILDREN WITH CEREBRAL PALSY
CR1089657
Executive Officer: Mr Peter Evans
Fundraising Manager: Mrs Shirley Illsley
Trust Office, Ingfield Manor, Five Oaks,
Billinghurst, West Sussex RH14 9AX
Tel: 01403 780444; 01403 783111
Fax: 01403 780444
Objects: W3,G,3

DANCE NORTH
See Dance City

DANCE EAST
CR1066825
Office Manager: Ms Karen Matthews
Northgate Arts Centre, Sidegate Lane West,
Ipswich, Suffolk IP4 3DF
Tel: 01473 639230
Fax: 01473 639236
Email: . . . . info@danceeast.co.uk
Objects: F,W3,J,W2,S,W5,G,W10,W4,H,3,P

DANENBERG OBERLIN-IN-LONDON PROGRAM
Founded: 1991 CR297071
Dr Donna Vinter
F.S.U. Study Centre, Room 29, 99-103 Great
Russell Street, London WC1B 3LA
Tel: 020 7419 1178
Fax: 020 7419 1178
Objects: W3,G

DAPHNE JACKSON TRUST, THE
Founded: 1992 CR1125867
Trust Director: Dr Katie Perry
Department of Physics, University of Surrey,
Guildford, Surrey GU2 7XH
Tel: 01483 689166
Fax: 01483 686781
Email: . . . . djmft@surrey.ac.uk
Objects: G,W11,1A,B,W8

DARTFORD, GRAVESHAM & SWANLEY MIND
Founded: 1969 CR1103790
Business Manager: Ms Angie Lawrence
Services Manager: Ms Sally Pearson
The Almhouses, 16 West Hill, Dartford, Kent DA1 2EP
Tel: 01322 291380
Fax: 01322 285294
Email: . . . . email@dgsmind.freeserve.co.uk
Objects: F,E,G,D,H,3,C,P,K

DAVID AND FREDERICK BARCLAY FOUNDATION, THE
See The Barclay Foundation

DAVID LEWIS CENTRE FOR EPILEPSY
Founded: 1990 CR1000392
Chief Executive: Mr James Bisset
The David Lewis Centre, Mill Lane, Warford, Alderley Edge, Cheshire SK9 7UD
Tel: 01565 640000
Fax: 01565 640100
Email: . . . . enquiries@davidlewis.org.uk
Objects: W3,W5,G,N,2,W4,O,3,C,K

DAVID LIVINGSTONE INTERNATIONAL LTD
SC010894
47 Brynsworthy Park, Roundswell, Devon EX31 3RB
Tel: 01271 321210
Fax: 01271 321210
Email: . . . . upservant2008@talktalk.net
Web: . . . . www.davidlivingstone-int-ltd.com

Objects: W3,U
DLI the charity with a difference it enjoys free office accommodation, heating and telephone, no salaries or allowances are paid to the directors or officers in the UK or abroad. It operates through ministers and national workers and seeks to respond to crisis situations in emergencies. DLI supports nearly 2,000 orphans and children in homes and schools in **Thailand, The Philippines, India** and various parts of **Africa**. It carries out an active medical programme treating **cleft palate** children with follow up dentistry, speech therapy and catch up education. Care for patients with TB, cancer and the frail elderly is part of seeking to meet part of the family needs. **Clean water is a vital part** of the provision and every year new **bore holes and water pumps** are installed in slum villages where weekly feeding programmes for malnourished children and training of mothers to prepare food in hygienic conditions are provided. **Education is the only way out of poverty** and children are encouraged to obtain the highest qualifications academically or vocationally in 2013 a number of our students received university and college degrees. **"Sympathy is no substitute for action"** David Livingstone. **200 years of ministry, Donations and legacies are urgently needed.**

See advert on this page

DEAF DIRECT
CR1105044
Community Manager: Mr Gordon Hay
Vesta Tilley House, Lowesmoor, Worcester, Worcestershire WR1 2RS
Tel: .... 01905 746301; 01905 746300 (Text)
Fax: 01905 746302
Email: .... info@deafdirect.org.uk
Objects: F,J,W7,G,3
Working to promote independence and equality of opportunity for deaf and hard of hearing people of all ages, living in Herefordshire, Oxfordshire and Worcestershire. Deaf Direct provides communication services, training, support and advice.

DEAF EDUCATION THROUGH LISTENING AND TALKING - DELTA
Founded: 1988 CR1115603
Operations Manager: Mr Steve Matthews
The Con Powell Centre, Alfa House, Molesey Road, Walton-on-Thames, Surrey KT12 3PD
Tel: 0845 108 1437
Email: .... enquiries@deafeducation.org.uk
Objects: F,W3,W7,G,V,2,H

DEAFNESS RESEARCH UK
CR326915
Patron: HRH The Duke of York
Chief Executive: Ms Vivienne Michael
330-332 Gray's Inn Road, London WC1X 8EE
Tel: 020 7164 2290
Fax: 020 7278 0404
Email: ...... contact@deafnessresearch.org.uk

DELPHSIDE LTD
Founded: 1991 CR1006024
Finance Manager: Miss J Dunne
11 Standstone Drive, Prescot, Merseyside L35 7LS
Tel: 0151 431 0330

DEMAND - DESIGN AND MANUFACTURE FOR DISABILITY
Founded: 1992 CR1008128
The Old Chapel, Mallard Road, Abbots Langley, Hertfordshire WD5 0GQ
Tel: 01923 681800
Fax: 01923 682400
Email: .... info@demand.org.uk

DEMENTIA SERVICES DEVELOPMENT TRUST

 Dementia Services Development Trust

Founded: 1989SC016905
Convenor: Ms Hilary Mounfield OBE
Iris Murdoch Building, University of Stirling, Stirling FK9 4LA
Tel: 01786 467740
Fax: 01786 466846
Email: dementia@stir.ac.uk/ dsdtrust_stirling@yahoo.com
Web: .... http://www.dementia.stir.ac.uk
Objects: F,G,H,K
The Dementia Services Development Trust (DSDT) works to improve the lives of people with dementia, their families and carers. For over 20 years the DSDT has funded projects undertaken by the Dementia Services Development Centre (DSDC). The Centre is based in the Iris Murdoch Building, an innovative example of dementia friendly design. Visitors to this acclaimed centre can see how design can enhance the lives of people with dementia. The Centre works to reduce the impact of dementia by providing training, expertise and advice on dementia and best care practice to organisations in all sectors.

DEPRESSION UK
Founded: 1979 CR294482
Secretary: Mrs Kate Wilkins
Self Help Nottingham, Ormiston House, 32-36 Pelham Street, Nottingham, Nottinghamshire NG1 2EG
Tel: 0870 774 4320
Fax: 0870 774 4319
Email: .... info@depressionuk.org
Objects: F,2,H,O,W

DERBY COUNCIL FOR VOLUNTARY SERVICE
CR1043482
4 Charnwood Street, Derby, Derbyshire DE1 2GT
Tel: ... 01332 346266; 01332 341576 (Minicom)
Fax: 01332 205069
Email: .... cvs@cvsderby.co.uk

DEREK PRINCE MINISTRIES - CHINA
Founded: 1992 CR1010850
Executive Co-ordinator: Mr Neil Cornick
Kingsfield, Hadrian Way, Baldock, Hertfordshire SG7 6AN
Tel: 01462 492110
Fax: 01462 492102
Email: .... enquires@dpmuk.org

DERIAN HOUSE CHILDREN'S HOSPICE FOR THE NORTH WEST
Founded: 1991 CR1005165
General Manager: Mr T E Briggs
Chairman of Trustees: Miss M R Vinten
Derian House, Chancery Road, Astley Village, Chorley, Lancashire PR7 1DH
Tel: 01257 271271
Fax: 01257 234861
Email: .... derian.house@virgin.net
Objects: W3,3

DESIGN AND TECHNOLOGY ASSOCIATION

Founded: 1992 CR1062270
Chief Executive: Mr R. Green
Chairman: Dr R Peacock
Company Secretary: Miss B Van Bejnum

16 Wellesbourne House, Walton Road,
Wellesbourne, Warwickshire CV35 9JB
Tel: 01789 470007
Fax: 01789 841955
Email: .... data@data.org.uk
Objects: G,2,H

DEVELOPMENT TRUST FOR THE FRAIL OR PHYSICALLY DISABLED ELDERLY

See AgeCare (The Royal Surgical Aid Society)

DEVON AIR AMBULANCE TRUST

Founded: 1991 CR1077998
Chief Executive: Ms Helena Holt
PA to CEO: Mrs Melanie Stevens

5 Sandpiper Court, Harrington Lane, Exeter,
Devon EX4 8NS
Tel: 01392 466666
Fax: 01392 464329
Email: .... info@daat.org
Objects: N,3

DIABETES TRUST RESEARCH AND CARE FUND

CR1058284
c/o InDependent Diabetes Trust, PO Box 294,
Northampton, Northamptonshire NN1 4XS
Tel: 01604 622837
Fax: 01604 622838
Email: .... enquiries@iddtinternational.org
Web: .... www.iddtinternational.org

DIABETES UK

Founded: 1934 CR215199; SC039136
Chief Executive: Mr Douglas Smallwood

Macleod House, 10 Parkway, London NW1 7AA
Tel: 020 7424 1853
Fax: 020 7424 1001
Email: .... legacies@diabetes.org.uk
Objects: F,W3,J,G,W10,A,V,2,H,3

THE DIAGEO FOUNDATION

Founded: 1992 CR1014681
Secretary: Ms S M Adams

8 Henrietta Place, London W1G 0NB
Tel: 020 7927 5200
Fax: 020 7927 4600

THE DICK VET ANIMAL HEALTH AND WELFARE FUND

SC004307
The University of Edinburgh, Easter Bush
Veterinary Centre, Roslin, Midlothian EH25 9RG
Tel: 0131 650 6261
Fax: 0131 650 8838
Email: .... edinburghcampaign@ed.ac.uk

DIMBLEBY CANCER CARE

CR247558
**4th Floor Management Offices, Bermondsey
Wing, Guy's Hospital, Great Maze Pond,
London SE1 9RT**
Tel: 020 7188 7889
Email: ... admin@dimblebycancercare.org
The charity focuses on addressing the
psychological and social impact on patients and
their families which a cancer diagnosis
inevitably brings, and offering care throughout
the journey from diagnosis to recovery, or to the
end of life.
Dimbleby Cancer Care provides funding for the
Cancer Information and Support Services at
Guy's and St Thomas' Hospitals in London.
These drop-in centres offer information;
psychological support and counselling;
complementary therapies; benefit and financial
advice; and support groups for specific cancers.
The Dimbleby Cancer Care Research Fund
facilitates research into the support needs of
people with cancer, and those of their families
and carers – for example, how can older care
givers be helped to cope better? The Research
Fund is one of the UK's leading supporters of
this type of research.
Dimbleby Cancer Care is entirely dependent on
legacies and donations. Please remember us in
your will or, if you can, make a donation now.
See advert on previous page

DIOCESE OF CYPRUS AND THE GULF ENDOWMENT FUND

Founded: 1990 CR1000307
Clerk: Miss E Ashley

19 Little Breach, Chichester, West Sussex
PO19 5TX
Tel: 01243 787507

THE DISABILITIES TRUST

Founded: 1979 CR800797
Chief Executive: Mr Barrie Oldham
Head of Marketing and Fundraising: Ms Helen
Tridgell

1st Floor, 32 Market Place, Burgess Hill, West
Sussex RH15 9NP
Tel: 01444 239123
Fax: 01444 244978
Email: .... info@thedtgroup.org
Objects: W3,E,W5,G,D,2,O,3,C

The Disabilities Trust is a leading national charity
providing quality care, rehabilitation and support for
people with physical disabilities, autism, acquired brain
injury and learning disabilities. We offer a range of
purpose built accommodation, community-based
housing and other services – all aimed at improving
quality of life for people with complex and multiple
disabilities.

DISABILITY ADVICE BRADFORD

CR700084
103 Dockfield Road, Shipley, West Yorkshire
BD17 7AR
Tel: 01274 594173
Fax: 01274 530432
Email: .... enquiry@disabilityadvice.org.uk

DISABILITY ESSEX (ESSEX DISABLED PEOPLES ASSOCIATION LTD)
Founded: 1949 CR1102596
The Centre for Disability Studies, Adult Community College Rocheway, Rochford, Essex SS4 1DQ
Tel: 08444 121771
Email: . . . . info@disabilityessex.org
Objects: F,W6,W7,W5,G,V,2,W4,3,P

DISABLED DRIVERS' ASSOCIATION, THE
See Disabled Motoring UK

DISABLED LIVING
CR224742
Chief Executive: Debra Evans
Redbank House, 4 St Chad's Street, Cheetham, Manchester, Greater Manchester M8 8QA
Tel: 0161 214 5959
Fax: 0161 835 3591
Email: . . . . information@disabledliving.co.uk
Objects: F,W6,M,W3,E,W7,W5,G,V,O,3,P

DISABLED MOTORING UK
CR1111826
National Headquarters, Ashwellthorpe, Norwich, Norfolk NR16 1EX
Tel: 01508 489449
Fax: 01508 488173
Email: . . . . enquiries@mobilise.info
Objects: F,J,W5,2,H,3,P

DOG AID SOCIETY OF SCOTLAND
Founded: 1956SC001918
Secretary: Miss Lucy Taylor
60 Blackford Avenue, Edinburgh EH9 3ER
Tel: 0131 668 3633
Fax: 0131 668 1063
Email: . . . . enquiries@dogaidsociety.com
Object: W1
Since 1956 the Dog Aid Society has been providing support and assistance for families who face the difficult decision to re-home their much loved pets. Every dog that we re-home is provided with all the items it will require to settle into its new home, in addition to being neutered, vaccinated and micro-chipped. DASS will continue to take an active interest in the dog throughout its life; providing any ongoing veterinary treatment that it may require. It is our aim to educate the public on dog ownership and one way that we achieve this is by providing a free information service, giving advice on every aspect of dog ownership. We also offer a low cost neutering scheme and a veterinary aid scheme for dog owners on benefits. If you would like more information about the Society please contact the office.
See advert on this page

DOG CARE ASSOCIATION (AND CATS)
CR518996
Ponderosa Kennels (CC), Allerton Bywater, Castleford, West Yorkshire WF10 2EW
Tel: 01977 552303
Fax: 01977 552303
Email: . . . . . . michael@pondarosakennel.org.uk
Object: W1

We promise we'll never put down a healthy dog.

Please promise to help us with a gift in your Will.

Every year, Dogs Trust cares for around 16,000 dogs in our 20 rehoming centres across the UK. We never put down a healthy dog. By leaving a gift in your Will, your love of dogs can live on and help us make the world a better place for them.

Call: 020 7837 0006
Email: infopack@dogstrust.org.uk
Please quote **"CD2014"**

DogsTrust

DOGS TRUST
Founded: 1891 CR227523; SC037843
Veterinary Director: Ms Paula Boyden
Secretary & Chief Executive: Mrs Clarissa Baldwin (OBE)
Marketing Director: Mr Adrian Burder
Finance Director: Mr Jim Monteith

17 Wakley Street, London EC1V 7RQ
Tel: 020 7837 0006
Fax: 020 7833 2701
Email: .... feedback@dogstrust.org.uk
Objects: Q,F,W1,J,G,2,H

Dogs Trust is the UK's largest dog welfare charity, and last year cared for around 16,000 stray and abandoned dogs at our nationwide network of rehoming centres. We never put down a healthy dog, and work hard to match the right dog with the right owner, no matter how long this may take. We believe that all dogs should live in permanent, loving homes with responsible owners, and that a dog really is for life. We are working towards the day when no healthy dog is put down for want of a loving home.

Dogs Trust also offers peace of mind to dog owners with its special free service, the Canine Care Card. If you ever wonder "What would happen to my dog if I were to die suddenly?" Dogs Trust provides the answer. By carrying a Canine Care Card, we undertake to look after and find a new, loving home for your dog in the event of your death. That way, you can rest assured that your dog's future can be a safe and happy one after your lifetime.

Dogs Trust relies entirely on legacies and donations to fund its work. Every gift received helps more dogs in need.

See advert on previous page

DONCASTER PARTNERSHIP FOR CARERS LIMITED (DPFC)
Founded: 1991 CR1075455
Centre Co-ordinator: Miss K Osborne

St Wilfrid's, 74 Church Lane, Bessacarr, Doncaster, South Yorkshire DN4 6QD
Tel: 01302 531333
Fax: 01302 536645
Email: .... dpfc@doncastercarers.org.uk
Objects: F,W6,W3,W7,W5,G,W10,W4,3

DONKEY SANCTUARY, ISLE OF WIGHT
See Isle of Wight Donkey Sanctuary

THE DONKEY SANCTUARY

THE DONKEY SANCTUARY

Founded: 1973 CR264818
Chief Executive: Mr David Cook
Slade House Farm (Dept CD), Sidmouth, Devon EX10 0NU
Tel: 01395 578222
Fax: 01395 579266
Email: . enquiries@thedonkeysanctuary.org.uk
Web: ...... www.thedonkeysanctuary.org.uk
Objects: F,W1,M,G,N,U,H,3

We aim to prevent the suffering of donkeys through the provision of high quality professional advice, training and support on donkey care and welfare. Welfare officers in the UK and Ireland provide advice and practical support to donkey owners and follow up complaints of alleged maltreatment or neglect of donkeys; and our veterinary team shares their knowledge with practitioners around the world. Please see our advertisement...

See advert on next page

DORCAS MINISTRIES
Founded: 1996 CR1055427
Director: Miss Annette Akporiaye

62 Lebrun Square, Greenwich, London SE3 9NS
Tel: 020 8856 7876
Objects: F,W9,W3,D,R,U,O,3,C,P,W8

DORIS FIELD CHARITABLE TRUST
Founded: 1990 CR328687
Trustees Solicitor: Messrs Morgan & Cole

Buxton Court, 3 West Way, Oxford, Oxfordshire OX2 0SZ
Tel: 01865 262600
Objects: 1A,A,1B

DORSET RESIDENTIAL HOMES
Founded: 1991 CR1003779
Company Accountant: Mrs Joanne Johnston
Chief Executive & Company Secretary: Mrs Gillian Lacey

Connaught House, 22 Cornwall Road, Dorchester, Dorset DT1 1RU
Tel: 01305 267483
Fax: 01305 267483
Email: .... doresd@aol.com
Objects: W5,O,3,C

DORUS TRUST
Founded: 1990 CR328724
Senior Grants Officer: Mrs Abigail Hiscock
Kings Hill, West Malling, Kent ME19 4TA
Tel: 01732 520081
Objects: F,W6,W3,W2,W7,W5,A,1B,W4,O

DOWN'S SYNDROME ASSOCIATION
CR1061474
Director: Ms Carol Boys
Langdon Down Centre, 2a Langdon Park, Teddington, Middlesex TW11 9PS

REMEMBER THE DONKEYS IN YOUR WILL

THE DONKEY SANCTUARY

PROVIDING A SANCTUARY FOR LIFE FOR DONKEYS AND MULES IN NEED OF REFUGE IN THE UK, IRELAND AND EUROPE

HELP US TO CARE FOR THEM IN THE FUTURE BY REMEMBERING US IN YOUR WILL.

Any donation, no matter how small, will be gratefully received and your name will be inscribed on a Memorial Wall at the Sanctuary in Sidmouth.

THE DONKEY SANCTUARY
Dept CD, Sidmouth,
Devon EX10 0NU

T 01395 578222 **F** 01395 579266
E enquiries@thedonkeysanctuary.org.uk
www.thedonkeysanctuary.org.uk

The Donkey Sanctuary (registered charity number 264818) and its sole corporate trustee, The Donkey Sanctuary Trustee Limited (Company number 07328588) both have their registered office at Slade House Farm, Sidmouth, EX10 0NU Incorporating: The Elisabeth Svendsen Trust for Children and Donkeys (EST); The International Donkey Protection Trust (IDPT).

FRSB
give with confidence

WORKING WORLDWIDE

0264_12_DS

Tel: 0845 230 0372
Fax: 0845 230 0373
Email: . . . . paul.zanon@downs-syndrome.org.uk
Objects: F,W3,J,G,2,W4,H,P

DRIVE
Founded: 1990 CR703002
Secretary: Mr Barry Gallagher
Unit 8, Cefn Coed, Parc Nantgarw, Nantgarw,
Cardiff CF15 7QQ
Tel: 01443 845260
Fax: 01443 845287
Objects: W5,D,3,P

THE DUKE OF EDINBURGH'S AWARD
Founded: 1956 CR1072490
Finance Director: Mr Ken Coppock
Marketing and Communications Assistant: Miss
Fluer Nicholson
UK Services Director: Mr Philip Treleven
Chief Executive: Mr Peter Westgarth
Gulliver House, Madeira Walk, Windsor, Windsor
& Maidenhead SL4 1EU
Tel: 01753 727400
Fax: 01753 810666
Email: . . . . info@DofE.org
Objects: W6,W3,W2,S,W7,W5,G,W10,H,3,P,W8

DURHAM LESOTHO DIOCESAN LINK, THE
Founded: 1990 CR702809
Executive Officer: Mr Paul Jefferson
26 Allergate, Durham, Co. Durham DH1 4ET

Tel: 0191 384 8385
Fax: 0191 386 2863
Email: . . . . tpjeff@sagainternet.co.uk
Objects: W3,G,A,R,3,P,W8

DUTCH HOME FOR THE ELDERLY
See Wilhelmina House

DWARF SPORT ASSOCIATION UK

Founded: 1993 CR1041961
PO Box 4269, Dronfield, Derbyshire S18 9BG
Tel: 01246 296485
Web: . . . . http://www.dsauk.org
Objects: W5,W15

The Dwarf Sports Association UK provides sporting and recreational opportunities for people with restricted growth conditions or dwarfism.

We provide regular sporting events at a regional and national level. We also provide support for the parents and siblings of our members.

The association also provides a platform to organise teams to attend European and World events.

If you feel you can help with the DSAuk's work then please contact us.

See advert on this page

DYSLEXIA ACTION
Founded: 1972 CR208502, SC039177
Executive Director: Ms Shirley Cramer
Executive Director: Ms Shirley Cramer
Parkhouse, Wick Road, Egham, Surrey
TW20 0HH
Tel: 01784 222300
Fax: 01784 222333
Email: .... info@dyslexiaaction.org.uk
Objects: F,W3,G,W4,H,3

DYSLEXIA ASSOCIATION, BRITISH
See British Dyslexia Association

DYSPRAXIA FOUNDATION
Founded: 1987 CR1058352
Administrator: Ms Eleanor Howes
8 West Alley, Hitchin, Hertfordshire SG5 1EG
Tel: 01462 455016; 01462 454986 Helpline (Mon-Fri 10am 1pm)
Fax: 01462 455052
Email: ... dyspraxia@dyspraxiafoundation.org.uk
Objects: F,W3,J,H

E

EARL MOUNTBATTEN HOSPICE, NEWPORT, ISLE OF WIGHT
CR1039086
Fundraising, Halberry Lane, Newport, Isle of Wight
PO30 2ER
Tel: 01983 528989
Fax: 01983 528671
Email. .... Info@emhfunding.com

EARLS COURT COMMUNITY PROJECT (YWAM)
Founded: 1991 CR1002189
Care Worker: Miss Rebecca Hulme
Project Manager: Mr Samy Mansour
Care Worker: Mr Walter S. Nicora
24 Collingham Road, London SW5 0LX
Tel: 020 7370 4424
Fax: 020 7370 4424
Objects: F,E,G,R,O,3,P

EASINGTON DISTRICT COUNCIL OF VOLUNTARY SERVICE
CR1117642
Community House, Yoden Road, Peterlee, Co. Durham SR8 5DP
Tel: 0191 569 3511
Fax: 0191 569 3522
Email: .... info@eastdurhamtrust.org.uk
Objects: F,G,A,1B,H,3

EAST CHESHIRE HOUSING CONSORTIUM LTD
Founded: 1991 CR1001923
Business Manager & Company Secretary: Mrs B Wright
26A Jordangate, Macclesfield, Cheshire SK10 1EW
Tel: 01625 500166

EAST LONDON COMMUNITY FOUNDATION
Founded: 1990 CR1133535
Operations Manager: Mrs Helen Robertson
Chief Executive: Jessica Wanamaker
Unit G12, Office 7, Chadwell Heath Ind.Park, Chadwell Heath, Essex RM8 1SL
Tel: 0300 303 1203
Email: .... enquiries@elcf.org.uk
Objects: W6,W3,W7,W5,W10,W15,A,1B,W16,W4

EAST MIDDLESBROUGH COMMUNITY VENTURE
Founded: 1990 CR702916
Secretary to the Trustees: Mr C J Beety
The Greenway Centre, Thorntree, Middlesbrough, North Yorkshire TS3 9PA
Tel: 01642 230314

ECL DOOR OF HOPE
CR1083260
PO Box 60 (SCC), Battle, East Sussex TN33 0WW
Tel: 01424 870836
Fax: 01424 870836
Email: .... doorhope@aol.com
Objects: W3,G,W10,3

ECUMENICAL SOCIETY OF THE BLESSED VIRGIN MARY
CR282748
Hon Secretary: Mr Joseph Farrelly
11 Belmont Road, Wallington, Surrey SM6 8TE
Tel: 020 8647 5992

THE EDINBURGH DOG AND CAT HOME

Founded: 1883SC006914
26 Seafield Road East, Portobello, Edinburgh EH15 1EH
Tel: 0131 669 5331
Fax: 0131 657 5601
Email: .... info@edch.org.uk
Objects: F,W1
Founded in 1883, the Home provides care and welfare for lost and abandoned dogs and cats. Donations and legacies are essential for us to provide a caring environment for the many animals brought to us for help.

EDUCATION ACTION INTERNATIONAL (REFUGEE EDUCATION & TRAINING ADVISORY SERVICE)
Founded: 1920 CR1003323
The Administrator
3 Dufferin Street, London EC1Y 8NA
Tel: .... 020 7426 5800 RETAS; 020 7426 5820 International
Fax: .... 020 7251 1314 RETAS; 020 7251 1315 International
Email: ..... international@education-action.org; retas@educational-action.org
Objects: F,G,W10,2,U,3,W8

EDWARD LLOYD TRUST, THE
Founded: 1991 CR1005124
Mr Howard Kennedy
Harcourt House, 19 Cavendish Square, London
W16 0AJ
Tel: 020 7636 1616
Fax: 020 7830 8292
Object: 3

ELFRIDA SOCIETY, THE
CR282716
34 Islington Park Street, London N1 1PX
Tel: 020 7359 7443
Fax: 020 7704 1358
Email: .... elfrida@elfrida.com

ELISABETH SVENDSEN TRUST FOR CHILDREN AND DONKEYS, THE
Founded: 1989 CR801070
Founder: Dr Elisabeth Svendsen MBE
Slade House Farm (Dept ESJ), Sidmouth, Devon
EX10 0NU
Tel: 01395 573133
Fax: 01395 579266
Email: ..... info@elisabethsvendsentrust.org.uk
Objects: Q,W6,W3,W7,W5,G,O,3,P

ELIZABETH FINN CARE (FORMERLY KNOWN AS DISTRESSED GENTLEFOLK'S AID ASSOCIATION)
Founded: 1897 CR207812
Ms Rebecca Calder
Director of Finance: Mr Antony Leaver
Administrator: Mrs Margaret Scanlon
Chief Executive: Mr Jonathan Welfare
Director of Casework: Ms Lizzie Yeats
1 Derry Street, London W8 5HY
Tel: 020 7396 6700; 0800 413 220
Fax: 020 7396 6739
Email: .... info@elizabethfinn.org.uk
Objects: F,W9,J,W5,W11,1A,A,W4

ELIZABETH FINN TRUST
See Elizabeth Finn Care (formerly known as
Distressed Gentlefolk's Aid Association)

ELIZABETH FOUNDATION FOR DEAF CHILDREN
Founded: 1981 CR293835
Director: Ms Shirley Metherell
Southwick Hill Road, Cosham, Portsmouth,
Hampshire PO6 3LL
Tel: 023 9237 2735
Fax: 023 9232 6155
Email: .... info@elizabeth-foundation.org
Objects: F,W3,W7,G,3

ELLENORLIONS HOSPICES, NORTHFLEET
CR1121561
Coldharbour Road, Northfleet, Gravesend, Kent
DA11 7HQ
Tel: 01474 320007
Fax: 01474 564018
Objects: N,3

ELLYS EXTRA CARE LIMITED
Founded: 1990 CR703127
Company Secretary: Miss S Peters
1 Ellys Road, Radford, Coventry, West Midlands
CV1 4EW
Tel: 024 7625 6859

ELSE AND LEONARD CROSS CHARITABLE TRUST, THE
Founded: 1992 CR1008038
Trustee: Mrs Helen Gillingwater
The Wall House, 2 Lichfield Road, Richmond,
Surrey TW9 3JR
Tel: 020 8948 4950
Fax: 020 8948 4950

EMERGENCY EXIT ARTS
Founded: 1991 CR1004137
Administrator: Ms Elaine Clarke
PO Box 570, Greenwich, London SE10 0EE
Tel: 020 8853 4809
Fax: 020 8858 2025
Email: .... info@eea.org.uk
Objects: W3,W2,S,G,W10,W4,3

EMFEC
Founded: 1991 CR1004087
Chief Executive: Ms Jennie Gardiner
Robins Wood House, Robins Wood Road, Aspley,
Nottingham, Nottinghamshire NG8 3NH
Tel: 0115 854 1616
Fax: 0115 854 1617
Email: .... enquiries@emfec.co.uk
Objects: G,2,H,3

EMMANUEL CHRISTIAN SCHOOL ASSOCIATION
Founded: 1990 CR900505
Treasurer: Mr Christopher Taylor
Sandford Road, Littlemore, Oxford, Oxfordshire
OX4 4PU
Tel: 01865 395236
Objects: W3,G,3

EMMANUEL INTERNATIONAL UK

Founded: 1978 CR289036
Forum House, Stirling Road, Chichester, West
Sussex PO19 7DN
Tel: 01243 537040
Email: .... info@eiuk.org.uk
Web: .... http://www.eiuk.org.uk
Objects: W3,W11,W15,2,R,W4,U,W8
Emmanuel International works in Developing
Countries world-wide through practical, caring action
and culturally sensitive mission - to meet the needs
of people practically, spiritually and emotionally.

EMUNAH (IN AID OF CHILD RESETTLEMENT FUND)
CR215398
Shield House, Harmony Way, London NW4 2BZ
Tel: 020 8203 6066
Fax: 020 8203 6668
Email: .... info@emunah.org.uk
Objects: F,W3,E,G,W4,O,P,W8

ENABLE CARE & HOME SUPPORT LIMITED
Founded: 1990 CR1001704
Company Secretary: Miss Fay Keely
Ellen House, Heath Road, Holmewood,
Chesterfield, Derbyshire S42 5RB
Tel: 01246 599999
Fax: 01246 599980
Objects: E,W5,D,N,W4,3,P

ENABLE SCOTLAND
Founded: 1954SC009024
Chief Executive: Mr Norman Dunning
Head of Fundraising & Marketing: Ms Doreen Walkinshaw
2nd Floor, 146 Argyle Street, Glasgow G2 8BL
Tel: 0141 226 4541
Fax: 0141 204 4398
Email: .... enable@enable.org.uk
Objects: F,W3,E,W5,G,V,2,H,3,C,P,K

ENABLING PARTNERSHIP (FORMERLY THE ENHAM TRUST)
See Enham

ENDOMETRIOSIS UK
Founded: 1982 CR1035810
50 Westminster Palace Gardens, 1-7 Artillery Row, London SW1P 1RR
Tel: 020 7222 2781
Fax: 020 7222 2786
Email: .... info@endometriosis-uk.org
Objects: F,2,H,W8

ENFIELD COMMUNITY TRANSPORT
Founded: 1991 CR1086730
Manager: Mr S Peters
5 Melling Drive, Enfield, Middlesex EN1 4BS
Tel: 020 0000 2255

ENFIELD VOLUNTARY ACTION
Founded: 1991 CR1077857
Chairperson: Ms Virginia Moodie
Community House, 311 Fore Street, London N9 0PZ
Tel: 020 8373 6299

ENGLISH AND MEDIA CENTRE, THE
Founded: 1990 CR803031
Secretary to the Trustees: Mr M Simons
18 Compton Terrace, London N1 2UN
Tel: 020 7359 8080
Fax: 020 7354 0133
Email: .... info@englishandmedia.co.uk

ENHAM
Founded: 1917 CR211235
Community Fundraiser: Mrs Liz Cosgrove
Chief Executive: Mr Michael Smith
Enham Alamein, Andover, Hampshire SP11 6JS
Tel: 01264 345800
Fax: 01264 333638
Email: .... info@enham.co.uk
Objects: F,W6,M,J,E,W7,W5,G,D,O,C,K

ENTERTAINMENT ARTISTES' BENEVOLENT FUND
Founded: 1908 CR206451
Mr Keith Lascelles
Brinsworth House (CD), 72 Staines Road, Twickenham, Middlesex TW2 5AL

Tel: 020 8898 8164
Fax: 020 8894 0093
Email: .... admin@eabf.org.uk
Objects: M,J,1A,A,V,N,B

ENVIRON TRUST LTD
See Groundwork Leicester & Leicestershire Ltd

THE ENVIRONMENT COUNCIL
Founded: 1969 CR294075
Chairman: Doctor Malcolm Aickin
212 High Holborn, London WC1V 7BF
Tel: 020 7836 2626
Fax: 020 7242 1180
Email: .... info@envcouncil.org.uk
Objects: F,J,W2,G,2,H,3

ENVIRONMENTAL INVESTIGATION AGENCY TRUST

CR1145359
62-63 Upper Street, London N1 0NY
Tel: 020 7354 7960
Fax: 020 7354 7961
Email: ...... legacy@eia-international.org
Objects: W1,W2
"ONE OF BRITAIN'S MOST EFFECTIVE CONSERVATION GROUPS" BBC Wildlife Magazine.
EIA's vision is a future where humanity respects, protects and celebrates the natural world for the benefit of all. For three decades EIA has been protecting animals and the environment with intelligence.
Every day many species face increasing threats from the cruel and lucrative illegal wildlife trade.
Our undercover investigations and determined campaigns have exposed this trade and helped to save the lives of hundreds of thousands of wild animals from tigers, elephants and orangutans to whales and dolphins and many other endangered species.
We also protect their habitats by exposing environmental crimes such as illegal logging and the illegal trade in chemicals that damage the ozone layer and contribute to climate change.
But it is only through the generosity of people who share our passion for the natural world that we are able to achieve outstanding results year after year.
A gift to EIA can help protect wildlife and the environment for generations to come.
For further information about remembering EIA in your Will, please call us or send us an e-mail or letter.

ENVIRONMENTAL PROTECTION UK
Founded: 1959 CR221026
44 Grand Parade, Brighton, Brighton & Hove BN2 9QA
Tel: 01273 878770
Fax: 01273 606626
Email: .... admin@nsca.org.uk
Objects: J,W2,G,2,H,3

You can help change the future.
Here are the facts now...
Epilepsy affects some 450,000 people in the UK.
30% of these people have epilepsy that cannot be controlled by drugs.
Every year 1,000 people die as a result of epilepsy.
By leaving Epilepsy Research UK a gift in your will, or by making a donation, you will be funding ground-breaking research that will help change the future for people with epilepsy.
funding research changing lives
epilepsy research uk
Dept CD120, Epilepsy Research UK
PO Box 3004 London W4 4XT
020 8995 4781
info@eruk.org.uk
www.epilepsyresearch.org.uk
Registered charity no: 1100394

EPIGONI TRUST
Founded: 1990 CR328700
Senior Grants Officer: Mrs Abigail Hiscock
Charities Aid Foundation, The Trust Department,
Kings Hill, West Malling, Kent ME19 4TA
Tel: 01732 520028
Objects: F,W6,W3,W2,W7,W5,A,1B,N,O

EPILEPSY RESEARCH UK
Founded: 2003 CR1100394
Chief Executive: Mr Leigh Slocombe
PO Box 3004, London W4 4XT
Tel: 020 8747 5024
Fax: 0870 838 1069
Email: .... info@eruk.org.uk
Objects: W3,W5,A,1B,N,W4,W8

See advert on previous page

EPILEPSY SOCIETY (THE WORKING NAME FOR THE NATIONAL SOCIETY FOR EPILEPSY)

Founded: 1892 CR206186
Head of fundraising: Ms Ropinder Gill
Chesham Lane, Chalfont St Peter,
Buckinghamshire SL9 0RJ
Tel: .. 01494 601300 Helpline 01494 601400
Email: fundraising@epilepsysociety.org.uk
Objects: F,M,W3,E,W5,G,W10,N,2,H,O,3,C,P, K

About one in every 100 people in the UK has epilepsy and many more are affected, especially close family. Our vision is a full life for everyone affected by epilepsy. Together we make a real and lasting contribution to people's lives in every way we can. We inform and connect people, campaign and raise awareness. Our pioneering medical research and expert medical services reduce seizures. And we are always here for people needing emotional support with our much valued helpline and forum.

How you can help: Much of our work is made possible by the gifts people leave behind in their wills. Without them we simply wouldn't have the resources to help people deal with this condition. Leave a legacy to Epilepsy Society and give hope to the future.

EQUITY CHARITABLE TRUST
Founded: 1989 CR328103
Plouviez House, 19-20 Hatton Place, London
EC1N 8RU
Tel: 020 7831 1926
Fax: 020 7242 7995
Email: .... info@equitycharitabletrust.org.uk
Objects: F,W11,1A,A,3
The Equity Charitable Trust provides Educational Bursaries to enable professional actors with a minimum of ten years professional adult experience to retrain, re-qualify and develop a new skill set. Depending on your circumstances, grants can cover some or even all of the fees. We also provide debt advice to industry members who are experiencing financial hardship and may qualify for a one-off financial grant. For information and to download an application form for either a Welfare or Education Grant, please call us or visit our website www.equitycharitabletrust.org.uk

ERIC (EDUCATION AND RESOURCES FOR IMPROVING CHILDHOOD CONTINENCE)
Founded: 1991 CR1002424
Director: Ms Penny Dobson
34 Old School House, Britannia Road, Kingswood,
Bristol BS18 8DB
Tel: 0845 370 8008
Fax: 0117 960 0401
Email: .... info@eric.org.uk
Objects: F,W3,H,3

ERMULI TRUST
See Music Libraries Trust, The

ESSEX AUTISTIC SOCIETY
See Autism Anglia

ESSEX DISABLED PEOPLE'S ASSOCIATION LIMITED
See Disability Essex (Essex Disabled Peoples Association Ltd)

EUROPEAN CHILDREN'S TRUST
Founded: 1990 CR803070
Head of Public Affairs: Ms Louise Baker
Chief Executive: Mr Robert Pritchett
4 Bath Place, Rivington Street, London EC2A 3DR
Tel: 020 7749 2468
Fax: 020 7729 8339
Email: .... gen@everychild.org.uk
Objects: Q,W3,J,G,U

EUROPEAN SIDHALAND ASSOCIATION
Founded: 1991 CR1002335
Director: Mr J C Collins
The Dome Woodley, Park Road, Ashurst,
Skelmersdale, Lancashire WN8 6UQ
Tel: 01695 728847
Fax: 01695 50306
Objects: W3,G,1A,A,2,W4,U,O,3

EVANGELICAL FELLOWSHIP IN THE ANGLICAN COMMUNION
CR212314
Trinity College, Stoke Hill, Bristol BS9 1JP
Tel: 0117 968 2803
Objects: W3,J,S,G,W10,R,W8

EVANGELICAL LIBRARY, THE
Founded: 1928 CR1040175
Librarian: Mr Stephen Taylor
5/6 Gateway Mews, Ringway, Bounds Green
Road, London N11 2UT
Tel: 020 8362 0868
Email: .... elenquire@gmail.com
Objects: F,G,3

EVELYN NORRIS TRUST
Founded: 1969 CR260078
Secretary to Trustees: Ms Kaethe Cherney
Honorary Chairman: Mr Frederick Pyne
Plouviez House, 19-20 Hatton Place, London
EC1N 8RU
Tel: 020 7831 1926
Fax: 020 7242 7995
Email: .... info@equitycharitabletrust.org.uk
Objects: W11,V
Charity that provides convalescent and recuperative holidays for members of the concert and theatrical professions following illness, injury or surgery.

EVERGREEN TRUST
Founded: 1991 CR1004289
Trustee Director General: Mr Laurence Ascott
Brixton Warehouse Shop, 126-128 Brixton Hill,
London SW2 1RP
Tel: 020 8674 3065

EVERYMAN - ACTION AGAINST MALE CANCER
See The Institute of Cancer Research: The Royal
Cancer Hospital

EWELL CHRISTIAN FELLOWSHIP TRUST
Founded: 1991 CR1002721
Generation Resource Centre, Ruxley Lane,
Epsom, Surrey KT19 0JG
Tel: 020 8786 8221
Fax: 020 8393 2918
Email: .... info@generation.co.uk
Objects: F,W3,W5,G,R,W4,3,P

EX-SERVICES HOUSING SOCIETY
 CR1004070
Chairman: Mr Anthony P Tynan
Kingsley Place, 46 Mote Road, Maidstone, Kent
ME15 6ES
Tel: 01622 768400
Fax: 01622 768500
Email: .... tony@primesafety.com
Objects: F,D

EYELESS TRUST, THE
Founded: 1993 CR1028896
Director: Mrs Lillian Ramsay AIMSW
Quemerford Cottage, 50 Malthouse Square, Lakes
Lane, Beaconsfield, Buckinghamshire HP9 2LE
Tel: 01494 672006
Objects: M,J,S,A,V,R

F

FACTORY COMMUNITY PROJECT AND YOUTH CENTRE
Founded: 1991 CR291360
Treasurer: Mr Ian Stewart
Project Director: Mr David Vandivier
The Walnut Tree, Bronte House, Mayville Est,
London N16 8LG
Tel: 020 7241 1520
Fax: 020 7275 7798
Objects: W3,G,W10,W4,3,W8

FACULTY OF PHARMACEUTICAL MEDICINE OF THE ROYAL COLLEGES OF PHYSICIANS OF THE UNITED KINGDOM
Founded: 1992 CR1130573
Treasurer: Mrs Kathryn Swanston
Faculty of Pharmaceutical Medicine, 1 St
Andrew's Place, Regent's Park, London NW1 4LB
Tel: 020 7224 0343

FAIRBRIDGE
Founded: 1909 CR206807
Director: Mr Nigel Haynes CBE
207 Waterloo Road, London SE1 8XD
Tel: 020 7928 1704
Fax: 020 7928 6016
Email: .... info@fairbrige.org.uk
Objects: F,W3,G,P

FAMILIES NEED FATHERS
Founded: 1974 CR276899
Chair: Mr John Baker
134 Curtain Road, London EC2A 3AR
Tel: 0300 030 0110
Fax: 020 7739 3410
Email: .... fnf@fnf.org.uk

FAMILY ACTION
Founded: 1869 CR264713
Chief Executive: Ms Helen Dent
501-505 Kingsland Road, Dalston, London
E8 4AU
Tel: 020 7254 6251
Fax: 020 7249 5443
Email: .... fwa.headoffice@fwa.org.uk
Objects: F,M,W3,E,G,1A,A,V,D,O,3

FAMILY HOLIDAY ASSOCIATION
Founded: 1975 CR800262
Chairholder: Mr Keith Graham
Director: Ms Jenny Stephenson
16 Mortimer Street, London W1T 3JL
Tel: 020 3117 0650
Fax: 020 7436 3302
Email: .... info@fhaonline.org.uk
Objects: W3,A,1B,V,P,W8

FATHER MAREK SUJKOWSKI, CHILDREN'S AID TO UKRAINE, ROMANIA AND POLAND
Founded: 1994 CR1031451
Trustee: Mrs Catherine E. Kyriakides
Founder: His Lordship The Rt. Rev. Fr. Abbot
Marek Sujkowski
48 Achilles Road, London NW6 1EA
Tel: 020 7794 7891 (10am-10pm)
Fax: 020 7431 5265
Objects: W6,W3,W5,N,U

FAUNA & FLORA INTERNATIONAL (CONSERVATION OF SPECIES AND HABITATS WORLDWIDE)
Founded: 1903 CR1011102
Senior Trusts & Foundation Officer: Ms Emma
Morris
Great Eastern House, Tenison Road, Cambridge,
Cambridgeshire CB1 2TT
Tel: 01223 571000
Fax: 01223 461481
Email: .... info@fauna-flora.org
Objects: W1,W2

FEEL HAPPY CHILDREN'S PROJECT
See Living Paintings Trust, The

FEGANS CHILD & FAMILY CARE
Founded: 1870 CR209930
Senior Social Worker: Ms Mary Dicker
Chief Executive: Mr D P Waller
160 St James' Road, Tunbridge Wells, Kent
TN1 2HE
Tel: 01892 538288
Fax: 01892 515793
Objects: F,W3,E,R,3

FEILDING (MARY) GUILD
See Mary Feilding Guild

FELINE ADVISORY BUREAU
See International Cat Care

FELTHAM COMMUNITY SCHOOL ASSOCIATION
Founded: 1991 CR1001996
Trustee Head Teacher: Mrs Gillian Smith BSc, MA
Feltham Community College, Browells Lane,
Feltham, Middlesex TW13 7EF
Tel: 020 8831 3000
Fax: 020 8751 4914
Objects: W3,W5,2

FERN STREET SETTLEMENT
Founded: 1907 CR250500
Manager: Mrs Pat Burton
Fern Street, Bow, London E3 3PS
Tel: 020 7987 1949
Fax: 020 7538 3148
Email: . . . . pat.burton@classmail.co.uk
Objects: F,W3,E,G,V,W4,3,P

FERNE ANIMAL SANCTUARY, CHARD
CR245671
Wambrook, Chard, Somerset TA20 3DH
Tel: 01460 65214
Fax: 01460 65230
Email: . . . . info@ferneanimalsanctuary.org

FHA - THE HOLIDAY CHARITY FOR FAMILIES IN NEED
See Family Holiday Association

FIELD - (FOUNDATION FOR INTERNATIONAL ENVIRONMENTAL LAW AND DEVELOPMENT)
Founded: 1990 CR802934
Trustee: Mr Alan Jenkins
Contact: Ms Karen Sherman
3 Endsleigh Street, London WC1H 0DD
Tel: 020 7388 2117
Fax: 020 7388 2826
Email: . . . . field@field.org.uk
Objects: F,J,W2,G,W10,H,3,K

FIELD LANE FOUNDATION
Founded: 1841 CR207493
Chief Executive: Mr Jeremy Lamb
Funding and Communications Manager: Mr Trevor O'Farrell
2nd Floor, The Victoria Charity Centre, 11 Belgrave Road, London SW1V 1RB
Tel: 020 7748 0303
Fax: 020 7821 6691
Email: . . . . info@fieldlane.org.uk
Objects: W3,E,D,N,W4,3,C

FIELDS IN TRUST
Founded: 1925 CR306070
Fundraising Manager: Mr Jonathan Cann
2nd Floor, 15 Crinan Street, London N1 9SQ
Tel: 0207 427 2110
Email: . . . . info@fieldsintrust.org
Objects: F,W3,J,W2,S,G,2,H,3,P

FIGHT FOR SIGHT
Founded: 1965 CR1111438
Executive Director: Mr Michael Roberts
5th Floor, 9-13 Fenchurch Buildings, Fenchurch Street, London EC3M 5HR
Tel: 020 7264 3900
Fax: 020 7488 3041
Email: . . . . info@fightforsight.org.uk
Objects: F,W6,M,W3,N,H

FINCHALE TRAINING COLLEGE FOR DISABLED PEOPLE
Founded: 1943 CR1001027
College Principal: Doctor David Etheridge
Company Secretary: Mr Anthony Ford
College Lifeline Project Development Officer: Mrs Sally Robinson-Lundy
Finchale Training College, Durham, Co. Durham DH1 5RX
Tel: 0191 386 2634
Fax: 0191 374 4962
Email: . . . . enquiries@finchalecollege.co.uk
Objects: F,W9,W5,G,W10,W11,W4,O,3,W8

THE FIRCROFT TRUST (PREVIOUSLY KNOWN AS MENTAL AID PROJECTS)
Founded: 1967 CR802456
Chief Executive: Mr John L Balcomb
Assistant to Chief Executive: Ms Mo Houlden
Fircroft, 96 Ditton Road, Surbiton, Surrey KT6 6RH
Tel: 020 8399 1772
Fax: 020 8390 7627
Email: . . . . office@thefircrofttrust.org
Objects: F,E,W5,3,C

FISHERMEN'S MISSION - ROYAL NATIONAL MISSION TO DEEP SEA FISHERMEN
Founded: 1881 CR232822; SC039088
Chief Executive: Mr D. Conley
Legacy Officer: Mr John Field
Mather House (CC), 4400 Parkway, Solent Business Park, Whiteley, Fareham, Hampshire PO15 7FJ
Tel: 01489 566926
Fax: 01489 561929
Email: . . . . enquiries@rnmdsf.org.uk
Objects: F,M,W5,1A,R,W4,H,O,3,C

FLEDGELING CHARITY FUNDS, THE
Founded: 1992 CR1014756, 1014758
Finsbury Dials, 20 Finsbury Street, London EC2Y 9AQ
Tel: 020 7742 6000
Object: 3

FLORENCE NIGHTINGALE HOSPICE - FLORENCE NIGHTINGALE HOSPICE CHARITY
Founded: 1989 CR802733
Chair of Trustees: Mr Mike Bennett
Unit 4, Aylesbury Business Centre, Chamberlain Road, Aylesbury, Buckinghamshire HP19 8DY
Tel: 01296 429975
Fax: 01296 744715
Email: . . . . enquiries@fnhospice.org.uk
Web: . . . . http://www.fnhospice.org.uk
The aim of the Florence Nightingale Hospice Charity (FNHC) is to provide comprehensive care and support through in-patient and at-home services to local families affected by life-limiting illness.
This year the Florence Nightingale Hospice Charity has pledged to provide over £600,000 towards the costs of the hospice and its services, which covers Aylesbury Vale and surrounding Chiltern Hills.
The Charity completely funds:
• Florrie's Children's Team–giving care and support in the home to children and their families affected by life-limiting illness
• Lymphoedema Clinic– improving patients' physical discomfort and mobility
• Day Hospice– Complementary therapies and relaxation technique – help bring patients together

• A new Nightingale 24/7 Team – a 24-hour service providing day and night-time care to patients in the home at end of life
• Volunteers and their support along with the beautiful courtyard garden
• Bank Nurses– providing holiday and relief cover in the In-Patient Unit
• Part-funding of the Specialist Community Palliative Care Nursing Team
• **All the other small enhancements that make hospice care so special.**

FLUENCY TRUST, THE
Founded: 1995 CR1044910
Treasurer: Mr A Grey
31 Harrow Close, Swindon, Wiltshire SN3 4QD
Tel: 01793 823986
Objects: F,W3,O,P

FOCUS ON ISRAEL
CR803140
PO Box 3197, Leytonstone, London E11 1XT
Tel: 020 8556 3229
Fax: 020 8532 8684
Email: .... mervyn.tilley@ntlworld.com

FOLKESTONE & DISTRICT MIND RESOURCE CENTRE
Founded: 1989 CR1089472
Treasurer: Mrs Sian Jarman
Chairman: Mrs Norma Smyth
Folkestone MIND Resource Centre, 3 Mill Bay, Folkestone, Kent CT20 1JS
Tel: 01303 250090
Objects: F,E,W5,2,H,3,P

FOOTWEAR BENEVOLENT SOCIETY, THE (FOOTWEAR FRIENDS)
Founded: 1836 CR222117
Secretary: Mrs G O'Sullivan
5th Floor, 15-16 Margaret Street, London W1W 8RW
Tel: 020 7323 2362
Email: .... info@footwearfriends.org.uk
Objects: W11,1A,A

FORCES PENSION SOCIETY WIDOWS' FUND
Founded: 1972 CR264524
Secretary: Mr S P Hermelin
Trustee: Major.General J D Moore-Bick CBE DL
68 South Lambeth Road, Vauxhall, London SW8 1RL
Tel: 020 7820 9988
Fax: 020 7820 7583
Objects: F,A,1B

FOREST OF CARDIFF
Founded: 1991 CR1002867
Secretary: Mr Julian Wilkes
The Walled Garden, Old Coedarhydyglyn, St Nicholas, Cardiff CF5 6SG
Tel: 029 2059 9300
Fax: 029 2059 2929
Objects: W2,G,3

FOREST YMCA
Founded: 1970 CR803442
Chief Executive: Mr Timothy Pain
642 Forest Road, Walthamstow, London E17 3EF
Tel: 020 8509 4600
Fax: 020 8521 9073
Email: .... info@forestymca.org.uk
Objects: W3,W16,D,3,C,P

FORFARSHIRE SOCIETY FOR THE BLIND
Founded: 1869SC008915
Superintendent: Mr Thomas F Maplesden
Treasurer: Mrs J S Stevenson
76 High Street, Arbroath, Angus DD11 1AW
Tel: 01241 871215
Fax: 01241 874987
Objects: F,W6,M,1A,A,3

FORTUNE CENTRE OF RIDING THERAPY
Founded: 1976 CR1045352
Director: Mrs Jennifer Dixon-Clegg
Avon Tyrrell, Bransgore, Christchurch, Dorset BH23 8EE
Tel: 01425 673297
Fax: 01425 674320
Email: .... info@fortunecentre.org.uk
Objects: W3,G,O

THE FOSTERING NETWORK
Founded: 1974 CR280852
Head of External Affairs: Ms Lucy Peake
Chief Executive: Mr Robert Tapsfield
87 Blackfriars Road, London SE1 8HA
Tel: 020 7620 6400
Fax: 020 7620 6401
Email: .... info@fostering.net
Objects: Q,F,W3,G,2,H,3

THE FOUNDATION FOR LIVER RESEARCH
Founded: 1973 CR1134579
The Institute of Hepatology, Harold Samuel House, 69-75 Chenies Mews, London WC1E 6HX
Tel: 020 7255 9830
Fax: 020 7380 0405
Email: .... n.day@researchinliver.org.uk
Web: .... www.liver-research.org.uk
The Foundation for Liver Research was established in 1973 to support research into disorders of the liver. Current research programmes are looking at the hepatitis viruses; severe infection in acute and chronic liver disease; development, diagnosis and treatment of liver cell cancer and the study of factors promoting liver recovery and regeneration. It is the Trustees intention to make the Institute of Hepatology a Centre of Excellence in this country and to link it with other centres specialising in liver disease throughout the world. The Foundation depends entirely on voluntary donations and legacies.
For more details and discussion of collaborative/ sponsorship opportunities, please contact: Professor Roger Williams, CBE, Director, at the address above or on r.williams@researchinliver.org.uk

FOUNDATION FOR THEOSOPHICAL STUDIES
Founded: 1992 CR1014648
Keymer Haslam and Co, 4/6 Church Road, Burgess Hill, West Sussex RH15 9AE
Tel: 01444 247871
Fax: 01444 871071
Email: ... inquiries@theosophical-society.org.uk

FOUNDATION HOUSING
Founded: 1984 CR515517
Secretary: Mr Steve Woodford
Tennant Hall, Blenheim Grove, Leeds, West Yorkshire LS2 9ET
Tel: 0113 368 8800
Fax: 0113 368 8819
Objects: F,W3,G,D,3,C,W8

FPA - FORMERLY THE FAMILY PLANNING ASSOCIATION

Founded: 1930 CR250187
Director of Communications: Ms Karen Brewer
Chief Executive: Ms Anne Weyman

50 Featherstone Street, London EC1Y 8QU
Tel: 020 7608 5240
Fax: 0845 123 2349
Email: . . . . membership@fpa.org.uk

Objects: F,G,2,H

FRANCIS HOUSE CHILDREN'S HOSPICE (RAINBOW FAMILY TRUST), MANCHESTER

Founded: 1990 CR328659
Secretary: Revd David Ireland

390 Parrswood Road, East Didsbury, Manchester, Greater Manchester M20 5NA
Tel: 0161 434 4118
Email: . . . . sr.austin@francishouse.org.uk

Objects: W3,N,3

FRANCISCAN MISSIONARIES OF MARY

CR249515
5 Vaughan Avenue, London W6 0XS
Tel: 020 8748 4077
Fax: 020 8741 9618
Email: . . . . provsecuk@aol.com
A Roman Catholic missionary society working world-wide.

FREDERICK ANDREW CONVALESCENT TRUST

Founded: 1970 CR211029
Clerk to the Trust: Mrs Karen Armitage
Andrew & Co Solicitors LLP, St Swithin's Court, 1 Flavian Road, Nettleham Road, Lincoln, Lincolnshire LN2 4GR
Tel: 01522 512123
Fax: 01522 518911
Email: . . . . info@factonline.co.uk
Web: . . . . www.factonline.co.uk

Objects: 1A,A,1B,W8

Grants made to women towards the cost of medically recommend convalescence, HCPC registered therapy or help in the home after illness or injury. Further information and application forms from Andrew & Co LLP (ref KJA).

FREE CHURCHES GROUP, THE

CR236878
Moderator: Revd Michael Heaney
Moderator Commissioner: Ms Elizabeth Makear

27 Tavistock Square, London WC1H 9HH
Tel: 020 7529 8130
Fax: 020 7529 8134
Email: . . . . freechurch@cte.org.uk

Objects: J,G,2,H

FREEDOM CENTRE - WORKING WITH PEOPLE WITH PHYSICAL DISABILITIES

CR1007683
Chairman: Mr Tony Andrews
Centre Manager: Mrs Christine Kite
Hon Treasurer: Mr Alan Ogilvie

c/o Freedom Centre, Blain Pritchard & Co, 29 High Street, Blue Town, Sheerness, Kent ME12 1RN
Tel: 01795 666233
Fax: 01795 666239

Objects: W6,S,E,W7,W5,G,W10,W11,2,H,3,P,W8

FRIENDS OF AMWELL VIEW SCHOOL, THE

Founded: 1990 CR803181
The Head Teacher

Amwell View School, Stanstead Abbotts, Ware, Hertfordshire SG12 8EH
Tel: 01920 870027

Objects: W3,G,1B,2

FRIENDS OF CANTERBURY CATHEDRAL

CR256575
Executive Secretary: Ms Pam Doyle
8 The Precincts, Canterbury, Kent CT1 2EE
Tel: 01227 865292
Fax: 01227 456171
Email: . . . . friends@canterbury-cathedral.org

Objects: S,A,V,2,W12,H,P

FRIENDS OF CYNTHIA SPENCER HOSPICE

CR1002926
Manfield Health Campus, Kettering Road, Northampton, Northamptonshire NN3 6NP
Tel: 01604 678082
Email: . . . . . . cshfundraising@nhft.nhs.uk
Web: . . http://www.cynthiaspencerhospice. nhs.uk

Objects: N,3

Providing specialist palliative care for people with life-limiting and terminal illnesses and their families across Northamptonshire, either at the Hospice itself or in the Community through our Hospice at Home Team.

FRIENDS OF HARROGATE HOSPITAL

Founded: 1966 CR252376
c/o General Office, Harrogate District Hospital, Lancaster Park Road, Harrogate, North Yorkshire HG2 7SX

Friends of Harrogate Hospital

Tel: 01423 501513
Web: . . . . www.harrogate.co.uk/lof/
Objects: N,O

The Friends exists to enhance the patient experience both in hospital and in the community. Money raised is used to purchase equipment that is currently unaffordable. Purchases have ranged from an MRI scanner to smaller items for use in the community and in the hospital.

Any legacy received will make a huge difference to our work.

FRIENDS OF THE ELDERLY
Founded: 1905 CR226064
Chief Executive: Mr Richard Furze
40-42 Ebury Street, London SW1W 0LZ
Tel: 020 7730 8263
Fax: 020 7259 0154
Email: . . . . enquiries@fote.org.uk
Objects: F,M,J,E,1A,A,N,W4,3,C

FRIENDS OF THE HOLY FATHER
CR280489
Culver Farn, Old Compton Lane, Farnham, Surrey GU9 8GJ
Tel: 01252 724924
Fax: 01252 724924

FRIENDS OF THE UNITED INSTITUTIONS OF ARAD
Founded: 1992 CR1012222
Accountants
5 Windus Road, London N16 6UT
Tel: 020 8880 8910
Fax: 020 8880 8911

FRIENDS' SCHOOL, SAFFRON WALDEN
Founded: 1990 CR1000981
Bursar: Ms Jane Corwin
Friends School, Mount Pleasant Road, Saffron Walden, Essex CB11 3EB
Tel: 01799 525351
Fax: 01799 523808
Objects: W3,G,1A,B,3

FRONTIERS
Founded: 1992 CR1012566
British Director: Mr Phil Goodchild
PO Box 600, Hemel Hempstead, Hertfordshire HP3 9UG
Email: . . . . info@frontiers.org.uk
Objects: R,U,3

FULBRIGHT FOUNDATION, THE
Founded: 1990 CR328571
Finance Director: Ms Beverley Brown
Executive Director: Penny Egan
Fulbright House, 62 Doughty Street, London WC1N 2JZ
Tel: 020 7404 6880
Fax: 020 7404 6834
Email: . . . . education@fulbright.co.uk
Objects: G,U

FULL EMPLOYMENT UK TRUST
Founded: 1990 CR328739
Principle Consultant: Mr Peter Ashby
35 The Avenue, Richmond, Surrey TW9 2AL
Tel: 020 7348 5070

FUND FOR REFUGEES IN SLOVENIA, THE
Founded: 1992 CR1013193
Trustee: Mr Keith C Miles
Chairman of Trustees: Lady Nott
19 Elmtree Green, Great Missenden, Buckinghamshire HP16 9AF
Tel: 0870 410 0088
Objects: W3,W5,G,1A,N,W4,U,T,3

FUSILIERS' AID SOCIETY (WARWICKSHIRE)
See Royal Warwickshire Charitable Welfare Funds

G

THE G J & S LIVANOS CHARITABLE TRUST
Founded: 1991 CR1002279
Secretary & Trustee: Mr Philip Norman Harris
Jeffrey Green Russell, Apollo House, 56 New Bond Street, London W1S 1RG
Tel: 020 7339 7000

GADS HILL SCHOOL
CR803153
Headmistress: Mrs A Everitt
Bursar & Company Secretary: Mrs Carol Homden
Higham, Rochester, Kent ME3 7PA
Tel: 01474 822366
Objects: W3,W2,S,G,B

GALLOWAY'S SOCIETY FOR THE BLIND
Founded: 1867 CR526088
Mr Peter Taylor
Howick House, Howick Park Avenue, Penwortham, Preston, Lancashire PR1 0LS
Tel: 01772 744148
Email: . . . . peter.taylor@galloways.org.uk
Objects: F,W6,M,G,A,V,2,O,3,C,P

GALTON INSTITUTE
Founded: 1907 CR209258
General Secretary: Mrs Betty Nixon
19 Northfields Prospect, Northfields, London SW18 1PE
Tel: 020 8874 7257
Email: . . . . betty.nixon@talk21.com
Objects: G,2,P

THE GAMBIA HORSE AND DONKEY TRUST
Founded: 2002 CR1096814
Brewery Arms Cottage (CD), Stane Street, Ockley, Surrey RH5 5TH
Tel: 01306 627568
Email: . ghdt@gambiahorseanddonkey.org.uk
Web: http://www.gambiahorseanddonkey.org.uk
We aim to reduce rural poverty by increasing the productivity of the working equines through the provision of training in management and welfare. We train farriers, harness makers, paravets, farmers groups and we teach in schools. We would like to provide the Gambian people with the knowledge and skills to deal with and even prevent the problems that we see.

We believe that learning should be fun and we encourage the young boys who traditionally care for the donkeys to have fun and build a rapport with their donkeys through games and sport.

We provide basic veterinary treatment and have mobile clinics and hospital facilities at our centre and we run a bit exchange programme.

We believe that poverty is the cause of many of the animal welfare problems that we see so we are involved in community development projects which will increase the economic growth of the area.

See advert on this page

THE GAME AND WILDLIFE CONSERVATION TRUST
Founded: 1992 CR1010814
Chairman: Mr Mike Barnes
Project Leader: Dr A R Leake
Loddington House, Main Street, Loddington,
Leicestershire LE7 9XE
Tel: 01572 717220
Email: .... aleake@gct.org.uk
Objects: F,W1,W2,2

THE GARDEN TOMB (JERUSALEM) ASSOCIATION
Founded: 1894 CR1004062
Honorary Treasurer: Mr R J Barwick
Maybury Copse, The Ridge, Woking, Surrey
GU22 7EQ
Tel: 01483 763298
Email: .... mail@gardentomb.com
Objects: R,3

GARDENING FOR DISABLED TRUST
CR255066
Treasurer: Mrs C Parish
Chairman: Mrs Felicity Seton
The Freight, Cranbrook, Kent TN17 3PG
Tel: 01580 712196
Objects: F,W5,A,H

GATESHEAD CROSSROADS - CARING FOR CARERS
Founded: 1991 CR1059917
Chief Officer: Mr Jeff Gray
The Old School, Smailes Lane, Highfield,
Rowlands Gill, Tyne & Wear NE39 2DB
Tel: ... 01207 549780; 0191 478 6284 (Minicom)
Fax: 01207 549794
Email: .. enquiries@gatesheadcrossroads.org.uk
Objects: F,W6,M,W3,J,S,E,W7,W5,G,W10,R,W4, B,H,3,P,W8,K

GEFFRYE MUSEUM, LONDON
Founded: 1990 CR803052
Company Secretary: Ms C Lalumia
Geffrye Museum, Kingsland Road, London
E2 8EA
Tel: 020 7739 9893
Object: S

THE GENETIC ALLIANCE UK LTD
Founded: 1990 CR1114195
Director: Mr Alastair Kent
Chair: Ms Maggie Ponder
4D Leroy House, 436 Essex Road, London
N1 3QP

Tel: 020 7704 3141
Fax: 020 7359 1447
Email: . . . . mail@gig.org.uk
Objects: F,J,W5,N,2,O

GIRL GUIDES ASSOCIATION
See Girlguiding UK

GIRLGUIDING UK
Founded: 1910 CR306016
Fundraising & Marketing Manager: Ms Donna Holland
Chief Executive: Miss Denise King BA Hons.
17-19 Buckingham Palace Road, London SW1W 0PT
Tel: 020 7834 6242
Fax: 020 7828 8317
Email: . . . . supporters@girlguiding.org.uk
Objects: W3,G,2,H,P,W8

GLASGOW CHILDREN'S HOLIDAY SCHEME

Founded: 1955SC022654
Fifth Floor, 30 George Square, Glasgow G2 1EG
Tel: 0141 248 7255
Email: . admin@glasgowchildrensholidayscheme.org.uk
Objects: W3,V,P
Since 1955 we have provided holidays for disadvantaged or disabled children in the Glasgow area. To enhance self-esteem, social skills and educational experience. Holidays may be with one of our volunteer host families, an activity week for teenagers or a week in one of our family caravans at Wemyss Bay.

GLASGOW EDUCATIONAL & MARSHALL TRUST

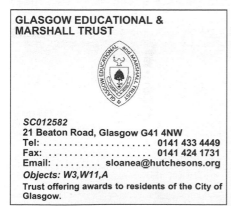

SC012582
21 Beaton Road, Glasgow G41 4NW
Tel: **0141 433 4449**
Fax: **0141 424 1731**
Email: . . . . **sloanea@hutchesons.org**
Objects: W3,W11,A
Trust offering awards to residents of the City of Glasgow.

GLOBAL PARTNERS UK
CR1009755
Secretary Director: Mr Michael C Barnett
Kingsgate House, High Street, Redhill, Surrey RH1 1SG
Tel: 01737 779040

GLOBE CENTRE, THE
Founded: 1991 CR1001582
Acting Director: Mr Simon Collier
159 Mile End Road, London E1 4AQ
Tel: 020 7791 2855
Fax: 020 7780 9551
Email: . . . . info@theglobecentre.co.uk
Objects: F,E,W5,W10,O,3,P,K

GLOUCESTERSHIRE ANIMAL WELFARE ASSOCIATION AND CHELTENHAM ANIMAL SHELTER
CR1081019
Gardners Lane, Cheltenham, Gloucestershire GL51 9JW
Tel: 01242 523521
Fax: 01242 523676
Email: . . . . fundraising@gawa.org.uk

GOAL UK
CR1107403
7 Hanson Street, London W1W 6TE
Tel: 020 7631 3196
Fax: 020 7631 3197
Email: . . . . info@goal.ie

GODINTON HOUSE PRESERVATION TRUST, THE
Founded: 1991 CR1002278
Agent: Mr N G Sandford
Estate Office, Godinton House, Godinton Lane, Ashford, Kent TN23 3BP
Tel: 01233 632652
Fax: 01233 647351
Email: . . . . ghpt@godinton.fsnet.co.uk
Objects: S,G,3

THE GORILLA ORGANIZATION
CR1117131
110 Gloucester Avenue, London NW1 8HX
Tel: 020 7916 4974
Email: . . . . info@gorillas.org
Objects: W1,W2,W10,2
The Dian Fossey Gorilla Fund was established by the acclaimed conservationist Dr Dian Fossey in 1978 after her favourite gorilla Digit was killed by poachers. Mountain gorilla numbers had fallen to an alarming 260 and trade in infant gorillas was rife. Today, with fewer than 1000 in existence, they still teeter on the edge of extinction. Human disease, war and the destruction of their African rainforest habitat are the main threats. Through a programme of community based conservation, anti-poaching patrols and conservation education, the fund continues to confront these threats with all the knowledge and compassion necessary to ensure the mountain gorilla's survival into the next century and beyond. Your support is vital and greatly appreciated.

See advert on previous page

GRACE & COMPASSION BENEDICTINES

Founded: 1954 CR1056064
38/39 Preston Park Avenue, Brighton, Brighton & Hove BN1 6HG

Tel: 01273 502129
Fax: 01273 552540
Email: .... osb@graceandcompassion.co.uk
Web: www.graceandcompassionbenedictines.org.uk
Founded in 1954 for the care of the old, sick and frail, we run care homes and retirement accommodation in the south of England. We also provide wide ranging services overseas, in India, Sri Lanka, Kenya and Uganda, where we work with the poor and sick of all ages, in care homes, hospital, village clinics, school of nursing, vocational training, farming, nursery and primary schools. There is so much to be done. Please support our work with a donation or a legacy.

GRACE WYNDHAM GOLDIE (BBC) TRUST FUND
Founded: 1950 CR212146
Administrator: Ms Cheryl Miles
BBC Pension and Benefits Centre, Ty Oldfield, BBC Broadcasting House, Llandaff, Cardiff CF5 2YQ
Tel: 029 2032 3772
Fax: 029 2032 2408
Objects: G,1A,A
The Fund makes modest grants for education and specific short term unexpected needs to persons who have been engaged in broadcasting or any associated activity and to their children and dependants.

GRAFF FOUNDATION
Founded: 1992 CR1012859
Trustee / Solicitor: Mr Anthony David Kerman
c/o Kerman & Co Solicitors, 7 Savoy Court, London WC2R 0ER
Tel: 020 7539 7272

GRAHAM KIRKHAM FOUNDATION, THE
Founded: 1991 CR1002390
Company Secretary: Mr Barry Todhunter FCCA
Bentley Moore Lane, Adwick Le Street, Doncaster, South Yorkshire DN6 7BD
Tel: 01302 330365
Fax: 01302 573456

GRAND LODGE OF MARK MASTER MASONS FUND OF BENEVOLENCE
Founded: 1868 CR207610
Honorary Secretary: Mr J Brackley
Trustees: Mr M Herbert
Mark Masons Hall, 86 St James's Street, London SW1A 1PL
Tel: 020 7839 5274
Fax: 020 7930 9750
Objects: 1A,A,1B,2

GRAND LODGE OF SCOTLAND
SC001996
Freemasons' Hall, 96 George Street, Edinburgh EH2 3DH
Tel: 0131 225 5577
Fax: 0131 225 3953
Email: ...... glhomes@grandlodgescotland.org

GRANGEWOOD EDUCATIONAL ASSOCIATION
Founded: 1990 CR803492
Chairman: Mr K S G Adams
Director & Company Secretary: Mr D Anderton
Grangewood School, Chester Road, Forest Gate, London E7 8QT
Tel: 020 8472 3552
Fax: 020 8552 8817
Objects: G,3

GREAT NORTH AIR AMBULANCE SERVICE
Founded: 1991 CR1092204
Chief Executive: Mr Grahame Pickering
Appeal Chairman: Mr R I Stewart
Northumberland Wing, The Imperial Centre, Grange Road, Darlington, Co. Durham DL1 5NQ
Tel: 01325 487263
Fax: 01325 489819
Email: ..... info@greatnorthairambulance.co.uk
Objects: N,3

GREATER NOTTINGHAM GROUNDWORK TRUST
Founded: 1991 CR1003426
Office Manager: Ms Jo Kerry
Executive Director: Mr Zbigniew Szulc
Denman Street East, Nottingham, Nottinghamshire NG7 3GX
Tel: 0115 978 8212
Fax: 0115 978 7496
Email: .... gn@groundwork.org.uk
Objects: F,W6,W3,J,W2,S,W7,W5,G,W10,A,1B, W4,H,3,P,W8,K

GREEN SHOOTS FOUNDATION
CR1138412
57/59 Gloucester Place, London W1U 8JH
Tel: 020 7935 8128
Email: ..... jm@greenshootsfoundation.org

GREENDOWN TRUST LIMITED
Founded: 1990 CR328465
Secretary to the Trustees: Mr Peter Mirfin
Dyneley House, 10 Alerton Hill, Chapel Allerton, Leeds, West Yorkshire LS7 3QB
Tel: 0113 268 1812
Fax: 0113 266 7356
Objects: W4,3,C

GREENFIELDS CENTRE LIMITED
Founded: 1990 CR702308
Centre Manager: Ms Judy Tate
Greenfields, 139 Russell Road, Forest Fields, Nottingham, Nottinghamshire NG7 6GX
Tel: 0115 841 8440
Objects: W3,3,W8

GREENPEACE ENVIRONMENTAL TRUST

CR284934
Canonbury Villas (CC), London N1 2PN
Tel: 020 7865 8116
Fax: 020 7865 8201
Email: .... andrew.sturley@greenpeace.org
Objects: W2,G,1A,A,1B,2,H
The Trust complements the activities of Greenpeace by engaging in educational activities and funding scientific research and investigative projects into world ecology. Some of the research activities funded by the Trust were increasing the efficiency of solar cells, the regional effects of the Chernobyl disaster on health and the environment, the effects of toxic pollution on marine mammals such as whales, seals and dolphins and the link between health and contamination of the environment and the food chain. The Trust also produces educational leaflets for students. For further information about the activities of the Trust, or for a legacy leaflet, please write to the above address.
See advert on next page

Canonbury Villas, London, N1 2PN
Tel: 020 7865 8100 Fax: 020 7865 8200

There are two Greenpeace organisations in the UK:
Greenpeace Limited and
Greenpeace Environmental Trust
(registered charity number 284934)

Greenpeace Limited campaigns in defence of the natural world. We work on issues ranging from climate change to oceans and promote solutions to environmental problems. A bequest to Greenpeace Limited will help keep our campaigners in action onland and at sea.

Greenpeace Environmental Trust funds scientific research and investigations into environmental issues. Our recent activities include documenting the effects of logging in the Amazon and surveying dolphin populations in the UK.

For more information on either organisation, please write to Andrew Sturley, Greenpeace, Canonbury Villas, London N1 2PN, call 020 7865 8116 or email: andrew.sturley@greenpeace.org

---

GREENSLEEVES HOMES TRUST
Founded: 1996 CR1060478
Chief Executive: Ms Kate James
Unit 2, Regent Terrace, Rita Road, London SW8 1AW
Tel: 020 7793 1122
Fax: 020 7793 1177
Email: .... headoffice@greensleeves.org.uk
Objects: M,N,W4,3

GRENFELL ASSOCIATION OF GREAT BRITAIN AND IRELAND (GAGBI)
Founded: 1928 CR210040
Treasurer: Doctor Raymond John Hambleton Chesworth
Ormonde, D'urton Lane, Broughton, Preston, Lancashire PR3 5LE
Tel: 01772 862212
Objects: N,O,C

GREYHOUNDS IN NEED
CR1069438
5 Greenways, Egham, Surrey TW20 9PA
Tel: 01784 436845
Fax: 01784 477490
Email: .... info@greyhoundsinneed.co.uk

GRIMSBY AND CLEETHORPES AREA DOORSTEP
Founded: 1990 CR702881
Secretary: Mrs M Chatterton MBE
115 Pasture Street, Grimsby, North East Lincolnshire DN32 9EE
Tel: 01472 321444
Objects: F,W3,E,G,D,3,C

GROUNDWORK LEICESTER & LEICESTERSHIRE LTD
Founded: 1990 CR703009
Executive Director & Company Secretary: Mr David Nicholls
Administration Manager: Mr Richard Wakefield
Parkfield, Western Park, Hinkley Road, Leicester, Leicestershire LE3 6HX
Tel: 0116 222 0222
Fax: 0116 255 2343
Email: .... info@gwll.org.uk
Objects: F,W1,W3,J,W2,G,1B,H,3,K

GROUNDWORK NORTH WALES
CR1004132
3-4 Plas Power Road, Tanyfron, Wrexham LL11 5SZ
Tel: 01978 757524
Fax: 01978 722402
Email: .... wx@groundwork.org.uk

GROUNDWORK UK
Founded: 1985 CR291558
Director of Finance: Mr Steve Dolphin
Development Director: Mr Graham Duxbury
Chief Executive: Mr Tony Hawkhead CBE
Director of Open Grants: Ms Wendy Jenkins
Director of HR and Performance: Mr Rob Williams
Lockside, 5 Scotland Street, Birmingham, West Midlands B1 2RR
Tel: 0121 236 8565
Fax: 0121 236 7356
Email: .... info@groundwork.org.uk
Objects: W3,J,W2,G,3

GROUNDWORK WREXHAM & FLINTSHIRE
See Groundwork North Wales

GROVE HOUSE
Founded: 1991 CR1003462
Company Secretary: Mr C F Pocock
St Albans and Dacorum Day Hospice, 4
Broadfields, Harpenden, Hertfordshire AL5 2HJ
Tel: 01582 621303
Objects: F,M,E,G,N,W4,O,3,P,W8

THE GUIDE DOGS FOR THE BLIND ASSOCIATION

Founded: 1934 CR209617; SC038979
Hillfields (C1), Reading Road, Burghfield
Common, Reading RG7 3YG
Tel: 0845 603 1477
Fax: 0118 983 6326
Email: . . . . giftsinwills@guidedogs.org.uk
Web: . . . http://www.guidedogs.org.uk/giftsinwills
Objects: W1,W6
Did you know it takes around 20 months of training and
costs almost £50,000 to train a puppy and fund their
working life as a qualified guide dog? That's why we rely
on the generosity of people who leave us a gift in their
Will. It all adds up to make a big difference for blind and
partially sighted people.

GUIDEPOSTS TRUST
CR272619
Two Rivers Industrial Estate, Station Lane,
Witney, Oxfordshire OX28 4BH
Tel: 01993 772886
Email: . . . . gpt@guidepoststrust.org.uk
Objects: M,E,W5,N,W4,3,P,K

GUILD OF AID FOR GENTLEPEOPLE
Founded: 1904FS 31BEN
10 St Christopher's Place, London W1U 1HZ
Tel: 020 7935 0641
Email: . . . . thead@pcac.org.uk
Objects: J,1A,A,W4

GUILD OF BENEVOLENCE OF THE INSTITUTE OF MARINE ENGINEERING, SCIENCE & TECHNOLOGY
Founded: 1934 CR208727
Honorary Treasurer: Mr Gary J McKenzie, CEng,
F.I.Mar EST
Aldgate House, 33 Aldgate High Street, London
EC3N 1EN
Tel: 020 7382 2600
Fax: 020 7382 2670
Email: . . . . guild@imarest.org
Objects: W9,W11,1A,A,3

GUILDHALL STRING ENSEMBLE CONCERTS TRUST, THE
Founded: 1990 CR1001256
Accountant to the Trustees: Mr C R Dean
13 West End, Whittlesford, Cambridge,
Cambridgeshire CB2 4LX
Tel: 01223 839744
Object: S

GUILDHE LIMITED
Founded: 1992 CR1012218
Executive Secretary: Ms Alice Hynes
Woburn House, 20 Tavistock Square, London
WC1H 9HB
Tel: 020 7387 7711
Fax: 020 7387 7712
Email: . . . . info@guildhe.ac.uk
Objects: G,2

THE GYDE CHARITY
Founded: 1909 CR311529
Clerk: Mrs Deirdre J Baker
Chairman: Mr P Oakley
6 Lawns Park, North Woodchester,
Gloucestershire GL5 5PP
Tel: 01453 872576

Objects: W3,A,1B

**Payment to assist in the education and
maintenance of blind and deaf and dumb
children of Protestant faith not provided for by
local education authorities and to assist in the
purchase of musical or other instruments, aids
and specialised equipment. Applicants must be
18 years or less but benefits may be extended to
21 years. Preference to residents of Painswick
and the County of Gloucestershire but open to
others.**

H

A H WHITELEY AND B C WHITELEY CHARITY
Founded: 1991 CR1002220
Trustee: Mr Edward George Aspley
Regent Chambers, 2A Regent Street, Mansfield,
Nottinghamshire NG18 1SW
Tel: 01623 655111

HABERDASHERS' ASKE'S HATCHAM COLLEGE
Founded: 1991 CR1001489
Secretary: Mr PW Durgan
Pepys Road, New Cross, London SE14 5SF
Tel: 020 7652 9500

HACT – THE HOUSING ACTION CHARITY
Founded: 1960 CR1096829
Director: Ms Heather Petch
Head of Programmes: Mr Andrew Van Doorn
78 Quaker Street, London E1 6SW
Tel: 020 7247 7800
Fax: 020 7247 2212
Email: . . . . hact@hact.org.uk
Objects: F,W5,W10,A,1B,D,W4,H,C,W8

HAEMOPHILIA SOCIETY
Founded: 1950 CR288260
Petersham House, 57A Hatton Garden, London
EC1N 8JG
Tel: 020 7831 1020
Fax: 020 7405 4824
Email: . . . . info@haemophilia.org.uk
Objects: F,W3,J,W5,1A,A,1B,2,W4,H,3,W8

HAIR AND BEAUTY BENEVOLENT (HABB)
Founded: 1853FS18BEN
136 Warren Road, Banstead, Surrey SM7 1LB
Tel: 01737 212494
Email: . . . . info@habb.org

Objects: 1A,2

We provide direct assistance to hairdressers or persons connected with the hairdressing and beauty industries, in times of hardship due to ill-health, disability or old age. One-off help or small pensions can be granted, dependant upon need. The past few years have seen a marked increase in the number of calls on our limited funds. Many fundraising events are organised each year, but as a small charity, we actively seek donations, Deeds of Covenant and legacies, which are very gratefully received.

HALLAM COMMUNITY PHYSIOTHERAPY PROJECT, THE

Founded: 1990 CR702486
Secretary to the Trustees: Mrs J Currie
24 Stumperlowe View, Sheffield, South Yorkshire S10 3QU
Tel: 0114 230 5044

HALLIWICK ASSOCIATION OF SWIMMING THERAPY

Founded: 1952 CR250008
Secretary: Mr Eric Dilley
c/o ADKC Centre, Whitstable House, Silchester Road, London W10 6SB
Tel: 01727 825 524
Fax: 020 8968 7609
Email: . . . . . . patrick.hastings@btopenworld.com
Objects: W6,M,J,W7,W5,G,H,O,3,P

HALO TRUST, THE

GETTING MINES OUT OF THE GROUND, FOR GOOD.

Founded: 1988 CR1001813; SC037870
Administrator: Ms Diana Roberts
Director: Mr Guy Willoughby
Carronfoot, Thornhill, Dumfries & Galloway DG3 5BF
Tel: 01848 331100
Fax: 01848 331122
Email: . . . . mail@halotrust.org
Web: . . . . http://www.halotrust.org
Objects: U,3

The HALO Trust is a British Charity whose main remit is the removal of debris of war - in particular landmines and unexploded ordnance (UXO). HALO currently works in Afghanistan, Cambodia, Abkhazia, Nagorno Karabakh, Kosovo, Mozambique, Angola, Colombia, Sri Lanka, Somaliland and Zimbabwe. We have suspended programmes in Chechnya and Eritrea.
HALO employs over 8,000 local staff and 30 international staff. HALO is primarily funded by governments and foundations. On average HALO Trust clears 200,000 mines and UXO each year. HALO's headquarters is in Dumfriesshire.
See advert on previous page

HAMELIN TRUST

Founded: 1991 CR1004432
Company Secretary: Mr Steve Fisher
Unit C, Radford Burn Centre, Radford Crescent, Billericay, Essex CM12 0DP
Tel: 01277 653889
Email: . . . . enquiries@hamelintrust.org.uk
Objects: M,W3,E,W5,V,2,3,C,P,K

HAMPSHIRE & ISLE OF WIGHT MILITARY AID FUND (1903)

Founded: 1903 CR202363
Secretary: Lt Col K R Bryan
Serles House, Southgate Street, Winchester, Hampshire SO23 9EG
Tel: 01962 852933
Email: . . . . hantsandiowmaf@dsl.pipex.com
Objects: W9,1A,A,3

HAMPSTEAD HEATH

Founded: 1990 CR803392
The Trustees Solicitors
Corporation of London, PO Box 270, Guildhall, London EC2P 2EJ
Tel: 020 7332 1334
Fax: 020 7710 8531

HANDICAPPED CHILDREN'S PILGRIMAGE TRUST AND HOSANNA HOUSE

See HCPT - The Pilgrimage Trust

HANDSWORTH COMMUNITY CARE CENTRE

Founded: 1991 CR1002669
Trustee: Ms Ava M Johnson
63 Heathfield Road, Handsworth, Birmingham, West Midlands B19 1HE
Tel: 0121 554 4755
Fax: 0121 240 1426

HAPPY DAYS CHILDREN'S CHARITY

Founded: 1992 CR1010943
Families Officer: Mrs M Bilborough
Chief Executive: Mr R Sinclair
3rd Floor, Clody House, 90-100 Collingdon Street, Luton, Bedfordshire LU1 1RX
Tel: 01582 755999
Fax: 01582 755900
Email: . . . . enquiries@happydayscharity.org
Web: . . . . http://www.happydayscharity.org
Objects: W3,S,W5,G,1A,A,1B,V,3,P
Holidays and day trips for children with special needs.

HARBOUR, THE (FORMERLY RED ADMIRAL PROJECT - BRISTOL)

Founded: 1992 CR1008360
Chief Executive: Ms Caroline Hutchins
30 Frogmore Street, Bristol BS1 5NA
Tel: 0117 925 9348
Email: . . . . info@the-harbour.co.uk
Objects: F,W5,W4,3,W8

HARINGEY IRISH CULTURAL AND COMMUNITY CENTRE

Founded: 1987 CR1003015
Manager: Mr Anthony Brennan
Haringey Irish Centre, Pretoria Road, Tottenham, London N17 8DX
Tel: 020 8885 3490
Fax: 020 8801 4839
Objects: F,E,W10,W4,P

HARRIS HOSPISCARE WITH ST CHRISTOPHER'S
Founded: 1984 CR1003903
Correspondent: Vanessa Casey
Caritas House, Tregony Road, Orpington, Kent BR6 9XA
Tel: 01689 825755
Fax: 01689 892999
Email: .... info@harrishospiscare.org.uk

HARRISON HOUSING
CR1101143
Chief Executive: Mr Raymond Bernstein
46 St James's Gardens, London W11 4RQ
Tel: 020 7603 4332
Fax: 020 7603 4370
Email: .... info@harrisonhousing.org.uk
Web: .... http://www.harrisonhousing.org.uk
Objects: W4,C

HARROGATE DISTRICT HOSPICE CARE
See Saint Michael's Hospice (Harrogate)

HARROW SCHOOL OF GYMNASTICS
Founded: 1991 CR1002258
Director: Mr Steve Tucker
186 Christchurch Avenue, Harrow, Middlesex HA3 5BD
Tel: 020 8427 5611
Fax: 020 8427 6171
Objects: W3,G,3

HASTINGS VOLUNTARY ACTION
Founded: 1990 CR802632
Company Secretary: Ms M Casey
31A Priory Street, Hastings, East Sussex TN34 1EA
Tel: 01424 444010
Fax: 01424 432877
Email: .. infoworker@hastingsvoluntaryaction.org

HAVERING CITIZENS ADVICE BUREAU
Founded: 1991 CR1002593
Company Secretary: Ms Lara Adeniran
Borough Director: Mrs Heather Ball
Chairman: Mr Dylan Champion
719 Victoria Road, Romford, Essex RM1 2JT
Tel: 01708 735325
Fax: 01708 735325
Email: .... advice@haveringcab.org.uk
Objects: F,3

HAWK CONSERVANCY TRUST
CR1092349
Visitor Centre (CC), Sarson Lane, Weyhill, Andover, Hampshire SP11 8DY
Tel: 01264 773850
Fax: 01264 773772
Email: .... info@hawkconservancy.org
Objects: W1,W2,G,O,3

HAYWARD HOUSE CANCER CARE TRUST
Founded: 1992 CR1014356
Chairman of Trustees: Dr D C Banks
Hayward House, Nottingham University Hospitals, City Campus, Hucknall Road, Nottingham, Nottinghamshire NG5 1PB
Tel: 0115 962 7996
Objects: M,N

HCPT - THE PILGRIMAGE TRUST
Founded: 1956 CR281074
Director of Communications
Chief Executive: Mr Tony Mills
Director of Communications: Mr Michael Orbell
Oakfield Park, 32 Bilton Road, Rugby, Warwickshire CV22 7HQ
Tel: 01788 564646
Fax: 01788 564640
Email: .... hq@hcpt.org.uk
Objects: W6,W3,W7,W5,V

HEADWAY THAMES VALLEY LIMITED
Founded: 1990 CR900591
Resource Centre Manager: Mrs Brian Pyle
Townlands Hospital, York Road, Henley-on-Thames, Oxfordshire RG9 2EB
Tel: 01491 411469; 01491 636108
Fax: 01491 636108
Email: .... hwthamesvalley@aol.com
Objects: F,J,E,W5,V,2,R,H,O,3,P

HEADWAY - THE BRAIN INJURY ASSOCIATION
Founded: 1979 CR1025852
Chief Executive: Mr Peter McCabe
190 Bagnall Road, Old Basford, Nottingham, Nottinghamshire NG3 8SF
Tel: .... 0115 924 0800; 0808 800 2244 Helpline
Fax: 0115 958 4446
Email: .... enquiries@headway.org.uk
Objects: F,J,E,W5,G,2,H,O,3,P

HEALTH CARE
See Tourism For All UK

HEALTHCARE FINANCIAL MANAGEMENT ASSOCIATION
Founded: 1952 CR1114463; SC041994
Chief Executive: Mr Mark Knight
Suite 32, Albert House, 111-7 Victoria Street, Bristol BS1 6AX
Tel: 0117 929 4789
Fax: 0117 929 4844
Email: .... info@hfma.org.uk
Objects: G,2,H

HEALTHLINK WORLDWIDE
Founded: 1977 CR274260
Executive Director: Mr Andrew Chetley
Office Manager: Ms Stephanie Hopkins
Leonie Try
Development House, 56-64 Leonard Street, London EC2A 4LT
Tel: 020 7549 0240
Fax: 020 7549 0241
Email: .... info@healthlink.org.uk
Objects: F,W3,W5,G,U,H,W8,K

Help the
Hospices

Can you help us make sure that everyone who needs it **has the best** possible care at the end of life?

Help the Hospices is the charity for hospice care, and we work with more than 200 local hospices to make sure that hospice care is there for everyone who needs it, helping people who are affected by life-limiting and terminal illnesses to live well.

By leaving a gift to us in your Will you will be helping hospices to continue to provide vital care and support to patients of all ages and their family and friends.

For more information, please contact:

Legacy Giving, Help the Hospices, Hospice House,
34–44 Britannia Street, London WC1X 9JG
Tel: **020 7520 8200**
fundraising@helpthehospices.org.uk
www.helpthehospices.org.uk

FRSB
FundRaising
Standards Board

HEARING DOGS FOR DEAF PEOPLE (HEAD OFFICE)
Founded: 1985 CR293358; SC040486
Director General: Mr Anthony Blunt
PR & Press Officer: Ms Victoria Klincke
The Grange, Wycombe Road, Saunderton,
Princes Risborough, Buckinghamshire HP27 9NS
Tel: 01844 348100
Fax: 01844 348101
Email: .... info@hearing-dogs.co.uk
Objects: W1,W3,W7

HELP FOR HEROES
CR1120920
14 Parker's Close (CC), Downton Business
Centre, Downton, Salisbury, Wiltshire SP5 3RB
Tel: 01725 513212
Email: .... info@helpforheroes.org.uk
Objects: W9,1B,O

HELP THE HOSPICES
Founded: 1984 CR1014851; SC041112
PA to Finance and Fundraising Directors: Heather
Oag
Hospice House, 34-44 Britannia Street, London
WC1X 9JG
Tel: 020 7520 8200
Fax: 020 7278 1021
Email: ..... fundraising@helpthehospices.org.uk
Objects: W3,N,W4

Now more than ever, it is vital to support hospices so
they can be there now and in generations to come.
Help the Hospices is the charity for hospice care, and
we work with more than 200 local hospices to make sure
that hospice care is there for everyone who needs it –
including children, young people, adults and their
families, carers and friends.
Hospice care helps people with life-limiting and terminal
illnesses to live well by providing the very best care and
support, in the place of their choice. Every year, this
care reaches 360,000 people in the UK – but with an
ageing population, more people will be dying with
complex needs and the demand for hospice care will
increase.
By leaving a gift to Help the Hospices in your Will, you
will enable us to champion and support hospice care in
years to come so that even more seriously ill people and
their families can make each day together count.
See advert on previous page

THE HENRY MOORE FOUNDATION
Founded: 1977 CR271370
Administrator: Mr Charles M Joint
Dane Tree House, Perry Green, Much Hadham,
Hertfordshire SG10 6EE
Tel: 01279 843333
Fax: 01279 843647
Email: .... admin@henry-moore-fdn.co.uk
Objects: G,A,1B,H

HEREFORDSHIRE ASSOCIATION FOR THE BLIND
CR220171
36 Widemarsh Street, Hereford, Herefordshire
HR4 9EP
Tel: 01432 352297

HEREFORDSHIRE LIFESTYLES
Founded: 1991 CR1003132
Director: Mr Richard Kelly
Secretary: Mrs P A Marson
41a Millbrook Street, Hereford, Herefordshire
HR4 9LF

Tel: 01432 277968
Fax: 01432 273507
Email: ...... mainoffice@lifestyles.demon.co.uk
Objects: M,W5,2,3,P

HERITAGE LINCOLNSHIRE
Founded: 1991 CR1001463
Assistant Director: Ms Rebecka Blenntoft
Director: Mr D Start
The Old School, Cameron Street, Heckington,
Sleaford, Lincolnshire NG34 9RW
Tel: 01529 461499
Fax: 01529 461001
Email: .... info@lincsheritage.org

HERPES VIRUSES ASSOCIATION
Founded: 1985 CR291657
Hon Treasurer: Mr G. Davies
Director: Ms Marian Nicholson
41 North Road, Islington, London N7 9DP
Tel: 020 7607 9661 & Minicom; 0845 123 2305
Helpline
Objects: F,W9,W6,W3,W7,W5,W10,W11,N,2,W4, H,W8

HERTFORDSHIRE CONVALESCENT TRUST
Founded: 1876 CR212423
Administrator: Mrs Janet Bird
Chairman: Mrs Mary Fuller
140 North Road, Hertford, Hertfordshire
SG14 2DZ
Tel: 01992 505886
Fax: 01992 582595
Objects: F,W9,W6,W3,W7,W5,W10,W11,1A,A,V, W4,W8

HESLEY FOUNDATION, THE
See Lloyd Family Foundation, The

HESTIA HOUSING AND SUPPORT
CR294555
Maya House, 134-138 Borough High Street,
London SE1 1LB
Email: .... info@hestia.org

HIGH BLOOD PRESSURE FOUNDATION
Founded: 1990SC022286
Director: Ms Rosalind Newton
Treasurer: Mr P. Yellowlees
Dept. of Medical Sciences (CD), Western General
Hospital, Edinburgh EH4 2XU
Tel: 0131 332 9211
Fax: 0131 537 1012
Email: .... hbpf@hbpf.org.uk
Objects: F,G,N,3

HIGHER EDUCATION INFORMATION SERVICES TRUST
See The Trust for Education

HIGHSCOPE GB
Founded: 1991
Anerley Business Centre, Anerley Road, London
SE20 8BD
Tel: 0870 777 7680; 0870 777 7681
Fax: 0870 777 7682
Email: .... highscope@btconnect.com
Objects: W3,G,3

HILDA MARTINDALE EDUCATIONAL TRUST
See Martindale (Hilda) Educational Trust

HISTORIC CHURCHES PRESERVATION TRUST
Founded: 1952 CR207402
Chief Executive: Mr Andrew Edwards
31 Newbury Street, London EC1A 7HU
Tel: 020 7600 6090
Fax: 020 7796 2442
Email: .... info@historicchurches.org.uk
Objects: W2,A,1B,3

HONOURABLE SOCIETY OF GRAY'S INN TRUST FUND
Founded: 1992 CR1014798
Director of Finance Gray's Inn: Mr W P Courage
8 South Square, Gray's Inn, London WC1R 5EU
Tel: 020 7458 7800
Fax: 020 7458 7801
Objects: G,2,3

HOPE AND HOMES FOR CHILDREN
CR1089490
Director: Colonel Mark Cook
Director: Mr James Whiting
East Clyffe, Salisbury, Wiltshire SP3 4LZ
Tel: 01722 790111
Fax: 01722 790024
Email: .... joe.sutton@hopeandhomes.org
Object: W3

HOPE FOR CHILDREN
CR1041258
22 Ben Sayers Park, North Berwick, East Lothian
EH39 5PT
Tel: 0844 779 9774
Fax: 0845 009 9628
Email: .... mw@hope4c.org

HOPE HOUSE CHILDREN'S HOSPICES
Founded: 1991 CR1003859
Chief Executive: Mr David Featherstone
Appeals Director: Ms Nuala O'Kane
Nant Lane, Morda, Oswestry, Shropshire
SY10 9BX
Tel: 01691 671671
Fax: 01691 671814
Email: .... appeals@hopehouse.org.uk
Objects: F,W3,J,W5,N,3

HOPE UK (DRUG EDUCATION) (FORMERLY THE BAND OF HOPE)
Founded: 1855 CR1044475
Executive Director: Mr George Ruston
25(f) Copperfield Street, London SE1 0EN
Tel: 020 7928 0848
Fax: 020 7401 3477
Email: .... a.wilson@hopeuk.org
Objects: W3,G,H,3

HORNIMAN MUSEUM AND GARDENS
CR802725
Secretary: Ms Grace Conacher
100 London Road, Forest Hill, London SE23 3PQ
Tel: 020 8699 1872
Email: .... development@horniman.ac.uk
Objects: S,3

HORSES AND PONIES PROTECTION ASSOCIATION
CR1085211
Taylor Building, Shores Hey Farm, Halifax Road, Briercliffe, Burnley, Lancashire BB10 3QU
Tel: 01282 455992
Fax: 01282 451992
Email: .... info@happa.org.uk

HORSEWORLD TRUST (FRIENDS OF BRISTOL HORSES SOCIETY)
CR1121920
Delmar Hall, Keynes Farm, Staunton Lane, Whitchurch, Bristol BS14 0QL
Tel: 01275 893033
Fax: 01275 836909
Email: .... info@horseworld.org.uk

HOSPICE AT HOME GWYNEDD AND ANGLESEY

CR1001428
Bodfan, Ysbyty Eryri, Caernarfon, Gwynedd LL55 2YE
Tel: .... 01286 662772 (Charity Office HQ); 01286 662775 (Nursing Office); 01248 354300 (Hafan Menai Day Hospice)
Fax: 01286 662792
Email: .. lynn.parry@wales.nhs.uk; gaynor.jones8@wales.nhs.uk
Web: .... www.hospiceathomega.co.uk
Hospice at Home Gwynedd and Anglesey is a small community based charity which cares for patients with cancer and other life limiting illness. 80% of the work done is in the patient's own home by a team of Hospice Nurses who are Registered General Nurses with additional palliative care training. The remaining 20% of the work consists of a Day Care Service at Hafan Menai Day Hospice located in Bangor and a Community Complementary Service in several clinics across the 2 counties and where necessary in the patient's own home. The Charity relies on the Public for its support and donations to continue its vital work.

HOSPICE AT HOME WEST CUMBRIA
CR1086837
Workington Community Hospital, Park Lane, Workington, Cumbria CA14 2RW
Tel: ... 01900 705200; 01900 873173 (Finance & Fundraising)
Fax: 01900 606003
Email: . info@hospiceathomewestcumbria.org.uk
Objects: F,E,N,3

HOSPICE INFORMATION SERVICE
See Counsel and Care

HOSPITAL SATURDAY FUND CHARITABLE TRUST
Founded: 1873 CR1123381
Chief Executive: Mr Keith Bradley MCMI
24 Upper Ground, London SE1 9PD
Tel: 020 7202 1365
Fax: 020 7928 0446
Email: .... charity@hsf.co.uk
Objects: 1A,A,1B,N,O

HOUSING 21
Founded: 1904 CR1015049
Chief Executive: Ms Melinda Phillips
The Triangle, Baring Road, Beaconsfield,
Buckinghamshire HP9 2NA
Tel: 01494 685200
Objects: M,D,W4,3,C

HOUSING FOR WOMEN
Founded: 1933 CR211351
Director of Finance: Ms Caroline Allen
Chief Executive: Ms Elizabeth Clarson
6th Floor, Blue Star House, 234-244 Stockwell
Road, London SW9 9SP
Tel: 020 7501 6120
Fax: 020 7924 0224
Email: .... info@h4w.co.uk
Objects: D,3,C,W8

HUDDERSFIELD MENCAP
See MENCAP in Kirklees

HUGGENS' COLLEGE
Founded: 1844 CR210336
Secretary to the Trustees: Mr David Newlyn
20 Sallows Shaw, Sole Street, Cobham,
Gravesend, Kent DA13 9BS
Tel: 01474 814587
Email: .... secretary@huggenscollege.org
Web: .... http://www.huggenscollege.org
Objects: W4,3,C

Homes for ladies and gentlemen in reduced circumstances, aged between 60 and 75, who are members of the Church of England. Huggens' College is an attractive almshouse complex of 30 bungalows with a chapel and common room set in well maintained grounds.

HUGO LONDON
Founded: 1992 CR1008230
Administrator: Doctor E Evans
20 Church Lane, Cheddington, Leighton Buzzard,
Bedfordshire LU7 0RU
Tel: 020 7935 8085

HULL AND EAST YORKSHIRE COUNCIL FOR DRUG PROBLEMS
See Council for Dependency Problems

HUMAN APPEAL INTERNATIONAL
Founded: 1991 CR1005733
Honorary Secretary: Doctor K Shadeed
Victoria Court, 376 Wilslow Road, Manchester,
Greater Manchester M14 6AX
Tel: 0161 225 0225
Fax: 0161 225 0226

HUNTINGDONSHIRE COMMUNITY CHURCH
Founded: 1990 CR803355
Staff Pastor: Mr Andy Stephens
83A High Street, Huntingdon, Cambridgeshire
PE29 3DP
Tel: 01480 411665
Objects: W3,W5,R,W4,3

HUNTINGDONSHIRE SOCIETY FOR THE BLIND
Founded: 1927 CR202573
Secretary: Mrs H Bosworth
F/R Chairman: Mr P Dronfield
Chairman: Mrs A White-Horan
8 St Mary's Street, Huntingdon, Cambridgeshire
PE29 3PE

IDS (Industrial Dwellings Society 1885)
Tel: 01480 453438
Fax: 01480 453556
Email: .... huntsblind@btconnect.com
Objects: F,W6,M,J,V,2,O,3,P

HYDE PARK APPEAL
Founded: 1991 CR1005326
Chairman: Mr Richard Briggs OBE
35 Sloane Gardens, London SW1W 8EB
Tel: 07767 498096
Fax: 020 7823 4512
Email: .... info@hydeparkappeal.org
Objects: W5,W4,3

HYELM
Founded: 1926 CR215575
Manager: Mr Keith Douglas
79 Fitzjohn's Avenue, Hampstead, London
NW3 6PA
Tel: 020 7435 8793
Fax: 020 7431 7873
Objects: W3,C

I

IA (ILEOSTOMY AND INTERNAL POUCH SUPPORT GROUP)
Founded: 1956 CR234472
IA National Office, Peverill House, 1-5 Mill Road,
Ballyclare BT39 9DR
Tel: 028 9334 4043
Fax: 028 9332 4606
Email: .... info@iasupport.org
Objects: F,M,J,G,H,O,P

IA is a patient support group run by and for people with ileostomies and ileo-anal pouches, their families, friends and carers. With approx 10,000 members, 53 local member organisations throughout the UK & Ireland and a team of specially trained visitors, IA is able to provide patients pre- and post-surgery with the invaluable support of talking to someone who has shared a similar experience. IA also promotes research into the causes of inflammatory bowel diseases (ulcerative colitis and Crohn's disease) which lead to this surgery in those cases that fail to respond to medical treatment.

ICHTHUS COMMUNITY PROJECTS LIMITED
Founded: 1990 CR1000655
Chair of Trustees: Anthony Gerry Armstrong
Company Secretary & Trustee: Mr Alistair Crow
7 Greenwich Quay, Clarence Road, Greenwich,
London SE8 3EY
Tel: 020 8694 7171
Fax: 020 8694 7172
Objects: F,W3,G,U,3

IDS (INDUSTRIAL DWELLINGS SOCIETY 1885)
FS14044R
Chief Executive: Mr Paul Westbrook BSc
5th Floor, Ockway House, 41 Stamford Hill,
London N16 5SR
Tel: 020 8800 9606
Fax: 020 8800 5990
Email: .... housing@ids.org.uk
Objects: W10,D,W4,3,C

IMMIGRATION INFORMATION AND ADVICE SERVICE
See Immigration Advisory Service

IMPACT FOUNDATION
Founded: 1985 CR290992
Chief Executive: Mrs Judi Stagg
Chairman: Mr David Walker CMG, CVO
151 Western Road, Haywards Heath, West Sussex RH16 3LH
Tel: 01444 457080
Fax: 01444 457877
Email: . . . . impact@impact.org.uk
Objects: W6,W3,W7,W5,G,1B,N,U,3
There are estimated to be 700 million disabled people in the world. Most of that disability was preventable and much of it is curable. The IMPACT Foundation's object is to take action, internationally and in the UK, to prevent and alleviate needless disability, using simple, appropriate and economical interventions.

IN-VOLVE
Founded: 1987 CR803244
HR & Finance Officer: Ms Marilyn Netley
Abbey House, 361 Barking Road, Plaistow, London E13 8EE
Tel: 020 7474 2222
Fax: 020 7473 5399
Email: . . . . headoffice@in-volve.org.uk
Objects: F,W3,E,G,W10,O,3,W8

INCLUDE
Founded: 1990 CR803333
Mrs Lesley Moore
c/o The Centre for British Teachers, 60 Queens Road, Reading RG1 4BS
Tel: 0118 902 1000; 0118 902 1404
Objects: W3,J,G,3

INCORPORATED BENEVOLENT FUND OF THE INSTITUTION OF GAS ENGINEERS AND MANAGERS
Founded: 1863 CR214010
President: Mr S Featherstone
Deputising Secretary / Chief Executive: Mr John Williams
Charnwood Wing, Holywell Park, Ashby Road, Loughborough, Leicestershire LE11 3GH
Tel: 01509 282728
Fax: 01509 283110
Email: . . . . general@igem.org.uk
Objects: M,1A,A,V,N,2,C

INCORPORATED HOMES FOR LADIES WITH LIMITED INCOME
See Lee House, Wimbledon

INDEPENDENT AGE
Founded: 1863 CR210729
Chief Executive: Janet Morrison
Finance Director: Mr Jonathan O'Shea
6 Avonmore Road (CC), London W14 8RL

Tel: 020 7605 4200
Fax: 020 7005 4201
Email: .... legacies@independentage.org
Objects: F,M,A,V,W4,H,P

INDEPENDENT DIABETES TRUST

CR1058284
PO Box 294, Northampton,
Northamptonshire NN1 4XS
Tel: 01604 622837
Fax: 01604 622838
Email: .... enquiries@iddtinternational.org
Objects: F,W3,N,W4

Supports people living with diabetes, represents their interests especially those experiencing difficulties with human insulin.

See advert on previous page

INDEPENDENT HEALTHCARE ASSOCIATION
See Independent Healthcare Forum

INDEPENDENT HEALTHCARE FORUM
CR296103
Chief Executive: Mr Barry Hassell
Centre Point, 103 New Oxford Street, London WC1A 1DU
Tel: 020 7379 7721
Fax: 020 7379 8586
Email: .... info@ihf.org.uk
Objects: F,W9,W6,W3,J,W7,W5,G,W11,N,2,W4, H,O,3,W8

INDIVIDUAL CARE SERVICES
Founded: 1992 CR1008195
Standards Director & Company Secretary: Mrs Helen Hodgetts
Client Services: Mr Alan Smith
Kingfisher Court, The Oaks, Clews Road, Redditch, Worcestershire B98 7ST
Tel: 01527 546000
Fax: 01527 546888

INFERTILITY NETWORK UK
Founded: 2003 CR1099960
Head of Business Development: Ms Sheena Young
Charter House, 43 St Leonards Road, Bexhill-on-Sea, East Sussex TN40 1JA
Tel: 01424 732 361
Fax: 01424 731858
Email: .... sheena@infertilitynetworkuk.com
Web: .... http://www.infertilitynetworkuk.com
Objects: Q,F,H,3,W8

Infertility Network UK is a national charity which provides information, help and support to all those who find they have a fertility issue. We are able to help people from the very day they think they have a problem, right through investigations and treatment then onwards, via our network More to Life for those who will remain childless and ACeBabes which provides support and information to those who have created their family through assisted conception, adoption/fostering or surrogacy.

INSTITUTE FOR EUROPEAN ENVIRONMENTAL POLICY, LONDON
Founded: 1990 CR802956
Director: Mr David Baldock
15 Queen Anne's Gate, London SW1H 9BU
Tel: 020 7799 2244
Fax: 020 7799 2600
Email: .... central@ieep.eu
Objects: F,W2,H,3

INSTITUTE FOR OPTIMUM NUTRITION
CR1013084
Managing Director: Mr Adam Porter-Blake
Avalon House, 72 Lower Mortlake Road, Richmond, Surrey TW9 2JY
Tel: 020 8614 7804
Fax: 0870 979 1133
Email: .... reception@ion.ac.uk
Objects: F,W3,G,2,W4,H,O,3,W8

THE INSTITUTE OF CANCER RESEARCH: THE ROYAL CANCER HOSPITAL
Exempt
Dept CD 2009, 123 Old Brompton Road, London SW7 3RP
Tel: 0800 731 9468
Fax: 020 7153 5313
Email: .... legacy@icr.ac.uk
Object: N

INSTITUTE OF CREDIT MANAGEMENT
Founded: 1939 CR1012200
Director General: Mr Philip King
The Water Mill, Station Road, South Luffenham, Oakham, Leicestershire LE15 8NB
Tel: 01780 722900
Fax: 01780 721333
Email: .... info@icm.org.uk
Objects: F,J,G,2,H

INSTITUTE OF DIRECT MARKETING, THE
Founded: 1991 CR1001865
Secretary to the Trustees: Mr Roger Wild
1 Park Road, Teddington, Middlesex TW11 0AR
Tel: 020 8977 5705
Objects: G,H

INSTITUTE OF JOURNALISTS
See Chartered Institute of Journalists

INSTITUTE OF NEUROLOGY
The National Hospital, Queen Square, London WC1N 3BG
Tel: .... 020 7837 3611 ext. 4137
Fax: 020 7278 5069
Objects: W5,N,W4,O,3

INSTITUTION OF ENGINEERING AND TECHNOLOGY
Founded: 1871 CR211014; SC038698
Head of Governance and Legal Affairs: Mr A F Wilson
Secretary & Chief Executive: Mr N Fine Bsc, MBA, Ceng,MICE, FIET
Michael Faraday House, Six Hills Way, Stevenage, Hertfordshire SG1 2AY
Tel: 01438 313311
Fax: 01438 765526
Email: .... postmaster@theiet.org
Objects: J,G,1A,A,2,H,W8

INSTITUTION OF INCORPORATED ENGINEERS
See Institution of Engineering and Technology

INSTITUTION OF STRUCTURAL ENGINEERS BENEVOLENT FUND
CR1049171
Chairman: Mr S M Craddy
Secretary: Mr H S Kitching
11 Upper Belgrave Street, London SW1X 8BH
Tel: 020 7235 4535
Fax: 020 7235 4294
Email: .... benfund@istructe.org
Objects: W11,1A,A,2

INTEGRATION TRUST LIMITED, THE
Founded: 1991 CR1003124
Trustee: Mr John Clifford
Howcans, Front Street, Esh, Durham, Co. Durham DH7 9QS
Tel: 0191 373 3804

INTERACT WORLDWIDE
Founded: 1991 CR1001698
Studio 325, Highgate Studios, 53-79 Highgate Road, London NW5 1TL
Tel: 020 7241 8500
Fax: 020 7267 6788
Email: .... maybea@interactworldwide.org
Objects: W3,U,3,W8

INTERCHANGE STUDIOS
Founded: 1975 CR267043
Chief Executive: Doctor Alan Tomkins
Hampstead Town, Hall Centre, 213 Haverstock Hill, London NW3 4QP
Tel: 020 7692 5808
Fax: 020 7692 5801
Email: .... bookings@interchange.org.uk

INTERCHANGE TRUST
See InterChange Studios

INTERCOUNTRY ADOPTION CENTRE
CR1067313
Chief Executive Officer: Ms Gill Haworth
Company Secretary: Mr Jeremy Muller
64-66 High Street, Barnet, Hertfordshire EN5 5SJ
Tel: 020 8449 2562
Fax: 020 8440 5675
Email: .... info@icacentre.org.uk
Objects: Q,F,H

INTERNATIONAL ANIMAL RESCUE

International Animal Rescue
internationalanimalrescue.org

CR1118277
Lime House, Regency Close, Uckfield, East Sussex TN22 1DS
Tel: 01825 767688
Fax: 01825 768012
Email: info@internationalanimalrescue.org
Objects: W1,W2

At International Animal Rescue (IAR) we do exactly what our name says: we save animals from suffering around the world.

In Borneo, our Orangutan Conservation Project rescues orphaned and displaced orangutans. We rehabilitate them at our Orangutan Rescue Centre, with the aim of releasing as many as possible back into protected areas of wild rainforest. We are working on holistic solutions to protect habitat from destruction and improving the welfare of the inhabitants.

Our clinics in India sterilise and vaccinate stray dogs and cats to regulate their numbers and protect them from diseases. The vets also treat snakes, monkeys and other wildlife, as well as sacred cows that roam the streets and beaches. When a disaster strikes like the Asian tsunami, our rescue teams rush to the aid of its victims.

IAR's sanctuaries in India are home to hundreds of dancing bears that we have rescued from the streets. The bears are nursed back to health and live free from fear and pain in a safe, semi-natural forest environment. At the end of 2009 IAR and our partners made animal welfare history by rescuing the last dancing bear in India and ending this cruel practice forever.

At our bird hospital in Malta we rescue and rehabilitate migrating birds that have been shot by hunters. We also campaign for better legislation to protect wild and domestic animals across the EU.

We cannot continue this work without your help. Please consider becoming a regular supporter to help us save an animal's life today, or pledge a lasting legacy that will provide sanctuary for suffering animals in future.

See advert on next page

INTERNATIONAL ASSOCIATION FOR RELIGIOUS FREEDOM (IARF)
CR1026699
Upper Chapel, Norfolk Street, Sheffield, South Yorkshire S1 2JD
Tel: 0114 276 7114
Email: .... hq@iarf.net
Objects: J,G,2

INTERNATIONAL CEREBRAL PALSY SOCIETY
CR273102
78 Romulus Court, 1 Justin Close, Brentford, Middlesex TW8 8QJ
Tel: 020 8568 0709
Email: .... anita.loring@mac.com

INTERNATIONAL CHINA CONCERN
Founded: 1990 CR1068349
Trustee: Mr P R Hubbard
PO BOX 20, Morpeth, Northumberland NE61 3YP

Tel: 01670 505622; 07799 413095
Email: . . . . uk@intichinaconcern.org
Objects: W3,W5,G,U,O,3

INTERNATIONAL CONNECTIONS TRUST
Founded: 1992 CR1113099
Trustee: Mr Tony Horswood
93 Acre Lane, Brixton, London SW2 5TU
Tel: 020 7924 9700
Fax: 020 7924 9800
Email: . . . . connuk@gol.com
Objects: 1A,1B,R,U,3

THE DONKEY SANCTUARY INTERNATIONAL

CR264818
Chief Executive: Mr David Cook
Slade House Farm (Dept CDO), Sidmouth,
Devon EX10 0NU
Tel: 01395 578222
Fax: 01395 579266
Email: . . enquiries@thedonkeysanctuary.org.uk
Web: . . http://www.thedonkeysanctuary.org.uk
Objects: F,W1,M,G,N,U,H,3
Our projects in five developing countries, Egypt,
Ethiopia, India, Kenya and Mexico, bring free
veterinary assistance and educational support to
working donkeys and their owners. Projects include
over 20 mobile clinics and five static clinics, which
concentrate on areas where there is a large donkey
population, where the economy is dependent on the
donkey, and where there is low economic status.
See advert on previous page

INTERNATIONAL FUND FOR CAT WELFARE FELINE ADVISORY BUREAU
Founded: 1958 CR1117342
Chief Executive: Ms Claire Bessant
Chair: Ms Kim Horsford
Taeselbury, High Street, Tisbury, Wiltshire
SP3 6LD
Tel: 01747 871872
Fax: 01747 871873
Email: . . . . info@icatcare.org
Objects: F,W1,G,2,B,H

INTERNATIONAL GLAUCOMA ASSOCIATION
Founded: 1974 CR274681; SC041550
Chief Executive: Mr David Wright FIAM FRSA
Woodcote House, 15 Highpoint Business Village,
Henwood, Ashford, Kent TN24 8DH
Tel: 01233 648170
Fax: 01233 648179
Email: . . . . info@iga.org.uk
Objects: W6,G,W4,H

INTERNATIONAL LEAGUE FOR THE PROTECTION OF HORSES (ILPH)
See World Horse Welfare

INTERNATIONAL ORGAN FESTIVAL SOCIETY LTD, THE
Founded: 1991 CR1006151
Company Secretary: Mrs Jenny Stroud
Spinney Corner, Green Lane, Apsley Guise, Milton
Keynes MK17 8EN
Object: S

INTERNATIONAL RECORDS MANAGEMENT TRUST, THE
Founded: 1991 CR1068975
Executive Director: Dr Anne Thurston
4th Floor, 7 Hatton Garden, London EC1N 8AD
Tel: 020 7831 4101
Fax: 020 7831 6303
Email: . . . . info@irmt.org
Objects: S,G,U,H,3,K

INTERNATIONAL STUDENTS HOUSE TRUST
CR294448
1 Park Crescent, Regents Park, London W1B 1SH
Tel: 020 7631 8300
Fax: 020 7631 8307
Email: . . . . info@ish.org.uk

INTERNATIONAL WATER ASSOCIATION
CR289269
Alliance House, 12 Caxton Street, London
SW1H 0QS
Tel: 020 7654 5500
Fax: 020 7654 5555
Email: . . . . water@iwahq.org.uk
Objects: J,2

INTERNATIONAL WHEELCHAIR & AMPUTEE SPORTS FEDERATION
Founded: 1992 CR1011552
IWAS Secretariat
IWAS Secretariat, Olympic Village, Guttmann
Road, Aylesbury, Buckinghamshire HP21 9PP
Tel: 01296 436179
Fax: 01296 436484
Email: . . . . info@iwasf.com
Objects: W3,J,W5,G,2,U,K

INVALIDS-AT-HOME TRUST
See Independence at Home

IPA TRUST, THE
Founded: 1991 CR1071752
Director General: Mr Piers Pendred
International Psychoanalytical Assn, Registered
Office, Bromhills, Woodside Lane, London
N12 8UD
Tel: 020 7380 7896

IRIE! DANCE THEATRE
Founded: 1985 CR1003947
Artistic Director: Ms Beverley Glean
The Moonshot Centre, Fordham Park, Angus
Street, New Cross, London SE14 6LY
Tel: 020 8691 6099
Fax: 020 8694 8464
Email: . . . . info@iriedancetheatre.org
Objects: W3,S,G,W10,W4,3,W8,K

IRIS FUND FOR PREVENTION OF BLINDNESS
See Fight for Sight

IRONBRIDGE (TELFORD) HERITAGE FOUNDATION LIMITED, THE
Founded: 1990 CR1001039
Secretary: Mr Arthur Adair
14 The Square, Broad Street, Edgbaston, Birmingham, West Midlands B15 1AS
Tel: 0121 603 9000

ISABEL HOSPICE (EASTERN HERTFORDSHIRE)
CR1046826
Director of Fundraising: Ms Lisa Seccombe
Deputy Director of Fundraising: Ms Charity Warnes
Head Office, 61 Bridge Road East, Welwyn Garden City, Hertfordshire AL7 1JR
Tel: 01707 382500
Fax: 01707 382598
Email: . . . . enquiries@isabelhospice.org.uk
Objects: M,E,N
Isabel Hospice provides a comprehensive range of specialist palliative care free of charge for patients and their families living with cancer and other life-limiting illnesses in The Borough of Welwyn and Hatfield, The Borough of Broxbourne and East Herts District. Services include a Community Nursing Team who are available from the point of diagnosis, In-Patient Care, Day Care, Hospice at Home and a Family Support team.
Almost two thirds of our funding has to be raised from charitable sources, and donations and legacies form a vital part of this income.

ISIS
Founded: 1989 CR1059698
Chairperson: Ms Alcina Humphrey
183-185 Rushey Green, Catford, London SE6 4BD
Tel: 020 8695 1955
Fax: 020 8695 5600
Objects: F,J,S,E,W5,G,W10,O,3,P,K

ISLE OF ANGLESEY CHARITABLE TRUST, THE
Founded: 1990 CR1000818
Treasurer: Mr David Elis-Williams
Isle of Anglesey Charitable Trust, County Offices, Llangefni, Anglesey LL77 7TW
Objects: A,1B

ISLE OF WIGHT DONKEY SANCTUARY
Founded: 1990 CR1001061
Charity Manager: Mrs Cherryl Clarke
Lower Winstone Farm (Dept. CD), Wroxall, Isle of Wight PO38 3AA
Tel: 01983 852693
Fax: 01983 866697
Email: . . . . info@iwdonkey-sanctuary.com

J

JAMES HOPKINS TRUST
Founded: 1990 CR1000870
Co-founder & General Manager: Mr Vance Hopkins
Kite's Corner, North Upton Lane, Gloucester, Gloucestershire GL4 3TR
Tel: 01452 612216
Fax: 08450 788 700
Email: . . . . info@jameshopkinstrust.org.uk
Web: . . . . www.jameshopkinstrust.org.uk
Objects: W3,W5,3
The James Hopkins Trust provides Nursing respite care to the severely disabled, life limited and life threatened young children of Gloucestershire, either in their family home or at our day care centre.

JAMI MOSQUE AND ISLAMIC CENTRE (BIRMINGHAM) TRUSTEES LIMITED
Founded: 1975 CR1000355
President: Dr A S M Rahim
Jami Masjid and Islamic Centre, 521 Coventry Road, Small Heath, Birmingham, West Midlands B10 0LL
Tel: 0121 772 6408
Fax: 0121 773 4340
Objects: F,W6,W3,J,S,W7,W5,G,W10,2,R,W4,H, T,O,3,P,W8,K

JAPAN ANIMAL WELFARE SOCIETY
Founded: 1966 CR244534
Chairman: Mr A.I. Crittenden
Office Manager: Akiko Yanagisawa
Lyell House, 51 Greencoat Place, London SW1P 1DS
Tel: 020 7630 5563
Fax: 020 7630 5563
Email: . . . . jawsuk@jawsuk.org.uk
Objects: W1,1A,2

JAWS
See Japan Animal Welfare Society

JENNIFER TRUST FOR SPINAL MUSCULAR ATROPHY
Founded: 1985 CR1106815
40 Cygnet Court, Timothys Bridge Road, Stratford-upon-Avon, Warwickshire CV37 9NW
Tel: 08707 743651; 08707 743652
Email: . . . . jennifer@jtsma.org.uk
Objects: F,W5,1A,3

JERRY GREEN DOG RESCUE
CR200232
Broughton, Brigg, Lincolnshire DN20 0BJ
Tel: 01652 650886
Email: . . . . fundraising@jerrygreendogs.org.uk
Objects: Q,F,W1,2,3

JERUSALEM AND THE MIDDLE EAST CHURCH ASSOCIATION
Founded: 1888 CR248799
Secretary to the Association: Mrs Shirley Eason
1 Hart House (Dept CD), The Hart, Farnham, Surrey GU9 7HJ
Tel: 01252 726994
Fax: 01252 726994
Email: . . . . secretary@jmeca.eclipse.co.uk
Objects: W6,W3,W7,W5,G,W10,W15,1A,A,1B,N, R,W4,U,Y,W8

JESMOND SWIMMING PROJECT
Founded: 1992 CR1010563
Company Secretary: Mr C Clarke
Jesmond Swimming Pool, St Georges Terrace,
Jesmond, Newcastle upon Tyne, Tyne & Wear
NE2 2DL
Tel: 0191 281 2482
Objects: W3,S,W7,W5,G,W10,W4,O,P,W8

JESSE MARY CHAMBERS ALMSHOUSES
Founded: 1924 CR1001479
Secretary & Clerk to the Trustees: Mrs Kathryn
Fleming
21 Rodney Road, Cheltenham, Gloucestershire
GL50 1HX
Tel: 01242 522180
Fax: 01242 522180
Objects: W4,3,C

JEWISH BLIND SOCIETY
See Jewish Care

JEWISH CARE
CR802559
Chief Executive: Mr Simon Morris
Merit House, 508 Edgware Road, The Hyde,
Colindale, London NW9 5AB
Tel: 020 8922 2000
Fax: 020 8201 3897
Email: .... info@jcare.org
Objects: F,W6,M,J,S,E,W5,N,W4,H,O,3,C,P,K

JEWISH CARE SCOTLAND
SC005267
May Terrace, Giffnock, Glasgow G46 6LD
Tel: 0141 620 1000
Fax: 0141 620 2409
Email: .... admin@jcarescot.org.uk

JEWISH CHILD'S DAY

Founded: 1947 CR209266
Executive Director: Mrs Melanie Klass
PA to Executive Director: Mrs Jackie Persoff
Chairman: Mrs Joy Moss MBE
707 High Road, London N12 0BT
Tel: 020 8446 8804
Fax: 020 8446 7370
Email: .... info@jcd.uk.com
Objects: M,W3,E,A,1B,V,U,O,Y

Jewish Child's Day has been providing support for
disabled, neglected, abused and underprivileged
Jewish children in the UK, Israel and worldwide for
more than 60 years. It provides the tangible items
required – wheelchairs, life-saving medical
equipment, hearing stimulus and special educational
materials to name but a few. Jewish Child's Day also
ensures that Jewish children receive the bare
essentials such as food and clothing. Relying entirely
on the generosity of the community and receiving
neither government nor statutory funding, Jewish
Child's Day grants provide Jewish children
throughout the world the chance to make a better life
for themselves. Every grant targets and improves the
lives of Jewish children in need.

JEWISH MARRIAGE COUNCIL
Founded: 1946 CR1078723
Treasurer: Mr Stuart Ifield FCA
Chairman: Judge Martyn Ziedman Q.C
23 Ravenshurst Avenue, London NW4 4EE
Tel: 020 8203 6311
Fax: 020 8203 8727
Email: .... info@jmc-uk.org
Objects: F,G,W10,3,P

JEWISH MUSIC INSTITUTE
Founded: 1989 CR328228
Director: Mrs Geraldine Auerbach MBE
PO Box 232, Harrow, Middlesex HA1 2NN
Tel: 020 8909 2445
Fax: 020 8909 1030
Email: .... jewishmusic@jmi.org.uk
*Objects: F,W6,W3,J,S,W7,W5,G,W10,1A,W4,H,T,
W8,K*

JEWISH WELFARE BOARD
See Jewish Care

JEWS FOR JESUS TRUST
Founded: 1991 CR1110425
Trustee: Mr Patrick Beresford
Office Manager: Mrs Wendy Burton
106-110 Kentish Town Road, London NW1 9PX
Tel: 020 7431 9636
Fax: 020 7431 6828
Email: ...... pbquestions@jews-for-jesus.org.uk
Object: R

JNF CHARITABLE TRUST (JEWISH NATIONAL FUND FOR ISRAEL, KKL EXECUTOR & TRUSTEE CO. LTD)
Founded: 1901 CR225910
Company Secretary: Mr H R Bratt
JNF House, Spring Villa Park, Edgware,
Middlesex HA8 7ED
Tel: 020 8732 6100
Fax: 020 8732 6111
Email: .... info@jnf.co.uk
Objects: W2,S,G,U,H

THE JOE HOMAN CHARITY
Founded: 1991 CR1006060
PO Box 54, Peterborough, Cambridgeshire
PE4 6JP
Tel: 01733 574886
Objects: W3,U

JOHN GROOMS (NOW LIVABILITY)
See Livability (the new name of John Grooms and
the Shaftesbury Society)

JOINT EDUCATIONAL TRUST
CR313218
Director: Ms Julie Burns
6-8 Fenchurch Buildings, London EC3M 5HT
Tel: 020 3217 1100
Fax: 020 3217 1110
Email: .... admin@jetcharity.org
Objects: W3,G,1A,A

JOSEPH WELD & TRIMAR HOSPICE AND CANCERCARE DORSET TRUST
See Weldmar Hospicecare Trust

JUBILEE ACTION
Founded: 1992 CR1013587
General Director: Mr D Smith
Carroll House, 11 Quarry Street, Guildford, Surrey
GU1 3UY
Tel: 01483 230250
Fax: 01483 565475
Email: .... info@jubileeaction.co.uk
Objects: W3,E,W10,A,1B,D,U,O,P,W8

JUBILEE DEBT CAMPAIGN
Founded: 1996 CR1055675
The Grayston Centre, 28 Charles Square, London
N1 6HT
Tel: 020 7324 4722
Fax: 020 7324 4723
Email: .... info@jubileedebtcampaign.org.uk
Objects: W3,J,W2,G,2,W4,H,W8

K

KENT ASSOCIATION FOR THE BLIND
CR1062354
72 College Road, Maidstone, Kent ME15 6SJ
Tel: 01622 691357
Fax: 01622 663999
Email: .... supportus@kab.org.uk

KENT COMMUNITY HOUSING TRUST
Founded: 1991 CR1002727
Bridgewood House, Rochester Airport Industrial
Estate, 8 Laker Road, Rochester, Kent ME1 3QX
Tel: 01634 869880
Fax: 01634 869824
Email: .... debbie.pert@kcht.org.uk
Objects: F,M,W3,E,W5,G,A,D,W4,O,3,C,P,K

KENT COUNTY AGRICULTURAL SOCIETY
CR1001191
General Manager: Mr Jonathan Day
County Showground, Detling, Maidstone, Kent
ME14 3JF
Tel: 01622 630975
Fax: 01622 630978
Email: .... info@kentshowground.co.uk
Objects: W1,W2,1A,1B,B

KENT WILDLIFE TRUST
Founded: 1958 CR239992
Supporter Relations Officer: Miss Emma Barnes
Director: Mr John Bennett
Chairman: Mr John Leigh Pemberton
Tyland Barn, Sandling, Maidstone, Kent
ME14 3BD
Tel: 01622 662012
Fax: 01622 671390
Email: .... info@kentwildlife.org.uk
Objects: W1,W2,G,2,P

KENTISBEARE COMMUNITY HALL FUND
Founded: 1990 CR1052482
Hon Secretary: Mr Q A Broom
Quenton House, Cullompton, Devon EX15 1PB
Tel: 01884 798342

KEYCHANGE CHARITY
Founded: 1920 CR1061344
Chief Executive: Mr Graham Waters
5 St George's Mews, 43 Westminster Bridge
Road, London SE1 7JB
Tel: 020 7633 0533
Fax: 020 7928 1872
Email: .... info@keychange.org.uk
Objects: W15,D,W4,H,C,W8

KEYRING-LIVING SUPPORT NETWORKS
Founded: 1990 CR1054234
Director: Ms Karyn Kirkpatrick
1st Floor Impact Centre, 12-18 Hoxton Street,
London N1 6NG
Tel: 020 7749 9411
Objects: W5,D,3

KIDASHA
CR1106156
Fundraising Manager: Ms Gurvinder Bans
55 East Road, London N1 6AH
Tel: 020 7017 8989
Email: .... enquiries@cwsuk.org
Objects: W3,G,N,3

KIDNEY WALES FOUNDATION
CR700396
1 Radnor Court, 256 Cowbridge Road East,
Cardiff CF5 1GZ
Tel: 029 2034 3940
Email: .... chris@kidneywales.com

KIDS KIDNEY RESEARCH
CR266630
10 Beechwood, Southwater, Horsham, West
Sussex RH13 9JU
Tel: 01403 732291
Email: .... paul@kidskidneyresearch.org
Object: W3

Each year a significant number of babies are born
with serious abnormalities of their kidneys, which
may result in total failure of kidney function, needing
dialysis treatment and/or a kidney transplant.
Treatments on offer allow varying extension of life.
However there is no cure.
Please help us to find ways of eradicating disease of
the kidney and bladder. We support the vital
research at the Institute of Child Health, which works
in conjunction with Great Ormond Street Hospital
renal unit. We also fund renal projects nationwide
under the guidance of the British Association for
Paediatric Nephrology. We are a member of the
Association of Medical Research Charities.

KING EDWARD VII'S HOSPITAL SISTER AGNES
Founded: 1899 CR208944
Chief Executive: Mr Clive Bath
Beaumont Street, London W1G 6AA
Tel: 020 7467 3920
Fax: 020 7467 3929
Email: .... fundraising@kingedwardvii.com
Objects: W9,W6,W7,W5,1A,A,N,W4,3,W8

KINGS CROSS-BRUNSWICK NEIGHBOURHOOD
CR1083901
Chair: Ms Pamela Mansi
Team Leader / Co-ordinator: Ms Sioned Williams
Marchmont Community Centre, 62 Marchmont
Street, London WC1N 1AB
Tel: 020 7278 5635
Fax: 020 7833 5709
Email: .... kcbna@aol.com
Objects: F,W3,W10,W4,3

KIRSTIN ROYLE TRUST
Founded: 1995 CR1040717
Trustee: Ms Lesley Metcalf
Secretary: Ms Katherine Owen
6/8 Valleyfield Street, Edinburgh EH3 9LS
Email: . . . . kirstinroyletrust@hotmail.com
Objects: W6,W3,W7,W5,W10,1A,A,1B,O,P,W8

KONING WILLEM FONDS
See Netherlands Benevolent Society

KRASZNA-KRAUSZ FOUNDATION
CR326601
Chairman: Mr Colin Ford CBE
Administrator: Ms Andrea Livingstone
3 Downs Court Road, Purley, Surrey CR8 1BE
Tel: 020 8668 3375
Email: . . . . info@kraszna-krausz.org.uk
Objects: 1A,A,1B

L

THE LABRADOR RESCUE TRUST
CR1088198
32 Award Road, Wimborne, Dorset BH21 7NT
Tel: 07791519084
Email: . . . . enquiries@labrador-rescue.com
Web: . . . . www.labrador-rescue.com
Objects: F,W1,G,P
The objects of the charity are to alleviate suffering and distress to Labradors which may be ill treated, abandoned, rejected or neglected.

LADY HOARE TRUST FOR PHYSICALLY DISABLED CHILDREN
See Contact a Family

LAMBETH AND SOUTHWARK HOUSING ASSOCIATION LIMITED
Founded: 192714888R
7A St Agnes Place, London SE11 4AU
Tel: 020 7735 3935
Objects: W3,W2,W7,W5,W10,W11,D,W4,3,W8

LAMBETH ELFRIDA RATHBONE SOCIETY (RATHBONE)
CR1096727
Contact: Andrew Preston
8 Chatsworth Way, West Norwood, London SE27 9HR
Tel: 020 8670 4039
Email: . . . . . . a.preston@rathbonesociety.org.uk
Objects: W3,W5,Z

LANCEFIELD CENTRE, THE
Founded: 1990 CR803214
Trustee: Ms Mary Nicholas
20a Lancefield Street, London W10 4PB
Tel: 020 8960 6006
Fax: 020 8960 7045
Email: . . . . lancefieldcent@aol.com

THE LANGFORD TRUST FOR ANIMAL HEALTH AND WELFARE
Founded: 1990 CR900380
School of Veterinary Science (CC), Langford House, Langford, North Somerset BS40 5DU
Tel: 0117 928 9207
Fax: 0117 928 9448
Email: . . . . langford-trust@bristol.ac.uk
Objects: W1,G

LAST CHANCE ANIMAL RESCUE
CR1002349
Hartfield Road, Edenbridge, Kent TN8 5NH
Tel: 01227 722 929; 01732 865 530
Fax: 01732 865838
Email: . . general@lastchanceanimalrescue.co.uk

LAURA CRANE TRUST
CR1058464
PO Box 437, Huddersfield, West Yorkshire HD1 9QH
Tel: 01484 510013
Fax: 01484 533995
Email: . . . . admin@lauracranetrust.org

LEAGUE OF FRIENDS OF THE WHITCHURCH HOSPITAL (SHROPSHIRE)
Founded: 1991 CR1002033
Chairman: Mrs M B Hiles
The Bungalow, Yockings Gate Mews, Black Park, Whitchurch, Shropshire SY13 4JP
Tel: 01948 664828

LEARNING THROUGH ACTION TRUST
CR1014350
Chief Executive: Ms Annette Cotterill MA, LRAM, ADB, Cert. Ed
Learning Through Action Centre, Fair Cross, Stratfield Saye, Reading RG7 2BT
Tel: 0870 770 7985
Fax: 0870 770 7986
Email: . . . . ltacentreoffice@aol.com
Objects: F,W3,G,H,3,P,K

LEARNING THROUGH LANDSCAPES TRUST
Founded: 1990 CR803270
Mr Graham Blight
Third Floor, Southside Offices, The Law Courts, Winchester, Hampshire SO23 9DL
Tel: 01962 040250
Fax: 01962 869099
Email: . . . . schoolgrounds-uk@ltl.org.uk
Objects: F,W6,W3,W2,W7,W5,G,W10,2,H,3

LEATHER AND HIDE TRADES BENEVOLENT INSTITUTION
Founded: 1860 CR206133
Treasurer: Mr Tim F Bigden
Secretary: Mrs Karen Harriman
143 Barkby Road, Leicester, Leicestershire LE4 9LG
Tel: 0116 274 1500
Fax: 0116 274 1500
Email: . . . . karenharriman@btconnect.com
Web: . . . . http://www.lhtbi.org.uk
Objects: W11,1A,A
Financial assistance available to former workers in the leather and hide or skin trades and their widows who are in need. Also one-off grants for special needs.

LEE HOUSE, WIMBLEDON
Founded: 1875 CR222043
Chairman: Lady Perring
Lee House, 2 Lancaster Avenue, Wimbledon, London SW19 5DE
Tel: 020 8946 0369
Objects: W4,3,C,W8

LEEDS REC
Founded: 1990 CR1000406
Director: Mr Tony Stanley
Sheepscar House, Sheepscar Street South, Leeds, West Yorkshire LS7 1AD

Lifeline 4 Kids / Handicapped Children's Aid Committee

Founded: 1961 CR200050
215 West End Lane, West Hampstead,
London NW6 1XJ
T: 020 7794 1661 F: 020 7794 1161
E: mail@lifeline4kids.org W: www.lifeline4kids.org

Most people realise the degree of stress suffered when a child is born with a disability, how many do something about it?

In 1961, a number of caring parents joined together to help children less fortunate than their own. To date over £16million in equipment and services has been dispensed. Appeals are investigated and if successful, funds are allocated and requirements are purchased directly by us.

We are a voluntary charity without paid staff or office expenses so virtually every penny raised is used to alleviate distress. We are determined never to let a child's cry for help go unheard.

Tel: 0113 243 8421
Fax: 0113 243 8434
Email: . . . . leedsrec@btinternet.com
Objects: F,W10,3

LEEDS TRAINING TRUST
Founded: 1990 CR1000380
Chief Executive: Mr C J Knight
Mitchell House, 139 Richardshaw Lane, Pudsey,
Leeds, West Yorkshire LS28 6AA
Tel: 0113 255 2417
Fax: 0113 236 1004

LEGISLATION MONITORING SERVICE FOR CHARITIES
CR1057767
Director: Ms Helen Donoghue
Church House, Great Smith Street, Westminster,
London SW1P 3JZ
Tel: 020 7222 1265
Fax: 020 7222 1250
Email: . . . . info@lmsconline.org.uk
Objects: F,H,3

LENNOX CHILDRENS CANCER FUND
Founded: 1992 CR1011325
Trustee: Mr V Fitzmaurice
57 Mawney Road, Romford, Essex RM7 7HL
Tel: 01708 734366

LEO TRUST, THE
Founded: 1993 CR1017367
CEO: Mr Joseph Graham
Boldshaves Oast, Frogshole, Woodchurch,
Ashford, Kent TN26 3RA

Tel: 01233 860060
Email: . . . . leotrust@btconnect.com
Objects: F,W5,3,P

LET'S FACE IT SUPPORT NETWORK FOR THE FACIALLY DISFIGURED
CR1043461
72 Victoria Avenue, Westgate-on-Sea, Kent
CT8 8BH
Tel: 01843 833724
Fax: 01843 835695
Email: . . . . chrisletsfaceit@aol.com

LEUKAEMIA & CANCER CHILDREN'S FUND
See CLIC Sargent (Scotland)

LEUKAEMIA & LYMPHOMA RESEARCH

LEUKAEMIA
& LYMPHOMA
RESEARCH

Beating Blood Cancers

Founded: 1960 CR216032; SC037529
Scientific Director: Professor Chris Bunce
Chief Executive: Ms Cathy Gilman
39-40 Eagle Street, London WC1R 4TH
Tel: 020 7504 2200
Email: . . . . info@beatingbloodcancers.org.uk
Objects: F,W3,J,A,1B,N,2,W4,H,3
Living my life to the full is important to me and it's important to Leukaemia & Lymphoma Research.

They want every person with blood cancer to survive and to go on to live a full life, free to do the things they enjoy and love.

I know they will use my legacy wisely because I've seen them develop treatments which now save the lives or nearly all children with acute lymphoblastic leukaemia. But the fight is not over so leave a legacy now. This could be the most important gift you've ever made.

LEUKAEMIA BUSTERS
CR1010957
Chair: Mr Stephen Christie
Southampton General Hospital, Southampton, Hampshire SO16 6YD
Tel: 023 8077 5590
Email: . . . . info@leukaemiabusters.org.uk
Object: W3

LEWIS W. HAMMERSON MEMORIAL HOME
Founded: 1993 CR286002
Secretary to the Trustees: Mrs Eleanor Angel
50A The Bishops Avenue, London N2 0BE
Tel: 020 8458 4523
Fax: 020 8458 2537
Objects: W7,W5,W4,3,C

LICENSED TRADE CHARITY
Founded: 2004 CR230011
Chief Executive: Mr James Brewster
Communications: Ms Elizabeth Gaffer
Heathorley, London Road, Ascot, Windsor & Maidenhead SL5 8DR
Tel: 01344 884440
Fax: 01344 884703
Email: . . . . info@licensedtradecharity.org.uk
Objects: F,W3,W5,G,W11,1A,A,2,W4,B,P

LIFE ACADEMY
Founded: 1964 CR80/310
9 Chesham Road, Guildford, Surrey GU1 3LS
Tel: 01483 301170
Email: . . . . info@pra.uk.com
Objects: F,G,2,H,3

LIFELINE 4 KIDS / HANDICAPPED CHILDREN'S AID COMMITTEE
Founded: 1961 CR200050
Chairman: Mr Roger Adelman
215 West End Lane, West Hampstead, London NW6 1XJ
Tel: 020 7794 1661
Fax: 020 7794 1161
Email: . . . . mail@lifeline4kids.org
Objects: M,W3,J,W5

Most people realise the degree of stress suffered when a child is born with a disability, how many do something about it? It is 51 years since a number of caring parents joined together to help children less fortunate than their own. To date almost £16million in equipment and services has been dispensed. Appeals are investigated and if successful, funds are allocated and requirements are purchased directly by us. We are a voluntary charity without paid staff or office expenses so virtually every penny raised is used to alleviate distress. We are determined never to let a child's cry for help go unheard.
See advert on previous page

THE LIFETRAIN TRUST
Founded: 1990 CR803697
Chief Executive: Mr Paul Wilkinson
Felbury House, Holmbury St Mary, Dorking, Surrey RH5 6NL

Tel: 01306 730929
Fax: 01306 730610
Email: . . . . info@lifetrain.org.uk
Objects: F,W3,W5,G,W10,V,3,P

THE LIND TRUST
Founded: 1990 CR803174
Trustee: Mr Gavin Croft Wilcock
c/o 74 The Close, Norwich, Norfolk NR1 4DR
Tel: 01603 610911

LINDSEY LODGE HOSPICE, SCUNTHORPE
Founded: 1990 CR702871
Chairman: Mr Peter Axe
Director: Ms Alison Tindall RGN, RCNT
Burringham Road, Scunthorpe, North Lincolnshire DN17 2AA
Tel: 01724 270835
Fax: 01724 843731
Email: . . fundraising@lindseylodgehospice.org.uk
Objects: W9,W6,W7,W5,W10,W11,N,W4,3,W8

LING TRUST LIMITED
Founded: 1991 CR1003366
Company Secretary: Ms Fiona Jayne Whitehouse
13 East Stockwell Street, Colchester, Essex CO1 1SS
Tel: 01206 769246
Fax: 01206 767287

LISTENING BOOKS
Founded: 1972 CR264221
Director: Mr Bill Dee
Marketing Co-ordinator: Ms Fiona Hutcheson
12 Lant Street, London SE1 1QH
Tel: 020 7407 9417
Fax: 020 7403 1377
Email: . . . . info@listening-books.org.uk
Objects: W6,W3,S,W5,G,2,W4,Y,3

LISTENING LIBRARY
See Listening Books

LITTLE FOUNDATION
Founded: 1990 CR803551
Chairman: Mr Christopher Robinson
c/o MacKeith Press, 30 Furnival Street, London EC4A 1JQ
Tel: 020 7831 4918
Fax: 020 7405 5365
Objects: W3,1B

THE LITTLE SISTERS OF THE POOR
CR234434
Sister Mary Chantel
St Peter's Residence (CC), 2a Meadow Road, London SW8 1QH
Tel: 020 7735 0788
Fax: 020 7582 0973
Email: . . . . mp.lond@lsplondon.co.uk
Object: W4

The Little Sisters of the Poor, an international congregation of Religious Sisters welcome into their homes elderly persons of modest means and of all nationalities and denominations. There are currently 16 homes in the UK, Jersey and Ireland.

LIVABILITY (THE NEW NAME OF JOHN GROOMS AND THE SHAFTESBURY SOCIETY)
CR1116530
Chief Executive: Mr Mike Smith O.B.E.
Legacies Marketing Manager: Mr Alastair Emblem
50 Scrutton Street, London EC2A 4XQ
Tel: 020 7452 2000
Fax: 020 7452 2001
Email: .... info@livability.org.uk
Objects: M,W3,E,W5,G,V,N,U,O,3,C,K

LIVER CANCER SURGERY APPEAL
CR1061703
The Old Farm House, Epsom Road, Merrow, Guildford, Surrey GU4 7AB
Tel: 01483 546321
Fax: 01483 453698
Email: .. livercancersurgeryappeal@yahoo.co.uk

LIVERPOOL MERCHANTS' GUILD
Founded: 1869 CR206454
Barratt House, 47-49 North John Street, Liverpool, Merseyside L2 6TG
Tel: 0151 236 9044
Fax: 0151 231 1267
Objects: 1A,A,W4,B

LIVING PAINTINGS TRUST, THE
Founded: 1989 CR1049103
Charity Director: Ms Camilla Oldland
Deputy to the Charity Director: Ms Julia Young
Queen Isabelle House, Unit 8, Kingsclere Park, Kingsclere, Newbury, West Berkshire RG20 4SW
Tel: 01635 299771
Fax: 01635 299771
Objects: W6,S,G,H,3,P

LIVING SPACE
Founded: 1991 CR1002762
Managing Director: Ms J Jolley
38 Marsh Hill, London E9 5PE
Tel: 020 8985 5575
Fax: 020 8525 0235
Email: .... office@livingspace.org
Objects: D,C

LIVING STREETS
Founded: 1929 CR1108448; SC039808
Director: Mr Tom Franklin
Finance Manager: Mr Ros Young
88-94 Wentworth Street, London E1 7SA
Tel: 020 7377 4900
Email: .... info@livingstreets.org.uk
Objects: F,W6,W3,W2,W7,W5,2,W4,H

LLANGOLLEN INTERNATIONAL MUSICAL EISTEDDFOD
CR504620
Ms Christine Dukes
Eisteddfod Office, Royal International Pavilion, Abbey Road, Llangollen, Denbighshire LL20 8SW
Tel: 01978 862007
Fax: 01978 862002
Email: ...... info@international-eisteddfod.co.uk

LLIW VALLEY WOMEN'S AID
Founded: 1991 CR1005646
Chairperson: Ms Christina Lambourne
PO Box 503, Portardawe, Swansea SA8 4WN

Tel: 01792 869480
Fax: 01792 862920
Email: .... info@luma.org.uk
Objects: W3,D,3,C,W8

LLOYD FOUNDATION, THE
Founded: 1972 CR314203
Secretary to the Trustees: Mrs M E Keyte
Fairway, Round Oak View, Tillington, Hereford, Herefordshire HR4 8EQ
Tel: 01432 760409
Objects: W3,G,1A,A,1B

LONDON BROOK ADVISORY CENTRE
Founded: 1992 CR1013037
Company Secretary: Ms Diane Noble
421 Highgate Studios, 53-79 Highgate Road, London NW5 1TL
Tel: 020 7284 6040

LONDON CATALYST
Founded: 1872 CR1066739
Chairman: Mr Tim Cook OBE
Secretary: Mr Graham Lawrence
45 Westminster Bridge Road, London SE1 7JB
Tel: 020 7021 4631
Fax: 020 7021 4011
Email: .... london.catalyst@peabody.org.uk
Objects: F,W6,M,W3,E,W7,W5,A,1B,N,W4,O,C

LONDON COMMITTEE OF THE METHODIST CHURCH
See Methodist London Mission Fund

LONDON COUNCIL FOR THE WELFARE OF WOMEN AND GIRLS (LCWWG)
See Women's Link

LONDON JEWISH CULTURAL CENTRE

Founded: 1992 CR1081014
Chief Executive: Ms Louise Jacobs
Chairman: Mr Michael Marx
Ivy House, 94-96 North End Road, London NW11 7SX
Tel: 020 8457 5000
Fax: 020 8457 5024
Email: .... admin@ljcc.org.uk
Objects: W3,S,G,W4,3

The mission of the LJCC is to educate, inspire and connect people to their Jewish identity and the wider world. Inclusive and independent, the Centre designs, delivers and facilitates the widest range of educational, cultural, social and family events for people of all ages, affiliations and interests. The LJCC also pioneers advances in Holocaust education, offers dynamic skill based Youth Programming, possesses the largest Jewish-film related archive and arranges tours to places of Jewish interest.

LONDON NORTH EAST COMMUNITY FOUNDATION
See East London Community Foundation

LONDON SHIPOWNERS' & SHIPBROKERS' BENEVOLENT SOCIETY
Founded: 1852 CR213348
Secretary: Mr R.J.M. Butler
The Annexe, 20 St. Dunstan's Hill, London
EC3R 8HL
Tel: 020 7283 6090
Fax: 020 7283 6133
Objects: W11,1A,A

LONDON SPORTS FORUM FOR DISABLED PEOPLE
CR1055683
Finance & Admin Officer: Ms Za Mayo-Candan
Chief Executive: Mr Stewart Lucas
Unit 2B07, London South Bank University, Technopark, 90 London Road, London SE1 6LN
Tel: 020 7717 1699
Email: .... info@interactive.uk.net
Objects: F,W6,W3,J,W7,W5,G,H,3

LONDON WEST TRAINING SERVICES
Founded: 1991 CR1002148
Chief Executive: Mr Brendan Tarring
Development Officer: Mr Christian Tileray
207 Waterlow Road, London SE1 8XD
Tel: 020 7928 2439
Fax: 020 7633 9105
Email: .... lwts@lwts.org.uk
Objects: F,G,3

LONDON YOUTH (FORMERLY THE FEDERATION OF LONDON YOUTH CLUBS)
Founded: 1887 CR303324
Chief Executive: Ms Joan Howard
47 - 49 Pitfield Street, London N1 6DA
Tel: 020 7549 8800
Fax: 020 7549 8801
Email: .... hello@londonyouth.org.uk

LOOK: NATIONAL FEDERATION OF FAMILIES WITH VISUALLY IMPAIRED CHILDREN
Founded: 1991 CR1140171
Office Manager: Mrs Steve Mundy
c/o Queen Alexandra College, 49 Court Oak Road, Harborne, Birmingham, West Midlands B17 9TG
Tel: 0121 428 5038; 0121 427 7111
Fax: 0121 427 9800
Email: .... steve@look-uk.org
Objects: F,W6,W3,G,V,2,H,P

LYTTELTON WELL LIMITED
Founded: 1990 CR1001139
General Manager: Mrs Jean Holt
Company Secretary: Mrs P. Hutchison
Church Street, Malvern, Worcestershire WR14 2AY
Tel: 01684 573702
Fax: 01684 572191
Email: .... manager@lytteltonwell.co.uk
Objects: F,W3,R,W4,3,W8

M

MACMILLAN CANCER RELIEF
See Macmillan Cancer Support

MACMILLAN CANCER SUPPORT
CR261017; SC039907, IoM 604
Chief Executive: Mr Peter Cardy
Ms Ruth Coleman
UK Office, 89 Albert Embankment, London SE1 7UQ
Tel: 0800 107 4448
Fax: 020 7840 7841
Email: .... leavealegacy@macmillan.org.uk

MACMILLAN CARING LOCALLY
Founded: 1974 CR268218
Macmillan Unit, Christchurch Hospital (CD), Fairmile Road, Christchurch, Dorset BH23 2JX
Tel: 01202 477628
Fax: 01202 705315
Email: .... enquiries@macmillanlocal.org
Macmillan Caring Locally is a Charity providing specialist end of life care and support to patients, families and carers in South East Dorset and South West Hampshire. We support the Macmillan Unit in Christchurch Dorset, which is a centre of excellence.

MACMILLAN NURSES (SEE MACMILLAN CANCER RELIEF)
See Macmillan Cancer Support

MAIDSTONE & NORTHWEST CROSSROADS
Founded: 1992 CR1090904
General Manager: Mrs Irene Jeffrey
The Lodge, Holborough Road, Snodland, Kent ME6 5PJ
Tel: 01634 249090
Objects: W6,M,W3,W7,W5,W10,N,W4,3,P,W8

MAKRO-AJY
Founded: 1927 CR305963
Head of AJY: Mr Eric Finestone
Balfour House, 741 High Road, London N12 0BQ
Tel: 020 8369 5000
Fax: 020 8369 5001
Objects: F,W3,J,S,G,H

MALCOLM SARGENT CANCER FUND FOR CHILDREN
See CLIC Sargent (Scotland)

MANCHESTER & CHESHIRE DOGS' HOME

Founded: 1893 CR1001346
Crofters House, Moss Brook Road,
Harpurhey, Manchester, Greater Manchester
M9 5PG
Tel: 0844 504 1212
Fax: 0161 277 6949
Email: .... appeals@dogshome.net
Web: .... www.dogshome.net
Objects: W1,G,3

The Home, founded in 1893 to take in and care for lost and stray dogs in order to re-unite them with their owners or to find new and caring homes for them, continues over a hundred years later to care for approximately 7,000 dogs annually. The Home is a charity maintained by voluntary donations to carry out its work in conjunction with local authorities. We receive no Government Funding. Our greatest challenge is to maintain our care of thousands of dogs each year on two sites - Manchester and Cheshire.

See advert on this page

MANCHESTER DEVELOPMENT EDUCATION PROJECT LTD
Founded: 1990 CR1000590
Ms Jane Angel
c/o Manchester Metropolitan University, 799 Wilmslow Road, Manchester, Greater Manchester M20 2RR
Tel: 0161 921 8020
Fax: 0161 921 8010
Email: .... info@dep.org.uk
Objects: F,W3,G,W10,H,3

MANCHESTER EDUCATION BUSINESS SOLUTIONS LTD
Founded: 1990 CR1093728
3rd Floor, Paragon House, 48 Seymour Grove, Old Trafford, Manchester, Greater Manchester M16 0LN
Tel: 0161 772 1000
Fax: 0161 873 7401

THE MANOR PREPARATORY SCHOOL TRUST
Founded: 1990 CR900347
Headmaster: Mr P Heyworth
Chair of Governors: Dr A Malmberg
Bursar: Mr D Ramm
Faringdon Road, Shippon, Abingdon, Oxfordshire OX13 6LN
Tel: ..... 01235 554814 Bursary; 01235 858458 School Office
Fax: 01235 559593
Email: .... bursar@manorprep.org
Objects: W3,G,3

MANOR TRAINING AND RESOURCE CENTRE LTD
Founded: 1990 CR1000516
Business Manager: Ms Kim Gervis
306-308 Prince of Wales Road, Sheffield, South Yorkshire S2 1FF
Tel: 0114 264 2194
Fax: 0114 265 9736
Email: .... kimg@matrec.org.uk
Objects: G,3

MARE AND FOAL SANCTUARY
CR1141831
Contact: Ms Rosemary Kind
Honeysuckle Farm, Buckland Road, Newton Abbot, Devon TQ12 4SA
Tel: 01626 355969
Fax: 01626 355959
Email: .... office@mareandfoal.org
Objects: W1,O

MARFAN ASSOCIATION UK
Founded: 1984 CR802727
Chairman / Support Co-ordinator: Mrs Diane Rust
Rochester House, 5 Aldershot Road, Fleet, Hampshire GU51 3NG
Tel: 01252 810472; 01252 617320 Answerphone
Fax: 01252 810473
Email: .... contactus@marfan-association.org.uk
Objects: F,M,W3,J,G,N,2,U,H,O,P

MARIE STOPES INTERNATIONAL
CR265543
1 Conway Street, Fitzroy Square, London W1T 6LP
Tel: 020 7034 2343
Fax: 020 7034 2371
Email: .... fundraising@mariestopes.org.uk

THE MARINE CONNECTION
CR1062222
Lime House, Regency Close, Uckfield, East Sussex TN22 1DS
Tel: 07931 366352
Fax: 020 7602 5318
Email: .... info@marineconnection.org
Objects: W1,W3,W2,G,2,H,3

MARINE CONSERVATION SOCIETY (MCS)
Founded: 1991 CR1004005; SC037480
Chief Executive: Mr A G Martin
Director of Conservation: Ms Samantha Pollard
11a Chester Street (CC), Edinburgh EH3 7RF
Tel: 0131 226 6360
Fax: 0131 226 2391
Email: .... info@mcsuk.org
Objects: F,W1,J,W2,G,2,H

MARITIME VOLUNTEER SERVICE - MVS (THE MARITIME FOUNDATION)
CR1048454
202 Lambeth Road, London SE1 7JW
Tel: 020 7928 8100
Fax: 020 7407 2537
Object: G

MARKET RESEARCH BENEVOLENT ASSOCIATION
Founded: 1977 CR274190
President: Mr Ian Brace
Secretary / Treasurer: Mrs Danielle Scott
11 Tremayne Walk, Camberley, Surrey GU15 1AH
Tel: 01276 0684 826
Email: .... marketresearchba@yahoo.co.uk
Objects: F,1A,A,V,N,O

MARLEBONE BANGLADESH SOCIETY
Founded: 1991 CR1001900
Co-ordinator: Mr Mesbah Uddin
19 Stamford Street, London NW8 8ER
Tel: 020 7724 7427
Fax: 020 7616 9740
Email: .... info@mbs-uk.org
Objects: F,W3,W5,G,W10,W4,B,3,P,W8

MARTHA TRUST
Founded: 1983 CR1067885
Chief Executive: Mr Graham Simmons
Homemead Lane, Hacklinge, Deal, Kent CT14 0PG
Tel: 01304 615223
Fax: 01304 615462
Email: .... contact@marthatrust.org.uk
Objects: E,W5,3

MARTINDALE (HILDA) EDUCATIONAL TRUST
Founded: 1952
Administrator to the Trust: Miss Sarah Moffat
c/o Registry, Royal Holloway, University of London, Egham, Surrey TW20 0EX
Tel: 01784 276158
Fax: 01784 473662
Email: .... hildamartindaletrust@rhul.ac.uk
Objects: G,1A,A,3,W8

MARY FEILDING GUILD
Founded: 1877 CR205563
Honorary Treasurer: Mr H Wiener
Chairman: Mrs Elizabeth Wright
103-107 North Hill, London N6 4DP
Tel: 020 8340 3915
Fax: 020 8341 0295
Objects: D,W4,3,C

THE MARY HARE FOUNDATION
CR1002680
Development Director: Ms Jane McMillan
Arlington Manor, Snelsmore Common, Newbury, West Berkshire RG14 3BQ
Tel: 01635 244204
Email: .... foundation@maryhare.org.uk
Objects: W7,G,3

MASONIC SAMARITAN FUND
Founded: 1990 CR1130424
Chief Executive & Secretary: Mr R Douglas
60 Great Queen Street, London WC2 5BL
Tel: 020 7404 1550
Fax: 020 7404 1544
Email: .... info@msfund.org.uk
Objects: 1A,A,N,2

MAST APPEAL
CR1000695
Chairman of Trustees: Mr David Evans
M A S T Appeal Office, Macclesfield District General Hospital, Prestbury Road, Macclesfield, Cheshire SK10 3BL
Tel: 01625 661988
Fax: 01625 661062
Objects: N,3

Pioneering research for lifelong health

MRC | Medical Research Foundation

Established in 1913, the Medical Research Council (MRC) is a world leader in biomedical science and the UK's major public funder of medical research. The Medical Research Foundation is the MRC's registered charity which funds research that compliments and extends that supported by the MRC.

The work of the MRC

The mission of the MRC and its charity is to improve human health, which means that everyone benefits from our work. We provide the funding needed to enable scientists, doctors and nurses to investigate many of the 21st century's most pressing health problems. They work in hospitals, GP practices, research centres and universities throughout the UK, on research that may involve patients or be laboratory-based.

Training tomorrow's research leaders

To date, 29 MRC-funded scientists have won Nobel Prizes for their achievements. To ensure that this standard of excellence continues, we place great importance on training and developing the next generation of researchers. Our aim is to give promising young scientists, doctors and nurses the skills and experience needed to become the research leaders of tomorrow.

Recent MRC discoveries

Recent achievements by MRC scientists include:

- Genetic discoveries that could lead to: new treatments for those at risk from coronary thrombosis; improved prediction of individuals who may be vulnerable to cardiac arrest; targeted new treatments for those genetically predisposed to asthma.
- Discovery of how the body produces toxic chemicals after stroke or brain injury that cause further, more serious brain damage; also ways of blocking the effects of these harmful chemicals.

Recent MRF grants

We recently awarded grants for new research including:

- £2 million to support liver disease research
- £2 million to train the next generation doctors to undertake research on mental health

How you can help

The MRC and its charity funds the best of UK medical research, so you can be sure that if you donate to the MRF your legacy will be invested in pioneering research that will improve people's health and quality of life. Although the MRC receives significant funding from central government, a private donation to its charity enables us to help more UK researchers to push back the frontiers of medical knowledge.

Please donate now

Would you like to help our researchers find ways of preventing, treating and curing major diseases? You can do so by supporting the Medical Research Foundation through a legacy in your will or through a one-off donation.

To find out more

Please contact the Medical Research Foundation, c/o Medical Research Council, 14th Floor, One Kemble Street, London, WC2B 4AN Tel: 020 7395 2270 Email: MedicalResearchFoundation@headoffice.mrc.ac.uk

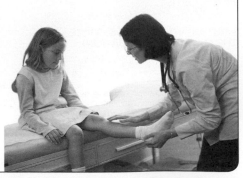

THE MATHILDA & TERENCE KENNEDY INSTITUTE OF RHEUMATOLOGY TRUST

Founded: 1966 CR260059
General Secretary: Mr Colin Boden
Director: Professor R N Maini

1 Aspenlea Road, Hammersmith, London W6 8LH
Tel: 020 8383 4444
Fax: 020 8383 4499
Email: .... c.boden@kirtrust.org
Object: 3

MATILWALA FAMILY CHARITABLE TRUST, THE

Founded: 1992 CR1012756
Managing Trustee: Mr A V Bux

9 Brookview, Fulwood, Preston, Lancashire
PR2 8FG
Tel: 01772 706501

MATTHEW TRUST - HELPING THE MENTALLY ILL IN THE COMMUNITY AND VICTIMS OF AGGRESSION

Founded: 1977 CR294966
Director: Mrs Annabel Thompson
PO Box 604, London SW6 3AG
Tel: 020 7736 5976
Fax: 020 7731 6961
Email: .... matthewtrust@ukonline.co.uk
Objects: F,M,G,1A,A,V,N,B,O,3,P

THE MEATH EPILEPSY TRUST

CR200359
Westbrook Road, Godalming, Surrey GU7 2QH
Tel: 01483 415095
Fax: 01483 414101
Email: .... info@meath.org.uk
Objects: E,N,O,3

MEDECINS SANS FRONTIERES MSF (DOCTORS WITHOUT BORDERS)

Founded: 1993 CR1026588
Chief Executive: Ms Anne-Marie Huby

Omega House, 67-74 Saffron Hill, London
EC1N 8QX
Tel: 020 7404 6600
Fax: 020 7404 4466
Email: .... office-ldn@london.msf.org
Object: U

MEDICAL COUNCIL ON ALCOHOL, THE

Founded: 1967 CR265242
Chairman: Professor Colin Drummond
Office Manager, Exec, Marketing & Acc Assistant:
Ms Sapphire Ellison
Medical Director: Dr Dominique Florin

5 St Andrew's Place, London NW1 4LB
Tel: 020 7487 4445
Fax: 020 7935 4479
Email: .... info@m-c-a.org.uk
Objects: F,W9,W3,J,W7,W5,G,W10,W15,W16,N, 2,W4,H,Z,W8,W

The MCA is an independent charity dedicated to the prevention and management by healthcare professionals of alcohol related harm. Its mission is to reduce alcohol related harm by improving the understanding and management of alcohol related health problems. To ensure that all doctors, medical students and other professions allied to medicine are aware of the risks to their patients and also aware of the risks related to their own alcohol consumption.

MEDICAL RESEARCH FOUNDATION

CR1138223
c/o Medical Research Council, 14th Floor, One
Kemble Street, London WC2B 4AN
Tel: 01793 416200
Fax: 020 7395 2421
Email: MedicalResearchFoundation@headoffice.
mrc.ac.uk
Object: G

The Medical Research Council (MRC) is the UK's major public funder of medical research. Our support enables scientists, doctors and nurses to investigate many of today's most pressing health problems, working in hospitals, GP practices, research centres and universities throughout the UK. To date, 27 MRC-funded scientists have won Nobel Prizes for their achievements in biomedical research. To ensure that this standard of excellence continues, we place great importance on training and developing the next generation of researchers. You can support the MRC through a legacy in your will, through a regular Gift Aid direct debit, or through a one-off donation to the MRC charity.

See advert on previous page

MENCAP IN KIRKLEES

Founded: 1990 CR702494
The Company Secretary

The Stables, Buckden Mount, 8 Thornhill Road,
Huddersfield, West Yorkshire HD3 3AU
Tel: 01484 340811
Fax: 01484 340822
Email: .... info@mencapinkirklees.org.uk
Objects: F,W3,E,W5,W4,3,P

MENCAP (ROYAL MENCAP SOCIETY)

CR222377
Chairman: Mr Brian Baldock CBE
Legacy Marketing Co-ordinator: Mrs Clair Lucy
Chief Executive: Dame Jo Williams CBE
MENCAP National Centre, 123 Golden Lane,
London EC1Y 0RT
Tel: 020 7454 0454
Fax: 020 7696 6014
Email: .... willsandtrusts@mencap.org.uk

MENIERE'S SOCIETY - HELPING PEOPLE WITH VERTIGO, TINNITUS AND DEAFNESS

Founded: 1984 CR297246
Director: Miss Lois Wolffe

The Rookery, Surrey Hills Business Park, Wotton,
Dorking, Surrey RH5 6QT
Tel: 0845 120 2975
Fax: 01306 876 057
Email: .... info@menieres.org.uk
Objects: F,J,2,H

MENTAL AID PROJECTS

See The Fircroft Trust (previously known as
Mental Aid Projects)

MENTAL HEALTH FOUNDATION

Founded: 1949 CR801130; SC039714
Finance Director: Mr Tony Clarkson
Director: Mr Andrew McCulloch

Colechurch House, 1 London Bridge Walk,
London SE1 2SX
Tel: 020 7803 1121
Fax: 020 7803 1111
Email: .... mhf@mhf.org.uk
Objects: F,W3,J,E,W5,G,A,W4,H,O,C,P,K

MERCHANT NAVY WELFARE BOARD
  CR212799
  8 Cumberland Place, Southampton, Hampshire
  SO15 2BH
  Tel: 023 8033 7799
  Email: . . . . enquiries@mnwb.org.uk

MERCHANT SEAMEN'S WAR MEMORIAL SOCIETY
  CR207500
  Sachel Court, Springbok Farm Estate, Alfold,
  Cranleigh, Surrey GU6 8EX
  Tel: 01403 752555
  Fax: 01403 753404
  Email: . . . . t.goacher@mswmsociety.org.uk

MERCURY PHOENIX TRUST
  Founded: 1992 CR1013768
  Administrator: Mr P Chant
  The Mill, Mill Lane, Cookham, Windsor &
  Maidenhead SL6 9QT
  Tel: 01628 527874

MERCY SHIPS
  CR1053055; SC039743
  Mercy Ships UK, The Lighthouse, 12 Meadway
  Court, Stevenage, Hertfordshire SG1 2EF
  Tel: 01438 727800
  Fax: 01438 721900
  Email: . . . . info@mercyships.org.uk

MERSEY KIDNEY RESEARCH
  Founded: 1964 CR250895
  Room 3,312A, School of Clinical Sciences, UCD
  Building, Royal Liverpool University Hospital,
  Liverpool, Merseyside L69 3GA

Tel: 0151 706 3598
Fax: 0151 706 5802
Email: . . . . annmkr@liv.ac.uk

MERSEYSIDE BROOK ADVISORY CENTRE
  Founded: 1990 CR703015
  Centre Manager: Helen Finney
  81 London Road, Liverpool, Merseyside L3 8JA
  Tel: 0151 207 4000
  Objects: F,W3,3,W8

MERSEYSIDE CHINESE COMMUNITY DEVELOPMENT ASSOCIATION
  Founded: 1989 CR1001288
  Trustee: Mr Andrew Green
  The Pagoda of Hundred Harmony, Chinese
  Community Centre, Henry Street, Liverpool,
  Merseyside L1 5BU
  Tel: 0151 233 8833
  Fax: 0151 233 8839
  Objects: F,W3,G,W10,W4,3

MERTON MUSIC FOUNDATION
  Founded: 1991 CR1004122
  Director of Merton Music Foundation
  MMF Office Chaucer Centre, Canterbury Road,
  Morden, Surrey SM4 6PX
  Tel: 020 8640 5446
  Fax: 020 8646 6990
  Email: . . . . admin@mmf.org.uk
  Objects: W3,G,3

MERU

CR269804
Unit 2, Eclipse Estate, 30 West Hill, Epsom,
Surrey KT19 8JD
Tel: 01372 725203
Fax: 01372 743159
Email: .... info@meru.org.uk

THE METHODIST CHURCH

The **Methodist** Church

CR1132208
Fundraising Officer: Mr Mencey Morera
Methodist Church House, 25 Marylebone
Road, London NW1 5JR
Tel: 020 7486 5502
Fax: 020 7467 5281
Email: . helpdesk@methodistchurch.org.uk
Web: .... http://www.methodist.org.uk/
information/worldchurch1.htm
Objects: W3,G,W10,1A,A,1B,N,2,R,W4,U,B,Y,
3,P,W8,L

Methodist Church World Mission Fund works
with and through churches overseas in a wide
variety of evangelistic and social work
throughout the world. Gives co-operative aid
through personnel and money for education,
medical, urban, agricultural and development
needs.
Please see www.methodist.org.uk World Church
pages for more details.
Methodist Church World Mission Fund supports
a wide range of evangelistic and social action
activities in Britain, including initiatives in
deprived areas, chaplaincy work, inter-faith
dialogue and projects in urban and rural areas.
Please see www.methodist.org.uk for more
details.

See advert on previous page

METHODIST LONDON MISSION FUND

Founded: 1861
Secretary: Reverend Dr Stuart Jordan
1 Central Buildings, Westminster, London
SW1H 9NH
Tel: 020 7222 8010
Fax: 020 7799 1452
Email: .... info@methodistlondon.org.uk
Objects: F,J,A,1B,R

METHODIST MINISTERS' HOUSING SOCIETY

Methodist Ministers Housing Society

Founded: 1948
Chief Executive: Peter Shearer EMBA FCIH MIoD
Chair: Revd Pat Billsborrow
Methodist Church House, 25 Marylebone Road,
London NW1 5JR
Tel: 020 7467 5272
Fax: 020 7467 5231
Email: .... admin@mmhs.org.uk

Object: D
Provides accommodation and associated services for
retired Methodist ministers, deacons and their
widow(er)s, of limited means.

METHODIST RELIEF AND DEVELOPMENT FUND

CR291691
Manager: Ms Kirsty Smith
Finance Accounts Payable, 25 Marylebone Road,
London NW1 5JR
Tel: 020 7467 5132
Fax: 020 7467 5233
Email: .... mrdf@methodistchurch.org.uk
Objects: W3,W2,W5,A,1B,W4,U,H,W8

METROPOLITAN HOSPITAL-SUNDAY FUND

See London Catalyst

METROPOLITAN POLICE BENEVOLENT FUND

Founded: 2008 CR1125409
Charities, PPAF & DMA Support Officer: Mr
William Tarrant
Treasurer: Mr Stephen Skirten
Exchequer Services (Charities) (CD 2014), 10th
Floor, Empress State Building, Empress
Approach, Lillie Road, London SW6 1TR
Tel: 020 7161 1667
Fax: 020 7161 1802
Email: .... william.tarrant@met.police.uk
Summary of Objects

The charity is predominantly funded via contributions
from police officers, however donations from members
of the public are greatly appreciated. The objects of the
charity are to:

• Provide financial support by way of a grant or a loan
to serving, former, ex and retired police officers and
their Widows, Widowers and dependants who are sick
or injured suffering financial hardship or distress.
• Provide grants to other charities who exist for the
relief of serving, former, ex and retired police officers
and their Widows, Widowers and dependants.
• Assist serving, former, ex and retired police officers
and their Widows, Widowers and dependants in such
ways as the Trustees think fit, provided that these shall
be exclusively charitable.
• Assist close family of deceased police officers who
died in the line of duty to attend police memorial
services.

MIDDLESEX ASSOCIATION FOR THE BLIND

CR207007
Head Office: The Sight Centre, Unit 3-4, Freetrade
House, Lowtner Road, Stanmore, Middlesex
HA7 1EP
Tel: 020 8423 5141
Fax: 020 8099 7053
Email: .... info@aftb.org.uk

MIDLANDS AIR AMBULANCE CHARITY (FORMERLY COUNTY AIR AMBULANCE)

Founded: 1991 CR1143118
Chief Executive: Hanna Sebright
Air Operations Manager: Becky Tinsley
Hawthorn House (CD), Dudley Road, Stourbridge,
West Midlands DY9 8BQ

Tel: 0800 840 2040
Fax: 01384 486621
Email: .... info@midlandsairambulance.com
Web: .... www.midlandsairambulance.com
Objects: M,N,3

MIGRAINE ACTION ASSOCIATION
Founded: 1958 CR207783
Director: Ms Lee Tomkins
27 East Street, Leicester, Leicestershire LE1 6NB
Email: .... info@migraine.org.uk
Objects: F,W3,J,W5,1A,A,1B,2,H,3,W8

MILITARY MINISTRIES INTERNATIONAL
CR284203
Havelock House, Barrack Road, Aldershot,
Hampshire GU11 3NP
Tel: 01252 311222
Fax: 01252 350722
Email: .... headoffice@m-m-i.org.uk
Objects: W9,R

MILL GROVE CHRISTIAN CHARITABLE TRUST
Founded: 1899 CR1078661
Director: Dr Keith White
Crescent Road, South Woodford, London E18 1JB
Tel: 020 8504 2702
Fax: 020 8506 0442
Email: .... millgrove@btinternet.com
Objects: W3,E,3

MILL HOUSE ANIMAL SANCTUARY - SAVE OUR OLD TIRED HORSES AND OTHER ANIMALS SANCTUARY
CR512905
Mayfields Road (CD), Fullwood, Sheffield, South Yorkshire S10 4PR
Tel: 01226 762732; 0114 230 2907
Fax: 01226 762732
Email: millhouseanimalsanctuary@btinternet.com

MIND
Founded: 1946 CR219830
Chief Executive: Mr Paul Farmer
Director of Finance & Resources: Ms Katherine Gardiner
Granta House, 15-19 Broadway, Stratford, London E15 4BQ
Tel: .. 020 8519 2122; 0845 766 0163 MIND Info Line
Fax: 020 8522 1725
Email: .... contact@mind.org.uk
Objects: F,G,W10,1A,A,1B,2,W4,H,W8

MISSION CARE
Founded: 1912 CR284967
General Manager: Ms Margaret Cornwell
Finance Manager: Mr Simon Couldry
Graham House, 2 Pembroke Road, Bromley, Kent BR1 2RU
Tel: 020 8289 7925
Fax: 020 8402 8629
Email: .... admin@missioncare.org.uk
Objects: M,G,D,C,P

MISSIONS TO SEAMAN (NORTHERN IRELAND)
See The Mission to Seafarers (Northern Ireland)

MOBILITY TRUST

MOBILITY TRUST
The Road to Freedom

Founded: 1972 CR1070975
Chief Executive: Mrs Anne Munn
17b Reading Road, Pangbourne, West Berkshire RG8 7LR
Tel: 0118 984 2588
Fax: 0118 984 2544
Objects: M,W5,3
We provide powered wheelchairs and scooters to severely disabled people who cannot obtain them through statutory sources or purchase such equipment themselves. We consider applications from all people living within the UK, regardless of age or cause of disability. We aim to help disabled people who have nowhere else to turn, whose disability falls outside the remit of major disability charities. Mobility Trust does not receive any government grants and relies on donations from trusts, corporate companies and individuals. We do not give grants to individuals or other organisations.

MONEY ADVICE TRUST
Founded: 1991 CR1099506
Director: Mr Alan Jarvis
Assistant Director: Mr Ian Whitcombe
21 Garlick Hill, London EC4V 2AU
Tel: 020 7653 9721
Fax: 020 7489 7704
Email: .... info@moneyadvicetrust.org
Objects: F,1B

MONOUX (SIR GEORGE) EXHIBITION FOUNDATION
CR310903
Life Long Learning Services, PO Box 416, Buildings 7 & 8, Uplands Business Park, Blackhorse Lane, Walthamstow, London E17 5QT
Tel: 020 8496 3509
Fax: 020 8496 3599
Objects: 1A,A

MOORCROFT RACEHORSE WELFARE CENTRE
CR1076278
Huntingrove Stud, Slinfold, Horsham, West Sussex RH13 0RB
Tel: 07929 666408
Fax: 01403 791916
Email: .... info@mrwc.org.uk
Objects: W1,O

MOORFIELDS EYE HOSPITAL - SPECIAL TRUSTEES
CR228064
City Road, London EC1V 2PD
Tel: 020 7566 2643
Fax: 020 7566 2459

MORDEN COLLEGE
Founded: 1695 CR215551
Major General David Rutherford-Jones CB
19 St Germans Place, Blackheath, London
SE3 0PW
Tel: 020 8463 8330
Fax: 020 8293 4887
Email: .... info@mordencollege.org
Web: .... www.mordencollege.org
Objects: 1A,A,1B,W4,C
An independent charity, governed by a Board of
Trustees. Our purpose is the relief of need in
older people by offering a home for either
independent or supported living, or 24/7 nursing
and care; accommodation available in
Blackheath and Beckenham. We also grant
direct financial support to non residents. We
support women and men, both single and those
in partnerships. Applicants must have in their
working lives held a position of responsibility in
a profession, commerce, trade or vocation; they
must not be in paid employment and must be at
or over the UK state pension age; and in need, by
reason of financial hardship, disability, infirmity
or other disadvantage.

MORRIS CERULLO WORLD EVANGELISM
Founded: 1990 CR1001361
European Director: Mr Julian Richards
PO Box 277, Hemel Hempstead, Hertfordshire
HP2 7DH
Tel: 01442 232432
Objects: 2,R

MORTHYNG LIMITED
Founded: 1990 CR1000381
Chairman: Mr Peter Broxham
Chief Executive: Mr Christopher MacCormac
14-16 Ship Hill, Rotherham, South Yorkshire
S60 2HG
Tel: 01709 372900
Fax: 01709 367500
Email: .... morthyng@btinternet.com
Objects: W3,W2,W5,G,W10,W11,W4,3,W8,K

MOTIONHOUSE
Founded: 1990 CR328693
Secretary to the Trustees: Mr Charles Vacy-Ash
Spencer Yard, Leamington Spa, Warwickshire
CV31 3SY
Tel: 01926 887052
Fax: 01926 316734
Objects: W3,S,G,W10,W4,W8

MR FEGAN'S HOMES
See Fegans Child & Family Care

MRS SMITH AND MOUNT TRUST, THE
Founded: 1992 CR1009718
Trust Administrator: Mrs Jayne Day
White Horse Court, 25C North Street, Bishop's
Stortford, Hertfordshire CM23 2LD
Tel: 01279 506421
Email: .... charities@pwwsolicitors.co.uk
Objects: F,W3,E,W5,G,W10,A,1B,D,W4,O,C,K

MSA FOR MIDLAND PEOPLE WITH
CEREBRAL PALSY
See Cerebral Palsy Midlands

MSF (UK)
See Medecins Sans Frontieres MSF (Doctors
Without Borders)

MUCOPOLYSACCHARIDE DISEASES
SOCIETY
See Society for Mucopolysaccharide Diseases

MULBERRY TRUST, THE
Founded: 1991 CR1005893
Trust Administrator: Mr R J Frost
PO Box 147, Aylesbury, Buckinghamshire
HP18 0WD
Tel: 01844 290154
Fax: 01844 299496

MULTIPLE SCLEROSIS SOCIETY
CR1139257; SC041990
Chief Executive: Mr Simon Gillespie
Marketing Manager: Ms Jennie Sullivan
MS National Centre, 372 Edgware Road, London
NW2 6ND
Tel: 020 8438 0700
Fax: 020 8438 0877
Email: .... info@mssociety.org.uk
Objects: F,J,E,G,A,2,H,P

MUSEUM OF EAST ASIAN ART, THE
Founded: 1990 CR328725
The Honorary Keeper: Mr B McElney
Chairman: Mr Alan White
12 Bennett Street, Bath, Bath & North East
Somerset BA1 2QL
Tel: 01225 464640
Fax: 01225 461718
Email: museum@east-asian-art.freeserve.co.uk
Objects: W9,W6,W3,W2,S,W7,W5,G,W10,W11,
W12,W4,H,3,W8

MUSIC LIBRARIES TRUST, THE
Founded: 1982 CR284334
Chairman: Dr David Wyn Jones
Jerwood Library of the Performing Arts, Trinity
Laban, King Charles Court, Old Royal Naval
College, King William Walk, Greenwich, London
SE10 9JF
Tel: 020 8305 4425
Email: .... e.speller@trinitylaban.ac.uk
Objects: J,S,G,1A,A,1B,H

MUSICIANS BENEVOLENT FUND
Founded: 1921 CR228089
Chief Executive: Ms Rosanna Preston
7-11 Britannia Street, London WC1X 9JS
Tel: 020 7239 9100
Email: .... info@helpmusicians.org.uk

MYELIN PROJECT
Founded: 1990 CR1000614
Honorary Secretary: Mrs Diana McGovern
32 The Croft, Hadfield, Glossop, Derbyshire
SK13 1HN
Tel: 01457 865639
Fax: 01457 865629
Email: .... info@myelinproject.co.uk

N

N.N.A.B.
See Norfolk and Norwich Association for the Blind

NABS
CR1070556
PR & Communications Manager: Ms Charlotte Dyball
6th Floor, 388 Oxford Street, London W1C 1JT
Tel: 020 7290 7070
Email: .... nabs@nabs.org.uk
Objects: F,W11,A

NACRO - THE CRIME REDUCTION CHARITY
Founded: 1966 CR226171
Chief Executive: Mr Paul Cavadino
Park Place, 10-12 Lawn Lane, London SW8 1UD
Tel: 020 7840 7200
Fax: 020 7840 7240
Email: .... communications@nacro.org.uk
Objects: F,W3,J,G,1A,A,2,H,3,C,K

NAGRYS LTD
Founded: 1990 CR803104
Trustee: Mrs M Monderer
45 Cheyne Walk, London NW4 3QH
Object: G

NARCOLEPSY ASSOCIATION (UK)
Founded: 1981 CR326361
Honorary Secretary: Mr Michael Armstrong
Operations Manager: Mrs Jannine Vallett
Vice Chairman: Mrs G Wood
PO Box 13842, Penicuik, Midlothian EH26 8WX
Tel: 0845 450 0394
Email: .... info@narcolepsy.org.uk
Objects: F,W3,W5,2,H,3,P

NATIONAL ALLIANCE OF WOMEN'S ORGANISATIONS (NAWO)
Founded: 1989 CR803701
Chair: Ms Roz Fraser
Treasurer: Ms Shirley Nelson
1-3 Berry Street, London EC1V 0AA
Tel: 020 7490 4100
Objects: F,J,G,H

NATIONAL AND LOCAL GOVERNMENT OFFICERS ASSOCIATION (NALGO)
See UNISON Welfare

NATIONAL ANIMAL WELFARE TRUST

National Animal Welfare Trust

Charity No 1090499

Founded: 1971 CR1090499
Chief Executive: Ms Clare Williams
Tylers Way, Watford By-Pass, Watford, Hertfordshire WD25 8WT
Tel: 020 8950 0177
Fax: 020 8420 4454
Email: .... watford@nawt.org.uk
The National Animal Welfare Trust was set up to find homes for unwanted dogs, cats and other domestic animals. Once in the Trust's care no healthy animal is put to sleep, however long its stay. The Trust has five Rescue Centres: the Watford centre based at the above address, the Somerset centre at Heaven's Gate Farm near Langport, the Berkshire Centre at Trindledown Farm, near Great Shefford, the Cornish Centre at

Wheal Alfred Kennels, Hayle and the Essex Centre at Clacton-on-Sea.

See advert on next page

NATIONAL ANKYLOSING SPONDYLITIS SOCIETY (NASS)
Founded: 1976 CR272258; SC041347
Director: Ms Jane Skerrett
Unit 0.2, One Victoria Villas, Richmond, Surrey TW9 2GW
Tel: 020 8948 9117
Fax: 020 8940 7736
Email: .... nass@nass.co.uk
Objects: F,J,G,2,H,O

NATIONAL ART COLLECTIONS FUND
See Art Fund, The

NATIONAL ASSOCIATION FOR FAMILY BASED RESPITE CARE, THE
See Shared Care Network

NATIONAL ASSOCIATION FOR VOLUNTARY AND COMMUNITY ACTION (NAVCA)
Founded: 1991 CR1001635
Information Officer: Mr Peter Horner
The Tower, 2 Furnival Square, Sheffield, South Yorkshire S1 4QL
Tel: .. 0114 278 6636; 0114 278 7025 Textphone
Fax: 0114 278 7004
Email: .... navca@navca.org.uk
Objects: F,J,G,2,H

NATIONAL ASSOCIATION OF BOYS' CLUBS
See Clubs for Young People (CYP)

NATIONAL ASSOCIATION OF CLUBS FOR YOUNG PEOPLE
See Clubs for Young People (CYP)

NATIONAL ASSOCIATION OF HOSPITAL AND COMMUNITY FRIENDS
See Attend

NATIONAL ASSOCIATION OF SWIMMING CLUBS FOR THE HANDICAPPED
Founded: 1966 CR247772
The Willows, Mayles Lane, Wickham, Hampshire PO17 5ND
Tel: 01329 833689
Objects: F,J,G,H,O,3,P

NATIONAL ASSOCIATION OF YOUTH CLUBS
See UK Youth

THE NATIONAL BENEVOLENT CHARITY
Founded: 1812 CR212450
Mr Paul Rossi
Peter Hervé House, Eccles Court, Tetbury, Gloucestershire GL8 8EH
Tel: 01666 505500
Fax: 01666 503111
Email: .... ce@nbi.org.uk

THE NATIONAL BRAIN APPEAL
Founded: 1984 CR290173
Unit 5, Nunhold Farm Business Centre, Dark Lane, Hatton, Warwick, Warwickshire CV35 8XB

Tel: 01926 840011
Fax: 01926 843958
Email. . . . . theresa.dauncey@ucih.nhs.uk
Objects: F,N,O

NATIONAL CARAVAN COUNCIL LIMITED BENEVOLENT FUND
CR271625
Membership Services Co-Ordinator: Mrs Lisa Howson
Catherine House, Victoria Road, Aldershot, Hampshire GU11 1SS
Tel: 01252 318251
Fax: 01252 322596
Email: . . . . info@nationalcaravan.co.uk
Objects: W6,W7,W5,W11,1A,A,W4,W8

NATIONAL CHILD MINDING ASSOCIATION
CR295981
Royal Court, 81 Tweedy Road, Bromley, Kent BR1 1TG
Tel: 029 2034 2336
Fax: 0845 880 0043
Email: . . . . ncma.wales@ncma.org.uk
Objects: F,W3,J,G,2,W4,H

NATIONAL CHILDREN'S ORCHESTRA OF GREAT BRITAIN
Founded: 1978 CR803026
Director of Operations: Mrs Jaqueline K Kingsley
57 Buckingham Road, Weston-super-Mare, North Somerset BS24 9BG

Tel: 01934 418855
Fax: 01934 418846
Email: . . . . g.jones@nco.org.uk
Objects: W3,S,3

NATIONAL COMMUNITIES RESOURCE CENTRE LTD
Founded: 1991 CR1005555
Chief Executive: Ms Sally Wyatt
Trafford Hall, Ince Lane, Wimbolds Trafford, Cheshire CH2 4JP
Tel: 01244 300246
Fax: 01244 300818
Objects: W3,W2,G,W10,D,H

NATIONAL COUNCIL FOR VOLUNTARY ORGANISATIONS (NCVO)
CR225922
Chief Executive: Sir Stuart Etherington
Regent's Wharf, 8 All Saints Street, London N1 9RL
Tel: . . 020 7713 6161; 0800 279 8798 Help Desk
Fax: 020 7713 6300; 020 7833 8637
Email: . . . . ncro@ncro-rol.org.uk
Objects: F,J,G,2,H,K

NATIONAL COUNCIL FOR VOLUNTARY YOUTH SERVICES
Founded: 1936 CR1093386
Chief Executive: Ms Susanne Rauprich
Second Floor, Solecast House, 13-27 Brunswick Place, London N1 6DX
Tel: 020 7253 1010
Email: . . . . mail@ncvys.org.uk
Objects: W3,J,G,2,H,P

NATIONAL CYRENIANS
See Homes for Homeless People

THE NATIONAL DEAF CHILDREN'S SOCIETY
Founded: 1944 CR1016532; SC040779
Head of Development: Mr Ian Govendir
15 Dufferin Street, London EC1Y 8UR
Tel: .. 020 7014 1102; 0808 800 8880 Freephone helpline (voice/text)
Fax: 020 7251 5020
Email: . . . . fundraising@ndcs.org.uk
Objects: F,M,W3,J,W7,G,W10,A,2,B,H,3,P

NATIONAL ECZEMA SOCIETY
Founded: 1976 CR1009671
Chief Executive: Mrs Margaret Cox
Team Assistant: Miss Grace Marshall
Manager - Information and Education: Ms Sue Ward
Hill House, Highgate Hill, London N19 5NA
Tel: 020 7281 3553
Fax: 020 7281 6395
Email: . . . . mcox@eczema.org
Objects: F,W3,G,W10,2,W4,H,W8

NATIONAL ENDOMETRIOSIS SOCIETY
See Endometriosis UK

NATIONAL EQUINE (AND SMALLER ANIMALS) DEFENCE LEAGUE
CR280700
The Animals' Refuge, Oak Tree Farm, Wetheral Shields, Carlisle, Cumbria CA4 8JA

Tel: 01228 560082
Fax: 01228 560985
Email: . . . . admin@animalrefuge.co.uk

NATIONAL EXAMINATION BOARD IN OCCUPATIONAL SAFETY AND HEALTH, THE (NEBOSH)
Founded: 1979 CR1010444
Chief Executive: Dr Stephen Vickers
Meridian Business Park, 3 Dominus Way,
Leicester, Leicestershire LE19 1QW
Tel: 0116 263 4700
Fax: 0116 282 4000
Email: . . . . info@nebosh.org.uk
Objects: G,3

NATIONAL EYE RESEARCH CENTRE
Founded: 1986 CR294087
Appeal Secretary: Colonel S C C Gaussen
Bristol Eye Hospital, Lower Maudlin Street, Bristol BS1 2LX
Tel: 0117 929 0024
Email: . . . . nerc-charity@bris.ac.uk

NATIONAL FEDERATION OF SPIRITUAL HEALERS (THE NFSH CHARITABLE TRUST LTD)
See NFSH Charitable Trust LTD (The Healing Trust)

NATIONAL FEDERATION OF WOMENS INSTITUTES
Founded: 1990 CR803793
General Secretary: Ms Jana Osborne
Finance Director: Mr David Wood
104 New Kings Road, London SW6 4LY
Tel: 020 7371 9300
Fax: 020 7736 3652
Email: .... hq@nfwi.org.uk
Objects: S,G,2,H,3,P,W8

NATIONAL FOUNDATION FOR EDUCATIONAL RESEARCH IN ENGLAND AND WALES - (NFER)
CR313392
The Mere, Upton Park, Slough SL1 2DQ
Tel: 01753 574123
Fax: 01753 691632
Email: .... enquiries@nfer.ac.uk
Objects: G,2

THE NATIONAL GARDENS SCHEME (NGS)
Founded: 1927 CR1112664
Hatchlands Park, East Clandon, Guildford, Surrey GU4 7RT
Tel: 01483 211535
Fax: 01483 211537
Email: .... ngs@ngs.org.uk
Web: .... www.ngs.org.uk
Each year over 3800 people, assisted by our volunteers, open their gardens to the public on behalf of the NGS. This raises money for nursing, caring and gardening charities including Macmillan Cancer Support, Marie Curie Cancer Care, Help the Hospices and the Carers Trust. In the last 10 years the National Gardens Scheme has made unrestricted donations of £22 million to the charities we support.
See advert on previous page

NATIONAL HEALTH SERVICE PENSIONERS' TRUST
Founded: 1991 CR1002061
Director: Mr Frank Jackson OBE
PO Box 456, Esher, Surrey KT10 1DP
Tel: 01372 805760
Fax: 01372 805760
Email: .... frankjackson1945@yahoo.com
Objects: W11,1A,A,1B,2

NATIONAL HEART FORUM
Founded: 1990 CR803286
Policy Communications Officer: Ms Jane Landon
Chief Executive: Mr Paul Lincoln
Tavistock House South, Tavistock Square, London WC1H 9LG
Tel: 020 7383 7638
Fax: 020 7387 2799
Email: .... nhf-post@heartforum.org.uk
Objects: J,G,2,H

NATIONAL INSTITUTE OF ADULT CONTINUING EDUCATION
Founded: 1991 CR1002775
Information Services
Director: Mr Alan Tuckett
21 De Montfort Street, Leicester, Leicestershire LE1 7GE
Tel: 0116 204 4200
Fax: 0116 285 4514
Email: .... enquiries@niace.org.uk
Objects: F,J,G,2,H

NATIONAL MEMORIAL ARBORETUM

Founded: 1994 CR1043992
Director: Mrs Sarah Montgomery
Croxall Road, Alrewas, Staffordshire DE13 7AR
Tel: 01283 792 333
Email: .... legacynma@thenma.org.uk
Objects: W9,W2,S,W12,3
The National Memorial Arboretum is the UK's year-round centre of Remembrance; a spiritually uplifting place which honours the fallen, recognises service and sacrifice, and fosters pride in our country. Sited in the heart of the Nation, with 50,000 maturing trees and over 280 significant memorials, it is a beautiful and lasting tribute to those who serve their country or who have died in conflict.

We want to ensure that the Arboretum remains a special place where future generations come to enjoy, learn and remember. Leave a gift in your will and help the Arboretum to flourish.

NATIONAL OSTEOPOROSIS SOCIETY
CR1102712; SC039755
Communications Director: Miss Juliette Brown
Chairman: Mrs Kate Tompkins
Camerton, Bath, Bath & North East Somerset BA2 0PJ
Tel: 01761 471771
Fax: 01761 471104
Email: .... info@nos.org.uk
Objects: F,W3,W5,G,1B,2,W4,H,3,W8

The National Osteoporosis Society is the only UK wide charity dedicated to improving the prevention, diagnosis and treatment of osteoporosis. We run national education campaigns to increase awareness of this disease and its prevention. We provide advice and information through a range of publications, run a specialist nurse-led national helpline and outreach vital support to through our network of local groups. We fund pioneering research into the causes, treatment and prevention of osteoporosis and we actively lobby the government as well as educate key health professionals to ensure people affected by osteoporosis can obtain the treatment and support they need.

NATIONAL POLICE FUND
CR207608
3 Mount Mews, High Street, Hampton, Middlesex TW12 2SH
Tel: 020 8941 7661
Fax: 020 8979 4323
Email: .... office@nationalpolicefund.org.uk
Objects: W3,G,W11,A,1B,W4

NATIONAL SOCIETY FOR MENTALLY HANDICAPPED PEOPLE IN RESIDENT
See RESCARE - National Society for Children and Adults with Learning Disabilities and their Families

NATIONAL SOCIETY FOR THE PREVENTION OF CRUELTY TO CHILDREN (NSPCC)

NSPCC ●™

Cruelty to children must stop. FULL STOP.

Founded: 1884 CR216401; SC037717
Ms Iona Bergius
Weston House, 42 Curtain Road, London
EC2A 3NH
Tel: 020 7825 2939
Email: .... legacyinfo@nspcc.org.uk
Web: .... www.nspcc.org.uk/legacies
Objects: F,W3,J,G,W15,X,H,O,3,P

The NSPCC is the only charity focused on ending child cruelty across the UK, driven by the simple belief that no child should suffer. Everything we do protects children and prevents abuse, helping children and families directly through local services, and providing training and support to people who work with children. The NSPCC also provides ChildLine and a helpline for adults who are worried about a child. Much of this work is possible thanks to the generosity of those who support us through gifts in wills. We understand that your loved ones come first, but once their needs are provided for in your will, a small percentage of whatever is left could help more children fulfill their potential.

NATIONAL TALKING NEWSPAPERS AND MAGAZINES (TNAUK)
CR293656
CEO: Mr John Kerby
National Recording Centre, Heathfield, East Sussex TN21 8DB
Tel: 01435 866102
Fax: 01435 865422
Email: .... legacyservices@rnib.org.uk
Objects: F,W6,M,W5,G,H,3

THE NATIONAL TRUST FOR SCOTLAND
Founded: 1931SC007410
Chief Executive: Mr Mark Adderly
Development Dept, Hermiston Quay, 5 Cultins Road, Edinburgh EH11 4DF
Tel: 0844 493 2100
Fax: 0131 243 9301
Email: .... legacy@nts.org.uk
Objects: W2,S,2

NATIONAL YOUTH BALLET
Founded: 1990 CR1000932
Director: Ms J Tookey
The Old Dairy, Wintersell Farm, Dwelly Lane, Edenbridge, Kent TN8 6QD
Tel: 01732 864781

NATIONAL YOUTH THEATRE OF GREAT BRITAIN
CR306075
443-445 Holloway Road, London N7 6LW
Tel: 020 7281 3863
Fax: 020 7281 8246
Email: .... info@nyt.org.uk
Objects: W3,J,G,P

NATURE IN ART TRUST
Founded: 1982 CR1000553
Chairman of Council: Doctor David Trapnell
Director: Mr Simon Trapnell
Wallsworth Hall, Twigworth, Gloucester, Gloucestershire GL2 9PA
Tel: 0845 450 0233
Fax: 01452 730937
Email: .... enquiries@nature-in-art.org.uk
Objects: S,G,W12,3

NAUTICAL INSTITUTE
Founded: 1971 CR1002462
Chief Executive: Mr C P Wake FNI
202 Lambeth Road, London SE1 7LQ
Tel: 020 7928 1351
Fax: 020 7401 2817
Email: .... sec@nautinst.org
Objects: J,G,2,B,H,3

NAWO
See National Alliance of Women's Organisations (NAWO)

NBFA ASSISTING THE ELDERLY
Founded: 1957 CR1147446
Mrs B Bewati
Mrs Jackie Wilkinson
32 Buckingham Palace Road, London SW1W 0RE
Tel: 020 7828 0200
Fax: 020 7828 0400
Email: .... info@nbfa.org.uk
Objects: M,W5,V,W4,P

NCH
Founded: 1869 CR1097940
Chief Executive Director: Mr Deryk Mead CBE
Central Office, 85 Highbury Park, London N5 1UD
Tel: 020 7226 2033
Fax: 020 7226 2537
Objects: Q,F,M,W3,G,H,O,3,C,P

NEA (NATIONAL ENERGY ACTION)
Founded: 1985 CR290511
Director of Communications: Ms Jenny Saunders
Communications Officer: Mrs Lesley Tudor-Snodin
Director of Communications: Mrs Maria Wardrobe
Level Six (Elswick) West One, Forty Banks, Newcastle upon Tyne, Tyne & Wear NE1 3PA
Tel: 0191 261 5677
Fax: 0191 261 6496
Email: .... info@nea.org.uk
Objects: F,J,W7,W5,G,W15,W4,H,Y,Z

NETHERLANDS BENEVOLENT SOCIETY
Founded: 1874 CR213032
Treasurer: Mr P Broek
Chairman: Mr L Broese van Groenou
Administrator: Mr P Eliott-Lockhart
Honorary Secretary: Mrs B B Geesink
PO Box 36, Burwash, Etchingham, East Sussex TN19 7WR
Tel: 01932 355885
Fax: 01932 355885
Email: .... info@koningwillemfonds.org.uk
Objects: F,1A,A,2,B,3

NEW COVENANT CHURCH
Founded: 1991 CR1004343
National Administrator: Revd A O Omisade
506-510 Old Kent Road, London SE1 5BA

Tel: 020 7231 9817
Fax: 020 7231 8959
Email: . . . . admin@newcovenant.org.uk
Objects: F,W3,W5,G,W10,2,R,W4,H,T,P,W8

NEW FOREST AGRICULTURAL SHOW SOCIETY, THE
Founded: 1992 CR1004255
The Showground, New Park, Brockenhurst,
Hampshire SO42 7QH
Tel: 01590 622400
Fax: 01590 622637
Email: . . . . info@newforestshow.co.uk
Objects: A,1B,3

NEW FRONTIERS INTERNATIONAL
Founded: 1991 CR1060001
Company Secretary: Mr Kevin Rose
17 Clarendon Villas, Hove, Brighton & Hove
BN3 3RE
Tel: 01273 234555
Fax: 01273 234556
Email: . . . . office@newfrontiers.xtn.org
Objects: G,R

NEW LIFE CROYDON
Founded: 1991 CR1123257
Treasurer / Administrator: Mr C D Parker
5 Cairo New Road, Croydon, Surrey CR0 1XP
Tel: 020 8680 7671
Fax: 020 8686 7692
Email: . . . . chris.parker@nlcc.croydon.org.uk
Objects: W3,G,R

NEWBURY AND DISTRICT AGRICULTURAL SOCIETY, THE
Founded: 1991 CR1003090
Chief Executive & Secretary: Doctor V A Brown
Treasurer: Mr G West
Newbury Showground, Priors Court Road,
Hermitage, Thatcham, West Berkshire RG18 9QZ
Tel: 01635 247111
Fax: 01635 247227
Email: . . . . . . office@newburyshowground.co.uk
Objects: W1,W3,W2,G,2,W4

NEWHAM ASIAN WOMEN'S PROJECT
CR1001834
Ms Baljit Banga
661 Barking Road, Plaistow, London E13 9EX
Tel: 020 8472 0528
Fax: 020 8503 5673
Email: . . . . info@nawp.org
Objects: F,W3,G,W10,D,C,W8

NEWMARTIN COMMUNITY YOUTH TRUST
CR298557
The Newmartin Youth Centre, 25 Claughton Road,
London E13 9PN
Tel: 020 8471 1749
Fax: 020 8552 6926
Email: . . . . lindar@ncytrust.org

NEWPORT (SHROPSHIRE) COTTAGE HOSPITAL TRUST LIMITED
Founded: 1990 CR1001348
Manager: Mrs Sylvia Harland Davies
Secretary: Mr Ron Jones
Chairman: Mr Derek Tremayne
Upper Bar, Newport, Shropshire TF10 7EH
Tel: 01952 820893
Fax: 01952 810633
Object: E

NEWTEC
Founded: 1990 CR802868
Chief Executive: Ms Chris Leigh
22 Deanery Road, Stratford, London E15 4LP
Tel: 020 8519 5843
Fax: 020 8519 9704
Email: . . . . enq@newtec.ac.uk
Objects: G,3,W8

NFSH CHARITABLE TRUST LTD (THE HEALING TRUST)
Founded: 1955 CR1094702
Finanacial Controller: Mr Satwan Singh Bhangra
General Manager: Mrs Veronica Burnett
21 York Road, Northampton, Northamptonshire
NN1 5QG
Tel: 01604 603247
Fax: 01604 603534
Email: . . . . office@thehealingtrust.org.uk
Objects: F,W1,W9,W6,W3,J,E,W7,W5,G,W10,
W11,W15,2,W4,U,H,P,W8,K

NHSPT
See National Health Service Pensioners' Trust

NIGEL MOORES FAMILY CHARITABLE FOUNDATION
Founded: 1991 CR1002366
Accountant: Mr Paul Kurthausen
Macfarlane and Co, 2nd Floor, Cunard Building,
Water Street, Liverpool, Merseyside L3 1DS
Tel: 0151 236 6161
Fax: 0151 236 1095

NOMAD HOMELESS ADVICE AND SUPPORT UNIT
Founded: 1991 CR1078089
Director: Miss Hilda Francis
90 - 92 West Street, Sheffield, South Yorkshire
S1 4EP
Tel: 0114 263 6624
Fax: 0114 263 6622
Email: . . . . director@nomadsheffield.co.uk
Objects: F,D,3,C

NORDOFF-ROBBINS MUSIC THERAPY CENTRE
CR280960
2 Lissenden Gardens (CC), London NW5 1PP
Tel: 020 7267 4496
Fax: 020 7267 4369
Email: . . . . admin@nordoff-robbins.org.uk

NORFOLK AND NORWICH ASSOCIATION FOR THE BLIND
Founded: 1805 CR207060
Director: Mr P J S Child
106 Magpie Road, Norwich, Norfolk NR3 1JH
Tel: 01603 629558
Fax: 01603 766682
Email: . . . . office@nnab.co.uk
Objects: F,W6,M,S,G,V,3,C,P

NORTH EAST ENGLAND GUIDE ASSOCIATION
CR1000858
Region Administrator
Unit 7, Alpha Court, Monks Cross Drive,
Huntington, York, North Yorkshire YO32 9WN
Tel: 01904 676076
Email: . . . . northeast@girlguiding.org.uk
Objects: W3,G,2

The Northern Counties Kidney Research Fund - NCKRF

Fundraising in the North for research in the North.

This Newcastle-based Fund began in 1971, becoming independent in1988.
It relies on bequests, covenants and donations, having no professional fund-raisers.
All income is dedicated to research into kidney failure and kidney transplantation.
Achievements include funding six full-time research workers, and establishing
a pathology laboratory and establishing a transplant laboratory studying
kidney graft rejection - still the greatest cause of graft loss.

Newcastle has one of the largest clinical and research programmes in
kidney transplant and kidney disease.
To maintain its pre-eminence, it needs the support of those who wish the
north of the country to flourish.

Please help us!

Northern Counties Kidney Research Fund, Clinical Deanery, 3rd Floor William Leech Building
The Medical School, Newcastle University, Newcastle upon Tyne, NE2 4HH
Tel: 0191 222 7067 Fax: 0191 282 0702
Email: info@nckrf.org.uk Web: http://www.nckrf.org.uk
RCN: 700037

NORTH HUMBERSIDE MOTOR TRADES GROUP TRAINING ASSOCIATION
Founded: 1990 CR702894
Director of Training: Mr G E Clark

The Riley Centre, Parkfield Drive, Anlaby Road,
Kingston upon Hull, East Riding of Yorkshire
HU3 6TB
Tel: 01482 353022
Fax: 01482 568193
Email: .... edward@motortradesgta.org
Objects: G,2

NORTH OF ENGLAND REFUGEE SERVICE, THE
Founded: 1991 CR1091200
Treasurer: Ms Dorothy Stoker
2 Jesmond Road West, Newcastle upon Tyne,
Tyne & Wear NE2 4PQ
Tel: 0191 245 7311
Email: .... info@refugee.org.uk

NORTH STAFFS HEART COMMITTEE

CR508743
Sneyd Cottage (CD), 5 Herm Close, Seabridge,
Newcastle-under-Lyme, Staffordshire ST5 3LL

Tel: 01782 622463
Fax: 01782 622463
Email: ...... tony.berry@northstaffsheart.org.uk
Web: ...... www.northstaffsheart.org.uk/charity

NORTHAMPTONSHIRE ASSOCIATION OF YOUTH CLUBS (NAYC)
Founded: 1990 CR803431
The Secretary to the Board
Kings Park, Kings Park Road, Moulton Park,
Northampton, Northamptonshire NN3 6LL
Tel: 01604 647580
Fax: 01604 499656
Email: .... nayc@nayc.org

NORTHERN COUNTIES KIDNEY RESEARCH FUND
CR700037
Institute of Cellular Medicine, 4th Floor William
Leech Building, Newcastle University, Newcastle
upon Tyne, Tyne & Wear NE2 4HH
Tel: 0191 222 7067
Fax: 0191 222 0723
Email: .... info@nckrf.org.uk
Web: .... www.nckrf.org.uk
Fundraising in the North for research in the North. This
Newcastle-based Fund began in 1971, becoming
independent in 1988. It relies on bequests, covenants
and donations, having no professional fund-raisers. All
income is dedicated to research into kidney failure and
kidney transplantation. Achievements include funding
six full-time research workers, and establishing a
pathology laboratory and establishing a transplant
laboratory studying kidney graft rejection - still the
greatest cause of graft loss. Newcastle has one of the
largest clinical and research programmes in kidney
transplant and kidney disease. To maintain it's pre-

eminence, it needs the support of those who wish the north of the country to flourish. Please help us!

See advert on previous page

NORTHERN IRELAND COMMUNITY RELATIONS COUNCIL

Community Relations Council

Founded: 1990XR16701
Director of Communications: Mr Ray Mullan
Glendinning House, 6 Murray Street, Belfast
BT1 6DN
Tel: 028 9022 7500
Fax: 028 9022 7551
Email: .... info@nicrc.org.uk
Objects: 1B,H,T

The Community Relations Council promotes a peaceful and fair society in Northern Ireland based on reconciliation, tolerance, inclusion and mutual trust. It provides advice and financial support for community relations and cultural diversity work in the voluntary and community sector and works in partnership with many public bodies to help create a more shared society.

NORTHUMBRIA COALITION AGAINST CRIME LIMITED
Founded: 1990 CR702756
Youth Programme Co-ordinator: Mr Danny Gilchrist
Chief Executive: Mrs Anne Tate
Block 33, Northumbria Police Headquarters, Newcastle upon Tyne, Tyne & Wear NE20 0BL
Tel: 01661 868424
Fax: 01661 868488
Email: .... lesley@ncac.org.uk
Objects: W3,J,G,2,H,3

NORTON FOUNDATION, THE
Founded: 1990 CR702638
Correspondent: Mr R C Perkins
PO Box 10282, Redditch, Worcestershire
B97 9ZA
Objects: W3,1A,A,1B,2

NOTTINGHAM AND DISTRICT REC
See Nottingham and Nottinghamshire REC

NOTTINGHAM AND NOTTINGHAMSHIRE REC
Founded: 2005 CR1104984
Chief Executive Officer: Afzal M Sadiq
67 Lower Parliament Street, Nottingham, Nottinghamshire NG1 3BB
Tel: 0115 958 6515
Fax: 0115 959 0624
Email: .... mall@nottsrec.com
Objects: F,G,D,3,K

THE NUCLEAR INDUSTRY BENEVOLENT FUND
CR208729
Chairman: Mr Gareth Beynon
Unit CUI, Warrington Business Park, Long Lane, Warrington, Cheshire WA2 8TX
Tel: 01925 633005
Fax: 01925 633455
Email: .... info@tnibf.org

Eligibility is restricted to current and past non-industrial employees of the UKAEA, BNFL, Amersham International, and successor organisations and their dependants. Where single status exists, all current staff are eligible. The Fund was set up to provide assistance in times of financial hardship.

NUFFIELD ORTHOPAEDIC CENTRE APPEAL
See Nuffield Orthopaedic Centre Appeal

NUFFIELD ORTHOPAEDIC CENTRE APPEAL
CR1006509
Nuffield Orthopaedic Centre, Headington, Oxfordshire OX3 7HE
Tel: 01865 227722

NZ - UK LINK FOUNDATION
Founded: 1990 CR802457
Treasurer: Mr Timothy Alston
Chairman: Mr Martin Williams
New Zealand House, Haymarket, London SW1Y 4TQ
Tel: .... 07776 147885 (mobile)
Email: .... link@linkuknz.demon.co.uk
Objects: S,G,1A

O

OAKWOOD SCHOOL FUND
Founded: 1990 CR1000982
Trustee: Mr D White
Oakwood School, Balcombe Road, Horley, Surrey RH6 9AE
Tel: 01293 785363

OCKENDEN INTERNATIONAL
Founded: 1951 CR1053720
Chief Executive: Mr James Beale
PO Box 1275, Woking, Surrey GU22 2FT
Objects: W3,W10,U,3,W8

OFF THE RECORD (BRISTOL)
Founded: 1965 CR1085351
2 Horfield Road, St Michael's Hill, Bristol BS2 8EA
Tel: 0117 922 6747
Objects: F,W3
• To become a young person led and centered organisation.
• To support young people to emotionally and practically empower themselves through the provision of counselling, information, participation, and development work.
• To promote the positive mental health and well-being of all young people.
• To promote young people's rights and participation in relation to mental health and well-being in all areas of public life.

OFFICERS' CHRISTIAN UNION
See Armed Forces' Christian Union

OILY CART COMPANY, THE
Founded: 1990 CR1000799
General Manager: Ms Kathy Everett
Artistic Director: Mr Tim Webb
Smallwood School Annexe, Smallwood Road, London SW17 0TW

Tel: 020 8672 6329
Fax: 020 8672 0792
Email: .... oilies@oilycart.org.uk
Objects: W3,S,W5,G,3,P

OMF INTERNATIONAL (UK)
Founded: 1865 CR1123973; SC039645
National Director: Dr Peter & Christine Rowan
UK Headquarters, Station Approach, Borough Green, Sevenoaks, Kent TN15 8BG
Tel: 01732 887299
Fax: 01732 887224
Email: .... omf@omf.org.uk
Objects: 2,R,H

OPEN LEARNING FOUNDATION, THE
Founded: 1990 CR1000055
Managing Director: Professor Collin Harrison
Administrator: Ms Fiona Paul
3 Devonshire Street, London W1W 5BA
Tel: 020 7636 4186
Fax: 020 7631 0132
Email: .... olf2@btconnect.com
Objects: G,2,H

OPEN SPACES SOCIETY (FORMERLY COMMONS, OPEN SPACES & FOOTPATHS PRESERVATION SOCIETY)
Founded: 1865 CR214753
General Secretary: Miss Kate Ashbrook
25A Bell Street, Henley-on-Thames, Oxfordshire RG9 2BA
Tel: 01491 573535
Email: .... hq@oss.org.uk
Objects: F,W2,S,1B,2,H,P

OPERATION MOBILISATION
Founded: 1992 CR1008196
Company Secretary: Mr Peter Copestake
The Quinta, Weston Rhyn, Oswestry, Shropshire SY10 7LT
Tel: 01691 773388
Email: .... info@uk.om.org

OPPORTUNITY INTERNATIONAL UK
Founded: 1992 CR1107713; SC039692
Director: Mr Edward Fox
Angel Court, 81 St Clements, Oxford, Oxfordshire OX4 1AW
Tel: 01865 725304
Fax: 01865 295161
Email: .... impact@opportunity.org.uk
Objects: U,3

OPUS DEI CHARITABLE TRUST
Founded: 1991 CR1005860
Trustee: Mr J N Pickering
6 Orme Court, London W2 4RL
Tel: 020 7229 7574
Objects: G,3

ORBIS UK
Founded: 1986 CR1061352
Head of Fundraising: Mr Allan Thompson
Fourth Floor, Fergusson House, 124-128 City Road, London EC1V 2NJ
Tel: 020 7608 7260
Fax: 020 7253 8483
Email: .... info@orbis.org.uk
Objects: W6,G,N,U,3

ORDER OF ST JOHN
Founded: 1888 CR235979
Secretary General: Rear Admiral Andrew Gough CB
Priory House, 25 St John's Lane, Clerkenwell, London EC1M 4PP
Tel: 020 7251 3292
Fax: 020 7251 3287
Objects: W6,W3,J,W5,W10,N,2,W4,3,W8

ORFACT: ORPHANS RELIEF FUND AND CHARITABLE TRUST
CR803125
The Studio, Jubilee Close, Kingsbury, London NW9 8TR
Tel: 020 8205 8272; 020 8358 4483
Email: .... info@orfact.org

ORGANISATION OF BLIND AFRICAN CARIBBEANS
CR1042756
1st Floor Gloucester House, 8 Camberwell New Road, London SE5 0RZ
Tel: 020 7735 3400
Fax: 020 7582 8334
Email: .... orgblindafricarib@ukonline.co.uk

ORMSBY CHARITABLE TRUST, THE
Founded: 1990 CR1000599
Trustee: Mrs Katrina McCrossan
Wasing Old Rectory, Shalford Hill, Aldermaston, Reading RG7 4NB
Tel: 0118 981 9663
Objects: W6,W3,W7,W5,A,1B,W4

ORPHEUS CENTRE
CR1105213
Orpheus Centre, North Park Lane, Godstone, Surrey RH9 8ND
Tel: 01883 744664
Fax: 01883 744994
Email: .... marketing@orpheus.org.uk
Objects: W6,W3,S,W7,W5,G,D

ORTHOPAEDIC INSTITUTE LIMITED
Founded: 1971 CR1044906
The Robert Jones and Agnes Hunt Orthopaedic Hospital NHS Foundation Trust, Oswestry, Shropshire SY10 7AG
Tel: 01691 404661
Fax: 01691 404170
Email: .... alison.whitelaw@rjah.nhs.uk
The Orthopaedic Institute is a registered charity and funds research at the Robert Jones & Agnes Hunt Orthopaedic Hospital at Oswestry, Shropshire. The hospital has a national and international reputation for
its research into orthopaedic disease and disability. Research programmes investigate a wide range of subjects such as bone disease, spinal disorders, hip and knee joint replacements, arthritis and rheumatism, stem cells and chondrocyte therapies. aim of the research is to find new and improved methods of treatment. Funds are needed for a wide range of research programmes in orthopaedic medicine. Please write or ring for a brochure 01691 404661.

ORTHOPAEDIC RESEARCH UK
Founded: 1988 CR1111657
Furlong House, 10a Chandos Street, London W1G 9DQ

Tel: 020 7436 1919
Fax: 020 7636 4351
Email: .... info@oruk.org
Objects: G,A,1B,W4

OSCAR BIRMINGHAM
Founded: 1990 CR1109849
The Chairman
251-253 Rookery Road, Handsworth, Birmingham, West Midlands B21 9PU
Tel: 0121 551 6553
Fax: 0121 554 6354
Email: .... admin@oscarbirmingham.org.uk

OSTEOPATHIC CENTRE FOR CHILDREN, LONDON
Founded: 1991 CR1003934
Finance Manager: Ms Sherlene Pusey
15a Woodbridge Street, London EC1R 0ND
Tel: 020 7490 5510
Fax: 020 7490 3414
Objects: W3,G,N,H,3

OUR LADY OF FIDELITY CHARITABLE TRUST
Founded: 1991 CR1002216
Trustee: Sister Betty Mary Hampson MBE
15-17 Marten Road, Folkestone, Kent CT20 2JR
Tel: 0131 325 3713
Objects: W3,E,G,2

OVACOME: THE OVARIAN CANCER SUPPORT CHARITY

the ovarian cancer support charity

Founded: 1996 CR1058026
B5 New City Cloisters, 196 Old Street, London EC1V 9FR
Tel: 0845 371 0554 (Support line); 020 7299 6654 (Admin)
Email: ...... ovacome@ovacome.org.uk
Web: .... http://www.ovacome.org.uk
We are a UK-wide support and information network for all those affected by ovarian cancer.

OVER FORTY ASSOCIATION FOR WOMEN WORKERS
See Housing for Women

OVERSEAS ADOPTION HELPLINE
See Intercountry Adoption Centre

OVERSEAS BISHOPRICS' FUND
Founded: 1841 CR245334
Clerk to Council: Mr Paul Burrage
Secretary: Mr Stephen Lyon
Church House, Great Smith Street, London SW1P 3AZ
Tel: 020 7898 1677
Objects: 1A,A,1B,R,U,3

OVERSEAS MISSIONARY FELLOWSHIP
See OMF International (UK)

OXFORD COLLEGES INTERNATIONAL (FORMERLY NORTH LONDON SCHOOLS TRUST)
Founded: 1991 CR1002034
Chairman: Mr D Simons

11 Golders Green Road, London NW11 8DY
Tel: 020 8905 5467
Fax: 020 8455 6528
Email: . . . . ggcol@easynet.co.uk
Objects: G,3

OXFORDSHIRE CHINESE COMMUNITY & ADVICE CENTRE
CR1006710
44b Princes Street, Oxford, Oxfordshire OX4 1DD
Tel: 01865 204188
Fax: 01865 242188
Email: . . . . occac@dial.pipex.com

OXFORDSHIRE RURAL COMMUNITY COUNCIL
Founded: 1990 CR900560
Chief Executive: Mr John Hardwicke

Jericho Farm, Worton, Witney, Oxfordshire OX29 4SZ
Tel: 01865 883488
Fax: 01865 883191
Email: . . . . orcc@oxonrcc.org.uk
Objects: F,J,1B,H,3

P

PACE CENTRE LTD, THE
Founded: 1992 CR1011133
Administrator: Ms Susan Muir

Philip Green House, Coventon Road, Aylesbury, Buckinghamshire HP19 9JL
Tel: 01296 392739
Fax: 01296 334836
Objects: W3,G,O,3

PACT (PRISON ADVICE & CARE TRUST)

Prisoners · Families · Communities
A Fresh Start Together

CR219278
Park Place, 12 Lawn Lane, Vauxhall, London SW8 1UD
Tel: 020 7735 9535
Email: . . . . info@prisonadvice.org.uk
Web: . . . . http://www.prisonadvice.org.uk
Pact supports prisoners and their families in making a fresh start and reduces the damage imprisonment causes to children and families.

Every day we see the children and families of prisoners suffering – not only with the emotional strain of being separated from a parent, but with the shame and isolation attached to the stigma of imprisonment.

Our family Visitors' Centres and children's projects offer hope and dignity to thousands of children, parents, grandparents and siblings who want to stay in touch with a family member in prison.

Please get in touch if you would like to support us, or find out more about our work.
See advert on previous page

PAIN RELIEF FOUNDATION

PAIN RELIEF FOUNDATION
RELIEVING CANCER AND OTHER PAIN THROUGH RESEARCH

Founded: 1979 CR277732
Administrator: Mr David E Emsley
Clinical Sciences Centre, University Hospital Aintree, Lower Lane, Liverpool, Merseyside L9 7AL
Tel: 0151 529 5820
Fax: 0151 529 5821
Email: administrator@painrelieffoundation. org.uk
Web: . . . . www.painrelieffoundation.org.uk
Objects: N,O,W

Pain Relief Foundation is situated in Liverpool and works in co-operation with the Walton Centre Pain Clinic. The Walton Centre Pain Clinic is the largest Pain Relief Clinic in Europe and is attended by more than pain patients 6,000 patients each year.

Researchers at the Foundation's 'Research Institute' take advantage of these large numbers of patients to conduct multidisciplinary research into the causes, mechanisms and relief of chronic pain and no animal experiments are carried out here. Cancer is obviously one of the forms of pain on which active research is pursued, because unfortunately the trust deeds of many cancer charities and research organisations prevent them from funding this work, because they specify 'research into the causes and cures of cancer'.

Our other research at the Foundation is directed at improving the treatment of many other forms of chronic pain, from phantom limb pain to arthritis and from cancer pain to back pain and neuralgia following shingles, which are not fatal, but can leave sufferers in agony for decades. The Foundation is entirely dependent for its income upon charity and, amazingly, it is the only research institute in the world devoted to multidisciplinary work on chronic human pain.
See advert on next page

PAINTINGS IN HOSPITALS SCOTLAND
See Art in Healthcare

PAPWORTH TRUST
Founded: 1917 CR211234
Supporter Relations Manager: Mr Marcus Barber
Chief Executive: Mr Adrian Bagg
Director of Development: Ms Sarah Coward
Director of Marketing & Communications: Mr David Martin

Bernard Sunley Centre, Papworth Everard, Cambridge, Cambridgeshire CB23 3RG
Tel: 01480 357200
Fax: 01480 357201
Email: . . . . info@papworth.org.uk
Objects: F,W6,M,W3,W7,W5,G,D,W4,O,3,C,K

PAIN RELIEF FOUNDATION

RELIEVING CANCER AND OTHER PAIN THROUGH RESEARCH

<u>Pain</u> is a vital alarm bell to the brain, telling us that we have damaged ourselves and that something is wrong. So, when the damage is treated, the pain has normally done its job and usually goes away.

But then there is **chronic pain,** and that is very, very different. No matter how much treatment you give the painful area it doesn't go away; painkilling drugs often don't work; even opioids often don't kill the pain, it is relentless and sufferers are subject to a lifetime of agony!!

Here are just a few hard facts to consider:

- 1 in 7 people in the UK suffer from chronic pain – which does <u>not</u> go away.
- Chronic pain is a desperate debilitating pain bringing a life sentence of agony.
- Over half of sufferers endure chronic pain all day, every day of their lives.
- Many sufferers say they can't remember what it is like <u>not</u> to be in pain.
- 1 in 5 chronic pain sufferers say their pain is so bad that they just want to die.
- Pain stops sufferers from enjoying simple activities like walking, shopping, sleeping, or just playing with their children.
- Many thousands of chronic pain sufferers lose their jobs because the pain is so bad that they cannot work.
- When a chronic pain sufferer lose their job, they are often on the downward spiral to poverty.
- A quarter of chronic pain sufferers are diagnosed with depression.

We obviously pursue active research on Cancer Pain, because many cancer charities and research organisations are prevented from funding work on cancer pain. Their Trust Deeds specify 'research into the cause and cure of cancer' and this, of course, excludes pain. Yet, for every £1.57p donated to cancer research, chronic pain research receives a donation of less than one (1p) penny.

The Pain Relief Foundation in Liverpool is a research charity working to find the causes of chronic pain; seeking new ways of improving the available treatments; educating all doctors and all other medical professionals on treatment methods to ease the pain; providing information packs for patients, sufferers and carers. If you need help, don't hesitate to contact us.

Research costs money, and there is always an urgent need for more and more research. The Pain Relief Foundation <u>DOES NOT</u> receive funding from the NHS or any other Government body. Instead, our vital work depends entirely on donations and the generosity of people like you. Will you please help?? – each and every £1 counts!!

Please help us to end the suffering!! There is a <u>serious</u> lack of funding for chronic pain research and <u>you can help</u> to change that!!

You can make a donation in many ways - making a subscription monthly, quarterly or yearly is usually the easiest way!!

You can also help to defeat chronic pain by leaving a Legacy in your will. For help and advice on how to pledge a Legacy and what you need to do, we are here to help and advise you – just contact us!!

Pain Relief Foundation
Clinical Sciences Centre
University Hospital Aintree
Liverpool L9 7AL

FundRaising
Standards Board

Telephone: 0151 529 5820   Fax: 0151 529 5821
Email   secretary@painrelieffoundation.org.uk
Website   www.painrelieffoundation.org.uk
Charity No 277732

PAPYRUS PREVENTION OF YOUNG SUICIDE

CR1070896
47 Bewsey Street, Warrington, Cheshire WA2 7JQ
Tel: 01925 572444; 0800 068 4141 HOPELineUK
Fax: 01925 240502
Email: . . . .   admin@papyrus-uk.org

PARKINSON'S UK

PARKINSON'SUK CHANGE ATTITUDES. FIND A CURE. JOIN US.

CR258197; SC037554
215 Vauxhall Bridge Road, London
SW1V 1EJ
Tel: 020 7931 8080; 0808 800 0303
Freephone Helpline
Fax: 020 7233 9908
Email: . . . . . enquiries@parkinsons.org.uk
Web: . . . . . www.parkinsons.org.uk/legacy
Objects: F,M,W3,J,W5,G,W10,V,N,2,W4,H,O, 3,P,K
A lasting legacy...
Did you know there are 120,000 people in the UK who have Parkinson's in the UK?
Parkinson's UK has over 40 years experience of caring for people living with Parkinson's and is working hard towards finding a cure. We are the leading UK charity supporting people with Parkinson's.
Parkinson's campaigns for a better quality of life for people with Parkinson's throughout the UK, and invests in a wide range of research projects into all aspects of Parkinson's, in five key areas – Cause, Prevention, Cure, Progression and Care.
Over 50% of our income comes from legacies. Put simply – much of our work caring for people with Parkinson's and our endeavours to find a cure would not be possible without people leaving us gifts in their Will.
For more information on leaving a legacy to the Parkinson's UK please telephone 020 7931 8080 or visit www.parkinsons.org.uk/legacies

PARTIALLY SIGHTED SOCIETY

 The Partially Sighted Society
Helping people with a visual impairment

Founded: 1973 CR254052
1 Bennetthorpe, Doncaster, South Yorkshire
DN2 6AA
Tel: 0844 477 4966
Fax: 0844 477 4969
Email: . . . . info@partsight.org.uk
Web: . . . . www.partsight.org.uk
Objects: F,W6,M,J,G,H,3,P

THE PASSAGE

 **THE PASSAGE**
HELPING HOMELESS PEOPLE since 1980

Founded: 1980 CR1079764
Business Director: Mr Andrew Hollingsworth
St Vincent's Centre, Carlisle Place, London SW1P 1NL
Tel: 020 7592 1856
Fax: 020 7592 1870
Email: . . . . info@passage.org.uk
Web: . . . . www.passage.org.uk
Objects: E,W16,C
The Passage's Mission is to provide resources that encourage, inspire, and challenge homeless people to transform their lives. It fulfils its mission by providing:
• Day Centre services offering basic care, Health including mental health, substance misuse and primary care, Housing and advice, education, training and employment
• Street link services to contact rough sleepers
• Hostel accommodation moving towards re-settlement.

See advert on next page

PAUL FOUNDATION

Founded: 1991 CR1003143
Trustee: Mr P R D Paul
Haycroft, Sherborne, Cheltenham, Gloucestershire GL54 3NB
Tel: 01451 844500
Objects: W3,A,1B

PAWS AND CLAWS ANIMAL RESCUE SERVICE, MID-SUSSEX

CR281075
Coombe Down (CC), London Road, Sayers Common, Hurstpierpoint, West Sussex BN6 9HZ
Tel: 01444 831286
Email: . . . . info@pawsandclaws-ars.org.uk

THE PEACE HOSPICE (SOUTH WEST HERTFORDSHIRE HOSPICE CHARITABLE TRUST)

Founded: 1991 CR1002878
Trustee & Solicitor: Mr P D Nicholas
Reynolds Porter Chamberlain, 278-282 High Holborn, London WC1V 7HA
Tel: 020 7242 2877
Email: . . . . fundraising@peacehospice.org.uk
Objects: F,E,W10,N,W4,3,W8

PELICAN TRUST LIMITED

CR703143
General Manager: Mrs S. Gillott
20-22 Crofton Road, Allenby Industrial Estate, Lincoln, Lincolnshire LN3 4NL
Tel: 01522 513533
Fax: 01522 540093
Email: . . . . jayne@pelicantrust.org
Objects: S,W5,G,O,3,K

News from The Passage

The Passage is about long term, lasting solutions and seeks to address the root causes that led to a person becoming homeless in the first place so that their cycle of homelessness can be broken for good. Recent achievements include:

- 92% of all new rough sleepers in South Westminster were either supported to return to their home area or linked into support services and accommodation off the streets within 2 contacts by The Passage Street Outreach team during 2011/12.

- The Passage helped 117 entrenched rough sleepers off the streets of South Westminster during the same period.

- For the 3rd year running every client moving on from The Passage's supported accommodation scheme and into their own tenancy has sustained that tenancy.

- Over the last 10 years The Passage has helped nearly 600 homeless people into full time employment.

The Passage has ninety staff and a volunteer to staff ratio of over 3:1. It costs nearly £4 million per year to run The Passage, and half of that income is dependent on voluntary donations. For every £1 donated in voluntary income, over 90% goes straight to our frontline services.

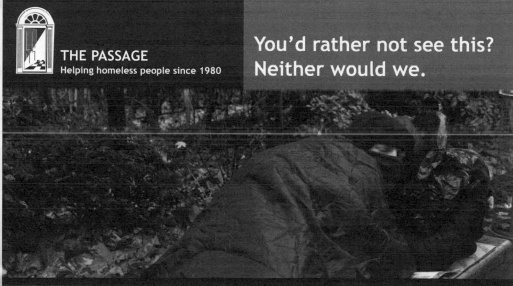

THE PASSAGE
Helping homeless people since 1980

You'd rather not see this? Neither would we.

At The Passage, we'd rather see vulnerable people with a roof over their head, and support at hand, than out and alone on the streets. To that end, our Day Centre opens its doors to up to 200 people every day, whilst our hostel, Passage House, has beds for 40 people and is open every night of the year.

In addition, Montfort House provides 16 studio flats preparing people for independent living. Our aim is to support individuals back into a settled way of life, as well as meeting basic needs.

If you're interested in being a volunteer, would like to make a donation or would simply like more information, we'd love to hear from you.

Give us a call on 0845 880 0689, email info@passage.org.uk or visit www.passage.org.uk

Alternatively, if you would like to make a postal donation, please make cheques payable to The Passage; and send to: St Vincent's Centre, Carlisle Place, London SW1P 1NL.

HELP NOW. Call us on 0845 800 0689

Reg. Charity No.1079764

PEMBROKE HOUSE, HOME FOR AGED EX-NAVAL MEN, THEIR WIVES AND WIDOWS AND FORMER WRENS
CR206243
Chief Executive: Commander Stephen Farrington QGM RN
Home Manager: Mrs Jo Trembeth RGN
11 Oxford Road, Gillingham, Kent ME7 4BS
Tel: 01634 852431
Fax: 01634 281709
Email: . . . . pembrokehouse@rnbt.org.uk
Objects: W9,1A,A,N

PENNY BROHN CANCER CARE
Founded: 1980 CR284881
Chief Executive: Mr Glyn Berwick
Head of Education: Mr Michael Connors
Therapy Director: Dr Helen Gunson
Chapel Pill Lane, Pill, Bristol BS20 0HH
Tel: . 01275 370110 Switchboard; 08451 232310 Helpline
Fax: 01275 370124
Email: . . . . info@pennybrohn.org
Objects: F,W3,J,W5,G,W10,W4,H,O,3,W8

PENTREATH LTD
Founded: 1991 CR1004477
General Manager: Ms Louise Knox
1st Floor Offices, Formal Ind Est, Treswithian, Camborne, Cornwall TR14 0PY
Tel: 01209 719632
Fax: 01209 610759
Email: . . . . penreath@penreath.co.uk
Objects: F,W5,G,O,3,K

PEOPLE'S TRUST FOR ENDANGERED SPECIES
CR274206
15 Cloisters House, 8 Battersea Park Road, London SW8 4BG
Tel: 020 7498 4533
Fax: 020 7498 4459
Email: . . . . enquiries@ptes.org
In the UK 90% of water voles and 75% of dormice living in hedgerows have been lost in just the last few years. Overseas turtles are caught and killed in fishing gear, lions are illegally shot and the seahorse population in south East Asia has halved. People's Trust for Endangered Species was founded in 1977 with the aim of helping to ensure a future for threatened species worldwide. We work to preserve endangered species in their natural habitats for future generations to enjoy. Every legacy we receive will enable us to plan ahead and use our resources in the best way to ensure the survival of threatened species. For more information please contact us. Thank you.
See advert on this page

PEPER HAROW FOUNDATION
See Childhood First

PERENNIAL - GARDENERS' ROYAL BENEVOLENT SOCIETY
SC040180
Chief Executive: Mr Richard Capewell
Director of Finance: Mrs Sally Hanson
Director of Marketing & Fundraising: Ms Debbie Lyne
Director of Services: Ms Sheila Thomson
115/117 Kingston Road, Leatherhead, Surrey KT22 7SU

Tel: 0845 230 1830
Fax: 01372 384 055
Email: . . . . info@perennial.org.uk
Objects: W3,W5,1A,A,V,D,N,B,H,3,C

PERTH & KINROSS SOCIETY FOR THE BLIND
SC001152
St Paul's Centre, 14 New Row, Perth, Perth & Kinross PH1 5QA
Tel: 01738 626969
Fax: 01738 448544
Email: . . . . pkbs.perth@virgin.net

PESTALOZZI INTERNATIONAL VILLAGE TRUST
CR1098422
Sedlescombe, Battle, East Sussex TN33 0RR
Tel: 01424 870444
Fax: 01424 870655
Email: . . . . office@pestalozzi.org.uk

PHAB
Founded: 1957 CR283931
Corporate Fundraising Events: Ms Anne Joyce
Corporate Fundraising: Mrs Anne Joyce
Summit House, Wandle Road, Croydon, Surrey CR0 1DF
Tel: 020 8667 9443
Fax: 020 8681 1399
Email: . . . . info@phab.org.uk
Objects: F,W3,J,S,W5,G,1A,1B,V,2,W4,H,3,P

PHARMACIST SUPPORT

 Pharmacist Support
working for pharmacists & their families

Founded: 1841 CR221438
5th Floor (CD), 196 Deansgate, Manchester, Greater Manchester M3 3WF
Tel: **0808 168 2233**
Fax: **0161 441 0319**
Email: . . . . . . **info@pharmacistsupport.org**
Objects: F,W5,W11,W15,1A,W4,O,Y

Pharmacist Support is an independent charity providing free and confidential support services to pharmacists and their families, former pharmacists and pharmacy students in times of need. Our services include financial assistance, a stress helpline, debt, benefits and employment advice, addiction support and an information and enquiry service. The Charity relies on the generosity of pharmacists to enable us to continue our work.

PIED PIPER TRUST, THE
Founded: 1992 CR1011611
Chairman: Mr Peter Hichman
Gloucestershire Royal Hospital, Great Western Road, Gloucester, Gloucestershire GL1 3NN
Tel: 01452 394119
Objects: W3,1B,N

PIMLICO OPERA
Founded: 1991 CR1003836
Trustee: Mr M Andrews
The Coach House, 12 St Thomas Street, Winchester, Hampshire SO23 9HF

Tel: 01962 868600
Fax: 01962 868968
Objects: S,G,3

PINE RIDGE DOG SANCTUARY
Founded: 1958 CR256728
Priory Road (CC), Ascot, Windsor & Maidenhead SL5 8RJ
Tel: 01344 882689
Fax: 01344 882689
Email: . . . . pineridgedogs@yahoo.co.uk
Objects: W1,W15,W4

Pine Ridge Dog Sanctuary has been saving stray and unwanted dogs since 1958. Established by the late Bernard Cuff. We spay and neuter all dogs, if old enough, prior to rehoming. We also help the elderly or needy families with veterinary costs. We can only do this through the generosity of animal lovers who support our work with regular donations. Please do not let the dogs down, they are relying on you. Please remember Pine Ridge in your Will. Legacies are of utmost importance to enable us to continue our work in giving the dogs the love and care they deserve.

POD CHARITABLE TRUST
Founded: 1977 CR279743
Chairman Trustees: Mr David Jamilly
Administrator: Mrs Margaret Munford
Mount Hall, Llanfair Caereinion, Welshpool, Powys SY21 0BH
Tel: 01938 810374
Email: . . . . podcharity@btinternet.com
Objects: W3,O,3,P

POLDEN PUCKHAM CHARITABLE FOUNDATION
Founded: 1991 CR1003024
The Secretary
BM PPCF, London WC1N 3XX
Objects: W2,1B

POLESWORTH GROUP HOMES ASSOCIATION
Founded: 1991 CR1003230
Secretary: Mr P R Boucher
Laurel End, Laurel Avenue, Tamworth, Staffordshire B78 1LT
Tel: 01827 896124
Objects: W5,3,C

THE POLICE DEPENDANTS' TRUST
Founded: 1966 CR251021
Chief Executive: Mr David French
3 Mount Mews, High Street, Hampton, Middlesex SW12 2SH
Tel: 020 8941 6907
Fax: 020 8979 4323
Email: . . . . office@pdtrust.org
Objects: M,W3,1A,A,V

POLICE MEMORIAL TRUST
CR289371
219 Kensington High Street, London W8 6BD
Tel: 020 7734 8385
Fax: 020 7602 9217
Object: W12

POLICE REHABILITATION CENTRE
CR210310
Flint House, Reading Road, Goring-on-Thames, Reading RG8 0LL
Tel: 01491 874499
Fax: 01491 875002
Email: . . . . enquiries@flinthouse.co.uk

THE POLICE TREATMENT CENTRES
CR1147449; SC043396
St Andrews, Harlow Moor Road, Harrogate, North
Yorkshire HG2 0AD
Tel: 01423 504448
Fax: 01423 527543
Email: . enquiries@thepolicetreatmentcentres.org

POLISH EX-COMBATANTS ASSOCIATION
Founded: 1946 CR249509
The Secretary
240 King's Street, London W6 0RF
Tel: 020 8741 1911; 020 8748 6136
Objects: F,H

PONTEFRACT FAMILY CENTRE
Founded: 1982 CR1100754
The Centre Manager: Mr Rodney Hermon
4 Harropwell Lane, Pontefract, West Yorkshire
WF8 1QY
Tel: 01977 706932
Objects: E,W5,W4,3,P

PONTESBURY PROJECT FOR PEOPLE WITH SPECIAL NEEDS, THE
Founded: 1990 CR702609
Manager: Mrs J Curtis
Hill Farm, Pontesford, Shrewsbury, Shropshire
SY5 0UH
Tel: 01743 791975

POPPYSCOTLAND (THE EARL HAIG FUND SCOTLAND)
SC014096
Chief Executive: Mr Jim Panton
New Haig House, Logie Green Road, Edinburgh
EH7 4HR
Tel: 0131 550 1567
Fax: 0131 557 5819
Email: . . . . supportercare@poppyscotland.org.uk
Objects: F,W9,M,J,1A,A,1B,2,H,3,K

POSITIVE EAST
Founded: 1990 CR1001582
159 Mile End Road, Stepney, London E1 4AQ
Tel: 020 7791 2855
Fax: 020 7780 9551
Email: . . . . . . patrick.barker@positiveeast.org.uk
Objects: F,W3,W10,3,W8

POSITIVE PLACE
Founded: 1992 CR1009957
Secretary to the Trustees: Mr Peter Strickland
52 Deptford Broadway, London SE8 4PH
Tel: 020 8694 9988
Fax: 020 8694 9900
Email: . . . . info@thepositiveplace.org.uk
Objects: 2,3

POSITIVELY UK
Founded: 1987 CR1007685
Director: Ms Elisabeth Crafer
345 City Road, London EC1V 1LR
Tel: . . . . 020 7713 0444 (admin) 9:30-5
Email: . . . . info@positivelyuk.org
Objects: F,W3,G,H,3,P,W8

POTENTIAL PLUS UK [FORMERLY NATIONAL ASSOCIATION FOR GIFTED CHILDREN (NAGC)]
Founded: 1966 CR313182
Education Consultant: Ms Fritha Fletcher
Education Consultant: Ms Elaine Hook
Director: Dr Stephen Tommis
Suite 1.2, Challenge House, Sherwood Drive,
Bletchley, Milton Keynes, Buckinghamshire
MK3 6DP
Tel: 01908 646433
Email: . . amazingchildren@potentialplusuk.org
Objects: F,W3,J,G,2,H,3,P
NAGC supports gifted children to enable them to
fulfil their potential. We make a real difference in
helping the children of today become the scientists,
inventors and musicians of tomorrow.

POTTERY & GLASS TRADES' BENEVOLENT FUND
Founded: 1881 CR208227
Flat 57, Witley Court, Coram Street, London
WC1N 1HD
Tel: 020 7837 2231
Fax: 020 7837 2231
Objects: W11,1A,A,B

PRACTICAL ACTION (FORMERLY ITDG)
Founded: 1965 CR247257
**The Schumacher Centre, Bourton on
Dunsmore, Rugby, Warwickshire CV23 9QZ**
Tel: 01926 634400
Fax: 01926 634401
Email: . . . . . legacy@practicalaction.org.uk
Objects: W2,U,W8
**Making a difference – Technology Challenging
Poverty**
**Practical Action makes a real difference by
helping people to access food, clean water,
sanitation, housing, and energy, to improving
livelihoods, helping them to adapt to climate
change and prepare for natural disasters.
Founded over 45 years ago by radical economist
and author of \\b Small is Beautiful\\plain, Dr E F
Schumacher, Practical Action works hand in
hand with local people in 13 of the poorest
countries in the world, building on their skills to
create simple, innovative and long term
solutions to poverty. Using appropriate
technologies, we ensure that all our projects are
sustainable, use local materials and are
managed by local communities, empowering
them to help themselves.
Practical Action is a registered charity and
company limited by guarantee.**

PRAYER BOOK SOCIETY

PBS
Prayer Book
Society

Founded: 1975 CR1099295
**The Studio, Copyhold Farm, Goring Heath,
Oxfordshire RG8 7RT**
Tel: **0118 984 2582**
Fax: **0118 984 5220**
Email: .... **pbs.admin@pbs.org.uk**
Objects: 2,R,H,P
**Founded to preserve the use of the Book of
Common Prayer for this and future generations.
Join online via the website or by contacting the
phone number above.
Co Ltd by Guarantee no 4786973 & Registered
Charity 1099295.**

THE PRE-RETIREMENT ASSOCIATION
See Life Academy

PRESTON AND WESTERN LANCASHIRE REC
Founded: 1990 CR1095261
Chief Executive: Mr M F Desai MBE
Town Hall Annexe, Birley Street, Preston,
Lancashire PR1 2RL
Tel: 01772 906422
Fax: 01772 906685
Email: .... admin@prestonrec.org.uk
Objects: F,S,W10,2,3

PREVENT UNWANTED PETS (PUP)
CR702569
Ms Alison Guest
14 Friars Close, Tyldesley, Manchester, Greater
Manchester M29 8QB
Tel: 07772 722709
Email: .... aguest@cat.com

PRIMARY IMMUNODEFICIENCY ASSOCIATION (PIA)
Founded: 1990 CR1107233
Chief Executive: Mr Christopher Hughan
Alliance House, 12 Caxton Street, London
SW1H 0QS
Tel: 020 7976 7640
Fax: 020 7976 7641
Email: .... info@pia.org.uk
Objects: F,W3,W5,1B,2,H,3,P

PRINCE OF WALES FOUNDATION FOR ARCHITECTURE AND THE URBAN ENVIRONMENT
See The Prince's Foundation for the Built
Environment

THE PRINCE'S FOUNDATION FOR THE BUILT ENVIRONMENT
CR1069969
19-22 Charlotte Road, London EC2A 3SG
Tel: 020 7613 8500
Fax: 020 7613 8599
Email: .... enquiry@princes-foundation.org
Objects: F,W3,W2,G,2,3

PRINCESS ALICE HOSPICE
CR1010930
Fundraising Manager: Mrs Margeret Robinson
West End Lane, Esher, Surrey KT10 8NA
Tel: 01372 468811
Email: .... fundraising@pah.org.uk
Objects: F,G,N,O,3

PRISON REFORM TRUST
Founded: 1981 CR1035525
Finance and Development Officer: Ms
Charlotte Story
Director: Mrs Juliet Lyon
2nd Floor, The Old Trading House, 15
Northburgh Street, London EC1V 0JR
Tel: 020 7251 5070
Fax: 020 7251 5076
Email: .... prt@prisonreformtrust.org.uk
Web: .... http://www.prisonreformtrust.org.uk
Objects: F,H
We aim to create a just, humane and effective penal
system. We do this by inquiring into the workings of
the system; informing prisoners, staff and the wider
public; and by influencing parliament, government
and officials towards reform.

PRISONERS ABROAD
Founded: 1978 CR1093710
Chief Executive: Ms Pauline Crowe
89-93 Fonthill Road, London N4 3JH
Tel: 020 7561 6820
Fax: 020 7561 6821
Email: .... info@prisonersabroad.org.uk
Objects: F,J,G,1A,A,U,H,3

PROGRESSIO
Founded: 1940 CR294329
Executive Director: Ms Christine Allen
Units 9-12, The Stableyard, Broomgrove Road,
London SW9 9TL
Tel: 020 7733 1195
Email: .... ciir@ciir.org
Objects: W3,W2,W7,W5,G,W10,W4,U,H,3,W8

PROSPECT EDUCATION (TECHNOLOGY) TRUST LTD
Founded: 1990 CR803497
Company Secretary: Mr R J Perry
100 West Hill, Wandsworth, London SW15 2UT
Tel: 020 8877 0357
Fax: 020 8877 0617
Objects: W3,G,3

PROSPECTS FOR PEOPLE WITH LEARNING DISABILITIES
Founded: 1976 CR1060571
Director of Operations: Mr Mike Howard
Chief Executive: Mr Paul Ashton
Director of Causeway Prospects: Mr Tony Phelps-Jones
Director of Finance: Miss Helen Preece
69 Honey End Lane, Reading RG30 4EL
Tel: 0118 950 8781
Fax: 0118 939 1683
Email: .... info@prospects.org.uk
Objects: M,E,W5,R,3,C,P,K

PROSTATE ACTION
Founded: 1994 CR1135297
Ms Ann Rolfe
6 Crescent Stables, 139 Upper Richmond Road,
London SW15 2TN

Tel: 020 8788 7720
Fax: 020 8789 1331
Email: . . . . info@prostateaction.org.uk
Objects: F,1B,H,3

PROSTATE CANCER UK

Founded: 1996 CR1005541; SC039332
Director of Fundraising: Mr Mark Bishop
4th Floor, Counting House, 53 Tooley Street,
London SE1 2QN
Tel: 020 3310 7000
Fax: 020 3310 7107
Email: . corporatepartnerships@prostate-cancer.
org.uk
Objects: F,H,W

One man dies of prostate cancer every hour. Prostate Cancer UK fights to help more men survive prostate cancer and enjoy a better quality of life. We support men, find answers and lead change.

PROVIDENCE ROW CHARITY
Founded: 1860 CR207454
Chief Executive: Mr Jo Ansell
The Dellow Centre, 82 Wentworth Street, London
E1 7SA
Tel: 020 7375 0020
Fax: 020 7377 5366
Email: . . . . info@providencerow.org.uk
Objects: F,E,W4,3,C,W8

PROVIDENCE ROW HOUSING ASSOCIATION
FS19322R
Chief Executive: Mr Gary Lashko
PA to Chief Executive: Mrs Maureen Pratt
Providence House, 458 Bethnal Green Road,
London E2 0EA
Tel: 020 7920 7300
Fax: 020 7729 8253
Objects: F,E,D,C

PROVISION TRADE BENEVOLENT INSTITUTION
Founded: 1835 CR209173
Secretary / Treasurer: Mr Mette Barwick
Secretary / Treasurer: Mr Peter Denhard
17 Clerkenwell Green, London EC1R 0DP
Tel: 020 7253 2114
Fax: 020 7608 1645
Objects: W11,1A,A,2,B

THE PSP ASSOCIATION
CR1037087
PSP House (CC), 167 Watling Street West,
Towcester, Northamptonshire NN12 6BX
Tel: 01327 322410
Fax: 01327 322412
Email: . . . . psp@pspeur.org

PSYCHIATRY RESEARCH TRUST
Founded: 1982 CR284286
Trust Director: Mr L Paine
Chief Administrator: Ms Lesley Pease
The Institute of Psychiatry, 16 De Crespigny Park,
Denmark Hill, London SE5 8AF

Tel: 020 7703 6217
Fax: 020 7848 5115
Email: . . . . psychiatry_research_trust@kcl.ac.uk
Object: 1A

PUBLIC LAW PROJECT, THE
Founded: 1991 CR1003342
Director: Mr Conrad Haley
Administrator: Ms Pamela Powell
150 Caledonian Road, London N1 9RD
Tel: 020 7697 2190
Fax: 020 7837 7048
Email: . . . . admin@publiclawproject.org.uk
Objects: W3,W5,G,W4,3

Q

QED UK
Founded: 1991 CR1004608
Chief Executive: Dr Mohammed Ali
Quest House, 243 Manningham Lane, Bradford,
West Yorkshire BD8 7ER
Tel: 01274 483267
Fax: 01274 482277
Email: . . . . info@qed-uk.org
Objects: F,J,G,W10,3,P

QUARRIERS - TRANSFORMING LIVES
SC001960
Fundraising, The Exchange, Quarrier's Village,
Bridge of Weir, Renfrewshire PA11 3SX
Tel: 01505 616057
Fax: 01505 616014
Email: . . . . fundraising@quarriers.org.uk

QUEEN ALEXANDRA'S ROYAL ARMY NURSING CORPS ASSOCIATION (QARANC)

CR270278
Regimental Headquarters QARANC, AMS HQ,
Slim Road, Camberley, Surrey GU15 4NP
Tel: 01276 412754; 01276 412791
Fax: 01276 412793
Email: . . . . regtsecqaranc@hotmail.com
Objects: W9,1A

Exists for the relief of past and present members of the Corps who are in conditions of need, hardship or distress. Maintains contact with past and present members of the Corps fostering mutual comradeship.

QUEEN VICTORIA SEAMEN'S REST - FOR UNEMPLOYED, RETIRED AND ACTIVE SEAFARERS
Founded: 1843 CR1106126
General Secretary: Mr T J Simco MBE
121-131 East India Dock Road, Poplar, London
E14 6DF
Tel: 020 7987 5466
Fax: 020 7537 0665
Email: . . . . personalassistant@qvsr.org.uk

QUIT
Founded: 1926 CR1042482
Chief Executive: Mr Steve Crone
Ground Floor, 20-22 Curtain Road, London
EC2A 3NF
Tel: 0207 539 1700
Email: . . . . info@quit.org.uk
Objects: F,W3,W5,G,W10,W4,H,3,W8

R

RAINER
Founded: 1788 CR229132
Chief Executive: Ms Joyce Moseley
Rectory Lodge, High Street, Brasted, Westerham,
Kent TN16 1JF
Tel: 01959 578200
Fax: 01959 561891
Email: . . . . mail@raineronline.org
Objects: W3,G,D,3,P,Z,I

RAINER FOUNDATION, THE
See Rainer

RAINY DAY TRUST (INCORPORATING THE POTTERY & GLASS TRADES' BENEVOLENT FUND)
Founded: 1843 CR209170
Brooke House, 4 The Lakes, Northampton,
Northamptonshire NN4 7YD
Tel: 01604 622023
Fax: 01604 631252
Email: . . . . rainyday@brookehouse.co.uk
Objects: W9,W6,J,W7,W5,W10,W11,1A,A,V,2, W4,W8

RAMBLERS' ASSOCIATION
Founded: 1935 CR1093577; SC039799
Chief Executive: Mr Nick Barrett
2nd Floor, Camelford House, 87-89 Albert
Embankment, London SE1 7TW
Tel: 020 7339 8500
Fax: 020 7339 8501
Email: . . . . rememberus@ramblers.org.uk
Objects: W2,S,G,2,P

THE RATHBONE CENTRE
See Lambeth Elfrida Rathbone Society
(Rathbone)

RAVENSCOURT
Founded: 1990 CR1000296
Centre Director: Mr J D Harman
15 Ellasdale Road, Bognor Regis, West Sussex
PO21 2SG
Tel: 01243 862157
Fax: 01243 867126
Objects: O,3

RAYNAUD'S & SCLERODERMA ASSOCIATION
CR326306
Press Officer: Miss Fiona Trotter
Chief Executive: Mrs Anne H Mawdsley MBE
112 Crewe Road, Alsager, Cheshire ST7 2JA

Tel: 01270 872776
Fax: 01270 883556
Email: . . . . info@raynauds.org.uk
Objects: F,W3,W5,1A,A,2,W4,H

RAYSTEDE CENTRE FOR ANIMAL WELFARE

RAYSTEDE
GIVING ANIMALS A BETTER LIFE

Founded: 1952 CR237696
Raystede, Ringmer, Lewes, East Sussex BN8 5AJ
Tel: 0844 875 1252
Fax: 01825 840995
Email: . . . . info@raystede.org
Objects: W1,2
A sanctuary for unwanted, abandoned & injured
animals and birds. 1500 animals in residence many
looking for new homes. Visitors welcome 10-4 daily.
Donations and legacies always gratefully received.

RCH CONVALESCENT CENTRES
Founded: 1899 CR207528
General Manager: Mr K. Alldread
245 Victoria Avenue, Ockbrook, Derby, Derbyshire
DE72 3RL
Tel: 01332 280552
Fax: 01332 280552
Email: . . . . keithalldread@aol.com
Objects: W6,W7,W5,W11,V,N,W4,3

REACH - THE ASSOCIATION FOR CHILDREN WITH UPPER LIMB DEFICIENCY
CR1134544
Pearl Assurance House, Brook Street,
Tavistock, Devon PL19 0BN
Tel: 0845 130 6225
Email: . . . . reach@reach.org.uk
Web: . . . . www.reach.org.uk
Objects: F,W3,W5,O,3
Reach is a family support organisation. It
provides information and advice on treatment
and living with an upper limb deficiency. We have
branches throughout the UK. For further
information contact: Jo Dixon at above address.

READING COUNCIL FOR RACIAL EQUALITY
Founded: 1990 CR900448
Director: Mr Rajinder Sohpal
2-4 Silver Street, Reading RG1 2ST
Tel: 0118 986 8755
Fax: 0118 931 4786
Email: . . . . admin@rcre.co.uk
Objects: F,J,W5,W10,3,K

RED SHIFT THEATRE COMPANY LTD
Founded: 1981 CR1004213
General Manager: Ms Emma Rees
TRG2 Trowbray House, 108 Weston Street,
London SE1 3QB
Tel: 020 7378 9787
Fax: 020 7378 9789
Email: . . . . mail@redshifttheatreco.co.uk
Objects: S,3

REDBRIDGE CVS
Founded: 1991 CR1005075
3rd Floor, Forest House, 16-20 Clements Road, Ilford, Essex IG1 1BA
Tel: 020 8553 1004
Fax: 020 8911 9128
Email: . . . . info@redbridgecvs.net
Objects: F,W3,J,G,W10,2,H,3

REDBRIDGE, EPPING & HARROW CROSSROADS - CARING FOR CARERS
Founded: 1991 CR1005208
Business Manager: Mrs Karen Kent
106 Charter Avenue, Newbury Park, Ilford, Essex IG2 7AD
Tel: 020 8518 4090; 020 8554 0790
Objects: M,W3,W5,W10,2,W4,3

REDCAR & CLEVELAND MIND
Founded: 1991 CR1142520
Treasurer: Mr Dennis Kiff
Director: Ms Sharon Street
Dove House, 5 Turner Street, Redcar, Redcar & Cleveland TS10 1AY
Tel: 01642 296052
Fax: 01642 296053
Email: . . . . main@randcmind.org
Objects: F,J,E,W5,2,H,O,3,P

REDDITCH CITIZENS ADVICE BUREAU
Founded: 1967 CR1003414
Manager: Mrs Moira Morris
Mrs Nina Wood-Ford
Suite E, Canon Newton House, Kingfisher Shopping Centre, Redditch, Worcestershire B97 4HA
Tel: 08444 152221
Email: . . . . manager@redditchcab.cabnet.org.uk
Objects: F,W9,W6,W3,W7,W5,G,W10,W11,D,W4, 3,W8

REDR UK
CR1079752
Ms Jo Barratt
250a Kennington Lane, London SE11 5RD
Tel: 020 7840 6000
Fax: 020 7582 8669
Email: . . . . info@redr.org
Objects: F,W3,G,W10,2,W4,U,H,3,W8,K

REDWINGS ADA COLE RESCUE STABLES
CR1068911
c/o Hapton, Norwich, Norfolk NR15 1SP
Tel: 01508 481000; 08700 400033
Fax: 0870 458 1947
Email: . . . . info@redwings.co.uk

REDWINGS HORSE SANCTUARY
Founded: 1984 CR1068911
Chief Executive: Ms Lynn Cutress
Hapton, Norwich, Norfolk NR15 1SP
Tel: 01508 481000
Fax: 0870 458 1947
Email: . . . . info@redwings.co.uk
Objects: Q,F,W1,G,N,H,O,3
Working to provide and promote the welfare, care and protection of horses, ponies, donkeys and mules.
See advert on this page

REED'S SCHOOL

Founded: 1813 CR312008
Bursar: Mr A D Bott FCCA
Headmaster: Mr David Jarrett MA
Sandy Lane, Cobham, Surrey KT11 2EP
Tel: 01932 869025
Fax: 01932 869046
Email: . . . . . . rgarrett@reeds.surrey.sch.uk
Web: . . . . . http://www.reeds.surrey.sch.uk
Objects: W3,G,A,3

Founded as an orphanage in 1813 by philanthropist Andrew Reed, Reed's School is now a thriving independent school which provides Bursaries for children in need. In addition the Reed's School Forums aim to break down barriers between state and independent education by creating a network that delivers opportunities to over 5000 disadvantaged children from low income families. The Forums provide a host of academic, sporting and creative enrichment activities, together with bursary and scholarship funding. The aim is to raise aspirations and improve the performance of young people facing hardship.

See advert on this page

REFUGEE LEGAL CENTRE
Founded: 1992 CR1012004
Secretary: Mr B Stoyle
Nelson House, 153-157 Commercial Road, London E1 2DA
Tel: 020 7780 3200
Fax: 020 7780 3201
Email: . . . . rlc@refugee-legal-centre.org.uk
Objects: F,W10,3

RELATE, THE RELATIONSHIP PEOPLE
Founded: 1938 CR207314
Chief Executive: Ms Sarah Bowler
Chief Executive: Ms Angela Sibson
Relate Premier House, Carolina Court, Lakeside, Doncaster, South Yorkshire DN4 5RA
Tel: 0845 456 1310
Email: . . . . enquiries@relate.org.uk
Objects: F,G,H,3

RELATIONSHIP COUNSELLING FOR LONDON
See London Marriage Guiding Council

RELATIVES & RESIDENTS ASSOCIATION
Founded: 1993 CR1020194
Director: Ms Jenny Stiles
1 The Ivories, 6-18 Northampton Street, London N1 2HY
Tel: 020 7359 8148
Email: . . . . info@relres.org
Objects: F,J,G,2,W4,H,P

RELEASE - THE NATIONAL DRUGS & LEGAL HELPLINE
Founded: 1967 CR801118
Director: Mr Sebastian Saville
388 Old Street, London EC1V 9LT
Tel: 020 7729 9904
Email: . . . . ask@release.org.uk
Objects: F,G,H,3

RELIEF FUND FOR ROMANIA
Founded: 1989 CR1046737
Director: Mr Edward Parry
54-62 Regent Street, London W1B 5RE
Tel: 020 8761 2277
Email: . . . . mail@relieffundforromania.co.uk
Objects: U,3

RESCARE - NATIONAL SOCIETY FOR CHILDREN AND ADULTS WITH LEARNING DISABILITIES AND THEIR FAMILIES
Founded: 1984 CR5631419
Honorary Chairman: Mr R S Jackson MBE, CEng, MIMechE
Steven Jackson House, 31 Buxton Road,
Heavlley, Stockport, Greater Manchester SK2 6LS
Tel: 0161 474 7323
Fax: 0161 480 3668
Email: . . . . office@rescare.org.uk
Objects: F,W5,1A,2,H,3

RESEARCH INSTITUTE FOR CONSUMER AFFAIRS
See Ricability

RESTRICTED GROWTH ASSOCIATION
Founded: 1970 CR261647
National Development Officer: Mrs Honor Rawlings
PO Box 1024, Peterborough, Cambridgeshire PE1 9GX
Tel: 01733 759458
Email: . . . . office@restrictedgrowth.co.uk
Objects: Q,F,W3,2,H,P

RETIRED GREYHOUND TRUST
Founded: 1975 CR269668
2nd Floor, Park House, 1 - 4 Park Terrace,
Worcester Park, Surrey KT4 7JZ
Tel: 020 8335 3016
Fax: 020 8337 5426
Email: . . . greyhounds@retiredgreyhounds.co.uk

THE RETIRED NURSES NATIONAL HOME
Founded: 1934 CR1090202
General Administrator: Mrs Elaine Brace
Chairman: Mrs Joyce Deacon SRN
Company Secretary / Treasurer: Mr Brian Newman
Riverside Avenue, Bournemouth BH7 7EE
Tel: 01202 396418
Fax: 01202 302530
Email: . . . . anything@rnnh.co.uk
Objects: M,N,3,C,P

RETRAINING OF RACEHORSES (ROR)
CR1084787
75 High Holborn, London WC1V 6LS
Tel: 020 7152 0178
Fax: 020 7152 0081
Email: . . . . info@ror.org.uk

RICABILITY
Founded: 1991 CR1007726
Company Secretary: Mr Andrew Day
Outreach Manager: Mr Chris Lofthouse
30 Angel Gate, City Road, London EC1V 2PT
Tel: .... 020 7427 2460; 020 7427 2469 Minicom
Fax: 020 7427 2468
Email: .... mail@ricability.org.uk
Objects: W6,W7,W5,W4,H,3

RICHARD LEWIS AWARD FUND, THE
Founded: 1992 CR1010272
Treasurer & Trustee: Ms Elizabeth Muir-Lewis
Manor Barn, 8 Manor Way, Eastbourne, East
Sussex BN20 9BN
Objects: W3,S,G,1B

RICHMOND FELLOWSHIP
Founded: 1959 CR200453
CEO: Ms Maggie Hysel
Executive Officer: Ms Marise Willis
Richmond Fellowship, 80 Holloway Road,
Islington, London N7 8JG
Tel: 020 7697 3300
Fax: 020 7697 3301
Email: communications@richmondfellowship.org.
uk
Objects: F,E,G,D,O,3,C,P,K

RIDING FOR THE DISABLED ASSOCIATION (NORTHERN IRELAND) INCORPORATING CARRIAGE DRIVING
Founded: 1969 CR244108
Julie Jordan, Kilmore House, Lurgan, Co. Armagh
BT67 9JP
Tel: 028 3822 2292
Email: .... rdaniregion@yahoo.co.uk
Objects: F,M,,I,W5,G,V,2,H,O,3

THE RIGHT TO LIFE CHARITABLE TRUST
CR1099319
PO Box 354, Sevenoaks, Kent TN13 9GA
Tel: 01732 460911
Fax: 01732 460911
Email: .... eleanor@righttolife.org.uk

RIVER & ROWING MUSEUM FOUNDATION
Founded: 1990 CR1001051
Chief Executive: Mr Paul Mainds
Mill Meadows, Henley-on-Thames, Oxfordshire
RG9 1BF
Tel: 01491 415600
Fax: 01491 415601
Email: .... museum@rrm.co.uk
Objects: W3,W2,S,G,W12,H

RIVERSIDE VINEYARD CHURCH
Founded: 1992 CR1013545
The Company Secretary
The Vineyard Centre, 513 Browells Lane, Feltham,
Middlesex TW13 7EQ
Tel: 020 8890 3535
Fax: 020 8890 3999
Objects: W3,2,R

ROALD DAHL'S MARVELLOUS CHILDREN'S CHARITY
Founded: 1991 CR1137409
Director: James Fitzpatrick
81A High Street, Great Missenden,
Buckinghamshire HP16 0AL

Tel: 01494 890465
Fax: 01494 890459
Objects: W3,1A,A,1B,N

ROCK REHABILITATION AND OCCUPATIONAL THERAPY CENTRE LTD
See Rock Work Opportunity Centre Ltd

ROCK WORK OPPORTUNITY CENTRE LTD
Founded: 1992 CR1011392
Managing Director: Mr G W Brown
230 Bristol Avenue, Blackpool FY2 0JF
Tel: 01253 593173
Fax: 01253 593683
Email: .... dt@rockwork.freeserve.co.uk

ROTHERHAM CROSSROADS CARING FOR CARERS
Founded: 1990 CR1062664
Chairman: Mr Bennett
Scheme Manager: Mrs Elizabeth Bent
Unit H, The Point, Broadmarsh, Rotherham, South
Yorkshire S60 1BP
Tel: 01709 360272
Fax: 01709 360272
Objects: W6,M,W7,W5,W4,3,P

THE ROWANS HOSPICE
CR299731
Purbrook Heath Road (CC), Purbrook,
Waterlooville, Hampshire PO7 5RU
Tel: 023 9225 0001
Fax: 023 9226 8567
Email: .... info@rowanshospice.co.uk
Objects: F,M,E,W5,W10,N,W4,3

ROYAL AIR FORCE BENEVOLENT FUND – RAFBF
Founded: 1919 CR1081009; SCO38109
Controller: Air Marshal Chris Nickols
67 Portland Place, London W1B 1AR
Tel: 020 7580 8343
Fax: 020 7636 7005
Email: .... info@rafbf.org.uk
See advert on previous page

ROYAL ALEXANDRA AND ALBERT SCHOOL, THE
Founded: 1758 CR311945
Secretary: Mrs Diana Bromley
Gatton Park, Reigate, Surrey RH2 0TD
Tel: 01737 649000
Fax: 01737 649002
Email: .... bursar@gatton-park.org.uk
Objects: W3,G,1A,B,3

A voluntary-aided junior and secondary boarding and
day boarding school for boys and girls aged from 7-18,
catering especially for those without one or both parents
or whose circumstances make boarding education
advantageous.
Children of all abilities admitted. Superb facilities,
bursaries available.
Management: Jointly by School Foundation and Surrey
Education Authority through Governing Body.
See advert on next page

ROYAL ARCHAEOLOGICAL INSTITUTE
CR254543
Administrator: S Gerber-Parfitt
Hon Secretary: Miss G Hey BA, PhD, FSA, MIFA
c/o Society of Antiquaries, Burlington House, Piccadilly, London W1J 0BE
Tel: 0116 243 3839
Fax: 0116 243 3839
Email: .... admin@royalarchinst.org
Objects: W2,1A,A,1B,H

ROYAL ARMY PAY CORPS REGIMENTAL ASSOCIATION
Founded: 1928 CR270477
RHQ AGC, Worthy Down, Winchester, Hampshire SO21 2RG
Tel: 01962 887436
Fax: 01962 887074
Email: .... regsec.rapc@virgin.net
Objects: W9,1A,A,V,2,P

ROYAL ARTILLERY CHARITABLE FUND
Founded: 1839 CR210202
General Secretary: Lt Col I A Vere Nicoll MBE
Artillery House, Royal Artillery Barracks, Larkhill, Salisbury, Wiltshire SP4 8QT
Tel: 01980 845895
Email: .. artycen-rhqra-racf-raa-gensec@mod.uk
Objects: F,W9,J,G,1A,A,1B,V,B,P
For relief and assistance of all past and present members of the Royal Regiment of Artillery, and their families and dependants, and the families and dependants of any deceased members, who are in need.

ROYAL ASSOCIATION FOR DEAF PEOPLE (RAD)
Founded: 1841 CR1081949
Administrator: Ms Tracey Barlow
Chief Executive: Mr Tom Fenton
Walsingham Road, Colchester, Essex CO2 7BP
Tel: 01206 509509
Fax: 01206 769755
Email: .... info@royaldeaf.org.uk
Objects: F,J,S,W7,W5,H,T,3,P

ROYAL BLIND, EDINBURGH
Founded: 1793SC017167
Chief Executive: Mr R G Hellewell
Box No: 500, Gillespie Crescent, Edinburgh EH10 4HZ
Tel: 0131 229 1456
Fax: 0131 229 4060
Email: .... enquiries@royablind.org
Objects: F,W6,M,W3,W5,G,N,W4,3

ROYAL BRITISH LEGION
CR219279
Ms Laura Buckley
Controller of Public Relations: Mr Charles Lewis
Secretary General: Mr Ian Townsend
Haig House, 199 Borough High Street, London SE1 1AA
Tel: 020 3207 2100
Fax: 020 3207 2276
Email: .... info@britishlegion.org.uk
Objects: F,E,A,B,O,C,K

ROYAL BRITISH LEGION WOMEN'S SECTION
CR219279
Haig House, 199 Borough High Street, London SE1 1AA
Tel: 020 3207 2188
Fax: 020 3207 2358
Email: .... women@britishlegion.org.uk
Objects: F,W9,M,W3,W5,G,1A,A,V,D,2,W4,3,P, W8

ROYAL COLLEGE OF ANAESTHETISTS
Founded: 1992 CR1013887
Finance Director
Churchill House, 35 Red Lion Square, London WC1R 4SG
Tel: 020 7092 1500
Fax: 020 7092 1730
Email: .... info@rcoa.ac.uk

ROYAL COMMONWEALTH EX-SERVICES LEAGUE
Founded: 1921 CR231322
Secretary General: Colonel P.A. Davis CBE
Controller Finance / Assistant Secretary General: Lieutenant Colonel C F Warren
199 Borough High Street, London SE1 1AA
Tel: 020 3207 2413
Fax: 020 3207 2115
Email: .. mgordon-roe@commonwealthveterans. org.uk
Objects: F,W9,J,1A,A,1B,U,W8

ROYAL ENGINEERS ASSOCIATION
Founded: 1868 CR258322
Controller: Lt Col John McLennan
Deputy Controller: Mr B J White
Brompton Barracks, Chatham, Kent ME4 4UG
Tel: 01634 847005
Email: .... info@reahq.org.uk
Objects: F,W9,J,1A,A,1B,V,W4,P,W8

ROYAL ENGINEERS CENTRAL CHARITABLE TRUST
Founded: 1991 CR1003032
Corps Treasurer: Lt Col (Retd) Roy Wilsher
Regimental HQ, Ravelin Building, Brompton Barracks, Dock Road, Chatham, Kent ME4 4UG
Tel: 01634 822355
Fax: 01634 822003
Email: .... info@reahq.org.uk
Objects: W9,1A,A,1B,2,W12

ROYAL FOUNDATION OF ST. KATHARINE
Founded: 1147 CR223849
The Master: The Revd Preb Ronald Swan MA
2 Butcher Row, London E14 8DS
Tel: 020 7790 3540
Fax: 020 7702 7603
Email: ...... michael@stkatherine.demon.co.uk
Objects: F,S,G,D,R,H,P

ROYAL GARDENERS' ORPHAN FUND
See Royal Fund for Gardeners' Children

ROYAL GENERAL THEATRICAL FUND ASSOCIATION
See Royal Theatrical Fund

ROYAL HORTICULTURAL SOCIETY – THE UK'S LEADING GARDENING CHARITY
CR222879; SC038262
80 Vincent Square, London SW1P 2PB
Tel: 020 7821 3125
Fax: 020 7821 3010
Email: .... developmentoffice@rhs.org.uk
Web: .... www.rhs.org.uk
The RHS is the UK's leading gardening charity. Our goal is to help people share a passion for plants, to encourage excellence in horticulture and inspire all those with an interest in gardening. Our four RHS gardens: Wisley in Surrey, Hyde Hall in Essex, Harlow Carr in North Yorkshire and Rosemoor in Devon, demonstrate horticultural excellence and bring joy and inspiration to thousands. We research how best to cultivate plants and protect them against pests and diseases, garden sustainably in a changing climate and encourage biodiversity. We enthuse gardeners of every age and ability to get growing and the RHS Campaign for School Gardening has so far proved a huge success by engaging with over 17,000 schools in the UK. As a charity we receive no direct government funding; we rely on donations as well as income from memberships, flower shows, shops and raffles. Legacies are at the heart of the Society's funding. By leaving a legacy to the RHS you can help us to pass on a love of gardening, giving joy and inspiration to gardeners of all ages, including thousands of school children and young people. Legacies also help us to fund the vital scientific research that underpins our understanding of plants and the development of horticultural knowledge for gardeners worldwide.

ROYAL LIVERPOOL PHILHARMONIC SOCIETY, THE
Founded: 1841 CR1002122
Chief Executive: Mr Michael Elliott
Fundraiser: Ms Claire Hughes
Head of Fundraising: Ms Kath Russell
Philharmonic Hall, Hope Street, Liverpool, Merseyside L1 9DP
Tel: 0151 210 2895
Fax: 0151 210 2902
Email: .... lisa.murray@liverpoolphil.com
Objects: 3,G

ROYAL LONDON SOCIETY FOR BLIND PEOPLE
Founded: 1838 CR307892
Chief Executive: Mr Brian Cooney
Dorton Campus, Wildernesse Avenue, Seal, Sevenoaks, Kent TN15 0EB
Tel: 01732 592500
Fax: 01732 592506
Email: .... ceosoffice@rlsb.org.uk
Objects: F,W6,M,W3,W5,G,W4,B,H,O,3,P,K

ROYAL MARINES ASSOCIATION
Founded: 1946 CR206003
Chief Executive: Brigadier Charlie W P Hobson
Central Office, Building 32, Whale Island, Portsmouth, Hampshire PO2 8ER
Tel: 023 9265 1519
Email: .... chiefexec@rma.org.uk
Objects: F,W9,1B,2,P

ROYAL MARINES CHARITABLE TRUST FUND
CR1134205
Corps Funds Treasurer: Capt Steve Marr RM
Building 32, H M S Excellent, Whale Island, Portsmouth, Hampshire PO2 8ER
Tel: 023 9254 7201
Fax: 023 9254 7207
Email: .... fundraising@rmctf.org.uk
Objects: W9,1A,A

ROYAL MARSDEN CANCER CHARITY
Founded: 1851 CR1095197
Chief Executive: Miss Cally Palmer
203 Fulham Road, London SW3 6JJ
Tel: 020 7808 2233
Fax: 020 7808 2268
Email: .... charity@royalmarsden.org

ROYAL MASONIC BENEVOLENT INSTITUTION
Founded: 1842 CR207360
Chief Executive: Mr Peter Gray FCIH ACIEH
Director of Communications: Mr Peter Williams
60 Great Queen Street, London WC2B 5AZ
Tel: 020 7596 2400
Fax: 020 7404 0724
Email: .... enquiries@rmbi.org.uk
Objects: F,1A,V,W4,B,3,C

THE ROYAL MEDICAL FOUNDATION
Founded: 1855 CR312046
Caseworker: Mrs Helen Jones
Administrator: Mr Chris Titman
Epsom College, College Road, Epsom, Surrey KT17 4JQ
Tel: 01372 021010
Fax: 01372 821013
Email: . caseworker@royalmedicalfoundation.org
Objects: W3,W5,G,1A,A,W4,B

ROYAL METAL TRADES BENEVOLENT SOCIETY
See RAINY DAY TRUST (Incorporating the Pottery & Glass Trades' Benevolent Fund)

ROYAL NATIONAL COLLEGE FOR THE BLIND (RNC)
Founded: 1872 CR1000388
Venns Lane, Hereford, Herefordshire HR1 1DT
Tel: 01432 376371
Fax: 01432 376628
Email: .... fundraising@rnc.ac.uk
Objects: W6,W5,G,O,3

ROYAL NATIONAL INSTITUTE OF BLIND PEOPLE (RNIB)
Founded: 1868 CR226227
Director General: Prof Ian Bruce BSocSc. CIMgt
Head of Communications: Ms Lynne Stockbridge
105 Judd Street, London WC1H 9NE
Tel: .... 020 7388 1266; 0845 766 9999 Helpline
Fax: 020 7388 2034
Email: .... helpline@rnib.org.uk
Objects: F,W6,M,W3,J,S,W5,G,A,V,D,W4,H,O,C, P

ROYAL NATIONAL MISSION TO DEEP SEA FISHERMEN
See Fishermen's Mission - Royal National Mission To Deep Sea Fishermen

ROYAL NAVAL ASSOCIATION - ONCE NAVY, ALWAYS NAVY
Founded: 1950 CR266982
Room 209, Semaphore Tower, PP70, HM Naval Base, Portsmouth, Hampshire PO1 3LT
Tel: 02392 723823
Email: .... paddy@royalnavalassoc.com
Objects: F,W9,J,G,1A,A,1B,2,B,H,P

ROYAL NAVAL BENEVOLENT TRUST (GRAND FLEET & KINDRED FUNDS)
Founded: 1922 CR206243
Events and Publicity Officer: Ms Corinne Day
Chief Executive: Commander Stephen Farrington QGM RN
Castaway House (CD), 311 Twyford Avenue, Portsmouth, Hampshire PO2 8RN
Tel: ... 023 9269 0112 Administration; 023 9266 0296 Welfare
Fax: 023 9266 0852
Email: .... rnbt@rnbt.org.uk
Web: .... http://www.rnbt.org.uk
Objects: F,W9,1A,A
The RNBT was established in 1922 to give help, in cases of need, to those who are serving or have served as ratings in the Royal Navy or as other ranks in the Royal Marines, and their dependants.
See advert on previous page

ROYAL NAVY SUBMARINE MUSEUM
Founded: 1996 CR1142123
Director: Commander J J Tall OBE, RN
Haslar Jetty Road, Gosport, Hampshire PO12 2AS
Tel: 023 9251 0354
Fax: 023 9251 1349
Email: rnsubs@submarine.museum.demon.co.uk
Objects: W2,G,W12

ROYAL PARKS FOUNDATION
CR1097545
The Old Police House, Hyde Park, London W2 2UH
Tel: 020 7036 8043
Email: ...... support@royalparksfoundation.org

ROYAL SAILORS REST (RSR)
Founded: 1876 CR238748
Mr David Rogerson
Castaway House, 311 Twyford Avenue, Portsmouth, Hampshire PO2 8RN
Tel: 023 9265 0505
Fax: 023 9265 2929
Email: .... info@rsr.org.uk
Objects: W9,W3,R,3,P

ROYAL SCHOOL FOR DEAF CHILDREN MARGATE
CR325109
Victoria Rd, Margate, Kent CT9 1NB
Tel: 01843 227561
Email: .... enquiries@rsdcm.org.uk
Objects: W3,W7,G

ROYAL SCHOOL FOR THE BLIND, LIVERPOOL
Founded: 1791 CR526090
Ms Jo-Anne McMullin
Church Road, North Wavertree, Liverpool, Merseyside L15 6TQ
Tel: 0151 733 1012
Fax: 0151 733 1703
Email: .... rsblind@globalnet.co.uk
Objects: W6,W3,W5,G

ROYAL SCHOOL FOR THE DEAF DERBY

CR1062507
Ashbourne Road, Derby, Derbyshire DE22 3BH
Tel: 01332 362512
Fax: 01332 299708
Email: .... principal@rsdd.org.uk
RSD Derby welcomes deaf learners from across the United Kingdom. We value British Sign Language and English equally, respecting the cultures of deaf and hearing people. The School promotes a positive sense of identity for each pupil, preparing them for the opportunities of adulthood and full participation in their community.
See advert on previous page

ROYAL SCHOOL OF CHURCH MUSIC

RS✦M

Founded: 1927 CR312828
Director: Mr Andrew Reid
Head of Development: Ms Catherine Demetriadi
19 The Close, Salisbury, Wiltshire SP1 2EB
Tel: 01722 424848
Fax: 01722 424849
Email: .... enquiries@rscm.com
Objects: F,W3,S,G,2,H,3
The RSCM is an ecumenical charity promoting the best use of music in Christian worship, church life, and the wider community. We support church music through education, vocational training, advice, planning tools, performance opportunities, and publishing. Our aim is to secure the future, enrich the present, and sustain the traditions that inspire worship through music.

THE ROYAL SCOTTISH CORPORATION
See ScotsCare

ROYAL SOCIETY FOR NATURE CONSERVATION/ RSNC
See The Wildlife Trusts

THE ROYAL SOCIETY FOR THE PREVENTION OF ACCIDENTS
Founded: 1916 CR207823
Edgbaston Park, 353 Bristol Road, Birmingham, West Midlands B5 7ST
Tel: 0121 248 2000
Fax: 0121 248 2001
Email: .... info-ni@rospa.com
Objects: F,W3,J,G,2,W4,H,3

ROYAL SOCIETY FOR THE PREVENTION OF CRUELTY TO ANIMALS, LIVERPOOL BRANCH

Founded: 1809 CR232254
Secretary: Mr John Smallwood
19 Tapton Way, Liverpool, Merseyside L13 1DA
Tel: 0151 220 3812
Fax: 0151 220 3821
Web: . http://www.rspcaliverpoolbranch.co.uk
Objects: W1,A
• The RSPCA Liverpool Branch formed in 1809 as "The Liverpool Society for Preventing Wanton Cruelty to Brute Animals" is the oldest Animal Charity in the world.
• Our core activity at the RSPCA Liverpool Branch Animal Centre in Halewood is accepting hundreds of cruelty case dogs and cats brought to us by RSPCA Inspectors from all over the north of England. These unfortunate cruelly treated, abused and neglected animals are nursed back to health on site by our dedicated veterinary and animal care staff. All animals are then neutered and cared for until they are suitable for rehoming.
• We are open to the public for viewing from 11.30 p.m. to 4.30 p.m. every day except Wednesday.
See advert on next page

THE ROYAL SOCIETY FOR THE PROMOTION OF HEALTH
Founded: 1876 CR215520
Chief Executive: Prof. Richard Parish
Chief Executive: Mr Stuart Royston
38A St George's Drive, London SW1V 4BH
Tel: 020 7630 0121
Fax: 020 7976 6847
Email: .... rsph@rsph.org
Objects: W6,W3,W2,W7,W5,G,2,W4,H,3,W8

THE ROYAL SOCIETY FOR THE PROTECTION OF BIRDS
CR207076; SC037654
Director of Marketing: Ms Karen Rothwell
Chief Executive: Mr Graham Wynne
The Lodge, Sandy, Bedfordshire SG19 2DL
Tel: 01767 680551
Fax: 01767 692365
Email: .... info@rspb.org.uk

ROYAL SOCIETY FOR THE RELIEF OF INDIGENT GENTLEWOMEN OF SCOTLAND, THE
Founded: 1847SC 016095
Senior Caseworker: Mrs Anne Metcalfe
14 Rutland Square, Edinburgh EH1 2BD
Tel: 0131 229 2308
Fax: 0131 229 0956
Email: .... info@igf.org
Web: .... www.igf.org
Objects: F,1A,A,2,W4,W8
The Society provides regular financial assistance, awarding grants of up to £1100 per annum. The service is confidential and personal: Caseworkers visit ladies in

Liverpool Branch

Reg. Charity No. 232254

Working for Animal Welfare Since 1809

Good homes always wanted for dogs and cats in our care

Branch Office: 19 Tapton Way, Liverpool L13 1DA
0151 220 3812

Animal Centre: Higher Road, Halewood Liverpool L26 9TX
0151 486 1706

www.rspcaliverpoolbranch.co.uk

their own homes, offering support if required, with other benefits available to meet specific needs.

Applications are considered in May and November each year from Scottish ladies who are widowed, divorced or unmarried, aged 50 or over - specifically, of Scottish birth or education with professional or business backgrounds, who exist on low incomes and savings. Over the last five years our Society has distributed nearly £4.5 million to ladies and the help in the current year will be approximately £1 million.

Contact the Society for Information and Application.

THE ROYAL SOCIETY OF ST GEORGE CHARITABLE TRUST
Founded: 1971 CR263076
Trust Secretary: Mrs E M Robinson
Chairman: Mr A Temple
127 Sandgate Road, Folkestone, Kent CT20 2BL
Tel: 01303 241795
Fax: 01303 850162
Email: .... info@rssg.u-net.com
Objects: W3,G,1A,A,1B,2

ROYAL SURGICAL AID SOCIETY, THE
See AgeCare (The Royal Surgical Aid Society)

ROYAL TANK REGIMENT BENEVOLENT FUND
Founded: 1919 CR248487
Regimental Secretary: Major.(Retd) A Henzie MBE
Regimental Colonel: Colonel (Retd) J L Longman
Stanley Barracks, Bovington, Wareham, Dorset BH20 6JB

Tel: 01929 403331
Fax: 01929 403488
Objects: F,W9,1A,A,1B

ROYAL THEATRICAL FUND
Founded: 1839 CR222080
Secretary: Ms Roslyn Foster
11 Garrick Street, London WC2E 9AR
Tel: 020 7836 3322
Fax: 020 7379 8273
Email: .... admin@trtf.com
Objects: W6,M,W5,1A,A,N,W4,O

ROYAL ULSTER CONSTABULARY GEORGE CROSS - POLICE SERVICE NORTHERN IRELAND BENEVOLENT FUND
XN48380
77-79 Garnerville Road, Belfast BT4 2NX
Tel: 028 9076 4200; 028 9076 4215
Fax: 028 9076 1548
Email: .... benfund.pfni@btconnect.com
Objects: W9,W6,W3,J,W7,W5,W15,1A,1B,2,W4, O,Y,3,P,W8

ROYAL UNITED KINGDOM BENEFICENT ASSOCIATION
See Independent Age

THE ROYAL VETERINARY COLLEGE
See Animal Care Trust

Samaritan's Purse™
INTERNATIONAL RELIEF

Helping in Jesus' Name

'A good man will leave an inheritance....' Proverbs 13.22 (NKJV)

By leaving a legacy in your Will you will be investing in the future of many underprivileged children and families, making a real difference in the lives of people across the world even though you are no longer here. Leaving a legacy is one way to ensure you are being a good steward of what God has given in your lifetime, to benefit future generations.

Samaritan's Purse is committed to providing long term support for victims of war, poverty, famine, disease and natural disaster whilst sharing the Good News of Jesus Christ.

If you share our passion for the world, giving a legacy means you can positively change the future of suffering people, giving them a will to live!

If you need any further assistance please don't hesitate to contact us on 020 8559 2044.

Samaritan's Purse, Victoria House, Victoria Road, Buckhurst Hill, Essex IG9 5EX.
Registered Charity Number 1001349.

RP FIGHTING BLINDNESS
Founded: 1975 CR271729
Chief Executive: Mr David Head
Hon President Trustee: Mrs Lynda Cantor MBE
PO Box 350, Buckingham, Buckinghamshire
MK18 1GZ
Tel: . 01280 821334; RP Helpline: 08451 232354
Email: . . . . info@rpfightingblindness.org.uk
Objects: F,A,1B,2,H
Retinitis pigmentosa is a hereditary disease of the retina that results in progressive loss of sight. We fund research to find a cure and support people with the condition.

RSABI
SC009828
Development Manager: Mr Paul Tinson
CEO: Ms Nina Clancy
Welfare Manager: Mr John Macfarlane
The Rural Centre, West Mains of Ingliston,
Newbridge, Midlothian EH28 8LT
Tel: 0131 472 4166
Fax: 0131 472 4156
Email: . . . . rsabi@rsabi.org.uk
Web: . . . . www.rsabi.org.uk
Objects: F,W6,W3,W7,W5,W11,1A,A,W4,W8
RSABI is the Scottish charity dedicated to helping people who have depended on the land. Anyone who has worked in agriculture, fish farming, forestry, horticulture and rural estate work and their dependants may be eligible. Each case is sympathetically and confidentially reviewed and assistance given in the form of crisis grants, annual payments or in kind, depending on circumstances. The charity is dependent upon voluntary donations and legacies to further its work.

Further details, applications, Gift Aid forms etc. available from the Chief Executive at the above address.

RSPCA BRISTOL BRANCH AND BRISTOL DOGS AND CATS HOME
CR205858
48 Albert Road, St Philips, Bristol BS2 0XA
Tel: 0117 924 3147
Fax: 0117 971 4809
Email: . . . . info@rspca-bristol.org.uk
Objects: Q,W1,3
Each year our Clinic treats over 12000 animals, providing a 24hr veterinary service for lost, sick & injured animals, subsidised treatment for those on low incomes & first aid for wildlife casualties. The Dogs Home provides care & a rehoming service to 2000 unwanted, abandoned & mistreated animals annually. With no funding from National RSPCA we reply entirely upon donations from the public to give animals in need a life free from pain & neglect.

RUDOLF STEINER PRESS
Founded: 1992 CR1013276
Secretary to the Trustees: Mr S Gulbekian
Hillside House, The Square, Forest Row, East
Sussex RH18 5ES
Tel: 01342 824433
Fax: 01342 826437
Email: . . . . office@rudolfsteinerpress.com
Objects: H,3

RUKBA
See Independent Age

S

SADACCA LIMITED
Founded: 1990 CR702393
Secretary: Mr Frank Heywood
Chairman: Mr Milton Samuel
48 Wicker Street, Sheffield, South Yorkshire
S3 8JB
Tel: 0114 275 3915
Fax: 0114 275 5629
Email: .... sadacca@yahoo.co.uk
Objects: F,W3,S,E,W5,G,W10,2,W4,3,P

SAILORS' FAMILIES' SOCIETY
Founded: 1821 CR224505
Chief Executive: Mr R B Vernon
Francis ReckittHouse, Newland, Kingston upon
Hull, East Riding of Yorkshire HU6 7RJ
Tel: 01482 342331
Fax: 01482 447868
Email: .... info@sailors-families.org.uk
Objects: F,W3,G,1A,A,V,3,C

SAILORS' SOCIETY
Founded: 1818 CR237778
The General Secretary
General Secretary: Mr Robert Adams
350 Shirley Road (CC), Southampton, Hampshire
SO15 3HY
Tel: 023 8051 5950
Fax: 028 8051 5951
Email: .... admin@biss.org.uk
Objects: F,M,J,W11,1A,A,B,3

SAINT MICHAEL'S HOSPICE (HARROGATE)
CR518905
Crimple House, Hornbeam Park Avenue,
Harrogate, North Yorkshire HG2 8QL
Tel: ..... 01423 879687; 01423 872658 Nursing
Fax: . 01423 872654; 01423 878199 Fundraising
Email: ...... cnorton@saintmichaelshospice.org

SALFORD FOUNDATION LIMITED
Founded: 1991 CR1002482
Mr P Collins
1st Floor Charles House, Albert Street, Eccles,
Manchester, Greater Manchester M30 0PD
Tel: 0161 787 8500

SAMARITAN'S PURSE

Founded: 1990 CR1001349
**Victoria House, Victoria Road, Buckhurst
Hill, Essex IG9 5EX**
Tel: 020 8559 1180
Fax: 020 8502 9062
Email: ..... info@samaritans-purse.org.uk
Web: www.samaritans-purse.org.uk; www.
operationchristmaschild.org.uk
Samaritan's Purse International Relief. Helping
in Jesus' name. Samaritan's Purse is committed
to providing long term support for the victims of
war, poverty, famine, disease and natural
disaster whilst sharing the Good News of Jesus
Christ.
See advert on previous page

SAMARITANS
Founded: 1953 CR219432; SC040604
The Upper Mill, Kingston Road, Ewell, Surrey
KT17 2AF
Tel: 08709 000032
Fax: 020 8394 8301
Email: .... admin@samaritans.org
*Objects: F,W9,W6,W3,W7,W5,W10,W11,2,R,W4,
3,W8*

SANDES SOLDIERS' & AIRMEN'S CENTRES
CR250718
Unit 7, 30 Island Street, Belfast BT4 1DH
Tel: 028 9050 0250
Fax: 028 9022 6233
Email: .... info@sandes.org.uk
Objects: F,W9,R,3,P

SANDS - STILLBIRTH AND NEONATAL DEATH SOCIETY
Founded: 1978 CR299679
28 Portland Place, London W1B 1LY
Tel: .... 020 7436 5881 Helpline; 020 7436 7940
Administration
Fax: 020 7436 3715
Email: .... support@uk-sands.org
Objects: F,J,G,1A,2,H,3,P,W8,K

SAVE THE CHILDREN

CR213890; SC039570
Chief Executive: Justin Forsyth
Chair: Alan Parker
Patron: HM Queen Elizabeth II
President: HRH The Princess Royal
Honorary Treasurer: Mr Richard Winter
1 St. John's Lane (CD), Farringdon, London
EC1M 4AR
Tel: 020 7012 6400
Email: .... leavelife@savethechildren.org
Web: .... www.savethechildren.org.uk
Objects: F,W3,J,G,U,H,3
Save the Children works in more than 120 countries.
We save children's lives. We fight for their rights. We
help them fulfil their potential.

Gifts in wills are a vital part of funds at Save the
Children. By remembering Save the Children in your
will, you are leaving vulnerable children the
opportunity for a similarly rich and fulfilling life. For
further information please contact us on 020 7012
6400.

SCHOOLMISTRESSES & GOVERNESSES BENEVOLENT INSTITUTION
Founded: 1843 CR205366
Case Manager: Mrs Gillian Mumford
Director & Secretary: Ms Sarah Brydon
Queen Mary House, Manor Park Road,
Chislehurst, Kent BR7 5PY
Tel: 020 8468 7997
Fax: 020 8468 7200
Email: .... sarah.brydon@sgbi.net / gillian.
mumford@sgbi.net
Objects: W11,1A,A,V,W4,U,B,W14,3,W8
The SGBI gives free annuities and grants for many
special needs.

Leave a legacy of hope

'Your will be done, here on earth as it is in heaven'. Matthew 6:10.

Leaving your legacy with Scripture Union will make Jesus known and bring to faith more children and young people who live in England and Wales.

That is the motivation that has inspired our work for over 140 years.

We invite you to join us in this vital mission by including Scripture Union in your will. Your legacy will be a powerful and on-going statement of hope and help to grow God's kingdom beyond your lifetime.

To request your free SU Legacy Information Pack please: visit our website **www.scriptureunion.org.uk/mylegacy** or call our Legacy Administrator on **01908 856120** or email **legacy@scriptureunion.org.uk**

www.scriptureunion.org.uk/mylegacy
Scripture Union, Department CC, 207-209 Queensway,
Bletchley, Milton Keynes, MK2 2EB
Registered Charity No. 213422 Limited Company No. 39828

Applicants must have been employed for the major period of their working lives in the private sector of education as governesses, or as schoolmistresses, or as self-employed teachers of language, music, dancing, art, etc., or as matrons, secretaries, or actively employed in an administrative capacity in the care and welfare of children in schools, or as teachers of students of more mature years and the comparable staff in universities, colleges etc.

Queen Mary House, the residential home, will also accept applications from ladies from comparable professions or careers.

SCIENCE, ENGINEERING & MANUFACTURING TECHNOLOGIES ALLIANCE (FORMERLY ENGINEERING & MARINE TRAINING AUTHORITY)

See SEMTA

SCOLIOSIS ASSOCIATION UK

Founded: 1981 CR285290
Chair: Ms Stephanie Clark PhD
Information Officer: Ms Pauline Grey
4 Ivebury Court, 323-327 Latimer Road, London W10 6RA
Tel: .... 020 8964 5343; 020 8964 1166 Helpline
Fax: 020 8964 5343
Email: .... sauk@sauk.org.uk
Objects: F,J,2,H,3,P

SCOPE

Founded: 1952 CR208231
Chief Executive: Mr Richard Hawkes
6 Market Road (Room CD14), London N7 9PW
Tel: 020 7619 7100
Fax: 020 7619 7399
Email: .... legacies@scope.org.uk
Web: .... http://www.scope.org.uk/cd
Scope exists to make this country a better place for disabled people and their families.

SCOTSCARE

Founded: 1611 CR207326
37 King Street, Covent Garden, London WC2E 8JS
Tel: .... 020 7240 3718; 0800 652 2989 Helpline
Fax: 020 7497 0184
Email: .... info@scotscare.com
Objects: F,1A,A,V,D,B,C

SCOTTISH CATHOLIC INTERNATIONAL AID FUND (SCIAF)

SC012302
19 Park Circus, Glasgow G3 6BE
Tel: 0141 354 5555
Fax: 0141 354 5533
Email: .... sciaf@sciaf.org.uk

SCOTTISH SOCIETY FOR THE MENTALLY HANDICAPPED

See ENABLE Scotland

SCOTTISH SOCIETY FOR THE PREVENTION OF CRUELTY TO ANIMALS (SCOTTISH SPCA)

SC006467
Head of Marketing and Fundraising: Miss Michelle Grubb
Braehead Mains, 603 Queensferry Road, Edinburgh EH4 6EA
Tel: 03000 999999
Fax: 0131 339 4777
Email: .... enquiries@scottishspca.org
Objects: W1,2,3

SCOTTISH WAR BLINDED

Founded: 1915SC002652
Chief Executive: Mr R G Hellewell
PO Box 500, Gillespie Crescent, Edinburgh EH10 4HZ
Tel: 0131 229 1456
Fax: 0131 229 4060
Objects: F,W9,W6,E,G,1A,A,1B,D,3,K

SCRIPTURE UNION ENGLAND AND WALES

Founded: 1867 CR213422
National Director: Rev Tim Hastie-Smith
207-209 Queensway, Bletchley, Buckinghamshire MK2 2EB
Tel: 01908 856000
Fax: 01908 856111
Email: .... info@scriptureunion.org.uk
Objects: W3,W15,V,R,11

We are a Christian charity working with churches, schools and local communities; providing people and resources to bring the good news about Jesus Christ to children, young people and families - and to encourage them to develop their relationship with God through the Bible and prayer.

As well as our network of volunteers, staff and Associate Trusts who run holidays, church based events and school Christian groups; we produce a wide range of Christian printed and digital publications and support those who use our resources through training programmes. Please see our website for more information: www.scriptureunion.org.uk

See advert on previous page

SEAFARERS UK

seafarers UK

the leading charity
for seafarers in need

Founded: 1917 CR226446; SC038191
King George's Fund for Sailors, 8 Hatherley
Street, London SW1P 2QT
Tel: 020 7932 0000
Fax: 020 7932 0095
Email: .... seafarers@seafarers-uk.org
Objects: W9,1B,W13
Seafarers UK is the leading maritime charity that
supports and promotes the many organisations
that look after seafarers in need across the
Merchant Navy, Fishing Fleets, Royal Navy and
Royal Marines, together with their families.

SECOND CHANCE: A CHARITY FOR CHILDREN WHO NEED SPECIAL HELP
CR1001462
Second Chance House (CC), Somers Road
Bridge, Portsmouth, Hampshire PO5 4NS
Tel: 023 9287 2790
Fax: 023 9273 7550
Email: .... second.chance@ukonline.co.uk
Objects: W3,G

SEMTA
Founded: 1990 CR1000328
Chief Executive: Mr Philip Whiteman
14 Upton Road, Watford, Hertfordshire WD18 0JT
Tel: 01923 238441
Objects: G,3

SENSE (THE NATIONAL DEAFBLIND & RUBELLA ASSOCIATION)
Founded: 1956 CR289868
Chief Executive: Mr Richard Brook
Director of Fundraising: Ms Claire Wood-Hill
101 Pentonville Road, London N1 9LG

Tel: 0845 127 0060
Fax: 0845 127 0061
Email: .... info@sense.org.uk
*Objects: F,W6,W3,J,E,W7,W5,G,V,D,2,W4,U,H,
O,3,C,P,K*

SEQUAL TRUST (SPECIAL EQUIPMENT & AIDS FOR LIVING)

the sequal trust .org.uk

Founded: 1969 CR260119
3 Ploughmans Corner, Wharf Road,
Ellesmere, Shropshire SY12 0EJ
Tel: 01691 624222
Fax: 01691 624222
Email: .... info@thesequaltrust.org.uk
Web: .... http://www.thesequaltrust.org.uk
Object: W5
The Sequal Trust, founded in 1969, is a national
charity which fund raises to provide
communication aids to British Citizens of all
ages with speech, movement or severe learning
difficulties. Applicants are accepted who do not
have the funds to buy such vital equipment
themselves and whose local authorities have no
budget for such devices. Liaison is conducted
with the person's health care professional, in
order to ensure that the recommended speech
aid fully meets the needs of the individual, to
allow them to lead more independent lives and
so 'Set lively minds free'.

SERVICE TO THE AGED
Founded: 1991 CR1001916
Auditors: Mr Cohen Arnold
c/o Cohen Arnold & Co, New Burlington House,
1075 Finchley Road, London NW11 0PU
Tel: 020 8731 0777
Objects: N,W4,C

SESAME INSTITUTE UK
Founded: 1964 CR263155
Director: Ms Di Cooper
Director: Ms Mary Smail
Christchurch, 27 Blackfriars Road, London
SE1 8NY
Tel: 020 7633 9690
Email: .... info@sesame-institute.org
Objects: F,W6,W3,W7,W5,G,2,R,W4,O,3,P,W8,K

SEVENOAKS AREA MIND
Founded: 1995 CR1044977
Chairman: Ms Mary-Ann Palmer
Chief Executive: Ms Jill Roberts
34 St John's Road, Sevenoaks, Kent TN13 3LW
Tel: 01732 744950
Email: ...... admin@sevenoaksareamind.org.uk
Objects: F,J,E,W5,G,2,3,C,P

SEVENOAKS DAY NURSERY TRUST
Founded: 1988 CR299319
Admin & Finance Manager: Mrs Ann Birch
Chairman of Trustees: Mr Peter Fitzpatrick
Treasurer: Mrs Anderson
Rear of Community Centre, Otford Road,
Sevenoaks, Kent TN14 5DN
Tel: 01732 460384
Objects: W3,G,W15,3,W8

SEVERN GORGE COUNTRYSIDE TRUST
Founded: 1991 CR1004500
Administrator: Ms Pauline Levesley
Wesley Rooms Annexe, Jockey Bank, Ironbridge, Telford, Shropshire TF8 7PD
Tel: 01952 433880
Objects: W2,3

SGRIPT CYMRU
See Sherman Cymru

THE SHAFTESBURY SOCIETY (NOW LIVABILITY)
See Livability (the new name of John Grooms and the Shaftesbury Society)

SHALOM EMPLOYMENT ACTION CENTRE
Founded: 1990 CR802730
The Project Manager
395 High Street North, London E12 6PG
Tel: 020 8472 3571

SHARED CARE NETWORK
Founded: 1990 CR1104216
National Co-ordinator: Ms Vicky Jones
Development Officer: Ms Sue Mennear
63-66 Easton Business Centre, Felix Road, Bristol BS5 0HE
Tel: .... 0117 941 5361; 0117 941 5364 Minicom
Fax: 0117 941 5362
Email: .... shared-care@bristol.ac.uk
Objects: Q,W6,W3,W7,W5,2,P

SHEFFIELD MEDIA AND EXHIBITION CENTRE LIMITED, THE
Founded: 1991 CR1002020
Company Secretary: Ms Julie Simpson
The Showroom, 7 Paternoster Row, Sheffield, South Yorkshire S1 2BX
Tel: 0114 279 6511
Objects: S,G,H,3,P,K

SHELTER - NATIONAL CAMPAIGN FOR HOMELESS PEOPLE

Founded: 1966 CR263710; SC002327
Legacy Manager: Mr John Ashley
88 Old Street, London EC1V 9HU
Tel: 0844 515 2062
Fax: 0844 515 2166
Email: .... info@shelter.org.uk
Objects: F,W9,W6,W3,W7,W5,W10,W11,W15, W16,D,W4,H,3,Z,W8

Shelter helps over a million people a year struggling with bad housing or homelessness – and we campaign to prevent it in the first place.
We're here so no-one has to fight bad housing or homelessness on their own.

We need your help. To join our campaign, make a donation, or get expert housing advice, visit shelter. org.uk

SHENLEY PARK TRUST
Founded: 1990 CR803520
Company Secretary: Mr John Ely
The Bothy, Shenley Park, Radlett Lane, Shenley, Hertfordshire WD7 9DW
Tel: 01923 852629
Fax: 01923 859644
Objects: W2,3

SHEPPARD'S COLLEGE
See Bromley & Sheppard's Colleges

THE SHEPPARD TRUST - HOUSING FOR ELDERLY LADIES
Founded: 1855 CR1133356
Chief Executive: Mr David Cash
12 Lansdowne Walk, London W11 3LN
Tel: 020 7727 5500
Fax: 020 7727 7730
Email: .... davidcash@sheppardtrust.org

SHINGLES SUPPORT SOCIETY
Founded: 1996 CR291657
Honorary Treasurer: Mr G Davies
Director: Ms Marian Nicholson
41 North Road, London N7 9DP
Tel: 020 7607 9661
Objects: F,W9,W6,W3,W7,W5,W10,W11,N,W4,H, 3,W8

SHIPWRECKED MARINERS' SOCIETY
Founded: 1839 CR212034
Chief Executive: Commodore M.S. Williams CBE, RN
1 North Pallant, Chichester, West Sussex PO19 1TL
Tel: 01243 789329; 01243 787761
Fax: 01243 530853
Email: .... general@shipwreckedmariners.org.uk
Web: .... www.shipwreckedmariners.org.uk
Objects: W11,1A,W4

Founded in 1839 to provide practical and financial assistance to survivors of shipwreck, the Society's main function today is to make grants to ex-merchant seafarers, fishermen and their dependants. Annual grant expenditure is currently £1.5 million in around 2, 500 cases of need.

SHUMEI EIKO LIMITED
Founded: 1991 CR1002647
Professor Clive H. Wake
Chaucer College Canterbury, University Road, Canterbury, Kent CT2 7LJ
Tel: 01227 787800
Fax: 01277 784267
Object: G

SHUTTLEWOOD CLARKE FOUNDATION, THE
Founded: 1990 CR803525
Chair of Trustees: Mr M. Freckelton
Chief Executive: Mr A.E. Norman
Ulverscroft Grange, Ulverscroft, Leicester, Leicestershire LE67 9QB
Tel: 01530 244914
Fax: 01530 249484
Objects: E,W5,W4,3

THE SICK CHILDREN'S TRUST (THE SCT)
Founded: 1982 CR284416
PR Co-ordinator: Ms Anna Nason
80 Ashfield Street, London E1 2BJ

Tel: 020 7791 2266
Fax: 020 7709 8358
Email: .... info@sickchildrenstrust.org
Objects: W3,E,3,C,P

SICKLE CELL SOCIETY
Founded: 1979 CR1046631
Health Education / Information Officer
54 Station Road, Harlesden, London NW10 4UA
Tel: 020 8961 7795; 020 8961 4006
Fax: 020 8961 8346
Email: .... sicklecellsoc@btinternet.com
Objects: F,M,J,G,1A,A,V,H,3,P

'SIGNALS' MEDIA ARTS CENTRE LIMITED
Founded: 1999 CR802376
Victoria Chambers, St Runwald Street,
Colchester, Essex CO1 1HF
Tel: 01206 560255
Fax: 01206 369086
Email: .... info@signals.org.uk
Objects: W3,W2,S,W7,W5,G,W10,W4,3,W8,K

SILOAM CHRISTIAN MINISTRIES - EDUCATION, HEALTHCARE & RELIEF AS A VEHICLE FOR THE GOSPEL
CR327396
'Clent House', 25 Beauchamp Avenue,
Leamington Spa, Warwickshire CV32 5RG
Tel: 01926 335037; 0800 027 7917
Fax: 01926 431193
Email: .... info@siloam.org.uk
Objects: W6,W3,W7,W5,W10,1A,1B,R,W4,U,W8

SIMON COMMUNITY, THE
Founded: 1963 CR283938
Community Leader: Mr Jonathan Burleigh
129 Malden Road, London NW5 4HS
Tel: 020 7485 6639
Fax: 020 7482 6305
Email: .... info@simoncommunity.org.uk

SIOBHAN DAVIES DANCE/ SIOBHAN DAVIES STUDIOS
Founded: 1992 CR1010786
Executive Director: Mr Andrew Broadley
Artistic Director: Ms Siobhan Davies CBE
Siobhan Davies Studios, 85 St George's Road,
London SE1 6ER
Tel: 020 7091 9650
Fax: 020 7091 9669
Email: .... info@siobhandavies.com
Objects: S,G,2,3

SIR ALISTER HARDY FOUNDATION FOR OCEAN SCIENCE
Founded: 1990 CR1001233
Director: Dr P C Reid
The Laboratory, Citadel Hill, Plymouth, Devon
PL1 2PB
Tel: 01752 633288
Fax: 01752 600015
Email: .... sahfos@wpo.nerc.ac.uk
Objects: W2,G

SIR GEORGE MONOUX EXHIBITION FOUNDATION
See Monoux (Sir George) Exhibition Foundation

SIR JAMES KNOTT TRUST, THE
CR1001363
Secretary: Mrs V R Stapley
16-18 Hood Street, Newcastle upon Tyne, Tyne &
Wear NE1 6JQ
Tel: 0191 230 4016
Objects: F,W9,W6,M,W3,W2,S,E,W7,W5,G,A,1B,
D,W4,O,C,P

SIR JOHN SUMNER'S TRUST
See Sumner's (Sir John) Trust

SIR RICHARD STAPLEY EDUCATIONAL TRUST
Founded: 1919 CR313812
Chairman: Dr Mary Wheater
Stapley Trust, Richmond, Surrey TW9 3AL
Email: .... admin@stapleytrust.org
Objects: G,1A,A

Grants, currently £300 to £1,000, are awarded to
students on an approved course at a university in the
UK leading to a post graduate degree (Masters MPhil or
PhD) and to students on degree courses leading to a
second degree in medicine, dentistry or veterinary
studies. Students must be over 24 on the 1st October of
the proposed academic year, with a 1st or 2nd upper
class degree. Applicants must not be in receipt of
awards from local authorities, Research Councils,
British Academy or similar public bodies. Grants are
awarded for one academic year.
All enquiries should be made to admin@stapleytrust.
org or to The Stapley Trust, PO Box 839, Richmond,
Surrey TW9 3AL. Closing date for applications is the
31st March.

SISTER AGNES
See King Edward VII's Hospital Sister Agnes

THE SISTERS OF THE SACRED HEARTS OF JESUS AND MARY
Founded: 1903 CR1004590
General Bursar: Sister Therese Cooney
Chigwell Convent, 803 Chigwell Road, Woodford
Green, Essex IG8 8AU
Tel: 020 8504 1624
Objects: W3,G,N,R,W4,U,T,3

SOBELL HOUSE HOSPICE CHARITY LIMITED

Sobell House

CR1118646
CEO: Ms Diane Gardner
Legacy Officer and Fundraiser: Ms Lindsay
Manifold
Churchill Hospital, Headington, Oxford,
Oxfordshire OX3 7LJ
Tel: 01865 857007
Fax: 01865 857015
Email: .... mail@sobellhospice.org
Object: N

SOCIAL MARKET FOUNDATION
Founded. 1990 CR1000971
Secretary to the Trustees: Ms Claire Newman
11 Tufton Street, London SW1P 3QB
Tel: 020 7222 7060
Objects: G,H,3

SOCIETY FOR MUCOPOLYSACCHARIDE DISEASES
Founded: 1982 CR1143472
Ms Christine Lavery
MPS House, Repton Place, White Lion Road,
Amersham, Buckinghamshire HP7 9LP
Tel: 0845 389 9901
Fax: 0845 399 9902
Email: .... mps@mpssociety.co.uk
Objects: F,W3,W5,A,V,N,2,H,P

SOCIETY FOR THE ASSISTANCE OF LADIES IN REDUCED CIRCUMSTANCES
Founded: 1886 CR205798
Secretary: Mr John Sands
Lancaster House, 25 Hornyold Road, Malvern,
Worcestershire WR14 1QQ
Tel: 0300 365 1886
Fax: 01684 577212
Email: .... info@salrc.org.uk
Objects: 1A,A,1B,Y,W8

SOCIETY FOR THE PROMOTION OF NATURE CONSERVATION
See The Wildlife Trusts

SOCIETY FOR THE PROMOTION OF NATURE RESERVES
See The Wildlife Trusts

SOCIETY FOR THE RELIEF OF DISTRESSED WIDOWS
See London Bereavement Relief Society

SOCIETY FOR THE STUDY OF ADDICTION TO ALCOHOL AND OTHER DRUGS
Founded: 1992 CR1009826
President: Dr Gillian Tober
SSA, Leeds Addiction Unit, 19 Springfield Mount,
Leeds, West Yorkshire LS2 9NG
Tel: 0113 295 1338
Objects: 1A,1B,2,H

SOCIETY OF FRIENDS OF FOREIGNERS IN DISTRESS
Founded: 1803 CR212593
Treasurer: Mrs A Schorr
68 Burhill Road, Horsham, Walton-on-Thames,
Surrey KT12 4JF
Tel: 01932 244916
Objects: W10,1A,A,3

SOCIETY OF JESUS CHARITABLE TRUST, THE
Founded: 1990 CR803659
Secretary: Mr K J Fox
114 Mount Street, London W1K 3AH
Tel: 020 7499 0285
Objects: R,3

SOCIETY OF LICENSED VICTUALLERS
See Licensed Trade Charity

SOCIETY OF THE PRECIOUS BLOOD
Founded: 1990 CR900512
The Reverend Mother
Burnham Abbey, Taplow, Maidenhead, Windsor &
Maidenhead SL6 0PW
Tel: 01628 604080
Objects: 2,R

SOFA (FURNITURE REUSE CHARITY)
Founded: 1984 CR1002980
Chief Executive: Jane Hammond
Towles Building, Nottingham Road,
Loughborough, Leicestershire LE11 1DY
Tel: 01509 262557
Fax: 01509 216208
Email: .... office@sofareuse.org
Objects: F,M,W2,G,W15,Y,3

SOIL ASSOCIATION
CR206862
Director: Ms Helen Browning
South Plaza, Marlborough Street, Bristol BS1 3NX
Tel: 0117 314 5000
Fax: 0117 314 5001
Email: .... info@soilassociation.org
Object: 2

SOUND SEEKERS
Founded: 1992 CR1013870
Chief Executive: Ms Lucy Carter
UCL Ear Institute, 332-336 Gray's Inn Road,
London WC1X 8EE
Tel: 020 7833 0035
Email: .... admin@sound-seekers.org.uk
Objects: W3,W7,G,2,U,3

SOUTH AMERICAN MISSION SOCIETY
CR221328
International Relations Director: Revd Canon John
Sutton
Financial Director: Mr Philip Tadman
Allen Gardiner Cottage, Pembury Road, Tunbridge
Wells, Kent TN2 3QU
Tel: 01892 538647
Fax: 01892 525797
Email: .... finsec@samsgb.org
Objects: F,W6,W3,W7,W5,G,W10,R,W4,U,H,T,3,
W8

SOUTH ASIAN CONCERN CHARITABLE TRUST
Founded: 1991 CR1002270
Chairman: Mr B Gidoomal
Secretary: Mr R Thomson
PO Box 43, Sutton, Surrey SM2 5WL
Tel: 020 8770 9717
Fax: 020 8770 9747
Email: .... info@southasianconcern.org
Objects: G,W10,R,H,3

SOUTH LONDON YMCA
CR1099051
Executive Director: Ms Toni Letts
Company Secretary: Mr Dennis Simmonds
The Old House, 2 Wellesley Court Road, Croydon,
Surrey CR0 1LE
Tel: 020 8667 9249
Fax: 020 8667 9250
Email: .... admin@croydonymca.org
Objects: F,W3,G,3,C,P

SOUTH WEST ACTION FOR LEARNING AND LIVING OUR WAY

Founded: 1993 CR1045893
General Manager: Mrs Beverley Craney
Fundraising and Finance Manager: Nicky Tew

The Old Engine House, Old Pit Road, Midsomer Norton, Somerset BA3 4BQ
Tel: 01761 414034
Email: .... info@swallowcharity.org
Web: .... http://www.swallowcharity.org
Objects: W5,G,D

SWALLOW supports people with learning disabilities to lead fulfilling, independent lives. The services that we provide include supported housing, training in independent living skills and creative courses such as art, pottery and drama. We also offer training for employment and social activities. Our centre provides a warm and welcoming environment for our members to meet and make friends.

SOUTH YORKSHIRE COMMUNITY FOUNDATION

South Yorkshire
Community Foundation
the charitable heart of the region

CR1140947
Unit 3, G1 Building, 6 Leeds Road, Sheffield, South Yorkshire S9 3TY
Tel: 0114 242 4857
Email: .... admin@sycf.org.uk
The Community Foundation is a proven manager of charitable endowments on behalf of companies, trusts and individuals, with a track record of ensuring that their money goes to the most worthy causes. Its grants support all charitable purposes for all age groups throughout the four boroughs of South Yorkshire.

SOUTHERN AREA HOSPICE SERVICES
XN47329/2
St John's House (CC), Courtenay Hill, Newry, Co. Down BT34 2EB
Tel: 028 3025 1333
Fax: 028 3026 8492
Email: ... info@southernareahospiceservices.org
Objects: M,N

SOUTHERN CONVALESCENT HOMES INC
See Bell Memorial Home (Inc)

SOUTHWARK DIOCESAN WELCARE
Founded: 1894 CR1107859
CEO: Revd. Anne-Marie Garton
St John's Community Centre, 19 Frederick Crescent, London SW9 6XN
Tel: 020 7820 7910
Fax: 020 7820 7912
Email: .... centraloffice@welcare.org
Objects: F,W3,J,G,W15,2,Y,3,P,Z,W8

SOVA
CR1073877
1st Floor, Chichester House, 37 Brixton Road, London SW9 6DZ

Tel: 020 7793 0404
Fax: 020 7735 4410
Email: .... mail@sova.org.uk
Objects: F,W3,J,G,W10,O,3,P,W8,K

SPADEWORK LIMITED
Founded: 1985 CR291198
Company Secretary: Jonathan Bryant
Teston Road, Offham, West Malling, Kent ME19 5NA
Tel: 01732 870002
Fax: 01732 842827
Objects: W5,G,3,K

SPARKS - SPORT AIDING MEDICAL RESEARCH FOR KIDS
Founded: 1991 CR1003825; SC039482
Chief Executive: Mr John Shanley
Heron House, 10 Dean Farrar Street, London SW1H 0DX
Tel: 020 7799 2111
Fax: 020 7222 2701
Email: .... info@sparks.org.uk
Objects: W3,A,1B

SPEAKABILITY (ACTION FOR DYSPHASIC ADULTS)
Founded: 1980 CR295094
Head of Fundraising: Mrs Melanie Derbyshire
1 Royal Street, London SE1 7LL
Tel: 020 7261 9572
Fax: 020 7928 9542
Email: .... speakability@speakability.org.uk
Objects: F,W5,G,2,W4,H,3,P

SPEECH, LANGUAGE AND HEARING CENTRE, THE
See Christopher Place

SPINA BIFIDA • HYDROCEPHALUS • INFORMATION • NETWORKING • EQUALITY - SHINE
Founded: 1966 CR249338
Chief Executive Officer: Mrs Jackie Bland
42 Park Road, Peterborough, Cambridgeshire PE1 2UQ
Tel: 01733 555988
Email: .... info@shinecharity.org.uk
Web: .... http://www.shinecharity.org.uk
Objects: F,W9,W6,W5,G,A,H,P

Shine work to support everyone living with spina bifida and hydrocephalus in England, Wales and Northern Ireland. Through a dedicated network of Support and Development Workers, Education Advisers, and Health Development Workers Shine are there from before birth and throughout the lives of those living with the conditions.

SPINAL INJURIES ASSOCIATION
CR1054097
Chief Executive: Mr Paul Smith
SIA House, 2 Trueman Place, Oldbrook, Milton Keynes MK6 2HH
Tel: 0845 678 6633 Switchboard; 0800 980 0501 Freephone Helpline
Fax: 0845 070 6911
Email: .... siahouse@spinal.co.uk
Objects: F,W5,2,H,3

SPINAL RESEARCH (INTERNATIONAL SPINAL RESEARCH TRUST)

SPINAL RESEARCH

fighting paralysis... and winning

Founded: 1981 CR1151015
Chief Executive: Mr Jonathan Miall
8a Bramley Business Centre, Station Road,
Bramley, Guildford, Surrey GU5 0AZ
Tel: 01483 898786
Fax: 01483 898763
Email: .... info@spinal-research.org
Web: .... www.spinal-research.org
Objects: W5,1B

Every day an average of three people in the UK and Ireland are paralysed by spinal cord injury. People who were once fit and active are now unable to move or feel below the level of injury and are dependent on family and carers. Paralysis does not just mean being unable to feel or move – it also affects other vital functions such as bladder and bowel control, blood pressure, breathing...

It takes courage to think about it, but we are all vulnerable to spinal cord injury – a serious fall, an accident on the road or the sports field. "I was paralysed after a rugby accident in 1983 and have helped Spinal Research since then. A treatment in my lifetime would be a bonus, but by making a legacy I can continue to help in the future as scientific research progresses further towards clinical trials and effective, safe treatments for paralysis". Martin Curtis, Honorary Treasurer, Spinal Research.

Spinal Research is the UK's leading charity funding research to develop reliable treatments for spinal cord injury. By leaving a legacy you can ensure vital research that could transform the life of paralysed people everywhere can carry on until the day when paralysis is finally beaten.

SPITALFIELDS MARKET COMMUNITY TRUST
Founded: 1991 CR1004003
Secretary: Mr T J Budgen
Spitalfields City Farm, Weaver Street, London
E1 5HJ
Tel: 020 7247 8762

SPORTS COUNCIL TRUST COMPANY, THE
Founded: 1990 CR803779
Company Secretary
3rd Floor, Victoria House, Southampton Row,
London WC1B 4SE
Tel: 020 7273 1648
Fax: 020 7273 1632
Objects: W6,W3,W7,W5,W10,A,1B,W4

SPRING HARVEST
Founded: 1992 CR1014540
Executive Director: Mr Alan Johnson
14 Horsted Square, Uckfield, East Sussex
TN22 1QG
Tel: 01825 769111
Fax: 01825 769141
Objects: G,V,3

SPRING PROJECT, THE
CR1067992
Trustee: Mr Richard Hubbard
PO BOX 20, Morpeth, Northumberland NE61 3YP
Tel: 01670 510725
Email: .... info@springproject.org.uk
Objects: R,3

SPURGEON'S CHILD CARE
CR1081182
Chief Executive: Mr D C Culwick
Head of Fundraising and Marketing: Mr A P Jaeger
74 Wellingborough Road, Rushden,
Northamptonshire NN10 9TY
Tel: 01933 412412
Fax: 01933 412010
Email: .... scc@spurgeons.org
Objects: F,W3,E,R,U,H,3,P,W8

ST ANDREW'S (ECUMENICAL) TRUST
Founded: 1991 CR1004126
Director: Mr Christopher J E Austen
Lambeth Palace, London SE1 7JU
Tel: 020 7898 1221
Objects: G,1A,R,B

ST ANNE'S COMMUNITY SERVICES
Founded: 1971 CR502224
Chief Executive: Ms Sharon Allen
6 St Mark's Avenue, Leeds, West Yorkshire
LS2 9BN
Tel: 0113 243 5151
Fax: 0113 245 1526
Email: .... info@st.annes.org.uk
Objects: F,E,W5,G,D,3,C,P

ST ANTHONY'S HOSPITAL, NORTH CHEAM
CR1068661
801 London Road, North Cheam, Surrey
SM3 9DW
Tel: 020 8337 6691
Fax: 020 8335 4537
Email: .... info@stanthonys.org.uk
Objects: N,3

The Hospital is founded by the Congregation of the Daughters of the Cross and has an international reputation for medical excellence, especially for open heart surgery.

ST AUGUSTINE'S FOUNDATION
Founded: 1979 CR307961
Treasurer: Mr C J Robinson
c/o Cathedral House, The Precincts, Canterbury,
Kent CT1 2EH
Tel: 01227 762862
Fax: 01227 865222
Objects: 1B,R

ST AUSTELL CHINA CLAY MUSEUM LIMITED
Founded: 1991 CR1001838
Company Secretary: Mr T D B Giles
Chairman: Mr R D Preston
Wheal Martyn, Carthew, St Austell, Cornwall
PL26 8XG
Tel: 01726 850362
Fax: 01726 850362
Email: .... info@chinaclaycountry.co.uk
Objects: W2,S,G,W12,3

ST BARNABAS HOUSE
Founded: 1973 CR256789
Chief Executive: Mr Hugh Lowson
Titnore Lane, Worthing, West Sussex BN12 6NZ
Tel: 01903 706300
Fax: 01903 706398
Email: .... info@stbh.org.uk
Objects: F,W3,E,G,N,O,3
St Barnabas House provides specialist palliative care, both at the hospice and in patients' homes, for adults with advanced, progressive, life-limiting illnesses – and their families – in the areas of Worthing, Adur, Arun and Henfield.

ST BRIGID'S SCHOOL LIMITED
Founded: 1991 CR1003157
Bursar: Miss Anne M H Spiller
Plas Yn Green, Mold Road, Denbigh,
Denbighshire LL16 4BH
Tel: 01745 815228
Fax: 01745 816928
Email: .... bursarst.brigids@denbighshire.gov.uk
Objects: G,3

ST CATHERINE'S HOSPICE
Founded: 1983 CR281362
Chief Executive: Mr Shaun O'Leary
Malthouse Road, Crawley, West Sussex
RH10 6BH
Tel: 01293 447333
Fax: 01293 611977
Email: .... info@stch.org.uk
Objects: F,E,G,N,O,3

ST CHRISTOPHER'S HOSPICE
CR210667
Head of Communication & Fundraising: Ms Claire Barracliffe
Chief Executive: Ms Barbara Monroe
51-59 Lawrie Park Road, London SE26 6DZ
Tel: 020 8768 4500
Fax: 020 8659 8680
Email: .... enquiries@stchris.ftech.couk
Objects: F,E,G,N,H,3

ST CLARE WEST ESSEX HOSPICE CARE TRUST
Founded: 1990 CR1063631
Secretary: Ms D Langridge
St Clare Hospice Centre, Hastingwood Road, Harlow, Essex CM19 9JX
Tel: 01279 413590
Email: .... fund@stclare-hospice.co.uk
Objects: F,M,E,N,3

ST CUTHBERT'S CENTRE
Founded: 1990 CR803638
Trustee (Chairman): Mr. Bruce Marquart
The Philbeach Hall,, 51 Philbeach Gardens, Earls Court, London SW5 9EB
Tel: 020 7835 1389
Fax: 020 7341 9889
Email: .... dropin@stcuthbertscentre.org.uk
Objects: F,E,G,3

ST DAVID'S FOUNDATION HOSPICE CARE

Founded: 1992 CR1010576
Chief Executive: Mrs V Morrey
Cambrian House, St Johns Road, Newport
NP19 8GR
Tel: 01633 271364
Fax: 01633 272593
Email: ..... enquiries@stdavidsfoundation.co.uk
Objects: N,3

ST ELIZABETH'S - POSITIVE LIVING & LEARNING FOR PEOPLE WITH EPILEPSY & OTHER COMPLEX NEEDS

Founded: 1901 CR1068661
Perry Green (CC), Much Hadham, Hertfordshire
SG10 6EW
Tel: 01279 843451
Fax: 01279 842198
Email: .... enquiries@stelizabeths.org.uk
St Elizabeth's specialises in the fields of epilepsy, associated neurological disorders and other complex medical conditions. St Elizabeth's also provides for children within the autistic spectrum. St Elizabeth's is the only national epilepsy centre offering services to all age groups with learning disabilities.

Situated near the village of Much Hadham, Hertfordshire, the charity has a national outreach with a strong regional presence. St Elizabeth's comprises:
A residential school for up to 80 pupils aged 5-19
A residential college with domiciliary care for 37 learners aged 18-25
A village of bungalow accommodation for 105 adult residents aged 18 and over
Day activities for residents, college learners and 12 day clients providing a varied range of leisure activities and vocational opportunities
A five-bed respite suite for those people requiring short-term care breaks

Our vision is that people with epilepsy and other complex needs should have the same opportunities for learning, work and leisure activities as everyone in the wider community, and to the maximum of their ability. This vision is grounded in Christian values of love, dignity and respect to those who we serve, although referrals to St Elizabeth's are accepted regardless of religious background. St Elizabeth's is administered by the Congregation of the Daughters of the Cross of Liège.

See advert on previous page

ST FRANCIS LEPROSY GUILD

Founded: 1895 CR208741
Hon Treasurer: Mr T G R Lawrence
Hon Secretary: Sister Helen McMahon
President: Mrs Gwen Sankey
73 St Charles Square, London W10 6EJ
Tel: 020 8969 1345
Email: .... enquiries@stfrancisleprosy.org
Objects: W6,W3,W7,W5,G,A,1B,D,N,2,R,W4,O,C, W8,K

ST JOHN CYMRU WALES

CR250523
Priory House, Beignon Close, Ocean Way, Cardiff
CF24 5PB
Tel: 029 2044 9629
Fax: 029 2044 9630
Email: .... fundraising@stjohnwales.org.uk

ST JOSEPH'S HOSPICE ASSOCIATION (JOSPICE INTERNATIONAL)

Founded: 1966 CR1090151
Mr Keith Cawdron
Ince Road, Thornton, Liverpool, Merseyside
L23 4UE
Tel: 0151 924 3812
Fax: 0151 932 6020
Email: .... jospice@3tc4u.net
Objects: N,R,U

ST JOSEPH'S SOCIETY (FORMERLY THE AGED POOR SOCIETY)

Founded: 1708 CR1010058
Secretary: Mr Simon Dolan
St Joseph's Almshouse, 42 Brook Green, London
W6 7BW
Tel: 020 7603 9817
Fax: 020 7602 1005

ST KATHARINE & SHADWELL TRUST

Founded: 1990 CR1001047
Director: Ms Jenny Dawes
Unit 1.4, 11-29 Fashion Street, London E1 6PX
Tel: 020 7422 7523
Fax: 020 7247 2938
Objects: G,A,1B,H

ST LUKE'S COLLEGE FOUNDATION

Founded: 1978 CR306606
Director: Dr David Benzie
15 St. Maryhaye, Tavistock, Devon PL19 8LR
Tel: 01822 613143
Email: ..... director@st-lukes-foundation.org.uk
Objects: G,1A,1B

For the advancement of Theology and Religious Education. Grants are made to individuals and to further and higher education organisations (not to schools, and for school-level education), for research, courses and facilities, for up to three years, but only in these subjects. One round of awards is made each year. Application Forms obtainable from the Director must be completed and returned by 1st May, for an Award commencing in the following September.

ST LUKE'S HEALTHCARE FOR THE CLERGY

Founded: 1892 CR1123195
Chief Executive: Mr John Cherry
Director of Finance & Administration: Mr Graham D Lloyd
14 Fitzroy Square, London W1T 6AH
Tel: 020 7388 4954
Fax: 020 7383 4812
Email: .... admin@stlukeshealthcare.org.uk
Objects: F,N,3

ST MARY'S CONVENT & NURSING HOME, LONDON

CR1080751
Sister Superior: Sister Jennifer Anne
Burlington Lane, Chiswick, London W4 2QE
Tel: 020 8994 4641
Fax: 020 8995 9796
Objects: W7,W5,W11,N,W4,W8

ST MICHAEL'S HOSPICE (NORTH HAMPSHIRE)

Founded: 1991 CR1002856
Basil De Ferranti House, Aldermaston Road,
Basingstoke, Hampshire RG24 9NB

St Michael's Hospice (North Hampshire)

Tel: 01256 844744
Fax: 01256 840357
Email: .... info@stmichaelshospice.org.uk
Objects: F,W9,W6,M,W3,J,E,W7,W5,G,W10, W11,N,W4,O,3,P,W8

ST PETER'S CONVENT
See St Peter's Home and Sisterhood

ST PETER'S HOME AND SISTERHOOD
Founded: 1861 CR240675
Chief Executive: Mrs Fiona Kergoat
St Peter's Convent, St Columbus House, Maybury Hill, Woking, Surrey GU22 8AB
Tel: 01483 750739
Fax: 01483 776208
Objects: F,G,3

ST RAPHAEL'S HOSPICE
CR1068661
London Road, North Cheam, Sutton, Surrey SM3 9DX
Tel: 020 8335 4576
Fax: 020 8335 4573
Email: .... fundraising@straphaels.org.uk
Objects: F,E,G,N,W4,3

ST RICHARD'S HOSPICE, WORCESTER
Founded: 1984 CR515668
Director of Fundraising: Ms Tricia Cavell
Communications Manager: Mrs Helen Griffee
Executive Director and Company Secretary: Mr Mark Jackson
Care Director: Ms June Patel
Wildwood Drive, Worcester, Worcestershire WR5 2QT
Tel: 01905 763963
Fax: 01905 351911
Email: .... enquiries@strichards.org.uk
Objects: F,G,N,3

ST SAVIOUR'S PRIORY
Founded: 1866 CR231926
Reverend Mother: Sister Elizabeth Crawford
Assistant Superior: Sister Anna Huston
18 Queensbridge Road, London E2 8NS
Tel: 020 7739 6775
Fax: 020 7739 1248
Objects: W3,E,R,W4,3

ST THOMAS'S COMMUNITY NETWORK
Founded: 1990 CR1093430
Director: Mrs Janet Hilkin
Blue Coat Base, Beechwood Road, Dudley, West Midlands DY2 7QA
Tel: 01384 818990
Fax: 01384 818991
Email: .... stcn@bcnet.org.uk
Objects: F,J,S,G,2,3

ST URSULA'S HIGH SCHOOL TRUST
Founded: 1990 CR900498
Bursar: Mr John McGill
Brecon Road, Westbury on Trym, Bristol BS9 4DT
Tel: 0117 962 2616
Objects: W3,G,3

STAFFORDSHIRE WILDLIFE TRUST

Founded: 1969 CR259558
The Wolseley Centre, Wolseley Bridge, Stafford, Staffordshire ST17 0WT
Tel: **01889 880100**
Fax: **01889 880101**
Email: .... **info@staffs-wildlife.org.uk**
Objects: W2,G,2,3
Staffordshire's largest environmental charity protects and enhances the wild places of the county for people and wildlife. It manages 26 sites covering 3,300 acres and has a membership of around 16,000.

STANDING CONFERENCE OF PRINCIPALS LTD
See GuildHE Limited

STAPLES TRUST
Founded: 1992 CR1010656
Director: Mr M A Pattison CBE
Allington House, 150 Victoria Street, London SW1E 5AE
Tel: 020 7410 0330

STEEPHILL SCHOOL
Founded: 1990 CR803152
Honorary Accountant & Trustee: Mrs V Hyndman
Honorary Company Secretary & Trustee: Mrs S M Scotting
off Castle Hill, Fawkham, Longfield, Kent DA3 7BG
Tel: 01474 702107
Fax: 01474 706011
Email: .... steephillprep@hotmail.com
Objects: W3,G

STEP BY STEP PARTNERSHIP LTD
Founded: 1990 CR900308
General Manager: Miss Amanda Laurie
36 Crimea Road, Aldershot, Hampshire GU11 1UD
Tel: 01252 346100
Email: .... generalmanager@emmaus.co.uk
Objects: F,W3,E,G,D,3,C,P

STEP FORWARD (TOWER HAMLETS)
Founded: 1990 CR802597
Chief Executive Officer: Ms Jennifer Fear
234 Bethnal Green Road, London E2 0AA
Tel: 020 7739 3082
Fax: 020 7613 2056
Objects: F,W3,G,3

STEPPING STONE PROJECT (ROCHDALE) LTD
Founded: 1991 CR1004375
Ms Sheena Marshall
Central Office, PO Box 153, Rochdale, Greater Manchester OL16 1FR
Tel: 01706 353000

STEPS CHARITY WORLDWIDE
CR1094040
Warrington Lane (CD), Lymm, Cheshire
WA13 0SA
Tel: 0871 717 0044
Fax: 01925 750270
Email: . . . . info@steps-charity.org.uk

STILLBIRTH AND NEONATAL DEATH SOCIETY
See SANDS - Stillbirth and Neonatal Death
Society

STOCK EXCHANGE BENEVOLENT FUND
Founded: 1801 CR245430
Assistant Secretary: Mrs Jennifer Golan
Secretary: Mr James L Cox
10 Paternoster Square, St Pauls, London
EC4M 7DX
Tel: 020 7797 1092; 020 7797 3120
Fax: 020 7374 4963
Email: . . . . stockxbf@yahoo.co.uk
Web: . . . . http://www.sebf.co.uk
Objects: 1A,2,Y

An occupational Benevolent Fund offering emergency
grants and long-term financial assistance to Members,
ex-Members and their dependants, at the discretion of
an elected Committee.

STOCKFIELD COMMUNITY ASSOCIATION
Founded: 1991 CR1003108
Mr Anthony Collins
St Philip's Gate, 5 Waterloo Street, Birmingham,
West Midlands B2 5PG
Tel: 0121 200 3242
Fax: 0121 212 7442
Email: . . . . acs@acollins-sol.co.uk

STOKE ON TRENT CITIZENS ADVICE BUREAU
Founded: 1990 CR1001204
Chief Executive: Mr Simon Harris
Advice House, Cheapside, Hanley, Stoke-on-
Trent, Staffordshire ST1 1HL
Tel: 01782 408600
Fax: 01782 408601
Objects: F,W9,W6,W3,W7,W5,W10,W4,3,W8

STOLL (FORMERLY SIR OSWALD STOLL FOUNDATION)
Founded: 1916 CR207939
Director: Mr R Brunwin
446 Fulham Road, London SW6 1DT
Tel: 020 7385 2110
Fax: 020 7381 7484
Email: . . . . fundraising@stoll.org.uk
Objects: F,W9,W5,D,W4,3,C

THE STROKE ASSOCIATION
CR211015; SC037789
Chief Executive: Mr Jon Barrick
Director of UK Operations: Mr Christopher R Clark
Director of Fundraising: Mr Jim Swindells
Stroke Association House, 240 City Road, London
EC1V 2PR
Tel: 020 7566 1505
Fax: 020 7490 2686
Email: . . . . legacy@stroke.org.uk

SUFFOLK REGIMENT OLD COMRADES ASSOCIATION
Founded: 1881 CR427780
Regimental Secretary: Lt Col A D Slaver
The Keep, Gibraltar Barracks, Bury St Edmunds,
Suffolk IP33 3PN
Tel: 01603 400290
Objects: W9,1A,A,2,B,C

SUMATRAN ORANGUTAN SOCIETY
CR1085600
The Old Music Hall, 106-108 Cowley Road,
Oxford, Oxfordshire OX4 1JE
Tel: 01865 403 341
Email: . . . . helen@orangutans-sos.org

SUMNER'S (SIR JOHN) TRUST
Founded: 1927 CR218620
Secretary: Mr I W Henderson
Chairman of Trustees: Mr J B Sumner
No. 1, Colmore Square, Birmingham, West
Midlands B4 6AA
*Objects: W9,W6,W3,W2,W7,W5,W10,W11,1A,A,
1B,W4,W8*

SUNSET HOME ALMSHOUSES
Founded: 1913 CR1070355
Secretary & Clerk to the Trustees: Ms Kathryn
Fleming
21 Rodney Road, Cheltenham, Gloucestershire
GL50 1HX
Tel: 01242 522180
Fax: 01242 522180
Objects: W4,3,C

SUSSEX AUTISTIC COMMUNITY TRUST LIMITED
See Sussex Autistic Community Trust Limited

SUSSEX DIOCESAN ASSOCIATION FOR THE DEAF
Founded: 1912 CR259713
Manager: Ms Chrissie Jenner
Chairman: Mrs P Hersey
Brighton Deaf Centre, Carlton Hill, Brighton,
Brighton & Hove BN2 0GW
Tel: 01273 671899
Fax: 01273 625283
Email: . . . . info@sussexdeaf.com
*Objects: F,W6,W3,E,W7,W5,G,1A,2,W4,H,3,P,
K*

SUSSEX HORSE RESCUE TRUST
CR297576
Hempstead Farm, Hempstead Lane, Uckfield,
East Sussex TN22 3DL
Tel: 01825 762010
Fax: 01825 762010
Email: . . . . sussexhorsetrust@yahoo.com
Objects: W1,O

SUSSEX WILDLIFE TRUST
CR207005
Woods Mill (Dept CD), Henfield, West Sussex
BN5 9SD
Tel: 01273 492630
Fax: 01273 494500
Email: . . . . enquiries@sussexwt.org.uk
Objects: W1,W2,G,2,H

SWALE CITIZENS ADVICE BUREAU
Founded: 1972 CR1103010
Chairman: Mrs Tricia Carr
Treasurer: Mr George Holdstock
17 Station Street, Sittingbourne, Kent ME10 3DU
Tel: 0870 121 2105
Objects: F,3

SWAN LIFELINE
Founded: 1986 CR299254
Chairman: Ms Kay Webb
Cuckoo Weir Island, South Meadow Lane, Eton,
Windsor & Maidenhead SL4 6SS
Tel: 01753 859397
Email: . . . . kaywebbsll@btinternet.com
Web: . . . . www.swanlifeline.org.uk
Objects: W1,W2,3

Voluntary 24 hour Swan rescue and treatment centre
for Thames Valley and home counties with the aim of
releasing back to the wild whenever possible. Funded
by public donations. Membership available.
See advert on next page

THE SWAN SANCTUARY

CR1002582
Trustee: Ms Dorothy Beeson BEM
Trustee: Mr Stephen Knight
Felix Lane, Shepperton, Middlesex TW17 8NN
Tel: 01932 240790
Email: . . . . info@theswansanctuary.org.uk
Web: . . . . www.theswansanctuary.org.uk
Objects: W1,W2

The Swan Sanctuary is a charity dedicated to the care
and treatment of swans and waterfowl with an
established reputation, not only within the British Isles
but worldwide

SWINBROOK NURSERY CENTRE
Founded: 1991 CR1001843
39-41 Acklam Road, London W10 5YU
Tel: 020 8968 5833
Email: . . . . swinbrooknursery@hotmail.com
Objects: W3,W10,3

SWINDON & DISTRICT CITIZENS ADVICE BUREAU
Founded: 1939 CR1115564
Manager: Mrs Judith Hawkins
Faringdon House, 1 Faringdon Road, Swindon,
Wiltshire SN1 5AR
Tel: 01793 618781
Fax: 01793 613270
Email: . . . . . bureau.swindoncab@cabnet.org.uk
*Objects: F,W9,W6,W3,W7,W5,G,W10,W11,2,W4,
3,W8*

SWINDON COUNSELLING SERVICE
Founded: 1990 CR1066502
Chairman: Mr Philip Powley
23 Bath Road, Swindon, Wiltshire SN1 4AS
Tel: 01793 514550
Objects: F,3

SWINDON REC
Founded: 1990 CR900449
The Director & Secretary
Faringdon House, 1 Faringdon Road, Swindon,
Wiltshire SN1 5AR
Tel: 01793 528545
Fax: 01793 430524
Objects: F,J,G,W10,3

SWISS BENEVOLENT SOCIETY
Founded: 1870 CR1111348
Treasurer: Mr M Lehmann
President: Mr A Martin
79 Endell Street, London WC2H 9DY
Email: . . . . info@swissbenevolent.org.uk
Objects: F,1A,A,2,B

SYNERGY ADDICTION
Founded: 1990 CR1001149
Treasurer: Mr J B. Davies
The Victoria Centre, Pettits Lane, Romford, Essex
RM1 4HP
Tel: 01708 740072
Email: . . . . admin@synergyaddiction.com
Objects: F,O,3

T

TAILORS' BENEVOLENT INSTITUTE
Founded: 1837 CR212954
Honorary Treasurer: Mr A Cundey
President: Mr M G Moss
68 Nightingale Road, Petts Wood, Orpington, Kent
BR5 1BQ
Tel: 01689 824405
Objects: W11,A

TALIESIN TRUST LTD, THE
Founded: 1991 CR1004108
Director: Ms Sally Baker
Assistant Director: Ms Sian Northey
Ty Newydd, Llanystumdwy, Criccieth, Gwynedd
LL52 0LW
Tel: 01766 522811
Fax: 01766 523095
Email: . . . . post@tynewydd.org
Objects: W6,W3,S,W7,W5,G,W10,W4,3,W8

TATE FOUNDATION
CR1085314
Tate Foundation, Millbank, London SW1P 4RG
Tel: 020 7887 8637
Fax: 020 7887 8098
Email: . . . . legacy.enquiries@tate.org.uk
Objects: S,G,W12

TEDWORTH CHARITABLE TRUST, THE
Founded: 1990 CR328524
Director: Mr A P Bookbinder
Allington House, 150 Victoria Street, London
SW1E 5AE
Tel: 020 7410 0330
Fax: 020 7410 0332

SWAN LIFELINE

☎ **01753 859 397**

www.swanlifeline.org.uk

Swan Lifeline is the oldest registered charity devoted entirely to the care of sick and injured swans in the Thames Valley and surrounding area. Originally known as Save Our Swans (SOS), it was founded in 1984 by a small group that had already long been involved with swan rescue and treatment.

- We rescue and provide shelter and treatment for sick, neglected and injured swans.
- We educate the public about the incidence and effects of pollution and human activities on swans and other wildfowl on the UK's rivers and waterways.
- We intend to maintain a professionally managed treatment centre to continue in perpetuity, not dependent upon any one person or group for its survival.

Our centre in Cuckoo Weir, Eton, is one of the biggest and best-equipped in the UK. Our site consists of a treatment centre and a series of outdoor recuperation pens with ponds and shelters. So far, we have rescued and treated more than 30,000 swans. Our work is possible only through generous donations and other support from the general public, our sponsors, trustees and volunteers.   Reg Charity No 299254

TEESSIDE POSITIVE ACTION
Founded: 1990 CR1121302
Business Manager: Mrs Julian Reynolds
15 Baker Street, Middlesbrough, North Yorkshire
TS1 2LF
Tel: 01642 254598
Fax: 01642 244558
Objects: F,W3,W5,G,H,3,W8

TEIKYO FOUNDATION (UK)
Founded: 1990 CR1001232
Company Secretary: Wing.Commander John
Frederick Thomas
Framewood Road, Wexham, Buckinghamshire
SL2 4QS
Tel: 01753 663756

TEIKYO UNIVERSITY OF JAPAN IN DURHAM
Founded: 1990 CR1000091
Company Secretary: Wing.Commander John F
Thomas
c/o Teikyo Foundation, Framewood Road,
Wexham, Buckinghamshire SL2 4QS
Tel: 01753 663756

TELECOMMUNICATIONS ACTION GROUP (TAG)
See TAG

TELEPHONES FOR THE BLIND FUND
Founded: 1967 CR255155
Honorary Secretary: Mrs J A Culling
7 Huntersfield Close, Reigate, Surrey RH2 0DX
Tel: 01737 248032
Objects: W6,1A,A,3

TENOVUS SCOTLAND
SC009675
Royal College of Physicians and Surgeons, 234
St. Vincent Street, Glasgow G2 5RJ
Tel: 0845 521 0783; 01292 311276
Fax: 0141 221 6268
Email: .... gen.sec@talk21.com

TERRENCE HIGGINS TRUST
Founded: 1983 CR288527
Communications Manager: Mr Mark Graver
Head of Media: Miss Sally Wright
314-320 Gray's Inn Road, London WC1X 8DP
Tel: .. 020 7812 1600; 0845 122 1200 THT Direct
Helpline
Fax: 020 7812 1601
Email: .... info@tht.org.uk
Objects: F,M,J,W5,G,W10,D,2,H,3,P,K

THAMES VALLEY CHARITABLE TRUST, THE
Founded: 1990 CR802595
Solicitor: Mr P J Lock
28-30 Beaumont Road, Windsor, Windsor &
Maidenhead SL4 1JP
Tel: 01753 861115
Fax: 01753 861113

THANET EARLY YEARS PROJECT & PALS
Founded: 1991 CR1100011
Project Manager: Ms E A Lucas
The Curran Building, Newlands Primary School, Dumpton Lane, Ramsgate, Kent CT11 7AJ
Tel: 01843 591200
Fax: 01843 591847
Email: . . . . maria@thanetearlyyears.org
Objects: W3,G,W10,3,W8

THEATRES TRUST CHARITABLE FUND
Founded: 1976 CR274697
Chairman: Rob Dickins CBE
Director: Mhora Samuel
22 Charing Cross Road, London WC2H 0QL
Tel: 020 7836 8591
Fax: 020 7836 3302
Email: . . . . info@theatrestrust.org.uk
Objects: F,W2,S,H

THEM WIFIES LIMITED
Founded: 1990 CR702946
Administrator: Ms Veronica Addison
Floor 2, British India House, Carliol Square, Newcastle upon Tyne, Tyne & Wear NE1 6UF
Tel: 0191 261 4090
Fax: 0191 2614091
Objects: W3,G,K

THOMAS CORAM FOUNDATION FOR CHILDREN
CR312278
Chief Executive: Dr Carol Homden
49 Mecklenburgh Square, London WC1N 2QA
Tel: 020 7520 0300
Fax: 020 7520 0301
Objects: Q,W3,3

THOMAS HOWELL'S TRUST
Founded: 1991 CR1004185
Head of Charities: Mrs Mei-Lin Edwards
c/o The Drapers Company, Drapers Hall, Throgmorton Avenue, London EC2N 2DQ
Tel: 020 7588 5001
Fax: 020 7628 1988
Objects: W3,A,1B

THOMAS MORE PROJECT, THE
Founded: 1992 CR1009917
Company Secretary: Mrs C K Lander
33 Fallodon Way, Henleaze, Bristol BS9 4HZ
Tel: 0117 962 0887; 0117 962 9899
Objects: W5,D

THOROUGHBRED REHABILITATION CENTRE
Founded: 1993 CR1089564
Whinney Hill, Aughton Road, Halton, Lancaster, Lancashire LA2 6PQ
Tel: 01524 812649
Email: . . . . fundraising@thetrc.co.uk

THREE COUNTIES DOG RESCUE

Three Counties Dog Rescue
Improving a Dog's Life

CR283209
Contact: Gyll Mauchline
High Park Cottage, Kirkby Underwood Road,
Aslackby, Sleaford, Lincolnshire NG34 0HP
Tel: 01778 440318; 077085 89792
Email: ..... info@threecountiesdogrescue.org
Web: . http://www.threecountiesdogrescue.org
Three Counties Dog Rescue has been improving
dogs' lives since 1971. We now find homes for
unwanted dogs and cats in the counties of
Lincolnshire, Rutland, Cambridgeshire,
Leicestershire and Northamptonshire. We operate
on an entirely unpaid and voluntary basis and all
money raised goes directly to the cause (primarily
veterinary and kennelling costs).

THROMBOSIS RESEARCH INSTITUTE

Founded: 1987 CR800365
Director: Professor The Lord Kakkar
Institute Secretary: Mr James To
Emmanuel Kaye Building, Manresa Road,
Chelsea, London SW3 6LR
Tel: 020 7351 8300
Fax: 020 7351 8324
Email: .... instsec@tri-london.ac.uk
Object: W

See advert on previous page

TIGGYWINKLES: THE WILDLIFE HOSPITAL TRUST

Tiggywinkles.
World's Leading Wildlife Hospital

Founded: 1978 CR286447
**Aston Road, Haddenham, Aylesbury,
Buckinghamshire HP17 8AF**
Tel: **01844 292292**
Fax: **01844 292640**
Email: .... mail@sttiggywinkles.org.uk
Object: W1
Specialising in hedgehogs, Tiggywinkles, the
Wildlife Hospital Trust, has been working for
over 30 years rescuing, treating and
rehabilitating ALL sick, injured and orphaned
British wildlife. Without large reserves and no
Government or Lottery funding, Tiggywinkles is
dependent upon the compassion of the general
public and corporate sponsorship to continue its
life-saving work. The hospital has a committed
team of hardworking veterinary staff and
volunteers dedicated to caring for their patients.
For the vital work of Tiggywinkles to continue
help is desperately needed and always so greatly
appreciated. Please HELP US HELP THEM.

TIMBER TRADES' BENEVOLENT SOCIETY
Founded: 1897 CR207734
General Manager: Mr Ivan Savage
Maçonç Croft, 10 Church Lane, Oulton, Stone,
Staffordshire ST15 8UL
Tel: 08448 922205
Fax: 08448 922205
Email: .... info@ttbs.org.uk
Objects: W11,1A,A,B

TORRIDGE TRAINING SERVICES LTD
Founded: 1990 CR900128
Chief Executive: Mr Michael Lillis
Finance Manager: Ms Heather Thompson
Woodville, Heywood Road, Bideford, Devon
EX39 3PG
Tel: 01237 479491
Fax: 01273 471208
Email: .... admin@ttser.demon.co.uk
Objects: G,3

TOURISM FOR ALL UK
Founded: 1981 CR279169
Manager
Chief Executive: Ms Jenifer Littman MBE
c/o Vitalise, Shap Road Industrial Estate, Shap
Road, Kendal, Cumbria LA9 6NZ
Tel: .... 0845 124 9971 Info
Fax: 01539 735567
Email: .... info@tourismforall.org.uk
Objects: F,W6,J,W7,W5,V,2,W4,H,3

TOWER HAMLETS AND CANARY WHARF FURTHER EDUCATIONAL TRUST, THE
Founded: 1991 CR1002772
Vice Chairman: Mr Abdul Asad
Administrator: Mr Errol de Silva
Chairman: Mr Gerald Rothman
c/o London Borough of Tower Hamlets, 3rd Floor, Mulberry Place, 5 Clove Crescent, London E14 2BG
Tel: 0207 364 4888
Fax: 020 7364 4311
Object: G

TOWN & COUNTRY PLANNING ASSOCIATION
Founded: 1899 CR214348
Chief Executive: Mr Gideon Amos
17 Carlton House Terrace, London SW1Y 5AS
Tel: 020 7930 8903
Fax: 020 7930 3280
Email: .... tcpa@tcpa.org.uk
Objects: W2,G,D,2,H

TOWNROW (ARTHUR) PENSIONS FUND
Founded: 1966 CR252256
Secretary: Mr Peter I King
PO Box 48, Chesterfield, Derbyshire S40 1XT
Tel: 01246 238086
Objects: 1A,3,W8

TOY TRUST, THE
Founded: 1991 CR1001634
Accountant: Mr Taz Khan
British Toy and Hobby Assn Limited, 80 Camberwell Road, London SE5 0EG
Tel: 020 7701 7271
Fax: 020 7708 2437
Email: .... admin@btha.co.uk
Objects: F,M,W3,E,1A,A,1B,V,N,U,H,O,P

TOYNBEE HALL
Founded: 1884 CR211850
Appeals Officer: Mrs Jill Goldsworthy
CEO: Russell Le Page
28 Commercial Street, Tower Hamlets, London E1 6LS
Tel: 020 7247 6943
Fax: 020 7377 5964
Email: .... info@toynbeehall.org.uk
Objects: F,M,W3,S,E,G,W10,V,D,W4,H,3,C,P,W8

TREBAH GARDEN TRUST
Founded: 1990 CR1000067
Administrator: Mr V. Woodcroft
Mawnan Smith, Falmouth, Cornwall TR11 5JZ
Tel: 01326 250448
Fax: 01326 250781
Email: .... mail@trebah-garden.co.uk
Objects: W2,G,2

TREE COUNCIL, THE

CR279000
71 Newcomen Street, London SE1 1YT
Tel: 020 7407 9992
Fax: 020 7407 9908
Email: .... info@treecouncil.org.uk
Object: W2
Founded in 1974, The Tree Council promotes the improvement of the environment by the planting and conservation of trees and woods in town and country throughout the UK. It is responsible for an annual programme that includes Seed Gathering Season, National Tree Week, and Walk in the Woods month, supporting the groups organising local events. It also co-ordinates the national volunteer Tree Warden scheme and operates a fund giving tree-planting grants to schools and communities.

TREE OF HOPE
CR1149254; SC042611
43a Little Mount Sion, Tunbridge Wells, Kent TN1 1YP
Tel: 01892 535525
Email: .... info@treeofhope.org.uk

TRINITARIAN BIBLE SOCIETY
Founded: 1831 CR233082; SC038379
General Secretary: Mr D P Rowland
Tyndale House, 200 Dorset Road, London SW19 3NN
Tel: 020 8543 7857
Fax: 020 8540 7777
Email: .... info@tbsbibles.org
Objects: W3,W7,W5,W10,1A,1B,2,R,W4,H,W8
We uphold the Bible as the inspired inerrant Word of God and promote accurate and trustworthy Bible translations; we publish Bibles in a range of languages for distribution for retail outlets, missionaries, churches, individuals etc, worldwide. We have a substantial ministry of free grant distribution of Bibles, New Testaments, Gospels and calendars worldwide.

TRINITY HOUSING RESOURCE CENTRE
Founded: 1991 CR1003826
Secretary: Ms M Osahan
Villa Road, Handsworth, Birmingham, West Midlands B19 1BL
Tel: 0121 554 8745; 0121 554 8746

TROLLOPE SOCIETY, THE
Founded: 1990 CR803130
Treasurer: Mr P Ravenscroft
Maritime House, Clapham Old Town, London SW4 0JW
Tel: 020 7720 6789
Fax: 020 7627 2965
Objects: S,2,H

THE TRUST FOR EDUCATION
Founded: 1990 CR1000408
Company Secretary: Mr Malcolm Lynch
c/o Wrigleys, 19 Cookridge Street, Leeds, West Yorkshire LS2 3AG
Tel: 0113 244 6100
Objects: W3,G,1B

TTE MANAGEMENT & TECHNICAL TRAINING
Founded: 1991 CR1001390
Managing Director: Mr K A Hunter
Finance Manager: Mr B Winspear FCCA
Edison House, Middlesbrough Road East, South
Bank, Middlesbrough, North Yorkshire TS6 6TZ
Tel: 01642 462266
Fax: 01642 460873
Email: .... info@tte.co.uk
Objects: W3,G,W4,3

TUBEROUS SCLEROSIS ASSOCIATION
Founded: 1977 CR1039549; SC042780
Community Fundraising Manager: Ms Emma
Damian-Grint
Administrator: Andreas Worth
PO Box 4923, Sheffield, South Yorkshire S2 9EU
Tel: 0114 270 1723
Email: . emma.damian-grint@tuberous-sclerosis.org
Web: .... www.tuberous-sclerosis.org
Providing support for affected families, raising
awareness and funding research to find a cure for
Tuberous Sclerosis Complex.

TURNERS COURT YOUTH TRUST
Founded: 1991 CR309562
Director: Mr Mike Cornfield
9 Red Cross Road, Goring, Reading RG8 9HG
Tel: 01491 874234
Fax: 01491 875370
Email: .... turnerscourt@turnerscourt.org.uk
Objects: F,W3,G,3

TYDFIL TRAINING CONSORTIUM LIMITED
Founded: 1990 CR702622
Secretary to the Trustees: Mr Colin A Parker
William Smith Building, High Street, Merthyr Tydfil
CF47 8AP
Tel: 01685 371747
Fax: 01685 379951
Email: .... training@tydfil.com
Objects: F,W6,W3,W7,W5,G,W11,W4,3,W8

U

UCCF: THE CHRISTIAN UNIONS
Founded: 1928 CR306137
Director: Mr Richard Cunningham
Blue Boar House, 5 Blue Boar Street, Oxford,
Oxfordshire OX1 4EE
Tel: 01865 253650
Email: .... rmc@uccf.org.uk
Objects: W3,G,R,H,3

UK SKILLS
Founded: 1991 CR1001586
Chief Executive: Mrs Linda Ammon CBE
Director of Corporate Management: Ms S Lynch
5 Portland Place, London W1B 1PW
Tel: 020 7580 1011
Email: .... ukskills@ukskills.org.uk
Objects: W3,J,G,H,3

UKJAID (UK JEWISH AID AND INTERNATIONAL DEVELOPMENT)
See Central British Fund for World Jewish Relief

UKJAID (UK JEWISH AID AND INTERNATIONAL DEVELOPMENT)
See Central British Fund for World Jewish Relief

UMBRELLA - WORKING FOR POSITIVE MENTAL HEALTH
Founded: 1991 CR1006778
Administrator: Mr Mark Calder
Chief Executive: Mr Gareth Pountain
354 Goswell Road, London EC1V 7LQ
Tel: 020 7278 3709
Fax: 020 7278 3831
Email: .... info@umbrellacare.org.uk
Objects: G,D,3,C

UNISON WELFARE
Founded: 1910 CR1023552
Head of UNISON Welfare: Ms Julie Grant
1 Mabledon Place, London WC1H 9AJ
Tel: 020 7551 1620
Fax: 020 7383 2617
Email: .... welfare@unison.co.uk
Objects: F,1A,A,2

UNIVERSITIES AND COLLEGES CHRISTIAN FELLOWSHIP
See UCCF: The Christian Unions

UNIVERSITIES FEDERATION FOR ANIMAL WELFARE (UFAW)
Founded: 1926 CR207996
Director: Dr James Kirkwood
The Old School, Brewhouse Hill,
Wheathampstead, Hertfordshire AL4 8AN
Tel: 01582 831818
Fax: 01582 831414
Email: .... ufaw@ufaw.org.uk
Objects: F,W1,G,1A,A,1B,2,B,H,3

UNIVERSITIES UK
Founded: 1990 CR1001127
Chief Executive: Ms Nicola Dandridge
Director of Resources: Mr Christopher Lambert
Woburn House, 20 Tavistock Square, London
WC1H 9HQ
Tel: 020 7419 4111
Fax: 020 7380 0137
Email: .... info@universitiesuk.ac.uk
Objects: G,2,H

UNIVERSITY OF CAMBRIDGE VETERINARY SCHOOL TRUST (CAMVET)
XO 979/86
Department of Veterinary Medicine (CC09),
Madingley Road, Cambridge, Cambridgeshire
CB3 0ES
Tel: .... 01223 337630 / 764475
Fax: 01223 337610
Email: .... trust.office@vet.cam.ac.uk
Objects: W1,2

UNIVERSITY OF CAPE TOWN TRUST
Founded: 1990 CR803042
Consultant Director: Mrs Sibylla Tindale
83a Esher High Street, Esher, Surrey KT10 9QA
Tel: 01372 477116
Fax: 01372 477118
Email: .... uct-trust@tecres.net
Objects: W3,G,1B,U

URBAN SAINTS
Founded: 1906 CR223798
Executive Director: Mr Matt Summerfield
Kestin House, 45 Crescent Road, Luton, Bedfordshire LU2 0AH
Tel: 01582 589850
Fax: 01582 721702
Email: . . . . email@urbansaints.org
Objects: W3,J,G,V,2,R,U,H

URBAN THEOLOGY UNIT
Founded: 1971 CR1115390
Support Services Manager: Ms Janet Ayres
Acting Director: Reverend Christine Jones
210 Abbeyfield Road, Sheffield, South Yorkshire S4 7AZ
Tel: 0114 243 5342
Fax: 0114 243 5356
Email: . . . . office@utusheffield.org.uk
Objects: G,2,H

THE URE ELDER FUND
SC003775
Solicitor: Mrs E M Kerr
Chairperson: Doctor C Joan McAlpine
1 George Square, Glasgow G2 1AL
Tel: 0141 248 5011
Fax: 0141 248 5819
Objects: 1A,A,B,W8

UXBRIDGE UNITED WELFARE TRUSTS
Founded: 1991 CR217066
Chairman: Mr P W F Hesford
Vice Chairman: Mr L Pond
Trustees Room, Woodbridge House, New Windsor Street, Uxbridge, Middlesex UB8 2TY
Tel: 01895 232976
Objects: A,1B

V

VEGETARIAN SOCIETY OF THE UK LTD, THE
Founded: 1968 CR259358
Chief Executive: Ms Annette Pinner
Parkdale, Dunham Road, Altrincham, Greater Manchester WA14 4QG
Tel: 0161 925 2000
Fax: 0161 926 9182
Email: . . . . support@vegsoc.org
Objects: F,W1,W3,W2,G,2,R,H,P

VEGFAM (FEEDS THE HUNGRY WITHOUT EXPLOITING ANIMALS)
Founded: 1963 CR232208
Honorary Secretary / Trustee: Ms Sandra Ozolins
c/o Cwm Cottage (CD), Cwmynys, Cilycwm, Llandovery, Carmarthenshire SA20 0EU

Tel: 01550 721197
Fax: .... Please Telephone First
Inland Revenue Ref: XN8555. **Self Assessment Gift Aid Ref:** XAD67AG

Online Donations: https://www.charitychoice.co.uk/vegfam

ABOUT VEGFAM
Vegfam "Feeds The Hungry Without Exploiting Animals" by funding sustainable, self-supporting projects: seeds and tools for vegetable growing, fruit/nut tree planting, irrigation and water wells. Also emergency relief in times of crisis and disaster. Vegfam helps people to help themselves.

WHY DONATIONS ARE NEEDED
Vegfam projects provide food security for children and adults worldwide - alleviating hunger, malnutrition, starvation and thirst. As little as £5 enables a family in India to be self-sufficient in fruit/nuts/vegetables or a family in Africa to have access to a safe water supply.

WHERE DONATIONS ARE SPENT
Beneficiaries: flood/earthquake survivors, HIV/AIDS sufferers, homeless people, marginalised communities, orphanages, refugees, schools/colleges, trafficked women and children, villagers and tribal people. In addition, the people who benefit from Vegfam funded projects are often suffering from disease and disabilities. For many, Vegfam is their only hope of help.

From 2008 to 2011, Vegfam funded 37 projects in 22 countries, helping over 950,000 people.

All donations and legacies are gratefully received and make a real difference to people's lives.

Please support our life saving work. Thank you.
See advert on previous page

VICTIM SUPPORT
CR298028
Octavia House, 50 Banner House, London EC1Y 8ST
Tel: 020 7336 1730
Email: .... info@victimsupport.org.uk

VICTORIA CONVALESCENT TRUST
Founded: 1897 CR1064585
Trustee: Mr N M Heath
Chair of Trustees: Mr N R Heath
Grants Co-ordinator: Mrs Anita Perkins
62 Wilson Street, London EC2A 2BU
Objects: W9,W6,W3,W7,W5,W10,W11,1A,A,2, W4,W8

VISION AID OVERSEAS
CR1081695
12 The Bell Centre, Newton Road, Manor Royal, Crawley, West Sussex RH10 9FZ
Tel: 01293 535016
Fax: 01293 535026
Email: .... info@visionaidoverseas.org
Objects: W6,W3,W5,G,W10,N,2,R,W4,U,3,W8

VISION SUPPORT
CR1068565
Chief Executive: Mrs Miriam Wright
Units 1 and 2, The Ropeworks, Whipcord Lane, Chester, Cheshire CH1 4DZ
Tel: 01244 381515
Fax: 01244 382337
Email: .... information@visionsupport.org.uk
Objects: F,W6,M,W3,W7,W5,W4,O,3,P,W8,K

VITILIGO SOCIETY
CR1069607
Administrator: Ms J Viles
125 Kennington Road, London SE11 6SF
Tel: 020 7840 0844
Fax: 020 7840 0866
Objects: F,2,H

VOLUNTARY ACTION CAMDEN
CR802186
The Secretary to the Trustees
293-299 Kentish Town Road, London NW5 2TJ
Tel: 020 7284 6550
Fax: 020 7284 6551
Email: .... vac@vac.org.uk

VOLUNTARY ACTION CARDIFF
Founded: 1991 CR1068623
Miss J Bell
3rd Floor, Brunel House, 2 Fitzalan Place, Cardiff CF24 0BE
Tel: 029 2048 5722; 029 2046 4196
Email: .... enquiries@vacardiff.org.uk
Objects: F,W3,J,W5,G,W10,A,2,W4,H,3,W8

VOLUNTARY ACTION KIRKLEES
Founded: 1991 CR1086938
Director: Ms Val Johnson
Volunteer Bureau Co-ordinator: Ms Sharon Wilkinson
15 Lord Street, Kirklees, Huddersfield, West Yorkshire HD1 1QB
Tel: 01484 518457
Fax: 01484 518457
Email: ...... info@voluntaryactionkirklees.co.uk
Objects: F,J,3

VOLUNTARY ACTION NORTH EAST LINCOLNSHIRE
Founded: 1991 CR1002624
Volunteer Bureau Co-ordinator: Ms Debbie Cattell
Secretary: Ms Julie Walmsley
14 Town Hall Street, Grimsby, North East Lincolnshire DN31 1HN
Tel: 01472 231123
Fax: 01472 231122
Email: .... peter@vanel.org.uk
Objects: F,J,G,2

VOLUNTEER CENTRE WOLVERHAMPTON
Founded: 1984 CR1079891
Volunteer Centre Manager: Ms Rita Beddard
Volunteer Centre: Mrs Rita Beddard
Chair: Ms Jean Lenoir MBE
Volunteer Centre, 5 Cleveland Street, Wolverhampton, West Midlands WV1 3HL
Tel: 01902 572323
Fax: 01902 572324
Email: .... info@wolvesvb.org.uk
Objects: F,W1,W9,W6,W3,J,W2,W7,W5,W10, W12,W4,H,3,W8

VRANCH HOUSE SCHOOL AND CENTRE
Founded: 1991 CR1002700
Business Manager: Colonel G F Wheeler
Vranch House, Pinhoe Road, Exeter, Devon EX4 8AD
Tel: 01392 468333
Fax: 01392 468333

VSA (FORMERLY VOLUNTARY SERVICE ABERDEEN)
SC012950
38 Castle Street, Aberdeen AB11 5YU
Tel: 01224 212021
Fax: 01224 580722
Email: .... fundraising@vsa.org.uk

W

WALDENSIAN CHURCH MISSIONS
CR277255
Executive Secretary: Mrs Erica Newbury
President: Mr Prescot Stephens
85 St Andrew's Road, Cambridge, Cambridgeshire CB4 1DH
Tel: 01223 315753
Fax: 01223 562605
Email: .... erica.newbury@gmail.com
Object: R

WASTE MANAGEMENT INDUSTRY TRAINING AND ADVISORY BOARD, THE
Founded: 1991 CR1006826
Director General: Dr Lawrence Strong
Peterbridge House, 3 The Lakes, Northampton, Northamptonshire NN4 7HE
Tel: 01604 231950
Fax: 01604 232457
Email: .... info.admin@wamitab.org.uk
Objects: G,W11,3

WATERAID

CR288701; SC039479
47-49 Durham Street, London SE11 5JD
Tel: **020 7793 4594**
Fax: **020 7793 4545**
Email: ...... supportercare@wateraid.org
Object: U
WaterAid is an international charity focused exclusively on improving poor people's access to safe water, improved hygiene and sanitation. We work in Africa, Asia, the Pacific region and Central America and campaign globally with our partners to realise our vision of a world where everyone has access to these basic human needs.
Today, 768 million people worldwide live without access to clean water and 2.5 billion people have nowhere safe or private to go to the toilet. As a result a child dies every 20 seconds from diseases caused by dirty water and poor sanitation.
Since WaterAid's foundation in 1981, we have reached over 19.2 million people.
Water, hygiene and sanitation underpin health, education and livelihoods, and form the first essential step in overcoming poverty.
A gift in your will can help us reach a day when everyone has access to safe water and sanitation. Leave something vital. Leave the world with water. Remember WaterAid in your will.
To find out more visit www.wateraid.org/giftinyourwill

WATERSIDE CENTRE, THE
Founded: 1990 CR1001330
63 Waterside, Kings Langley, Hertfordshire WD4 8HE
Tel: 01923 260092
Objects: E,W5,3

WATFORD MENCAP
CR1004431
Langwood House, Suites 1 & 2, 63-81 High Street, Rickmansworth, Hertfordshire WD3 1EQ
Tel: 01923 713620
Fax: 01923 773976
Email: .... admin@watfordmencap.org.uk

WATFORD NEW HOPE TRUST
Founded: 1991 CR1080784
Company Secretary: Mrs P Leese
C.E.O: Mr Mike Smith
Administration Office, Top Floor, 67 Queens Road, Watford, Hertfordshire WD17 2QN
Tel: 01923 210680
Fax: 01923 235329
Email: .... info@wnht.org
Objects: F,E,W5,W10,W16,W4,3,C,W8

WATSON'S (ANN) TRUST
Founded: 1721 CR226675
Chairman: Mr A A Dunn
Chairman: Dr J N Redfern
Flat 4, 14 College Street, Sutton-on-Hull, Hull, Kingston upon Hull HU7 4UP
Tel: 01482 709626
Objects: W3,G,1A,A,D,W4,B,W8

WDC, WHALE AND DOLPHIN CONSERVATION

WHALE AND DOLPHIN CONSERVATION

WDC

Founded: 1992 CR1014705
Brookfield House, 38 St Paul Street, Chippenham, Wiltshire SN15 1LJ
Tel: 01249 449500
Fax: 01249 449501
Email: .... legacy@whales.org
Objects: W1,J,W2,G,1A,A,1B,V,2,H
Whales and dolphins are intelligent and socially complex creatures which captivate us with their beauty, grace and dignity. Yet human actions and climate change have brought populations and even entire species to the brink of extinction.
Every year thousands of whales and dolphins are killed or injured in commercial fishing nets, poisoned by man-made pollutants, cruelly hunted for food or sold into captivity.
WDC, Whale and Dolphin Conservation, is the global voice dedicated to the protection of whales and dolphins and their environment.
We are entirely dependent upon the public's support for our campaigning, conservation and education work. Will you help us keep whales and dolphins safe and free?
See advert on next page

WEARSIDE WOMEN IN NEED
Founded: 1990 CR1000934
Co-ordinator: Ms Clare Phillipson
1st Floor, The Elms, Concord, Washington, Tyne
& Wear NE37 2BA
Tel: 0191 416 3550
Fax: 0191 416 3888
Email: .... wwinelms@aol.com
Objects: F,W3,D,C,W8

WELCARE SERVICE FOR PARENTS & CHILDREN (SOUTHWARK DIOCESE)
See Southwark Diocesan Welcare

WELDMAR HOSPICECARE TRUST
Founded: 1990 CR1000414
Chief Executive: Ms Alison Ryan
Hammick House, Bridport Road, Poundbury,
Dorchester, Dorset DT1 3SD
Tel: 01305 269898
Fax: 01305 266261
Email: .... reception@weld-hospice.org.uk
Objects: E,N,3

WELLBEING OF WOMEN

WELLBEING
OF WOMEN

Founded: 1964 CR239281; SC042856
Director: Liz Campbell
First Floor, Fairgate House, 78 New Oxford Street,
London WC1A 1HB
Tel: 020 3697 7000
Email: .... hello@wellbeingofwomen.org.uk
Web: ..... http://www.wellbeingofwomen.org.uk
Objects: W3,1A,1B,W8
Wellbeing of Women is the charity dedicated to
improving the health of women and babies, to make a
difference to everybody's lives today and tomorrow.
We provide information, to raise awareness of health
issues to keep women and babies well today.
We fund medical research and training grants, which
have and will continue to develop better treatments and
outcomes for tomorrow.
Wellbeing of Women has touched the lives of millions of
women thanks to its long history of fund-raising for vital
medical research. We are a member of the Association
of Medical Research Charities.

WELLCHILD
Founded: 1977 CR289600
Senior Fundraiser: Miss Sarah Howley
Chief Executive: Mrs Kedge Martin
16 Royal Crescent, Cheltenham, Gloucestershire
GL50 3DA
Tel: 01242 530007
Fax: 01242 530008
Email: .... info@wellchild.org.uk
Objects: W3,1B

WELSH KITE TRUST / YMDDIRIEDOLAETH BARCUDIAID CYMRU
CR1058210
"Samaria", Nantmel, Llandrindod Wells, Powys
LD1 6EN
Tel: 01597 825981
Email: .... info@welshkitetrust.org

WELSHPOOL AND LLANFAIR LIGHT RAILWAY PRESERVATION CO LIMITED
Founded: 1990 CR1000378
Company Secretary: Mr Reg Davies
Chaiman: Mr Alan Higgins
15 Valley Avenue, London N12 9PG
Tel: 020 8445 5581
Fax: 020 8445 5581
Email: .... regdavies@btinternet.com
Objects: W2,S,G,2,3,K

WESC FOUNDATION
CR1058937
Principal: Mr Paul Holland MEd, DipSpEd
Countess Wear, Exeter, Devon EX2 6HA
Tel: 01392 454336
Email: .... fundraising@westengland.org.uk
Objects: F,W6,M,W3,G,N,O,P

AUTISM WESSEX
Founded: 1990 CR1000792
Chief Executive: Mr R W Lowndes
22 Bargates, Christchurch, Dorset BH23 1QL
Tel: 01202 483360
Fax: 01202 483171
Email: .... enquiries@autismwessex.org.uk
Objects: F,W3,W5,G,2,3,C,P

WESSEX CANCER HELP CENTRE
See Cancerwise

WESSEX FOUNDATION, THE
Founded: 1991 CR1002373
Director: Mr Gyles Morris
The Magdalen Project, Magdalen Farm, Winsham,
Chard, Somerset TA20 4PA
Tel: 01460 30144
Fax: 01460 30177
Email: ...... admin@themagdalenproject.org.uk
*Objects: W6,W3,W2,S,W7,W5,G,W10,V,W4,O,3,
P,W8,K*

WEST HAMPSTEAD COMMUNITY CENTRE
Founded: 1990 CR1135778
Co-ordinator: Ms Pat Barnes
Secretary: Ms Lily Krikler
17 Dornfell Street, London NW6 1QN
Tel: .... info@westhampsteadcc.org.uk
Objects: F,W3,S,W7,W5,G,W10,V,W4,P,W8,K

WEST KENT YMCA - HELPING YOUNG PEOPLE BUILD THEIR FUTURE
Founded: 1990 CR803529
Chairman: Mr Graham Edwards
Treasurer: Mr Mark Farrar
Chief Executive: Mr Rob Marsh
Chief Executive: Mr Richard Mayhew
Ryder House, 1-23 Belgrave Road, Tunbridge
Wells, Kent TN1 2BP
Tel: 01892 542209
Fax: 0871 239 0677
Email: .... info@westkentymca.org.uk
Objects: F,W3,S,E,W5,G,D,3,C,K

THE WESTMINSTER SOCIETY FOR PEOPLE WITH LEARNING DISABILITIES
CR801081
16a Croxley Road, London W9 3HL

Tel: 020 8968 7376
Fax: 020 8968 9165
Email: .... westminstersociety@wspld.org

WHEELPOWER - BRITISH WHEELCHAIR SPORT
Founded: 1972 CR265498
Head of Fundraising: Mr Paul Rushton
Stoke Mandeville Stadium, Guttmann Road, Stoke Mandeville, Buckinghamshire HP21 9PP
Tel: 01296 395995
Fax: 01296 424171
Email: .... info@wheelpower.org.uk
Objects: F,J,W5,G,2,H,O,P

Each year, thousands of men, women and children become disabled due to an accident or illness or are born with a disability.
WheelPower help disabled people to play sport and lead healthy active lives.

WHEN YOU WISH UPON A STAR
CR1060963
2nd Floor, Futurist House, Valley Road, Basford, Nottinghamshire NG5 1JE
Tel: 0115 979 1210
Fax: 0115 979 1210

WHITE HORSE CARE TRUST, THE
Founded: 1990 CR900633
Director of Care: Ms Hilary Davidson
Chief Executive: Mr Ian Spalding
Washbourne House, 77A High Street, Wroughton, Wiltshire SN4 9JU

Tel: 01793 846000
Fax: 01793 846001
Email: .... staff@whct.co.uk
Objects: W5,D,N,O,3

WHITEHALL AND INDUSTRY GROUP, THE
Founded: 1991 CR1061584
Chief Executive: Ms Sally Cantello
22 Queens Annes Gate, London SW1H 9AA
Tel: 020 7222 1166
Fax: 020 7222 1167
Email: .... info@wig.co.uk
Objects: J,G,2

WHITELANDS SPRINGFIELD AND TYNING COMMUNITY ASSOCIATION
Founded: 1990 CR900420
Secretary to the Association: Mrs Shirley Diane Turner
39 Walnut Buildings, Radstock, Bath, Bath & North East Somerset BA3 3LJ
Tel: 01761 435101

WILDFOWL & WETLANDS TRUST

Founded: 1946 CR1030884; SC039410
Chief Executive: Mr Martin Spray
Slimbridge, Gloucestershire GL2 7BT

Tel: 01453 891900
Fax: 01453 890827
Email: .... enquiries@wwt.org.uk
Web: .... www.wwt.org.uk
Objects: W1,W2,G,2
Founded by the late Sir Peter Scott, WWT works to save wetlands for wildlife and people, at nine UK centres and internationally.

THE WILDLIFE AID FOUNDATION
Founded: 1987 CR1138944
Officer Manager: Becky Banning
Managing Trustee: Mr Simon Cowell
Randalls Farmhouse (CD), Randalls Road, Leatherhead, Surrey KT22 0AL
Tel: . 09061 800 132 - 24Hr Helpline calls 50p per minute
Fax: 01372 375183
Email: .... mail@wildlifeaid.org.uk
Objects: W1,G,3

See advert on previous page

WILDLIFE TRUSTS, THE
Founded: 1912 CR207238
Managing Director: Mr T P R Crane
Managing Director: Ms Stephanie Hilborne
Partnership Support Officer: Ms Catherine Sutherland
The Kiln, Mather Road, Newark-on-Trent, Newark, Nottinghamshire NG24 1WT
Tel: 01636 677711
Email: .... pdorans@wildlifetrusts.org
Objects: W3,J,W2,G,H

WILLIAM SUTTON TRUST
Founded: 1900 CR205847
Director of Corporate Affairs: Ms Stephanie Bamford
Chief Executive: Mr Mike Morris
12 Elstree Way, Borehamwood, Hertfordshire WD6 1JE
Tel: 020 8235 7000
Fax: 020 8313 0440
Email: .... south@williamsutton.org.uk
Objects: W9,W6,W3,W7,W5,W10,D,W4,3,C,W8

WILLOW FOUNDATION
CR1106746
Willow House, 18 Salisbury Square, Hatfield, Hertfordshire AL9 5BE
Tel: 01707 259777
Fax: 01707 259289
Email: .... info@willowfoundation.org.uk

WILTONS MUSIC HALL
Founded: 1991 CR1003041
Miss Flora Smith
Wilton's Music Hall, Graces Alley, Wellclose Square, London E1 8JB
Tel: 01622 690691
Fax: 01622 662022
Objects: S,G

THE WIMBLEDON GUILD
CR200424
Guild House, 30-32 Worple Road, Wimbledon, London SW19 4EF
Tel: 020 8946 0735
Fax: 020 8296 0042
Email: .... hbreen@wimbledonguild.co.uk
Objects: F,W9,M,W5,A,D,N,W4,P

WINCANTON RECREATIONAL TRUST
Founded: 1991 CR1003992
Chairman: Mr P W Rochford
Homestead Farm, Barrow Lane, Charlton Musgrove, Wincanton, Somerset BA9 8HW
Tel: 01963 34017

WINNICOTT FOUNDATION - IMPROVING CARE FOR PREMATURE AND SICK BABIES - SUPPORTING IMPERIAL'S NEONATAL UNITS AT ST MARY'S HOSPITAL AND QUEEN CHARLOTTE'S HOSPITALS
CR292668
Sam Segal Unit, Clarence Wing, St Mary's Hospital, Imperial College Healthcare NHS Trust, Praed Street, London W2 1NY
Tel: 020 3312 6773
Fax: 020 3312 5905
Email: .... info@winnicott.org.uk

WIRRAL COUNCIL FOR VOLUNTARY SERVICE
CR1003070
Chief Executive: Ms Jean Benfield
Information & Communications Officer: Mr Ronnie Wright
46 Hamilton Square, Birkenhead, Merseyside CH41 5AR
Tel: 0151 647 5432
Fax: 0151 647 5432
Email: .... admin@wirralcvs.org.uk
Objects: F,J,G,H

WISDOM HOSPICE (ROCHESTER), FRIENDS OF
CR284894
High Bank, Rochester, Kent ME1 2NU
Tel: 01634 831163
Fax: 01634 849975
Email: .... info@fowh.org.uk

WJAID (WORLD JEWISH AID)
See Central British Fund for World Jewish Relief

WOKING AND SAM BEARE HOSPICES
Founded: 1991 CR1082798, 1115439
Executive Services Manager: Mrs Lyn Clark
Chief Executive: Mr Nigel Hording
Woking & Sam Beare Hospices, Hill View Road, Woking, Surrey GU22 7HW
Tel: 01483 881750
Email: .... mail@woking-hospice.freeserve.co.uk
Objects: N,3

WOKING HOMES - A RESIDENTIAL RETIREMENT HOME (A RAILWAY CHARITY)
CR1120447
Oriental Road, Woking, Surrey GU22 7BE
Tel: 01483 763558
Fax: 01483 721048
Email: .... administration@woking-homes.co.uk

WOLVERHAMPTON MULTI-HANDICAP CARE AND RELIEF SERVICE
Founded: 1990 CR703005
Care Service Manager: Mrs Brenda Shortley
Easterling House, Hilton Street, Springfields, Wolverhampton, West Midlands WV10 0LF
Objects: W3,W5,3

WOMANKIND WORLDWIDE

Founded: 1989 CR328206
Marketing Officer: Ms Rosey Ellum
Head of Fundraising: Ms Disha Sughand

2nd Floor, Development House, 56-64 Leonard Street, London EC2A 4LT
Tel: 020 7549 0360
Fax: 020 7549 0361
Email: .... info@womankind.org.uk
Objects: G,U,W8

Womankind Worldwide is an international women's human rights charity working to help women transform their lives in Africa, Asia and Latin America. We partner with women's rights organisations who are tackling the day to day issues that affect women's lives. We work to end violence against women, increase women's civil and political participation and to increase women's control over economic resources. For twenty-five years Womankind Worldwide has been helping courageous individuals transform their lives.

WOMEN IN PRISON

Founded: 1992 CR1118727
Director: Ms Suzanne Sibillin

Unit 10, The Ivories, 6 Northampton Street, London N1 2HY
Tel: 020 7359 6674
Email: .... salma@womeninprison.org.uk
Objects: F,W3,G,W10,1A,A,W4,O,3,W8

WOMEN IN SUPPORTED HOUSING

Founded: 1991 CR1040476
Deputy Manager: Ms Tina Lee

Vernon House, 80 Edna Street, Hyde, Cheshire SK14 1DR
Tel: 0161 366 1355
Email: .... wishtameside@btconnect.com
Objects: F,D,3,C,W8

WOMEN'S CORONA SOCIETY

See Corona Worldwide

WOMEN'S ENVIRONMENTAL NETWORK

Founded: 1992 CR1010397
Co-ordinator: Ms Ann Link

PO Box 30626, London E1 1TZ
Tel: 020 7481 9004
Fax: 020 7481 9144
Email: .... info@wen.org.uk
Objects: F,W2,W10,2,H,W8

WOMEN'S TECHNOLOGY / BLACKBURNE HOUSE

Founded: 1992 CR1010546
Chief Executive Officer: Ms Claire Dove

Blackburne House, Hope Street, Liverpool, Merseyside L8 7PE
Tel: 0151 709 4356
Objects: G,3,W8

WOOD GREEN, THE ANIMALS CHARITY

CR298348
Supporter Services (CC), King's Bush Farm, London Road, Godmanchester, Cambridgeshire PE29 2NH
Tel: 0844 248 8181
Fax: 01480 832815
Email: .... info@woodgreen.org.uk

THE WOODLAND TRUST

Founded: 1972 CR294344; SC038885
Chief Executive: Ms Sue Holden
Director of Fundraising: Mr Karl Mitchell

Autumn Park, Dysart Road, Grantham, Lincolnshire NG31 6LL
Tel: 01476 581111
Fax: 01476 590808
Email: .... legacies@woodland-trust.org.uk
Objects: F,W1,W6,W3,J,W2,W7,W5,G,W10,W11, A,1B,2,W4,H,P,W8

WOODLANDS HOSPICE CHARITABLE TRUST, LIVERPOOL

CR1048934
University Hospital Aintree Campus (CC09), Longmoor Lane, Liverpool, Merseyside L9 7LA
Tel: 0151 529 2299
Fax: 0151 529 2638
Email: .... carole.riley@aintree.nhs.uk

WOODROFFE BENTON FOUNDATION

Founded: 1988 CR1075272
Secretary: Mr Alan King

16 Fernleigh Court, Harrow, Middlesex HA2 6NA
Tel: 020 8421 4120
Objects: M,W2,W5,G,A,1B,N,W4,C,P

WOODSIDE ANIMAL WELFARE TRUST

CR299789
Elfordleigh, Plympton, Plymouth, Devon PL7 5ED
Tel: 01752 347503
Fax: 01752 347654
Email: .... woodsidesanctuary@yahoo.co.uk

WORDSLEY HOUSING SOCIETY

Founded: 1990 CR1001178
Manager: Ms Karen Barr

30 Brook Street, Wordsley, Stourbridge, West Midlands DY8 5YW
Tel: 01384 480770
Fax: 01384 860507
Objects: F,V,O,3,C,P

WORKERS' EDUCATIONAL ASSOCIATION

Founded: 1903 CR1112775
General Secretary: Mr Richard Bolsin

4 Luke Street, London EC2 4XW
Tel: 020 7426 3450
Fax: 020 7426 3451
Email: .... national@wea.org.uk
Objects: S,G,2,3

WORKS TRUST, THE

Founded: 1990 CR1000463
Chief Executive: Mr M E Rushton

Prospect House, 19-21 Bucknall Old Road, Hanley, Stoke-on-Trent, Staffordshire ST1 2AF
Tel: 01782 263919
Fax: 01782 283971
Email: ... heritage@the-works-trust.demon.co.uk
Objects: W2,W12,3

WORLD CANCER RESEARCH FUND (WCRF UK)

Founded: 1990 CR1000739
Head of Fundraising: Mr Paul Fretwell
Chief Executive: Ms Marilyn Gentry
General Manager: Mr P Rushton

19 Harley Street, London W1G 9QJ

Tel: 020 7343 4200
Tax: 020 7343 4201
Email: .... giftsinwills@wcrf.org
Objects: 1A,2,H,3

WORLD CHRISTIAN MINISTRIES
Founded: 1991 CR1001691
Director: Reverend D David
6 Belfield Close, Marldon, Paignton, Devon
TQ3 1NZ
Tel: 01803 663681
Fax: 01803 665166
Objects: M,E,G,R,U

WORLD HORSE WELFARE
Founded: 1927 CR206658; SC038384
Director of Fundraising: Ms Linda Hams
Director (Operations): Mr Tony Tyler
UK Head Office, Anne Colvin House, Snetterton,
Norfolk NR16 2LR
Tel: 0870 870 1927
Fax: 0870 904 1927
Email: .... hq@ilph.org
Objects: Q,F,W1,G,A,1B,2,U,B,H,O

WORLD MEDICAL FUND

CR1063756
St Helens, Low Road, Saddlebow, Norfolk
PE34 3FN
Tel: 0800 783 3822
Email: .... info@ukwmf.org
See advert on previous page

WORLD OWL TRUST
CR1107529
World Owl Centre, Muncaster Castle, Ravenglass,
Cumbria CA18 1RQ
Tel: 01229 717393
Fax: 01229 717508
Email: .... barbara@owls.org

WORLD PARROT TRUST
Founded: 1989 CR800944
Chairman: Mrs Alison Hales
Glanmor House, Hayle, Cornwall TR27 4HB
Tel: 01736 751026
Fax: 01736 751028
Email: .... uk@parrots.org
Objects: W1,W2,2,H

WORLD WIDE FUND FOR NATURE
See WWF-UK

WORLD WILDLIFE FUND
See WWF-UK

WORLDWIDE HARVEST MINISTRIES TRUST
Founded: 1991 CR1005119
Trustee: Rev Terry Murphy
41 Marlow Road, Maidenhead, Windsor &
Maidenhead SL6 7AQ
Tel: 01628 621727
Objects: 1A,N,2,R,U

WORLDWIDE VETERINARY SERVICE (WVS)

CR1100485
Chief Executive: Luke Gamble
5-7 Castle Street (CD), Cranborne, Dorset
BH21 5PZ
Tel: 01725 551123
Fax: 01725 551125
Email: .... info@wvs.org.uk
Objects: W1,W2,G,U

WVS provides a free veterinary resource for charities
and sanctuaries all over the world. Getting to places
where there are no vets, WVS teams work to provide
animal welfare to help human welfare. With over 500
associated charities, WVS sends on average one
veterinary team every week and at least one veterinary
aid parcel every day.

WORM WATCH
6-14 Underwood Street, London N1 7JQ

**To ensure we
have the correct
details of your
organisation
please inform us
of any changes**

By post to:
The Editor
CHARITIES DIGEST
6-14 Underwood Street
London
N1 7JQ
By fax on:
020 7566 8213

Tel: 020 7566 5771
Email: .... crios@wilmington.co.uk

WRVS TRUSTEES LTD
See Greensleeves Homes Trust

WSPA - WORLD SOCIETY FOR THE PROTECTION OF ANIMALS

CR1081849
Chief Executive: Mike Baker
Senior Legacy Officer: Kathy Rich
5th Floor, 222 Grays Inn Road, London
WC1X 8HB
Tel: **0845 073 7500**
Fax: **020 7239 0654**
Email: .... **giftsinwills@wspa.org.uk**
Object: W1

The World Society for the Protection of Animals (WSPA) believes that cruelty to animals and their needless suffering is wrong.

Billions of animals around the world are brutally exploited for our entertainment, food or financial gain. Animals are farmed beyond their biological limits. Dogs are brutally killed in an attempt to control the spread of rabies. Bears are cruelly farmed for their bile, or caged and abused as tourist attractions. Wild animals are poached and traded as commodities. The cruelty and suffering endured by animals is both needless and wrong.

WSPA is determined to create a better world for animals. A world where animals can live free to express their natural behaviour and are protected from cruelty and suffering. But we can't create this world without you.

Leaving a gift to WSPA in your Will is your opportunity to leave behind this world – to help protect animals long into the future. If you would like a confidential chat with our Legacy Officer, please call 0845 0737 500. Thank you.

WWF-UK
Founded: 1961 CR1081247; SC039593
Campaign Manager: Ms Sarah Cunningham
President of WWF-UK: HRH Princess Alexandra the Hon Lady Ogilvy KG, GCVO
Panda House, Weyside Park, Godalming, Surrey GU7 1XR
Tel: 01483 426333
Fax: 01483 426409
Email: .... legacy@wwf.org.uk
Objects: W1,W2,G,A,1B,2,U,H

WYTHALL ANIMAL SANCTUARY
Founded: 1968 CR1137681
Middle Lane, Kings Norton, Birmingham, West Midlands B38 0DU
Tel: 01564 823288
Fax: 01564 826140
Email: ..... info@wythallanimalsanctuary.org.uk
Objects: W1,3
Founded 1968 to re-home unwanted dogs, cats and other small animals. All new homes checked and animals neutered. Our continued existence is only

possible through bequests, fundraising and voluntary donations. Running costs approx. £6000 weekly. We have membership, newsletter, adoption, 100 club schemes and a Charity shop. Please help us continue our work.

WYTHAM HALL LIMITED
Founded: 1983 CR289328
Registered Project Manager: Ms Julie Gaudion
Registered Owner: Dr P Reid
117 Sutherland Avenue, London W9 2QJ
Tel: 020 7289 1978
Fax: 020 7266 1518
Email: .... enquiries@wythamhall.co.uk
Objects: F,G,D,N,O,C,P

Y

YELDALL CHRISTIAN CENTRES
Founded: 1990 CR1000038
Chief Executive: Mr K Wiltshire
Yeldall Manor, Blakes Lane, Hare Hatch, Reading RG10 9XR
Tel: 0118 940 1093
Fax: 0118 940 4852
Email: .... info@yeldall.org.uk
Objects: F,O,3

YMCA ENGLAND
Founded: 1844 CR212810
National Secretary: Mr Nicholas Nightingale
640 Forest Road, London E17 3DZ
Tel: 020 8520 5599
Fax: 020 8509 3190
Email: .... info@england.ymca.org.uk
Objects: F,M,W3,S,E,G,U,H,C,P

YMCA - SLOUGH
Founded: 1991 CR1002442
Manager: Ms Kate Kimpton
30 Ladbrooke Road, Chalvey, Slough SL1 2SR
Tel: 01753 810684
Objects: G,D,C

YORKSHIRE CANCER RESEARCH
CR516898
Ms Clair Chadwick
39 East Parade (CC), Harrogate, North Yorkshire HG1 5LQ
Tel: 01423 501269
Fax: 01423 527929
Email: .... hq@ycr.org.uk

YORKSHIRE COUNTY CRICKET CLUB CHARITABLE YOUTH TRUST, THE
Founded: 1991 CR1001497
Secretary: Mr J P Honeysett
9 St Winifreds Road, Harrogate, North Yorkshire HG2 8LN
Tel: 01423 887978

YORKSHIRE WILDLIFE TRUST
CR210807
1 St George's Place, York, North Yorkshire YO24 1GN
Tel: 01904 659570
Fax: 01904 613467
Email: .... info@ywt.org.uk
Objects: W1,W2,G,2,3

YOUTH ALIYAH - CHILD RESCUE
Founded. 1944 CR1077913
Finance Manager: Ms Nellie Ebert
Executive Director: Ms Claudia Rubenstein
126 Albert Street, London NW1 7NE
Tel: 020 7485 8375
Email: . . . . info@youthaliyah.org.uk
Objects: Q,W3,G,1B,N,U

YWCA (ACCOMMODATION AND ADVISORY SERVICE)
See Women's Link

Z

ZOOLOGICAL SOCIETY OF GLASGOW & WEST SCOTLAND
Founded: 1936SC002651
Chief Executive Officer: Mr Roger Edwards
Morrisbank, Deans Road, Bathgate, West Lothian EH48 1JU
Objects: W1,J,W2,G,2,H

ZOOLOGICAL SOCIETY OF LONDON, THE
CR208728
Regent's Park, London NW1 4RY
Tel: 020 7449 6226
Fax: 020 7586 6177
Email: . . . . fundraising@zsl.org
Objects: W1,W2

ADOPTION SERVICES

The names of the Societies are listed under the areas in which their administrative headquarters are situated, though their activities are not necessarily confined to those areas. Local Authority Social Services Departments are also recognised Adoption Agencies. Societies based in England, Scotland and Wales were contacted individually to verify current details.

ENGLAND

Bristol

CATHOLIC CHILDREN'S SOCIETY (DIOCESE OF CLIFTON)
162 Pennywell Road, Easton, Bristol BS5 0TX
Tel: 0845 122 0077
Fax: 0117 935 0078
Email: .... info@ccsadoption.org

Cambridgeshire

ADOPT ANGLIA (THE EAST ANGLIA ADOPTION AND FAMILY CARE ASSOCIATION)
9 Petersfield, Cambridge, Cambridgeshire CB1 1BB
Tel: 01223 357397
Fax: 01223 576602

Co. Durham

DFW ADOPTION
Agriculture House, Stonebridge, Durham, Co. Durham DH1 3RY
Tel: 0191 386 3719
Fax: 0191 386 4940
Email: .... office@dfw.org.uk

Devon

FAMILIES FOR CHILDREN DEVON
Southgate Court, Buckfast, Buckfastleigh, Devon TQ11 0EE
Tel: 01364 645480
Fax: 01364 645499
Email: .... mail@familiesforchildren.org.uk

Greater Manchester

CATHOLIC CHILDREN'S SOCIETY (SALFORD DIOCESE)
Cathedral Centre, 34 ST, Salford, Greater Manchester M3 6DP
Tel: 0161 817 2250
Fax: 0161 833 1635

Hertfordshire

ACTION FOR CHILDREN, THE CHILDREN'S CHARITY
3 Boulevard, Ascot Road, Watford, Hertfordshire WD18 8AJ
Tel: 01923 620 111
Fax: 01923 361 500

Lancashire

CARITAS CARE LIMITED
218 Tulketh Road, Preston, Lancashire PR2 1ES
Tel: 01772 732313
Fax: 01772 768726
Email: .... info@caritascare.org.uk

London

BRITISH ASSOCIATION FOR ADOPTION AND FOSTERING
Saffron House, 6-10 Kirby Street, London EC1N 8TS
Tel: 0207 421 2669
Fax: 0207 421 2601
Email: .... southern@baaf.org.uk

IAS-TACT ADOPTION
303 Hither Green Lane, Hither Green, London SE13 6TJ
Tel: 020 8695 8111
Fax: 020 8695 8100
Email: .... enquiries@tactcare.org.uk

SSAFA FORCES HELP
19 Queen Elizabeth Street, London SE1 2LP
Tel: 020 7403 8783
Fax: 020 7403 8815
Email: .... info@ssafa.org.uk

Middlesex

NORWOOD JEWISH ADOPTION SOCIETY
Broadway House, 80-82 The Broadway, Stanmore, Middlesex HA7 4HB
Tel: 020 8954 4555
Fax: 020 8420 6800
Email: .... info@norwood.org.uk

Milton Keynes

ST FRANCIS CHILDREN'S SOCIETY
Collis House, 48 Newport Road, Woolstone, Milton Keynes MK15 0AA
Tel: 01908 572700
Fax: 01908 572701
Email: .... enquiries@sfcs.org.uk

Nottinghamshire

FAITH IN FAMILIES
7 Colwick Road, West Bridgford, Nottingham, Nottinghamshire NG2 5FR
Tel: 0115 955 8811
Fax: 0115 955 8822
Email: .... enquiries@ccfnotts.co.uk

FAMILY CARE
28 Magdala Road, Nottingham, Nottinghamshire
NG3 5DF
Tel: 0115 960 3010
Fax: 0115 962 8500
Email: . . . . . . info@familycare-nottingham.org.uk

Reading

FOSTERING ADOPTION TEAM - RBC (READING BOROUGH COUNCIL)
Placement Choice & Stability, PO Box 2943,
Reading RG1 9NT
Tel: 0118 955 3740
Fax: 0118 955 3746

PARENTS AND CHILDREN TOGETHER
7 Southern Court, South Street, Reading
RG1 4QS
Tel: 0118 938 7600
Email: . . . . info@pactcharity.org

South Yorkshire

ADOPTION AND FAMILY WELFARE SOCIETY
Jubilee House, 1 Jubilee Road, Wheatley,
Doncaster, South Yorkshire DN1 2UE
Tel: 01302 349909
Email: . . . web@yorkshireadoptionagency.org.uk

Staffordshire

SACCS FLYING COLOURS FOSTERING CARE
The Dairy House, Brockton Hall, Brockton,
Eccleshall, Stafford, Staffordshire ST21 6LY
Tel: 01785 857100
Fax: 01785 859272
Email: . . . . familyplacement@saccs.co.uk

Surrey

CATHOLIC CHILDREN'S SOCIETY (ARUNDEL & BRIGHTON, PORTSMOUTH AND SOUTHWARK DIOCESES)
49 Russell Hill Road, Purley, Surrey CR8 2XB
Tel: 020 8668 2181
Fax: 020 8763 2274
Email: . . . . info@cabrini.org.uk

Tyne & Wear

ST CUTHBERT'S CARE
St Cuthberts House, West Road, Newcastle upon
Tyne, Tyne & Wear NE15 7PY
Tel: 0191 228 0111
Fax: 0191 228 0177
Email: . . . . enquiries@stcuthbertscare.org.uk

NORTHERN IRELAND
Belfast

CHURCH OF IRELAND BOARD FOR SOCIAL RESPONSIBILITY (NI)
18 Heron Road, Belfast BT3 9LE
Tel: 028 9073 6080

FAMILY CARE SOCIETY (BELFAST)
Good Shepherd Centre, 511 Ormeau Road,
Belfast BT7 3GS
Tel: 028 9069 1133
Fax: 028 9064 9849
Email: . . . . email@family-care-society.org

Co. Londonderry

FAMILY CARE SOCIETY (LONDONDERRY)
1a Millar Street, Londonderry, Co. Londonderry
BT48 6SU
Tel: 028 7136 8592
Fax: 028 7137 2611

SCOTLAND
Edinburgh

BARNARDO'S SCOTLAND - GIVING CHILDREN BACK THEIR FUTURE
235 Corstorphine Road, Edinburgh EH12 7AR
Tel: 0131 334 9893
Fax: 0131 316 4008
Email: . . . . martin.crewe@barnardos.org.uk

ST ANDREWS CHILDREN'S SOCIETY LTD
7 John's Place, Edinburgh EH6 7EL
Tel: 0131 454 3370
Fax: 0131 454 3371
Email: . . . . info@standrewschildren.org.uk

Glasgow

ST MARGARET'S CHILDREN AND FAMILY CARE SOCIETY
Flat 2/1, 274 Bath Street, Glasgow G2 4JR
Tel: 0141 332 8371
Fax: 0141 332 8593
Email: . . . . info@stmargaretsadoption.org.uk

WALES
Cardiff

ST. DAVID'S CHILDREN'S SOCIETY (WALES)
28 Park Place, Cardiff CF10 3BA
Tel: 029 2066 7007
Email: . . . . info@stdavidscs.org

ALMSHOUSES

For those seeking almshouse accommodation, lists of local almshouse charities and their contact names and addresses should be obtainable from local authority Housing Departments or Social Services Departments and from Citizens' Advice Bureaux. Alternatively, the Almshouse Association can provide a list of the almshouse trusts in a locality.

The Almshouse Association
Billingbear Lodge, Maidenhead Road, Wokingham RG40 5RU
Tel: 01344 452922 Fax: 01344 862062
E-mail: naa@almshouses.org   Web: www.almshouses.org

For the last thousand years, almshouses have provided accommodation for older people and they continue to give this service today.

Early almshouses were called Hospitals, in the sense that they provided hospitality and shelter for those in need. Part of our national heritage, almshouses show the most complete examples of vernacular domestic architecture from the 12th century to the present day. There are more than 2,600 groups of almshouses in the United Kingdom, providing 30,000 separate homes for older people. New almshouses continue to be built today, some as extensions of existing trusts and others as new foundations.

The Almshouse Association is itself a charity which aims to assist and advise trustees of almshouses on their many problems. There are nearly 1,800 almshouse charities in membership of the Association throughout the United Kingdom. One of the main tasks is helping trustees to improve the accommodation in their almshouses up to modern housing standards. This often involves arranging or assisting with funding towards the cost of the work. A Common Investment Fund and Comprehensive Insurance Policy have been established for almshouse charities to help trustees further with the financial running of their trusts.

The Association publishes an Annual Report and quarterly Gazette to keep members up to date with legislation and other information and a series of regional meetings and training days are arranged annually. An Associate membership is available to individuals and bodies who are interested in supporting the work of the Association.

CITIZENS ADVICE BUREAUX

Citizens Advice Bureaux help people with legal, financial and other advice throughout the UK. They are all registered charities and rely on volunteers and donations to keep them going. The following pages list selected CAB offices throughout England, Scotland, Wales and Northern Ireland and are organised according to county/unitary authority/region.

For more information, contact the local CAB office, or visit www.citizensadvice.org.uk

CHANNEL ISLANDS
Guernsey

Guernsey
Bridge Avenue, The Bridge, St Sampsons,
Guernsey GY2 4QS
Tel: 01481 242266
Fax: 01481 200444

Jersey

St Helier
The Annexe, St Paul's Gate, New Street, St
Helier, Jersey JE2 3WP
Tel: 01534 724942
Fax: 01534 617508
Email: .... advice@cab.org.je

ENGLAND
Bath & North East Somerset

Bath
2 Edgar Buildings, George Street, Bath, Bath &
North East Somerset BA1 2EE
Tel: 0844 848 7919
Fax: 01225 481667

Bedfordshire

Ampthill
The Court House, Woburn Street, Ampthill,
Bedfordshire MK45 2HX
Tel: 0844 477 1600
Fax: 01525 402742

Bedford
7a St Paul's Square, Bedford, Bedfordshire
MK40 1SQ
Tel: 01234 354384

Dunstable
Grove House, 76 High Street North, Dunstable,
Bedfordshire LU6 1NF
Tel: .... 01582 661384; 01582 670003 Appts

Leighton Buzzard
Bossard House, West Street, Leighton Buzzard,
Bedfordshire LU7 1DA
Tel: 01525 373878
Fax: 01525 371161

Luton
24-26 King Street, Luton, Bedfordshire LU1 2DP
Tel: 01582 731616
Fax: 01582 488705

Blackpool

Blackpool
6-10 Whitegate Drive, Devonshire Square,
Blackpool FY3 9AQ
Tel: 01253 308400
Fax: 01253 308420
Email: .... advice@blackpoolcab.org.uk

Bournemouth

Bournemouth
The West Wing, Town Hall, Bourne Avenue,
Bournemouth BH2 6DX
Tel: 01202 290967
Fax: 01202 290975

Bracknell Forest

Bracknell
42 The Broadway, Bracknell, Bracknell Forest
RG12 1AG
Tel: 0844 499 4107
Fax: 01344 867171

Bristol

Bristol
12 Broad Street, Bristol BS1 2HL
Tel: 0844 499 4718
Fax: 0117 934 9829

Buckinghamshire

Amersham
Barn Hall Annexe, Chiltern Avenue, Amersham,
Buckinghamshire HP6 5AH
Tel: 0845 092 0137
Fax: 01494 431815

Aylesbury
2 Pebble Lane, Aylesbury, Buckinghamshire
HP20 2JH
Tel: 0844 4994714
Fax: 01296 338075

Buckingham
Wheeldon House, Market Hill, Buckingham,
Buckinghamshire MK18 1JX
Tel: 01280 816707
Fax: 01280 824494

High Wycombe
8 Easton Street, High Wycombe,
Buckinghamshire HP11 1NJ
Tel: 0844 499 4108
Fax: 01494 536437

Milton Keynes
Acorn House, 361 Midsummer Boulevard, Milton
Keynes, Buckinghamshire MK9 3HP
Tel: 01908 604475
Fax: 01908 545199

Cambridgeshire

Cambridge
66 Devonshire Road, Cambridge, Cambridgeshire
CB1 2BL
Tel: 0844 848 7979
Email: .... advice@cambridgecab.org.uk

Ely
70 Market Street, Ely, Cambridgeshire CB7 4LS
Tel: 0845 130 6442
Fax: 01353 669308

Huntingdon
6 All Saints Passage, Huntingdon,
Cambridgeshire PE29 3LE
Tel: 01480 388900
Fax: 01480 388903

March
March Library, City Road, March, Cambridgeshire
PE15 9LT
Tel: 01945 464367
Fax: 01945 475658

Peterborough
16-17 St Marks Street, Peterborough,
Cambridgeshire PE1 2TU
Tel: 0844 499 4120; 01733 558383
Fax: 01733 340028
Email: .... info@peterboroughcab.org.uk

St Neots
28 New Street, St Neots, Cambridgeshire
PE19 1AJ
Tel: 01480 388905
Fax: 01480 388908

Wisbech
Fenland CAB, 12 Church Mews, Wisbech,
Cambridgeshire PE13 1HL
Tel: 01945 464367
Fax: 01945 475658

Cheshire

Birchwood
46 Benson Road, Birchwood, Warrington,
Cheshire WA3 7PQ
Tel: 01925 824952
Fax: 01925 831861

Chester
Folliot House, 53 Northgate Street, Chester,
Cheshire CH1 2HQ
Tel: 0844 576 6111
Fax: 01244 315726

Crewe
50 Victoria Street, Crewe, Cheshire CW1 2JE
Tel: 01270 303003
Fax: 01270 251158

Crewe and Nantwich
The Gables, Beam Street, Nantwich, Cheshire
CW5 5NF
Tel: 01270 303004
Fax: 01270 629079

Ellesmere Port
1 Whitby Road, Ellesmere Port, Cheshire
CH65 8AA
Tel: 0151 355 3428
Fax: 0151 356 5440

Lymm
Lymm Library, Davies Way, Lymm, Cheshire
WA13 0QW
Tel: 01925 753247
Fax: 01925 750661

Macclesfield
Sunderland House, Sunderland Street,
Macclesfield, Cheshire SK11 6JF
Tel: ... 01625 426303 Client Line; 01625 432847
Fax: 01625 503108
Email: .... advice@cecab-north.org.uk

Runcorn
Runcorn Office, Ground Floor, Grosvenor House,
Runcorn, Cheshire WA7 2HF
Tel: 0845 130 4055
Fax: 0845 130 6075

Widnes
Unit 6, Lugsdale Road, Widnes, Cheshire
WA8 6DJ
Tel: 0845 130 4055
Fax: 0845 130 4053
Email: .... advice@haltoncab.org.uk

Winsford
The Brunner Guildhall, High Street, Winsford,
Cheshire CW7 2AU
Tel: 0844 576 6111

Co. Durham

Barnard Castle
21 Galgate, Barnard Castle, Co. Durham
DL12 8EQ
Tel: 01833 631486
Fax: 01833 631486
Email: .... teesdalecab@hotmail.com

Chester-le-Street
1a Front Street, Chester-le-Street, Co. Durham
DH3 3BQ
Tel: 0191 389 3000
Fax: 0191 389 1619

Darlington
Bennet House, 14 Horsemarket, Darlington, Co.
Durham DL1 5PT
Tel: .... 01325 256999 Advice Line
Fax: 01325 380324
Email: .... bureau@darlingtoncab.cabnet.org.uk

Durham
39 Claypath, Durham, Co. Durham DH1 1RH
Tel: .... 0191 384 2638; 0191 383 2885 -
appointment line
Fax: 0191 384 3886

Hartlepool
87 Park Road, Hartlepool, Co. Durham TS26 9HP
Tel: 01429 273223
Fax: 01429 868803

Peterlee
17-19 The Upper Chare, Castledene Shopping
Centre, Peterlee, Co. Durham SR8 1BW
Tel: 0191 586 2639

Wear Valley
Four Clocks, 154a Newgate Street, Bishop
Auckland, Co. Durham DL14 7EH
Tel: 01388 606661
Fax: 01388 661629
Email: .... enquiries@wearvalleycab.org.uk

Cornwall

Bodmin
Shire Hall, Mount Folly Square, Bodmin, Cornwall
PL31 2DQ
Tel: 01208 74835
Fax: 01208 79966

Bude
Neetside, Bude, Cornwall EX23 8LB
Tel: 01288 354531

Falmouth
Mulberry Passage, Market Strand, Falmouth,
Cornwall TR11 3DB
Tel: 0844 499 4188

Liskeard
Duchy House, 21 Dean Street, Liskeard, Cornwall
PL14 4AB
Tel: 0844 499 4188
Fax: 01579 348338

Newquay
The Public Library, Marcus Hill, Newquay,
Cornwall TR7 1BD
Tel: 0844 499 4188
Fax: 01637 851440

Penzance
The Guildhall, St John's Road, Penzance,
Cornwall TR18 2QR
Tel: 0844 499 4188
Fax: 01736 330240; 01736 330684

Truro
The Library, Union Place, Truro, Cornwall
TR1 1EP
Tel: 0844 499 4188
Fax: 01872 263481

Cumbria

Barrow-in-Furness
Ramsden Hall, Abbey Road, Barrow-in-Furness,
Cumbria LA14 5QW
Tel: 0844 4994132
Fax: 01229 830379

Carlisle
5-6 Old Post Office Court, Carlisle, Cumbria
CA3 8LE
Tel: 01228 633900

Eden
2 Sandgate, Penrith, Cumbria CA11 7TP
Tel: 01768 863564
Fax: 01768 899070

Ulverston
Town Hall Annexe, Theatre Street, Ulverston,
Cumbria LA12 7AQ
Tel: 01229 585585
Fax: 01229 580231

Whitehaven
Tangier Buildings, Gregg's Lane, (off Tangier
Street), Whitehaven, Cumbria CA28 7UH
Tel: 01946 693321
Fax: 01946 693137

Windermere
The Library, Ellerthwaite Road, Windermere,
Cumbria LA23 2AJ
Tel: 01539 446464
Fax: 01539 446504

Workington
Vulcans Lane, Workington, Cumbria CA14 2BT
Tel: 01900 604735
Fax: 01900 870482

Derbyshire

Clay Cross
126 High Street, Clay Cross, Chesterfield,
Derbyshire S45 9EE
Tel: 0844 848 9800
Fax: 01246 866206
Email: .... mail@nedcab.org.uk

Glossop
1st Floor, Bradbury Community House, Market
Street, Glossop, Derbyshire SK13 8AR
Tel: 01298 214550

Staveley
6 - 8 Broad Pavement, Chesterfield, Derbyshire
S40 1RP
Tel: 01246 209164
Fax: 01246 229909

Devon

Barnstaple
Ground Floor, Belle Meadow Court, Albert Lane,
Barnstaple, Devon EX32 8RJ
Tel: 01271 377077

Bideford
28a Bridgeland Street, Bideford, Devon EX39 2PZ
Tel: 01237 473161
Fax: 01237 425272

Exeter
Wat Tyler House, 3 King William Street, Exeter,
Devon EX4 6PD
Tel: 0844 4994101
Fax: 01392 201203

Exmouth
The Town Hall, St Andrew's Road, Exmouth,
Devon EX8 1AW
Tel: 01395 204045
Fax: 01395 269202

Honiton
Honiton Library and Information Centre, 48-50
New Street, Honiton, Devon EX14 IBS
Tel: 01404 44213
Fax: 01404 47927

North Devon
Ilfracombe Outreach, c/o The Ilfracombe Centre,
44 High Street, Ilfracombe, Devon EX34 8AL
Tel: 01271 377181
Fax: 01271 855325

Okehampton
The Ockment Centre, North Street, Okehampton,
Devon EX20 1AR
Tel: 01837 52574
Fax: 01837 52105

Paignton
29 Palace Avenue, Paignton, Devon TQ3 3EQ
Tel: 01803 521726
Fax: 01803 558262

Tavistock
Kingdon House, North Street, Tavistock, Devon
PL19 0AN
Tel: 01822 612359
Fax: 01822 618990

Teignbridge
Bank House Centre, 5b Bank Street, Newton
Abbot, Devon TQ12 2JL
Tel: 01626 203141
Fax: 01626 337801

Teignmouth

Teignmouth Library, Fore Street, Teignmouth, Devon TQ14 8DY
Tel: 01626 776770
Fax: 01626 770591
Email: ...... enquiries@teignbridgecab.org.uk

Tiverton (Mid-Devon)

Mid Devon District CAB, The Town Hall, St Andrew Street, Tiverton, Devon EX16 6PG
Tel: 01884 234926

Torquay

Debt Advice Unit, 11 Castle Road, Torquay, Devon TQ1 3BB
Tel: 01803 297803

Totnes

The Cottage, Follaton House, Plymouth Road, Totnes, Devon TQ9 5NE
Tel: 01803 862392
Fax: 01803 847652

Dorset

Bridport

45 South Street, Bridport, Dorset DT6 3NY
Tel: 01308 456594
Fax: 01308 456769
Email: .... advice@bridport-cab.org.uk

Christchurch

2 Sopers Lane, Christchurch, Dorset BH23 1JG
Tel: . 01202 482023 Advice; 01202 488442 Appts Only
Fax: 01202 488441

Dorchester

1 Acland Road, Dorchester, Dorset DT1 1JW
Tel: 0845 231 0400
Fax: 01305 257126

Gillingham

The Courtyard, Newbury Court, Gillingham, Dorset SP8 4QX
Tel: 01747 822117
Fax: 01747 826300

Sherborne

Manor House, Newland, Sherborne, Dorset DT9 3JL
Tel: 0844 848 7939
Fax: 01935 815694

Wareham

Mill Lane, Wareham, Dorset BH20 4RA
Tel: 01929 551257
Fax: 01929 550328
Email: ...... bureau@purbeckcab.cabnet.org.uk

Weymouth

2 Mulberry Terrace, Great George Street, Weymouth, Dorset DT4 8NQ
Tel: 01305 782798
Fax: 01305 770325

Wimborne

Hanham Road, Wimborne, Dorset BH21 1AS
Tel: 01202 884738
Fax: 01202 848110

East Riding of Yorkshire

Boothferry

80 Pasture Road, Boothferry, Goole, East Riding of Yorkshire DN14 6HE
Tel: . 01405 762054 Advice; 01405 720866 Appts Only
Fax: 01405 761035
Email: .... bureau@boothferrycab.cabnet.org.uk

Bridlington

5a Prospect Arcade, Bridlington, East Riding of Yorkshire YO15 2AL
Tel: ...... 01482 393180; 01262 605644 Appts

East Sussex

Crowborough

Thorpe House, Croft Road, Crowborough, East Sussex TN6 1DL
Tel: 01892 655303
Fax: 01892 653841

Eastbourne

Unit 6, Highlight House, 8 St Leonards Road, Eastbourne, East Sussex BN21 3UH
Tel: 01323 417177
Fax: 01323 412072

Hailsham

Southview, Western Road, Hailsham, East Sussex BN27 3DN
Tel: 01323 842336
Fax: 01323 849762

Lewes

3 North Court, Lewes, East Sussex BN7 2AR
Tel: 01273 473082

Seaford

37 Church Street, Seaford, East Sussex BN25 1HG
Tel: 01323 896209
Fax: 01323 894465

Essex

Barking

55 Ripple Road, Barking, Essex IG11 7NT
Tel: 020 8594 6715
Fax: 020 8591 0440

Billericay

Burghstead Lodge, 143 High Street, Billericay, Essex CM12 9AB
Tel: 01277 651858
Fax: 01277 633830

Braintree, Halstead & Witham

Collingwood Road, Witham, Essex CM8 2DY
Tel: 0844 499 4719
Fax: 01376 502190

Brentwood

8 - 12 Crown Street, Brentwood, Essex CM14 4BA
Tel: 0844 477 0808
Fax: 01277 264999

Chelmsford

47 Broomfield Road, Chelmsford, Essex CM1 1SY
Tel: 01245 257144; 01245 354720
Fax: 01245 281388

Colchester

Blackburn House, Ground Floor, 32 Crouch Street, Colchester, Essex CO3 3HH
Tel: 08444 770808
Fax: 01206 244827

Epping

50a Hemnall Street, Epping, Essex CM16 4LS
Tel: 01992 574989
Fax: 01992 576669

Grays

Voluntary & Community Resource Centre, High Street, Thurrock, Grays, Essex RM17 6XP
Tel: 0844 826 9689
Fax: 01375 389863

Loughton
St Mary's Parish Centre, High Road, Loughton,
Essex IG10 1BB
Tel: 020 8502 0031
Fax: 020 8532 0243

Maldon
St Cedds House, Princes Road, Maldon, Essex
CM9 5NY
Tel: 01621 841195
Fax: 01621 841282
Email: ...... bureau@maldoncab.cabnet.org.uk

Rochford
Rochford Day Centre, Back Lane, Rochford,
Essex SS4 1AY
Tel: 0844 477 0808
Fax: 01702 547521

Saffron Walden
Barnard's Yard, Saffron Walden, Essex CB11 4EB
Tel: 0844 775 986
Fax: 01799 513702

Southend-on-Sea
1 Church Road, Southend-on-Sea, Essex
SS1 2AL
Tel: 01702 610610
Fax: 01702 469999

Tendring
18 Carnarvon Road, Clacton-on-Sea, Essex
CO15 6QF
Tel: 0844 477 0808
Fax: 01255 689786

Waltham Abbey
Side Entrance, Town Hall, Highbridge Street,
Waltham Abbey, Essex EN9 1DE
Tel: 01992 710353
Fax: 01992 710802

Wickford
Gibraltar Walk, High Street, Wickford, Essex
SS12 9AX

Gloucestershire

Cirencester
2-3 The Mews, Cricklade Street, Cirencester,
Gloucestershire GL7 1HY
Tel: 01285 652908

Gloucester
75-81 Eastgate Street, Gloucester,
Gloucestershire GL1 1PN
Tel: . 01452 528017 Advice; 01452 527202 Appts
Fax: 01452 381507

Stroud
Unit 8, 1st Floor Brunel Mall, London Road,
Stroud, Gloucestershire GL5 2BP
Tel: 01453 762084

Greater Manchester

Altrincham
20 Stamford New Road, Altrincham, Greater
Manchester WA14 1EJ
Tel: 0844 499 4103

Ashton-under-Lyne
9 George Street, Ashton-under-Lyne, Greater
Manchester OL6 6AQ
Tel: 0161 330 2156

Bolton
26-28 Mawdsley Street, Bolton, Greater
Manchester BL1 1LF
Tel: 0844 826 9707
Fax: 01204 900212

Bury
1-3 Blackburn Street, Radcliffe, Greater
Manchester M26 1NN
Tel: 0845 120 3757

Irlam & Cadishead
595 Liverpool Road, Irlam, Manchester, Greater
Manchester M44 5BE
Tel: .... 08701 202424 District Advice Line
Fax: 0161 777 6626

Longsight
384 Dickenson Road, Longsight, Manchester,
Greater Manchester M13 0WQ
Tel: 0845 122 1112

Manchester
Swan Buildings, 20 Swan Street, Manchester,
Greater Manchester M4 5JW
Tel: 0161 834 9057
Fax: 0161 834 9163

Oldham
1 & 2 Ashcroft Court, Peter Street, Oldham,
Greater Manchester OL1 1HP
Tel: 0844 847 2638
Fax: 0161 621 4390

Prestwich
7 Fairfax Road, Prestwich, Greater Manchester
M25 1AS
Tel: 0845 120 3757

Radcliffe
1-3 Blackburn Street, Radcliffe, Manchester,
Greater Manchester M26 1NN
Tel: 0845 120 3757
Fax: 0161 725 5375

Sale
73 Chapel Road, Sale, Greater Manchester
M33 7EG
Tel: 0844 499 4103

Salford
25a Hankinson Way, Salford Precinct, Salford,
Greater Manchester M6 5JA
Tel: .... 08701 202424 District Advice Line
Fax: 0161 737 3759

Salford - Mental Health Services
Prestwich Psychiatric Hospital, Bury New Road,
Prestwich, Greater Manchester M25 3BL
Tel: 0161 772 3506
Fax: 0161 772 3508
Email: .... main.bureau@smhscab.org.uk

Stretford
Stretford Library, 55 Bennett Street, Stretford,
Greater Manchester M32 8SG
Tel: 0844 499 4103

Withington
Withington Methodist Church, 439 Wimslow Road,
Withington, Manchester, Greater Manchester
M20 4AN
Tel: 08444 111 444

Hampshire

Aldershot
Princes Gardens, High Street, Aldershot,
Hampshire GU11 1BJ
Tel: 0845 120 3765
Email: .... advice@aldershotcab.org.uk

Alton
7 Cross And Pillory Lane, Alton, Hampshire
GU34 1HL
Tel: 01420 84399
Fax: 01420 544645
Email: ..... altonoutreach@easthantscab.org.uk

Andover
Ground Floor, East Wing, Wessex Chambers, 1
South Street, Andover, Hampshire SP10 2BN
Tel: 01264 365534
Fax: 01264 333853

Ash
Ash Hill Road, Ash, Aldershot, Hampshire
GU12 5DP
Tel: 01252 315569
Fax: 01252 316612
Email: .... ashcan@cabnet.org.uk

Basingstoke
19-20 Westminster House, The Library, Potters
Walk, Basingstoke, Hampshire RG21 7LS
Tel: 01256 322814
Fax: 01256 327001

Bishop's Waltham
Well House, 2 Brook Street, Bishop's Waltham,
Hampshire SO32 1AX
Tel: 01489 896376
Fax: 01489 890815
Email: .... bishopswaltham@cabnet.org.uk

Fareham
2nd Floor, Country Library Building, Osborn Road,
Fareham, Hampshire PO16 7EN
Tel: 0844 477 2232
Fax: 01329 223119

Farnborough
Elles Hall Community Centre, Meudon Avenue,
Farnborough, Hampshire GU14 7LE
Tel: 0845 120 3752
Fax: 01252 894297

Fleet
Civic Offices, Harlington Way, Fleet, Hampshire
GU51 4AE
Tel: 01252 617922
Fax: 01252 626905

Fordingbridge
School House, Provost Street, Fordingbridge,
Hampshire SP6 1AY
Tel: 01425 652643
Fax: 01425 652643

Hythe
The Grove, 25 St Johns Street, Hythe,
Southampton, Hampshire SO45 6BZ
Tel: 0844 8269686
Fax: 023 8084 4050
Email: .... bureau@watersidecab.cabnet.org.uk

Leigh Park
Leigh Park Community Centre, Dunsbury Way,
Leigh Park, Havant, Hampshire PO9 5BG
Tel: 023 9271 7707

Lymington
91-92 High Street, Lymington, Hampshire
SO41 9AP
Tel: 0844 499 4119
Fax: 01590 677868

New Milton
2 Ashley Road, New Milton, Hampshire BH25 6AS
Tel: 0844 499 4136
Fax: 01425 629847
Email: .... bureau@newmiltoncab.cabnet.org.uk

Petersfield
The Old Surgery, 18 Heath Road, Petersfield,
Hampshire GU31 4DY
Tel: 01730 264887
Fax: 01730 233037

Portsmouth
1-3a London Road, Dugald Drummond Street,
Portsmouth, Hampshire PO2 0BQ
Tel: 023 9265 6300

Ringwood
5 Fridays Court, High Street, Ringwood,
Hampshire BH24 1AB
Tel: 01425 473330
Fax: 01425 480521

Romsey
5 Abbey Walk, Church Street, Romsey,
Hampshire SO51 8JQ
Tel: 01794 516378
Fax: 01794 519379

Southampton
3 Kings Park Road, Southampton, Hampshire
SO15 2AT
Tel: 023 8022 1406; 023 8033 3868
Fax: 023 8023 7284

Whitehill and Bordon
Forest Community Centre, Pinehill Road, Bordon,
Hampshire GU35 0BS
Tel: 01420 477747
Fax: 01420 488943

Winchester
The Winchester Centre, 68 St Georges Street,
Winchester, Hampshire SO23 8AH
Tel: 01962 848000
Fax: 01962 848005
Email: .... advice@winchestercab.org,uk

Yateley
Royal Oak Close, Yateley, Hampshire GU46 7UD
Tel: 01252 878410

Herefordshire

Hereford
8 St Owen Street, Hereford, Herefordshire
HR1 2PJ
Tel: 0844 826 9685
Fax: 01432 344843
Email: .... info@herefordshirecab.org.uk

Leominster
11 Corn Square, Leominster, Herefordshire
HR6 8LR
Tel: 0844 826 9685
Fax: 01432 383342

Hertfordshire

Abbots Langley
The Old Stables, St Lawrence's Vicarage, High
Street, Abbots Langley, Hertfordshire WD5 0AS
Tel: 01923 267949
Fax: 01923 266335

Barnet
30 Station Road, Barnet, Hertfordshire EN5 1PL
Tel: 08701 288080
Fax: 020 8441 2384

Bishop's Stortford
74 South Street, Bishop's Stortford, Hertfordshire
CM23 3AZ
Tel: 0844 848 9700
Fax: 01279 306698

Borehamwood
Community Centre, Vanstone Suite, 2 Allum Lane, Elstree, Borehamwood, Hertfordshire WD6 3PJ
Tel: .... 0870 121 2025 Phone advice; 0208 953 9961 Appointments

Buntingford
North Entrance, The Manor House, 21 High Street, Buntingford, Hertfordshire SG9 9AB
Tel: 0844 848 9700
Fax: 01763 274753
Email: ...... bureau@buntingfordcabnet.org.uk

Bushey
8 Rudolph Road, Bushey, Hertfordshire WD23 3DU
Tel: 0870 121 2025
Fax: 020 8421 8285

Cheshunt
Old Bishop's College, Churchgate, Cheshunt, Hertfordshire EN8 9XP
Tel: 01992 635858
Fax: 01992 629722

Hatfield
1st Floor, Queensway House, Queensway, Hatfield, Hertfordshire AL10 0LW
Tel: .... 01707 262607 Advice Line
Fax: 01707 275189

Hemel Hempstead
Dacre House, 19 Hillfield Road, Hemel Hempstead, Hertfordshire HP2 4AA
Tel: 0844 873 1303
Fax: 01442 239658

Hertford
Block D, Yeoman's Court, Ware Road, Hertford, Hertfordshire SG13 7HJ
Tel: 0844 848 9700
Fax: 01992 587436

Hitchin
Thomas Bellamy House, Bedford Road, Hitchin, Hertfordshire SG5 1HL
Tel: 0845 688 9897
Fax: 01462 441332
Email: .... info@nhsdistrictcab.org.uk

Letchworth
66-68 Leys Avenue, Letchworth, Hertfordshire SG6 3EG
Tel: 0845 688 9897
Email: .... infor@nhdistrictcab.cabnet.org.uk

Potters Bar
Wyllyotts Centre, 1 Wyllyotts Place, Darkes Lane, Potters Bar, Hertfordshire EN6 2HN
Tel: 0870 121 2025
Fax: 01707 664352

Rickmansworth
Northway House, High Street, Rickmansworth, Hertfordshire WD3 1EH
Tel: 01923 720424

Royston
Town Hall, Royston, Hertfordshire SG8 7DA
Tel: 0845 688 9897
Email: .... infor@nhdistrictcab.cabnet.org.uk

South Oxhey
4 Bridlington Road, South Oxhey, Watford, Hertfordshire WD19 7AF
Tel: 020 8421 0911
Fax: 020 8421 5266

St Albans
64 London Road, St Albans, Hertfordshire AL1 1NG
Tel: 01727 811118

Stevenage
Swingate House, Danestrete, Stevenage, Hertfordshire SG1 1AF
Tel: 0845 120 3789; 01438 759300 Answerphone
Fax: 01438 722067

Ware and District
Meade House, 85 High Street, Ware, Hertfordshire SG12 9AD
Tel: 0844 848 9700

Watford
St Mary's Churchyard, High Street, Watford, Hertfordshire WD17 2BE
Tel: 08448269726
Fax: 01923 231889

Isle of Wight

Newport
Exchange House, St Cross Lane, Newport, Isle of Wight PO30 5BZ
Tel: 0845 120 2959
Fax: 01983 520594

Kent

Bexleyheath
8 Brampton Road, Bexleyheath, Kent DA7 4EY
Tel: 020 8303 5100
Fax: 020 8303 9524

Bromley
Community House, South Street, Bromley, Kent BR1 1RH
Tel: 020 8315 1940
Fax: 020 8315 1066

Dartford
Trinity Resource Centre, High Street, Dartford, Kent DA1 1DE
Tel: 01322 224686
Fax: 01322 220448

Deal
26 Victoria Road, Deal, Kent CT14 7BJ
Tel: 0844 848 7978
Fax: 01304 374333

Dover, Deal & District
Maison Dieu Gardens, Maison Dieu Road, Dover, Kent CT16 1RW
Tel: 0844 848 7978
Fax: 01304 202442

Edenbridge
68 High Street, Edenbridge, Kent TN8 5AR
Tel: 01732 865131
Fax: 01732 863220

Erith
50 Pier Road, Erith, Kent DA8 1TA
Tel: 01322 357933
Fax: 01322 357934

Faversham
43 Stone Street, Faversham, Kent ME13 8PH
Tel: 0844 499 4125

Folkestone
20 Church Street, Folkestone, Kent CT20 1SE
Tel: 0844 499 4118
Fax: .... 01303 249310 Appts

Gillingham
46 Green Street, (Off High St.), Gillingham, Kent
ME7 5TJ
Tel: 0844 826 9709
Fax: 01634 380036
Email: .... advice@medway.cabnet.org.uk

Herne Bay
185-187 High Street, Herne Bay, Kent CT6 5AF
Tel: 01227 740647 (To make appointments only);
0844 499 4128 (Adviceline)
Fax: 01227 740647

Maidstone
2 Bower Terrace, Tonbridge Road, Maidstone,
Kent ME16 8RY
Tel: 01622 752420; 01622 757882
Fax: 01622 751816
Email: .... advice@maidstonecab.org.uk

Margate
The Old Town Hall, Market Street, Margate, Kent
CT9 1EU
Tel: . 01843 225973 Advice; 01843 232666 Appts
Fax: 01843 228643
Email: .... enquiries@thanetcitizensadvice.co.uk

Sevenoaks
Buckhurst Lane (next to the library), Sevenoaks,
Kent TN13 1HW
Tel: 01732 454443
Fax: 01732 463164
Email: .... info@sevenoakscab.org.uk

Sittingbourne
17 Station Street, Sittingbourne, Kent ME10 3DU
Tel: 0844 499 4124
Fax: 01795 431315

Swanley and District
16 High Street, Swanley, Kent BR8 8BG
Tel: 01322 664949
Fax: 01322 613636

Tonbridge
3-4 River Walk, Tonbridge, Kent TN9 1DT
Tel: 01732 350099
Fax: 01732 373838

Tunbridge Wells
29-31 Monson Road, Tunbridge Wells, Kent
TN1 1LS
Tel: 08701 264856 Advice; 01892 617256 Admin
Answerphone Only
Fax: 01892 539506
Email: .... advice@twcab.cabnet.org.uk

Kingston upon Hull

Hull
2 Charlotte Street Mews, Hull, Kingston upon Hull
HU1 3BQ
Tel: .... 01482 224608 General Line

Lancashire

Bacup
18 King Street, Bacup, Lancashire OL13 0AH
Tel: 0844 499 4121

Barnoldswick
10 Rainall Road, Barnoldswick, Lancashire
BB18 5AF
Tel: 01282 814814
Email: .... pris@cabnet.org.uk

Blackburn
St John's Centre, Victoria Street, Blackburn,
Lancashire BB1 6DW
Tel: 01254 671211
Fax: 01254 675934
Email: .... advice@blackburncab.co.uk

Chorley
35-39 Market Street, Chorley, Lancashire
PR7 2SW
Tel: 01772 424282
Fax: 01257 268086

Clitheroe
19-21 Wesleyan Row, Parson Lane, Clitheroe,
Lancashire BB7 2JY
Tel: 01200 428966

Colne
The Citadel, Market Place, Colne, Nelson,
Lancashire BB8 0HY
Tel: 01282 867188

Hyndburn
New Era Centre, Paradise Street, Accrington,
Lancashire BB5 1PB
Tel: 01254 304114; 01254 394210
Fax: 01254 304111

Kirkham
Council Offices, Moor Street, Kirkham, Preston,
Lancashire PR4 2AU
Tel: 01772 682588
Fax: 01772 673014
Email: .... kirkhamcab@cabnet.org.uk

Lancaster
87 King Street, Lancaster, Lancashire LA1 1RH
Tel: 08701 264035
Fax: 01524 846447
Email: .... enquiries@lancastercab.org

Morecambe and Heysham
Oban House, 87-89 Queen Street, Morecambe,
Lancashire LA4 5EN
Tel: .... 0844 499 4197 (Advice); 01524 400405
Appts
Fax: 01524 400401
Email: .... post@morecambecab.co.uk

Nelson
61-63 Every Street, Nelson, Lancashire BB9 7LT
Tel: 01282 616750
Fax: 01282 602731

Preston
Town Hall Annexe, Birley Street, Preston,
Lancashire PR1 2QE
Tel: . 01772 822416 Advice; 01772 906434 Appts
Fax: 01772 254407

Leicestershire

Coalville
87 Belvoir Road, Coalville, Leicestershire
LE67 3PH
Tel: 0844 499 2375
Email: .... advice@swlcab.org.uk

Harborough
Fountain Court, Rear of 42 High Street, Market
Harborough, Leicestershire LE16 7AF
Tel: 0844 848 9009
Fax: 01858 469986

Loughborough
John Storer House, Ward's End, Loughborough,
Leicestershire LE11 3HA
Tel: 01509 267376
Fax: 01509 213293

Melton Mowbray
9 Burton Street, Melton Mowbray, Leicestershire
LE13 1AE
Tel: 0844 499 2375
Fax: 01664 484088

Lincolnshire

Boston
The Len Medlock, Voluntary Centre, St Georges
Road, Boston, Lincolnshire PE21 8YB
Tel: 0844 499 4199

East Lindsey
20 Algitha Road, Skegness, Lincolnshire
PE25 2AG
Tel: 0844 491 4199
Fax: 01754 769527

Gainsborough
26 North Street, Gainsborough, Lincolnshire
DN21 2HU
Tel: 0844 499 4199
Fax: 01427 810914

Lincoln & District
Beaumont Lodge, Beaumont Fee, Lincoln,
Lincolnshire LN1 1UL
Tel: 0844 499 4199
Fax: 01522 828601

Sleaford
The Advice Centre, Moneys Yard, Carre Street,
Sleaford, Lincolnshire NG34 7TW
Tel: 0844 499 4199

Stamford
30 High Street, Stamford, Lincolnshire PE0 2DD
Tel: 0844 499 4199
Fax: 01780 480819

London

Battersea
125 Bolingbroke Grove, London SW11 1DA
Tel: 020 8333 6960
Fax: 020 7978 5348

Beckenham and Penge
20 Snowdown Close, Avenue Road, Penge,
London SE20 7RU
Tel: .... 020 8778 0921; 020 8776 9209 Minicom
Fax: 020 8776 6056

Bermondsey
8 Market Place, Southwark Park Road,
Bermondsey, London SE16 3UQ
Tel: 0844 499 4134
Fax: 020 7231 4410

Brent
270-272 High Road, Willesden, London
NW10 2EY
Tel: 0845 050 5250
Fax: 020 8451 3714
Email: .... brent.cab@brentcab.co.uk

Chelsea
Old Town Hall, Kings Road, Chelsea, London
SW3 5EE
Tel: 08448269708

Dalston
491-493 Kingsland Road, Dalston, London
E8 4AU
Tel: 0844 499 1195
Fax: 020 7249 7699

Fulham
The Pavilion, 1 Mund Street, Fulham, London
W14 9LY
Tel: 020 7385 1322
Email: .... advice@hfcab.org.uk

Grahame Park
The Concourse, Grahame Park, London
NW9 5XA
Tel: 0844 826 9336
Fax: 020 8205 8506

Green Lanes
Palmers Green CAB, Palmers Green Town Hall,
Green Lanes, London N13 4RY
Tel: 020 8350 2813
Email: ...... fiyaz.mughal@enfieldcabx.org.uk

Holborn
3rd Floor, Holborn Library, 32-38 Theobalds Road,
Holborn, London WC1X 8PA
Tel: 08451 202965
Fax: 020 7404 1507

Kentish Town
242 Kentish Town Road, Kentish Town, London
NW5 2AB
Tel: 0845 120 2965
Fax: 020 7485 5150

Kilburn
200 Kilburn High Road, Kilburn, London NW6 4JD
Tel: 0845 120 2965
Fax: 020 7328 4744

Leytonstone
Greater London House, 547-551 High Road,
Leytonstone, London E11 4PB
Tel: 020 8988 9620
Fax: 020 8558 7911

Morden
7 Crown Parade, Crown Lane, Morden, London
SM4 5DA
Tel: 0844 243 8430
Fax: 020 8715 0550
Email: .... advice@mertoncab.org.uk

Palmers Green
Town Hall, Green Lanes, Palmers Green, London
N13 4XD
Tel: 0870 126 4664
Fax: 020 8447 9343

Peckham
97 Peckham High Street, Peckham, London
SE15 5RS
Tel: 0844 499 4134
Fax: 020 7732 2497

Putney & Roehampton
Roehampton CAB, 166 Roehampton Lane,
Roehampton, London SW15 4HR
Tel: 020 8333 6960
Fax: 020 8780 1505

Sheen
Sheen Lane Centre, Sheen Lane, Sheen, London
SW14 8LP
Tel: 0844 826 9700
Fax: 020 8878 5105

Strand
Royal Courts of Justice, Strand, London
WC2A 2LL
Tel: ... 08458563534; 020 7947 6880 - voicemail

Streatham Hill
Ilex House, 1 Barrhill Road, Streatham Hill,
London SW2 4RJ
Tel: 0844 243 8430
Fax: 020 8678 6593

Whitechapel
Unit 32, Greatorex Street, Whitechapel, London
E1 5NP
Tel: 0844 826 9699
Fax: 020 7375 2256
Email: . . . . . . towerhamlets@eastendcab.org.uk

Woolwich
Old Town Hall, Polytechnic Street, Woolwich,
London SE18 6PN
Tel: 0300 303 8080
Fax: 020 8317 7571
Email: . . . . greenwichcab@btopenworld.com

Merseyside

Anfield
36-38 Breckfield Road North, Anfield, Liverpool,
Merseyside L5 4NH
Tel: 0844 848 7700
Fax: 0151 285 1088

Bootle
Goddard Hall, 297 Knowsley Road, Bootle,
Merseyside L20 5DF
Tel: 0151 288 5686
Fax: 0151 288 5685

Crosby
Prince Street, Crosby, Liverpool, Merseyside
L22 5PB
Tel: 0151 282 5666
Fax: 0151 282 5667

Formby
11a Duke Street, Formby, Liverpool, Merseyside
L37 4AN
Tel: 01704 875078; 01704 873009
Fax: 01704 385608

Garston
Garston Community House, Garston Village, 2
Speke Road, Liverpool, Merseyside L19 2PA
Tel: 0844 848 7700
Email: . . . . info@garstoncab.org.uk

Halewood
The Halewood Centre, Roseheath Drive,
Halewood, Merseyside L26 9UH
Tel: 0845 122 1300
Fax: 0151 288 7501
Email: . . . . advice@knowsleycab.org.uk

Heswall
Hillcroft, Rocky Lane, Heswall, Wirral, Merseyside
CH60 0BY
Tel: 0844 477 2121
Fax: 0151 342 4336

Kirkby
1st Floor, 2 Newton Gardens, Kirkby, Knowsley,
Merseyside L32 8RR
Tel: 0845 122 1300
Email: . . . . advice@knowsleycab.org.uk

Liverpool
2nd Floor, 1 Union Court, Cook Street, Liverpool,
Merseyside L2 4SJ
Tel: 0151 285 8534; 0844 848 7700
Fax: 0151 227 5535
Email: . . . . bureau@liverpoolcab.org

Netherley
Belle Vale Business Centre, 304 Childwall Valley
Road, Netherley, Liverpool, Merseyside L25 2XE
Tel: 0844 848 7700
Fax: 0151 487 8342

Prescot
10a Church Street, Prescot, Merseyside L34 3LA
Tel: 0845 122 1300; 0151 477 6012
Email: . . . . advice@knowsleycab.org.uk

Southport
24 Wright Street, Southport, Merseyside PR9 0TL
Tel: 01704 385630
Fax: 01704 385631

St Helens
Millenium Centre, Corporation Centre, St Helens,
Merseyside WA10 1HJ
Tel: . 08448 269694 Advice; 01744 737866 Appts
Fax: 01744 758720

Wallasey
237-243 Liscard Road, Wallasey, Merseyside
CH44 5TH
Tel: 0844 477 2121
Fax: 0151 630 5118
Email: . . . . advice@wirralcab.org.uk

Wirral
57 New Chester Road, New Ferry, Bebington,
Wirral, Merseyside CH62 1AB
Tel: 0844 477 2121
Fax: 0151 644 9478
Email: . . . . advice@wirralcab.org.uk
1- 3 Acacia Grove, West Kirby, Wirral, Merseyside
CH48 4DD
Tel: 0844 477 2121
Fax: 0151 625 0625

Middlesex

Harrow
Harrow Civic Centre, Civic 5, Station Road,
Harrow, Middlesex HA1 2XH
Tel: 0844 826 9711

Sunbury-on-Thames
Sunbury Library, The Parade, Staines Road West,
Sunbury-on-Thames, Middlesex TW16 7AB
Tel: 01932 765041

Twickenham
The Advice Centre, 61 Heath Road, Twickenham,
Middlesex TW1 4AW
Tel: . . . .

0844 826 9700
Fax: 020 8843 7228

Uxbridge
The Colonnade, Civic Centre, High Street,
Uxbridge, Middlesex UB8 1UW
Tel: 0844 848 7903
Fax: 01895 277306

Norfolk

Dereham
Assembly Rooms, Ruthen Place, Dereham,
Norfolk NR19 2TX
Tel: 01362 697776
Fax: 01362 692546

Diss & Thetford
Shelfanger Road, Diss, Norfolk IP22 4EH
Tel: . 01379 651333 Diss; 01842 752777 Thetford
Fax: . 01379 640530 Diss; 01842 750986 Thetford
Email: . . . . advice@disscab.cabnet.org.uk

Holt
Kerridge Way, Holt, Norfolk NR25 6DN
Tel: 01263 713849
Fax: 01263 713076

North Walsham & District
New Road, North Walsham, Norfolk NR28 9DE
Tel: 01692 402570
Fax: 01692 408290

Thetford
15 Earls Street, Thetford, Norfolk IP24 2AB
Tel: 01842 752777
Fax: 01842 750986
Email: ...... advice@thetfordcab.cabnet.org.uk

Watton
The Cabin, Harvey Street, Watton, Norfolk
IP25 6EB
Tel: 01953 882746

West Norfolk
Whites House, 26 St Nichols Street, King's Lynn,
Norfolk PE30 1LY
Tel: 0844 499 4104
Fax: 01553 660900

North East Lincolnshire

Grimsby
4 Town Hall Street, Grimsby, North East
Lincolnshire DN31 1HN
Tel: 01472 252500

North Lincolnshire

Scunthorpe
12 Oswald Road, Scunthorpe, North Lincolnshire
DN15 7PT
Tel: 0870 126 4854 Advice; 01724 870941 Appts

North Somerset

Weston-super-Mare
The Badger Centre, 3-6 Wadham Street, Weston-
super-Mare, North Somerset BS23 1JY
Tel: 0870 121 2017
Fax: 01934 836206

North Yorkshire

Hambleton
277 High Street, Northallerton, North Yorkshire
DL7 8DW
Tel: 0845 122 8689 Advice; 01609 776551 Appts
Email: .... advice@hambletoncab.cabnet.org.uk

Harrogate
Victoria Park House, 18 Victoria Avenue,
Harrogate, North Yorkshire HG1 5QY
Tel: 01423 503576
Fax: 01423 565192

Middlesbrough
3 Bolckow Street, Middlesbrough, North Yorkshire
TS1 1TH
Tel: 0844 499 4110
Fax: 01642 802312

Richmond
23 Newbiggin, Richmond, North Yorkshire
DL10 4DX
Tel: 01748 823978
Email: ..... enquiries@richmondshirecab.org.uk

Ryedale
Ryedale Community House, Wentworth Street,
Malton, North Yorkshire YO17 7BN
Tel: 01653 692740

Selby
Rear of 4 Park Street, Selby, North Yorkshire
YO8 4PW
Tel: 08451 203718
Fax: 01757 213325

Skipton
St Andrew's Church Hall, Newmarket Street,
Skipton, North Yorkshire BD23 2JE
Tel: 01756 700210
Fax: 01756 796631
Email: ...... bureau@skiptoncab.cabnet.org.uk

Whitby
Church House, Flowergate, Whitby, North
Yorkshire YO21 3BA
Tel: 0845 120 2930 Advice; 01723 368710 Appts

York
3 Blossom Street, York, North Yorkshire
YO24 1AU
Tel: .... 0844 826 9705 Advice Line
Fax: 01904 620571
Email: .... admin@yorkcab.org.uk

Northamptonshire

Daventry
The Abbey, Market Square, Daventry,
Northamptonshire NN11 4XG
Tel: .... 0844 855 2122; 01327 701693 Minicom
Fax: 01327 701644

Kettering
5 Horsemarket, Kettering, Northamptonshire
NN16 0DG
Tel: 0844 855 2122
Fax: 01536 312313

Northampton
Town Centre House, 7/8 Mercers Row,
Northampton, Northamptonshire NN1 2QL
Tel: 0844 855 2122
Fax: 01604 235089

Wellingborough
2b High Street, Wellingborough, Northamptonshire
NN8 4HR
Tel: 0870 126 4865
Fax: 01933 273716
Email: ...... advice@wellingboroughcab.org.uk

Northumberland

Amble
The Fourways, Bridge Street, Amble,
Northumberland NE65 0DR
Tel: 01665 604135

Ashington
39-91 Station Road, Ashington, Northumberland
NE63 8RS
Tel: 01670 818360
Fax: 01670 812573
Email: .... cab@wansbeck80.fsnet.co.uk

Berwick-upon-Tweed
Berwick, 5 Tweed Street, Berwick-upon-Tweed,
Northumberland TD15 1NG
Tel: 01289 330222

Blyth Valley
Eric Tolhurst Centre, 3-13 Quay Street, Blyth,
Northumberland NE24 2AS
Tel: 01670 367779
Email: . emailenquiries@blythvalley.cabnet.org.uk

Castle Morpeth
Tower Buildings, 9 Oldgate, Morpeth,
Northumberland NE61 1PY
Tel: 01670 518814

Hexham
The Community Centre, Gilesgate, Hexham,
Northumberland NE46 3NP
Tel: 01434 605254
Fax: 01434 607611
Email: . . westnorthumberlandcab@cabnet.org.uk

Nottinghamshire

Bassetlaw
Central Avenue, Worksop, Nottinghamshire
S80 1EJ
Tel: 08448563411
Fax: 01909 530566

Beeston
Ground Floor, Council Offices, Foster Avenue,
Beeston, Nottinghamshire NG9 1AB
Tel: 0844 499 1193
Fax: 0115 917 3818
Email: .... bureau@eastwood.cabnet.org.uk

Eastwood
Library and Information Centre, Wellington Place,
Eastwood, Nottingham, Nottinghamshire
NG16 3GB
Tel: 0844 499 4194
Fax: 01773 533687

Sutton-in-Ashfield
22 Market Street, Sutton-in-Ashfield,
Nottinghamshire NG17 1AG
Tel: 0870 126 4873
Fax: 01623 555345

Oxfordshire

Didcot
Civic Hall, Britwell Road, Didcot, Oxfordshire
OX11 7JN
Tel: 01235 813632
Fax: 01235 512839

Oxford
95 St Aldates, Oxford, Oxfordshire OX1 1DA
Tel: 08445730608
Fax: 01865 202715

Poole

Poole
54 Lagland Street, Poole BH15 1QG
Tel: .... 01202 680838 Advice line
Fax: 01202 644479
Email: .... advice@poolecab.co.uk

Reading

Reading
Minster Street, Reading RG1 2JB
Tel: .... 0845 071 6379 Advice; 01189 583 5313
Training Services line
Fax: 01189 523 050

Woodley
Headley Road (Next to Library), Woodley,
Reading RG5 4JA
Tel: 0118 9699006
Email: .... public@wokingham-cab.org.uk

Redcar & Cleveland

Redcar & Cleveland
88 Westgate, Guisborough, Redcar & Cleveland
TS14 6AP
Tel: 01642 469880
Fax: 01287 630541

Rutland

Oakham
56 High Street, Oakham, Rutland LE15 6AL
Tel: 0845 120 3705
Fax: 01572 722568
Email: .... advice@rutlandcab.org.uk

Shropshire

Bridgnorth and District
Westgate, Bridgnorth, Shropshire WV16 5AA
Tel: 0844 499 1100
Fax: 01746 713361

Ludlow
Stone House, Corve Street, Ludlow, Shropshire
SY8 1DG
Tel: 0844 499 1100
Fax: 01584 838070

Oswestry
34 Arthur Street, Oswestry, Shropshire SY11 1JN
Tel: 0844 499 1100
Fax: 01691 677375

Slough

Slough
Hasland, 27 Church Street, Slough SL1 1PL
Tel: 0845 120 3712

Somerset

Frome
5 King Street, Frome, Somerset BA11 1BH
Tel: 01373 465496
Fax: 01373 452289

Shepton Mallet
9/9a Market Place, Shepton Mallet, Somerset
BA4 5AZ
Tel: 01749 343010
Email: .... advice@mendipcab.org.uk

Yeovil
40 - 42 Hendford, Yeovil, Somerset BA20 1UW
Tel: 01935 421167
Fax: 01935 410561
Email: .... cab@southsomcab.org.uk

South Gloucestershire

Yate
Kennedy Way, Yate, South Gloucestershire
BS37 4DQ
Tel: 0870 121 2019
Fax: 01454 329288

South Yorkshire

Mexborough
The Happy Childrens Nursery, Adwick Road,
Mexborough, South Yorkshire S64 0BP
Tel: 01709 572400

Rotherham
Wellgate Old Hall, 120-126 Wellgate, Rotherham,
South Yorkshire S60 2LN
Tel: 01709 515680

Sheffield

Mental Health Unit CAB, Michael Carlisle Centre, Nether Edge Hospital, Osborne Road, Sheffield, South Yorkshire S11 9BF
Tel: 0114 271 8025
Fax: 0114 271 8683
Sheffield Debt Support Unit, Unit 9b The Old Dairy, Broadfield Road, Sheffield, South Yorkshire S8 0XQ

Staffordshire

Cheadle

Harbourne Road, Cheadle, Staffordshire ST10 1JY
Tel: 01538 753189
Fax: 01538 752319

East Staffordshire

Suite 8, Anson Court, Horninglow Street, Burton-on-Trent, Staffordshire DE14 1NG
Tel: 01283 566722
Fax: 01283 527983
Email: . . . . info@eaststaffordshirecab.co.uk

Lichfield

29 Levetts Fields, Lichfield, Staffordshire WS13 6HY
Tel: 01543 252730
Fax: 01543 414255

Newcastle-under-Lyme

25-27 Well Street, Newcastle-under-Lyme, Staffordshire ST5 1BP
Tel: . . . . 0844 499 4115 Information Line
Fax: 01782 713202

Rugeley

7 Brook Square, Rugeley, Staffordshire WS15 2DU
Tel: 01889 580633
Fax: 01889 586126

Stafford

Stafford District, Vol Services Centre, 131-141 North Walls, Stafford, Staffordshire ST16 3AD
Tel: 01785 258673; 01785 242524
Fax: 01785 243625

Stafford & Stone (Stone)

St Mary's Chambers, 15 Station Road, Stone, Staffordshire ST15 8JP
Tel: 01785 814806

Stoke-on-Trent District

Advice House, Cheapside, Hanley, Stoke-on-Trent, Staffordshire ST1 1HL
Tel: 01782 408600
Fax: 01782 408601
Email: . . . . advice@stoke-cab.org.uk

Suffolk

Beccles

12 New Market, Beccles, Suffolk NR34 9HB
Tel: 01502 717715
Fax: 01502 716212

Brandon

11 High Street, Brandon, Suffolk IP27 0AQ
Tel: 01842 811511
Fax: 01842 813116
Email: . . . . advice@brandoncab.co.uk

Bungay

8 Chaucer Street, Bungay, Suffolk NR35 1DT
Tel: 01986 895827
Fax: 01502 716212

Bury St Edmunds

The Risbygate Centre, 90 Risbygate Street, Bury St Edmunds, Suffolk IP33 3AA
Tel: 01284 753675
Fax: 01284 763056

Felixstowe & District

2-6 Orwell Road, Felixstowe, Suffolk IP11 7HD

Haverhill - Centre for Voluntary Agencies

Lower Downslade, Haverhill, Suffolk CB9 9HB
Tel: 01440 704012
Fax: 01440 713212

Ipswich

19 Tower Street, Ipswich, Suffolk IP1 3BE
Tel: 01473 219777
Fax: 01473 286548

Leiston

14 Colonial House, Station Road, Leiston, Suffolk IP16 4JD
Tel: 01728 832193
Fax: 01728 832544

Mildenhall

Willow House, 40 St Andrews Street, Mildenhall, Bury St Edmunds, Suffolk IP28 7HB
Tel: 01638 712094
Fax: 01638 715567
Email: . . . . mildenhall@brandoncab.co.uk

Newmarket

Foley Gate, Wellington Street, Newmarket, Suffolk CB8 0HY
Tel: 01638 665999
Fax: 01638 668111
Email: . . . adviser@newmarketcab.cabnet.org.uk

North East Suffolk (Lowestoft)

The Advice Centre, 36 Gordon Road, Lowestoft, Suffolk NR32 1NL
Tel: 01502 518510
Fax: 01502 515825

Stowmarket

5 Milton Road South, Stowmarket, Suffolk IP14 1EZ
Tel: 01449 676060; 01449 676280
Fax: . . . . 01449 675634 (Ring before Faxing)

Sudbury

Belle Vue, Newton Road, Sudbury, Suffolk CO10 2RG
Tel: 01787 374671
Fax: 01787 881564
Email: . . . . . . bureau@sudburycab.cabnet.org.uk

Surrey

Addlestone

The Old Library, Church Road, Addlestone, Surrey KT15 1RW
Tel: 01932 842666
Fax: 01932 827187

Camberley

Rear of Library, Knoll Road, Camberley, Surrey GU15 3SY
Tel: 01276 684342
Fax: 01276 683192

Caterham

Soper Hall, Harestone Valley Road, Caterham, Surrey CR3 6YN
Tel: 01883 344777
Fax: 01883 341745

Cranleigh
Village Way, Cranleigh, Surrey GU6 8AF
Tel: 0844 848 7969
Fax: 01483 271054

Croydon
1 Overbury Crescent, New Addington, Croydon, Surrey CR0 0LR
Tel: 01689 846890
Fax: 01689 845105

Epsom
The Old Town Hall, The Parade, Epsom, Surrey KT18 5AG
Tel: 01372 720205
Fax: 01372 732622

Esher
Harry Fletcher House, High Street, Esher, Surrey KT10 9RN
Tel: 01372 464770
Fax: 01372 470488

Farnham
Montrose House, South Street, Farnham, Surrey GU9 7RN
Tel: 0844 848 7969
Fax: 01252 726218

Frimley
Beech House, Church Road, Frimley, Camberley, Surrey GU16 7AD
Tel: 01276 21711
Email: . . . bureau@heathlandscab.cabnet.org.uk

Guildford
15-21 Haydon Place, Guildford, Surrey GU1 4LL
Tel: 01483 576699
Fax: 01483 450185
Email: . . . . guildford@cabnet.org.uk

Haselmere
Well Lane House, Well Lane, High Street, Haslemere, Surrey GU27 2LB
Tel: 0844 848 7969
Fax: 01428 656130

Horley
c/o Horley Help Shop, 4 Victoria Square, Consort Way, Horley, Surrey RH6 7AF
Tel: 0844 477 9394
Fax: 01293 773279
Email: . . . . info@redhillcab.cabnet.org.uk

Leatherhead
The Georgian House, Swan Mews, High Street, Leatherhead, Surrey KT22 8AE
Tel: . . 01372 375522 Advice; 01372 361160 Appts
Fax: 01372 379166

Leatherhead & Dorking
Lyons Court, Dorking, Surrey RH4 1AB
Tel: 01306 876805
Fax: 01306 741416

Mitcham
Kellaway House, 326 London Road, Mitcham, Surrey CR4 3ND
Tel: 0844 243 8430
Fax: 020 8685 9483

North Cheam
320 Malden Road, (Behind Cheam Leisure Centre), North Cheam, Sutton, Surrey SM3 8EP
Tel: 020 8405 3552

North Surrey Domestic Abuse Outreach Service
Elm Grove, Hersham Road, Walton-on-Thames, Surrey KT12 1LH
Tel: 01932 248660
Fax: 01932 221680

Oxted
1st Floor Library Building, 14 Gresham Road, Oxted, Surrey RH8 0BQ
Tel: 01883 715525
Fax: 01883 723252

Richmond
ASCA, 233 Lower Mortlake Road, Richmond, Surrey TW9 2LL
Tel: 0844 826 9700

Staines
Community Link, Knowle Green, Staines, Surrey TW18 1XA
Tel: . . 01784 444220 (advice line); 01784 444215 (appointment line only)
Fax: . . . . 01784 446394 (admin only)

Sutton
The Central Library, St Nicholas Way, Sutton, Surrey SM1 1EA
Tel: 020 8405 3552
Fax: 020 8770 4929

Thornton Heath
Strand House, Zion Road, Thornton Heath, Surrey CR7 8RG
Tel: 020 8684 2236
Fax: 020 8683 5204

Wallington
Carshalton & Wallington CAB, 68 Parkgate Road, Wallington, Surrey SM6 0AH
Tel: 020 8405 3552
Fax: 020 8405 3551

Waverley
10 Queen Street, Godalming, Surrey GU7 1BD
Tel: 0844 848 7969
Fax: 01483 527915

Woking
Provencial House, 26 Commercial Way, Woking, Surrey GU21 6EN
Tel: 0844 375 2975
Fax: 01483 776350

Tyne & Wear

Gateshead
5 Regent Terrace, Gateshead, Tyne & Wear NE8 1LU
Tel: 0191 477 1392

Washington
13-14 Arndale House, Concord, Washington, Tyne & Wear NE37 2SW
Tel: 0191 416 6848

Warwickshire

Bedworth
25 Congreve Walk, Bedworth, Warwickshire CV12 8LX
Tel: 0844 855 2322
Fax: 024 7664 0710
Email: . . . . info@brancab.org.uk

Rugby

1st Floor, Chestnut House, 32 North Street,
Rugby, Warwickshire CV21 2AG
Tel: 08448552322
Fax: 01788 544903
Email: .... adviser@brancab.org.uk

Stratford-upon-Avon

25 Meer Street, Stratford-upon-Avon,
Warwickshire CV37 6QB
Tel: . 01789 293299 Advice; 01789 261966 Appts

Warwick District

10 Hamilton Terrace, Leamington Spa,
Warwickshire CV32 4LY
Tel: 0844 855 2322
Fax: 01926 457905

West Berkshire

Newbury

16 Bartholomew Street, Newbury, West Berkshire
RG14 5LL
Tel: 08444 779980
Fax: 01635 524011

West Midlands

Bilston

William Leigh House, 15 Walsall Street, Bilston,
Wolverhampton, West Midlands WV14 0AT
Tel: 01902 572004
Fax: 01902 572008

Birmingham

Ground Floor, Gazette Buildings, 168 Corporation
Street, Birmingham, West Midlands B4 6TF
Tel: 0811 177 1010
Fax: 0121 683 6909

Brierley Hill

6b Maple Row, Mill Street, Brierley Hill, West
Midlands DY5 2RH
Tel: 01384 816222
Fax: 01384 816201
Email: .... dudleybureau@dudleycabx.org

Coventry

Kirby House, Little Park Street, Coventry, West
Midlands CV1 2JZ
Tel: 024 7625 2052
Fax: 024 7625 6635

Cradley Heath

Cradley Heath Community Centre, Reddal Hill
Road, Cradley Heath, West Midlands B64 5JG
Tel: 0121 500 2703
Fax: 01384 410760

Dudley District (Halesowen)

49 Summer Hill, Halesowen, West Midlands
B63 3BU
Tel: 01384 816222
Fax: 01384 816191
Email: .... dudleybureau@dudleycabx.org

Dudley District (Stourbridge)

69 Market Street, Stourbridge, West Midlands
DY8 1AQ
Tel: 01384 816222
Fax: 01384 816220
Email: .... dudleybureau@dudleycabx.org

Handsworth

171 Churchill Parade, Birchfield Road,
Handsworth, Birmingham, West Midlands B19 1LL
Tel: ...... 08444 771010; 0121 687 5323 Admin
Fax: 0121 687 5303

Kingstanding

392-394 Kingstanding Road, Kingstanding,
Birmingham, West Midlands B44 8LD
Tel: . 08444 771010 (Info line) 10:00am - 3:00pm;
0121 244 1090 (Admin Office)
Fax: 0121 244 1090

Low Hill

Ground Floor, Housing Office, Showell Circus,
Wolverhampton, West Midlands WV10 9JL
Tel: 01902 572175
Fax: 01902 572176

Northfield

734-740 Bristol Road South, Northfield,
Birmingham, West Midlands B31 2NN
Tel: .. 08444 771010 (Info 10am-3pm); 0121 687
5767 (Admin Office)
Fax: 0121 683 5766

Oldbury

Municipal Buildings, Halesowen Street, Oldbury,
Warley, West Midlands B69 3DB
Tel: 0121 552 2022
Fax: 0121 552 2442

Queensway

Administrative Office, 5th Floor, Norfolk House,
Smallbrook, Queensway, Birmingham, West
Midlands B5 4LJ
Tel: 0121 643 3456
Fax: 0121 633 3881

Sandell (Smethwick)

370-372 High Street, Smethwick, Warley, West
Midlands B66 3PJ
Tel: 0121 558 8500

Tipton

Neptune Health Park, Sedgley Road West, Tipton,
West Midlands DY4 8LX
Tel: 0121 612 1841
Fax: 0121 612 1843

Walsall

139-144 Lichfield Street, (opposite the Town Hall),
Walsall, West Midlands WS1 1SE
Tel: .... 01922 700600 Advice Line
Fax: 01922 648018
Email: .... advice@cab.walsall.org.uk

Wolverhampton

26 Snow Hill, Wolverhampton, West Midlands
WV2 4AD
Tel: 01902 572006
Fax: 01902 572214
Email: .... district@wcabx.org

Yardley

202-204 Church Road, Yardley, Birmingham,
West Midlands B25 8UT
Tel: 08444 771010
Fax: 0121 258 5008

West Sussex

Bognor Regis

Town Hall, Clarence Road, Bognor Regis, West
Sussex PO21 1LD
Tel: 0844 477 1171
Fax: 01243 842981
Email: ...... bureau@bognorcab.cabnet.org.uk

Burgess Hill

Delmon House, 38 Church Road, Burgess Hill,
West Sussex RH15 9AE
Tel: 0844 477 1171

Chichester
Bell House, 6 Theatre Lane, Chichester, West
Sussex PO19 1SR
Tel: 0844 477 1171
Fax: 01243 538914

Crawley
The Orchard, 1-2 Gleneagles Court, Brighton
Road, Southgate, Crawley, West Sussex
RH10 6AD
Tel: 0844 477 1171
Fax: 01293 657124

East Grinstead
Cantelupe House, Cantelupe Road, East
Grinstead, West Sussex RH19 3BZ
Tel: 0844 477 1171
Fax: 01342 410240

Haywards Heath
Oaklands, Paddockhall Road, Haywards Heath,
West Sussex RH16 1HG
Tel: 0844 477 1171
Fax: 01444 414799

Horsham
Lower Tanbridge Way, Horsham, West Sussex
RH12 1PJ
Tel: 0844 477 1171
Fax: 01403 218548
Email: .... advice@horshamcab.org.uk

Lancing and Sompting
Parish Hall, South Street, Lancing, West Sussex
BN15 8AJ
Tel: 01903 755585; 01903 754194
Fax: 01903 768474
Email: ...... bureau@lancingcab.cabnet.org.uk

Littlehampton
14-16 Anchor Springs, Littlehampton, West
Sussex BN17 6BP
Tel: 0844 477 1171
Fax: 01903 733237
Email: ..... enquiries@littlehampton-cab.org.uk

Shoreham-by-Sea
Pond Road, Shoreham-by-Sea, West Sussex
BN43 5WU
Tel: 01273 453756
Fax: 01273 462754

Worthing
11 North Street, Worthing, West Sussex
BN11 1DU
Tel: 08448 487912
Fax: 01903 231972
Email: .... contact@worthingcab.org

West Yorkshire

Batley
Town Hall Annexe, Brunswick Street, Batley, West
Yorkshire WF17 5DT
Tel: 08448 487970
Fax: 01924 326062

Chapeltown
Willow House, New Roscoe Buildings, Cross
Francis Street, Chapeltown, Leeds, West
Yorkshire LS7 4BZ
Tel: 0113 262 9479

Dewsbury
Units 5-6 Empire House, Wakefield Old Road,
Dewsbury, West Yorkshire WF12 8DJ
Tel: 0844 848 7970
Fax: 01924 487869

Elland
65/67 Southgate, Elland, West Yorkshire
HX5 0DQ
Tel: 01422 842848

Halifax
37 Harrison Road, Halifax, West Yorkshire
HX1 2AF
Tel: 01422 842848

Hebden Bridge
New Oxford House, Albert Street, Hebden Bridge,
West Yorkshire HX7 8AH
Tel: 01422 842848

Huddersfield
2nd Floor, Standard House, Half Moon Street,
Huddersfield, West Yorkshire HD1 2JF
Tel: .... 0844 848 7970 Advice
Fax: 01484 545683
Email: .... bureau@skcab.org.uk

Keighley
The Library Annexe, Spencer Street, Keighley,
West Yorkshire BD21 2BN
Tel: 0845 120 2909
Fax: 01535 601326

Leeds
Central Office, 31 New York Street, Leeds, West
Yorkshire LS2 7DT
Tel: 0844 477 4788
Fax: 0113 281 6727

Otley
The Courthouse, Courthouse Street, Otley, West
Yorkshire LS21 1BG
Tel: 0844 477 4788

Shipley
6 - 8 Windsor Road, Shipley, West Yorkshire
BD18 3EQ
Tel: 0845 120 2909

Spen Valley
The Town Hall, Church Street, Cleckheaton, West
Yorkshire BD19 3RH
Tel: 0844 848 7970
Fax: 01274 862491

Todmorden
Tormorden Community College, Burnley Road,
Todmorden, West Yorkshire OL14 7BX
Tel: ...... 01422 842848 Telephone Advice Line
Fax: 01706 811103

Wiltshire

Chippenham
3 Avon Reach, Monkton Hill, Chippenham,
Wiltshire SN15 1EE
Tel: 0845 120 3707
Fax: 01249 445812

Kennet
New Park Street, Devizes, Wiltshire SN10 1DY
Tel: 0844 375 2775
Fax: 01380 728848
Email: .... bureau.kennetcab@cabnet.org.uk

Salisbury and District
18 College Street, Salisbury, Wiltshire SP1 3AL
Tel: 0844 375 2775
Fax: 01722 410262
Email: .... advice@cabsalisbury.org.uk

Swindon

Faringdon House, 1 Faringdon Road, Swindon,
Wiltshire SN1 5AR
Tel: 0844 499 4114
Fax: 01793 613270
Email: .... advice@swindon.cabnet.org.uk

Tidworth

The Community Centre, Wyle Road, Tidworth,
Wiltshire SP9 7QQ
Tel: 01980 843377
Fax: 01980 846784

Trowbridge

1 Mill Street, Trowbridge, Wiltshire BA14 8BE
Tel: 0844 375 2775
Fax: 01225 781941

Wokingham

Wokingham

First Floor, 26-28 Market Place, Wokingham
RG40 1AP
Tel: 0844 499 4126
Email: .... public@wokingham-cab.org.uk

Worcestershire

Bromsgrove and District

50-52 Birmingham Road, Bromsgrove,
Worcestershire B61 0DD
Tel: .... 01527 831480; 01527 557397 (Housing
advice only)
Fax: 01527 574536

Evesham

116 High Street, Evesham, Worcestershire
WR11 4F,I
Tel: 01386 443737
Fax: 01386 444238
Email: .. enquiries@wychavoncab.cabnet.org.uk

Malvern Hills

The Grange, Grange Road, Malvern,
Worcestershire WR14 3HA
Tel: 01684 563611
Fax: 01684 567146
Email: ...... bureau@malvernhills-cab.org.uk

Redditch

Suite E Cannon Newton House, Kingfisher
Shopping Centre, Redditch, Worcestershire
B97 4HA
Tel: 0844 415 2221
Fax: 01527 67179

Worcester

The Hopmarket, The Foregate, Worcester,
Worcestershire WR1 1DL
Tel: 01905 611371
Fax: 01905 23354
Email: ..... advice@worcestercab.cabnet.org.uk

Wyre Forest

21-23 New Road, Kidderminster, Worcestershire
DY10 1AF
Tel: 01562 823953

NORTHERN IRELAND

Belfast

Falls

8 Springfield Road, Belfast BT12 7AG
Tel: 028 9050 3000
Fax: 028 9043 8741
Email: .... fallscab@citizensadvice.co.uk

Co. Antrim

Antrim

10D High Street, Antrim, Co. Antrim BT41 1AN
Tel: 028 9442 8176
Fax: 028 9446 9243
Email: ... antrimdistrictcab@citizensadvice.co.uk

Ballymena

28 Mount Street, Ballymena, Co. Antrim
BT43 6BW
Tel: 028 2564 4398
Email: ..... ballymenacab@citizensadvice.co.uk

Carrickfergus

65 North Street, Carrickfergus, Co. Antrim
BT38 7AE
Tel: 028 9335 1808
Fax: 028 9335 5850

Larne

Park Lodge, 49 Victoria Road, Riverdale, Larne,
Co. Antrim BT40 1RT
Tel: 028 2826 0379

Lisburn

Bridge Community Centre, 50 Railway Street,
Lisburn, Co. Antrim BT28 1XG
Tel: 028 9266 2251
Fax: 028 9260 2933
Email: .... lisburncab@citizensadvice.co.uk

Rathcoole

Dunanney Centre, Rathmullan Drive, Rathcoole,
Co. Antrim BT37 9DQ
Tel: 028 9085 2271; 028 9085 2400
Fax: 028 9036 5770
Email: ... enewtownabbey@citizensadvice.co.uk

Co. Armagh

Armagh

9 McCrums Court, Armagh, Co. Armagh
BT61 7RE
Tel: 028 3752 4041
Fax: 028 3752 8258
Email: .... armaghcab@citizensadvice.co.uk

Craigavon District (Lurgan)

The Town Hall, 6 Union Street, Lurgan, Co.
Armagh BT66 8DY
Tel: 028 3835 3260
Email: criagavondistrictcab@citizensadvice.co.uk

Co. Down

Ards

75 West Street, Newtownards, Co. Down
BT23 4EN
Tel: 028 9182 3966
Fax: 028 9181 9837
Email: .... ardscab@citizensadvice.co.uk

Banbridge

77 Bridge Street, Banbridge, Co. Down BT32 3JL
Tel: 028 4062 2201
Email: ..... banbridgecab@citizensadvice.co.uk

Bangor

Hamilton House, 1a Springfield Avenue, Bangor,
Co. Down BT20 5BY
Tel: 028 9127 0009
Fax: 028 9127 0574

Down District

Maghinnis House, 8-10 Irish Street, Downpatrick,
Co. Down BT30 6BP
Tel: .... 028 4461 4110; 028 4461 7907 Minicom
Fax: 028 4461 6432
Email: ... downpatrickcab@citizensadvice.co.uk

Newry and Mourne District
Ballybot House, 28 Cornmarket, Newry, Co. Down
BT35 8BG
Tel: 028 3026 2934
Email: .... newrycab@citizensadvice.co.uk

North Down (Holywood)
Queens Hall, Sullivan Place, Holywood, Co. Down
BT18 9JF
Tel: 028 9042 8288
Fax: 028 9042 6758
Email: ..... northdowncab@citizensadvice.co.uk

Co. Londonderry

Causeway
24 Lodge Road, Coleraine, Co. Londonderry
BT52 1NB
Tel: 028 7034 4817
Fax: 028 7034 2501
Email: ..... causewaycab@citizensadvice.co.uk

Londonderry
Embassy Court, 3 Strand Road, Londonderry, Co.
Londonderry BT48 7BJ
Tel: 028 7136 2444
Fax: 028 7126 1030
Email: ..... lmanderrycab@citizensadvice.co.uk

Co. Tyrone

Dungannon
5-6 Feeneys Lane, Dungannon, Co. Tyrone
BT70 1TX
Tel: 028 8772 5299
Fax: 028 8772 5872
Email: .... dungannoncab@citizensadvice.co.uk

Strabane
17 Dock Street, Strabane, Co. Tyrone BT82 8EE
Tel: 028 7138 2665
Fax: 028 7138 2185
Email: ...... strabanecab@citizensadvice.co.uk

SCOTLAND

Aberdeen

Aberdeen
41 Union Street, Aberdeen AB11 5BN
Tel: 01224 586255
Fax: 01224 210510
Email: .. bureau@aberdeencab.casonline.org.uk

Aberdeenshire

Banff and Buchan
Townhouse, Broad Street, Peterhead,
Aberdeenshire AB42 1BY
Tel: 01779 471515
Fax: 01779 478586
Email: .... bureau@banffcab.cabnet.org.uk

Angus

Arbroath
11 Millgate, Arbroath, Angus DD11 1NN
Tel: 01241 870661
Fax: 01241 870023
Email: .. bureauarbroath@arbroathcab.casonline.org.uk

Forfar
19 Queen Street, Forfar, Angus DD8 3AJ
Tel: 01307 467096
Fax: 01307 467097
Email: ...... bureau@forfarcab.casonline.org.uk

Montrose
32 Castle Street, Montrose, Angus DD10 8AG
Tel: 01674 673263
Fax: 01674 677309

Clackmannanshire

Alloa
47 Drysdale Street, Alloa, Clackmannanshire
FK10 1JA
Tel: 01259 723880
Fax: 01259 724326
Email: ..... bureau@alloacab.casonline.org.uk

Dumfries & Galloway

Annan
19a Bank Street, Annan, Dumfries & Galloway
DG12 6AA
Tel: 01461 201012
Fax: 01461 201724
Email: ..... bureau@annancab.casonline.org.uk

Castle Douglas
3 St Andrew Street, Castle Douglas, Dumfries &
Galloway DG7 1DE
Tel: 01556 502190
Email: ... bureau@cdouglascab.casonline.org.uk

Dumfries
81-85 Irish Street, Dumfries, Dumfries & Galloway
DG1 2PQ
Tel: 01387 252456
Fax: 01387 253212
Email: ... bureau@dumfriescab.casonline.org.uk

Stranraer
23 Lewis Street, Stranraer, Dumfries & Galloway
DG9 7AB
Tel: 01776 706355
Fax: 01776 889936
Email: ... bureau@stranraercab.casonline.org.uk

Dundee

Dundee
Dundee Central Library, Level 4, Wellgate Centre,
Dundee DD1 2DB
Tel: 01382 307494
Fax: 01382 431590
Email: .... bureau@dundeecab.casonline.org.uk

East Ayrshire

Kilbirnie
43 Main Street, Kilbirnie, East Ayrshire KA25 7BX
Tel: 01505 682830
Fax: 01505 682110
Email: .... bureau@kilbirniecab.casonline.org.uk

Kilmarnock
3 John Dickie Street, Kilmarnock, East Ayrshire
KA1 1HW
Tel: 01563 544744
Fax: 01563 571106

East Lothian

Haddington
46 Court Street, Haddington, East Lothian
EH41 3NP
Tel: 01620 824471
Fax: 01620 822390
Email: .... cab@haddingtoncab.casonline.org.uk

Musselburgh
141 High Street, Musselburgh, East Lothian
EH21 7DD
Tel: 0131 653 2748; 0131 653 2544
Fax: 0131 665 1141; 0131 665 1141
Email: bureau@musselburghcab.casonline.org.uk

Edinburgh

Edinburgh
58 Dundas Street, Edinburgh EH3 6QZ
Tel: 0844 848 9600
Fax: 0131 557 3543

Gorgie / Dalry
Fountainbridge Library, 137 Dundee Street,
Edinburgh EH11 1BG
Tel: . . . . . 0131 474 8080 Advice; 0131 558 3681
Appointments
Fax: 0131 474 8082
Email: . gorgiedalry@citizensadviceedinburgh.co.
uk

Leith
166 Great Junction Street, Leith, Edinburgh
EH6 5LJ
Tel: 0844 848 9600
Fax: 0131 553 5984
Email: . . . . . leith@citizensadviceedinburgh.co.uk

Pilton
661 Ferry Road, Pilton, Edinburgh EH4 2TX
Tel: 0844 848 9600
Fax: 0131 332 8549
Email: . . . . pilton@citizensadviceedinburgh.co.uk

Falkirk

Denny
24 Duke Street, Denny, Falkirk FK6 6DD
Tel: 01324 823118; 01324 825333
Fax: 01324 826063

Grangemouth and Bo'ness
1 Kerse Road, Grangemouth, Falkirk FK3 8HW
Tel: 01324 483467
Fax: 01324 666935
Email: . bureau@grangemouthcab.casonline.org.
uk

Glasgow

Bridgeton
35 Main Street, Glasgow G40 1QB
Tel: 0141 554 0336
Fax: 0141 556 5560

Castlemilk
27 Dougrie Drive, Castlemilk, Glasgow G45 9AD
Tel: 0141 634 0338
Fax: 0141 634 0549
Email: . . . . . . bureau@cmilkcab.casonline.org.uk

Drumchapel
195c Drumry Road East, Drumchapel, Glasgow
G15 8NS
Tel: . . . . . 0141 944 0205 Advice; 0141 944 2612
Fax: 0141 944 8066
Email: . bureau@drumchapelcab.casonline.org.uk

East Renfrewshire
216 Main Street, Barrhead, Glasgow G78 1SN
Tel: 0141 881 2032
Fax: 0141 881 3660
Email: . . bureau@eastrenfrewshirecab.casonline.
org.uk

Easterhouse
46 Shandwick Square, Easterhouse, Glasgow
G34 9DT
Tel: . . . . . 0141 771 2328 Advice; 0141 773 1349
Fax: 0141 781 1070
Email: . . adminuser@easterhousecab.casonline.
org.uk

Maryhill
25 Avenuepark Street, Glasgow G20 8TS
Tel: 0141 946 6373
Fax: 0141 576 5103
Email: . . . . bureau@maryhillcab.casonline.org.uk

Parkhead
1361-1363 Gallowgate, Parkhead, Glasgow
G31 4DN
Tel: 0141 554 0004
Fax: 0141 554 0339

Highland

Inverness
103 Academy Street, Inverness, Highland IV1 1LX
Tel: 01463 237664
Fax: 01463 714272

Lochaber
Dudley Road, Fort William, Highland PH33 6JB
Tel: 01397 705311
Fax: 01397 700610

Nairn
6 High Street, Nairn, Highland IV12 4BJ
Tel: 01667 456677
Fax: 01667 451081
Email: . . . . bureau@nairncab.casonline.org.uk

Ross and Cromarty
'Balallan', 4 Novar Road, Ross-shire, Alness,
Highland IV17 0QG
Tel: 01349 883333
Fax: 01349 884126
Email: . . . . adviser@alnesscab.casonline.org.uk

Thurso
7a Brabster Street, Thurso, Caithness, Highland
KW14 7AP
Tel: 01847 894243; 01847 896796
Fax: 01847 894243
Email: . . . . bureau@cnesscab.cabnet.org.uk

Midlothian

Dalkeith
8 Buccleuch Street, Dalkeith, Midlothian
EH22 1HA
Tel: 0131 663 3688
Fax: 0131 654 1844
Email: . . . . bureau@dalkeithcab.casonline.org.uk

Penicuik
14a John Street, Penicuik, Midlothian EH26 8AB
Tel: 01968 675259
Fax: 01968 677047

Moray

Elgin
30-32 Batchen Street, Elgin, Moray IV30 1BH
Tel: 01343 550088
Fax: 01343 559000
Email: . . . . . bureau@moraycab.casonline.org.uk

North Ayrshire

Arran
Park Terrace, Lamlash, Isle of Arran, North
Ayrshire KA27 8NB
Tel: 01770 600210
Fax: 01770 600210
Email: ...... bureau@arrancab.casonline.org.uk

Largs
36 Boyd Street, Largs, North Ayrshire KA30 8LE
Tel: 01475 673586
Fax: 01475 686100
Email: ...... bureau@largscab.casonline.org.uk

North Ayrshire
The Three Towns Centre for Enterprise, Moffat
House, 12-14 Nineyard Street, Saltcoats, North
Ayrshire KA21 5HS
Tel: 01294 467848
Fax: 01294 603427
Email: ... bureau@saltcoatscab.casonline.org.uk

Saltcoats
18-20 Countess Street, Saltcoats, North Ayrshire
KA21 5HW
Tel: 01294 602328

North Lanarkshire

Airdrie
Resource Centre, 14 Anderson Street, Airdrie,
North Lanarkshire ML6 0AA
Tel: 01236 754109
Fax: 01236 754376
Email: ..... advice@airdriecab.casonline.org.uk

Bellshill
6 Hamilton Road, Bellshill, North Lanarkshire
ML4 1AQ
Tel: 01698 748615
Fax: 01698 841876
Email: ... manager@bellshillcab.casonline.org.uk

Coatbridge
Unit 10, Fountain Business Centre, Ellis Street,
Coatbridge, North Lanarkshire ML5 3AA
Tel: 01236 421447; 01236 421448
Fax: 01236 435805
Email: . adviser@coatbridgecab.casonline.org.uk

Cumbernauld
2 Annan House, 3rd Floor, Town Centre,
Cumbernauld, North Lanarkshire G67 1DP
Tel: 01236 723201
Fax: 01236 735165
Email: bureau@cumbernauldcab.casonline.org.uk

Motherwell and Wishaw
32 Civic Square, Motherwell, North Lanarkshire
ML1 1TP
Tel: 01698 259389; 01698 251981
Fax: 01698 263250
Email: bureau2@motherwellcab.casonline.org.uk

Orkney Islands

Orkney
Anchor Buildings, 6 Bridge Street, Kirkwall,
Orkney Islands KW15 1HR
Tel: 01856 875266
Fax: 01856 870400

Perth & Kinross

Perth
4-12 New Row, Perth, Perth & Kinross PH1 5QB
Tel: . 01738 624301 Advice; 01738 564304 Appts
Fax: 01738 440870
Email: karencampbell@perthcab.casonline.org.uk

Renfrewshire

Paisley
45 George Street, Paisley, Renfrewshire PA1 2JY
Tel: 0141 889 2121
Fax: 0141 849 7116
Email: .... bureau@paisleycab.casonline.org.uk

Scottish Borders

Galashiels
111 High Street, Galashiels, Scottish Borders
TD1 1RZ
Tel: 01896 753889
Fax: 01896 756966
Email: bureau@centralborderscab.casonline.org.
uk

Hawick
1 Towerdykesside, Hawick, Scottish Borders
TD9 9EA
Tel: 01450 374266
Fax: 01450 370119
Email: . enquiries@roxburghcab.casonline.org.uk

Peebles
42 Old Town, Peebles, Scottish Borders
EH45 8JF
Tel: 01721 721722
Fax: 01721 723844
Email: .. manager@peeblescab.casonline.org.uk

Shetland Islands

Lerwick
Market House, 14 Market Street, Lerwick,
Shetland Islands ZE1 0JP
Tel: 01595 694696
Fax: 01595 696776
Email: .... sicab@zetnet.co.uk

South Lanarkshire

Clydesdale
10-12 Wide Close, Lanark, South Lanarkshire
ML11 7LX
Tel: 01555 664301
Fax: 01555 666674
Email: .. advice@clydesdalecab.casonline.org.uk

East Kilbride
9 Olympia Way, Town Centre, East Kilbride, South
Lanarkshire G74 1JT
Tel: 01355 263698
Fax: 01355 270282
Email: ..... bureau@ekilbridecab.cabnet.org,uk

Hamilton
Almada Tower, 67 Almada Street, Hamilton, South
Lanarkshire ML3 0HQ
Tel: 01698 283477
Fax: 01698 423923

Stirling

Stirling
The Norman MacEwan Centre, Cameronian
Street, Stirling FK8 2DX
Tel: 01786 470239
Fax: 01786 451951
Email: sessionsupervisor@sterlingcab.casonline.
org.uk

West Dunbartonshire

Dumbarton
Bridgend House, 179 High Street, Dumbarton,
West Dunbartonshire G82 1NW
Tel: 01389 744690
Fax: 01389 768019
Email: . . . . info@dumbartoncab.co.uk

West Lothian

West Lothian
Suite 7, Shiel House, Craigshill, Livingston, West
Lothian EH54 5EH
Tel: . . . . 01506 432977 Advice Lines
Fax: 01506 441986
Email: . . . . enquiries@cabwestlothian.org.uk

Western Isles

Barra
Castlebay, Isle of Barra, Western Isles HS9 5XD
Tel: 01871 810608
Fax: 01871 810875
Email: . . . . . . bureau@barracab.casonline.org.uk

Harris
Pier Road, Tarbert, Isle of Harris, Western Isles
HS3 3BG
Tel: 01859 502431
Fax: 01859 502431
Email: . . . . bureau@harriscab.cabnet.org.uk

Lewis
41-43 Westview Terrace, Stornoway, Isle of Lewis,
Western Isles HS1 2HP
Tel: 01851 706727
Fax: 01851 706913
Email: . . . . . . bureau@lewiscab.casonline.org.uk

Uist
45 Winfield Way, Balivanich, Isle of Benbecula,
Western Isles HS7 5LH
Tel: 01870 602421
Fax: 01870 602008
Email: . . . . bureau@uistcab.casonline.org.uk

WALES

Anglesey

Canolfan Cynghori Ynys Mon
6 Victoria Terrace, Holyhead, Anglesey LL65 1UT
Tel: 0844 477 2020
Fax: 01407 769300

Blaenau Gwent

Blaina
High Street, Blaina, Blaenau Gwent NP13 3AN
Tel: 01495 292659

Bridgend

Bridgend
Ground Floor, 26 Dunraven Place, Bridgend
CF31 1JD
Tel: 0844 477 2020
Fax: 01656 654603

Maesteg
Council Offices, Talbot Street, Maesteg, Bridgend
CF34 9BY
Tel: 0844 477 2020
Fax: 01656 810369

Caerphilly

Bargoed
41b Hanbury Road, Bargoed, Caerphilly
CF81 8QU
Tel: 0844 477 2020
Fax: 01433 839618

Caerphilly
2B De Clare House, 5 Alfred Owen Way,
Pontygwindy Industrial Estate, Caerphilly
CF83 2WB
Tel: 0844 477 2020
Fax: 029 2088 8440

Carmarthenshire

Ammanford
14 Iscennen Road, Ammanford, Carmarthenshire
SA18 3BG
Tel: 01269 590721
Fax: 01269 597674

Carmarthen
113 Lammas Street, Carmarthen,
Carmarthenshire SA31 3AP
Tel: 01267 234488
Fax: 01267 223748

Llanelli
4a Cowell Street, Llanelli, Carmarthenshire
SA15 1UU
Tel: 0844 477 2020

Ceredigion

Aberystwyth
12 Cambrian Place, Aberystwyth, Ceredigion
SY23 1NT
Tel: 01970 612817
Fax: 01970 612442

Cardigan
Napier Street, Cardigan, Ceredigion SA43 1ED
Tel: 01239 613707
Fax: 01239 612974
Email: . . . enquiries@cardigancab.cabnet.org.uk

Conwy

Clych Conwy District
7 South Parade, Llandudno, Conwy LL30 2LN
Tel: 0844 477 2020

Denbighshire

Denbigh
23 High Street, Denbigh, Denbighshire LL16 3HY
Tel: 01745 814336
Fax: 01745 818080

Llangollen
37 Hall Street, Llangollen, Denbighshire LL20 8EP
Tel: 01978 860983
Fax: 01978 869216

Rhyl
11 Water Street, Rhyl, Denbighshire LL18 1SP
Tel: 01745 334568
Fax: 01745 343036

Ruthin
The Old Fire Station, Market Street, Ruthin,
Denbighshire LL15 1BE
Tel: 01824 703483
Fax: 01824 704804

Flintshire

Holywell
The Old Library, Post Office Lane, Holywell,
Flintshire CH8 7LH
Tel: 01352 711262
Fax: 01352 713835

Mold
The Annexe Terrig House, Chester Street, Mold,
Flintshire CH7 1EG
Tel: 01352 753520
Fax: 01352 706821

Merthyr Tydfil

Merthyr Tydfil
Tramroadside North, Merthyr Tydfil CF47 0AP
Tel: 01685 379997; 01685 382188
Fax: 01685 370730

Monmouthshire

Abergavenny
26a Monk Street, Abergavenny, Monmouthshire
NP7 5NP
Tel: . . 08444 772020; 01873 735867 Admin Line
Email: . . . . abergavennycab@yahoo.co.uk

Chepstow
The Gate House, High Street, Chepstow,
Monmouthshire NP16 5LH
Tel: 0844 477 2020
Fax: 01291 622185

Monmouth
23a Whitecross Street, Monmouth,
Monmouthshire NP25 3BY
Tel: 0844 477 2020

Neath Port Talbot

Neath
44 Alfred Street, Neath, Neath Port Talbot
SA11 1EH
Tel: 0844 477 2020
Fax: 01639 637041

Port Talbot
36 Forge Road, Port Talbot, Neath Port Talbot
SA13 1NU
Tel: 0844 477 2020
Fax: 01639 892992

Newport

Newport
8 Corn Street, Newport NP20 1DJ
Tel: 0844 477 2020
Fax: 01633 213792

Risca
Park Road, Risca, Newport NP11 6BJ
Tel: 0844 477 2020
Fax: 01633 615780

Pembrokeshire

Haverfordwest
43 Cartlett, Haverfordwest, Pembrokeshire
SA61 2LH
Tel: 0844 477 2020
Fax: 01437 767936
Email: . . . . hwestcab@yahoo.com

Powys

Brecon
11 Glamorgan Street, Brecon, Powys LD3 7DW
Tel: 0845 601 8421

Newtown
Ladywell House, Frolic Street Entrance, Park
Street, Newtown, Powys SY16 1QS
Tel: 01686 624390
Fax: 01686 624873
Email: . . . . montycab@powys.org.uk

Ystradgynlais
Welfare Hall, Brecon Road, Ystradgynlais, Powys
SA9 1JJ
Tel: 0845 601 8421

Rhondda Cynon Taff

Cynon Valley
Old Library, Duffryn Road, Mountain Ash,
Rhondda Cynon Taff CF45 4DA
Tel: . . . . . . 08444772020; 08444 772020 Advice
Fax: 01443 473389
Email: . . . . cynonvalleycab@talk21.com

Rhondda Taff
5 Gelliwastad Road, Pontypridd, Rhondda Cynon
Taff CF37 2BP
Tel: 0844 477 2020
Fax: 01633 876121

Swansea

Swansea Citizens Advice Bureau
Llys Glas, Pleasant Street, Swansea SA1 5DS
Tel: 01792 474882
Email: . . . . enquiries@swanseacab.org.uk

Torfaen

Cwmbran
21 Caradoc Road, Cwmbran, Torfaen NP44 1PP
Tel: 01633 482464
Fax: 01633 876121

Vale of Glamorgan

Barry
119 Broad Street, Barry, Vale of Glamorgan
CF62 7TZ
Tel: 0844 477 2020

Wrexham

Wrexham
35 Grosvenor Road, Wrexham LL11 1BT
Tel: 01978 364639
Fax: 01978 363332

UK COMMUNITY FOUNDATIONS

Community Foundation Network represents the community foundation movement in the UK. Our aim is to help clients create lasting value from their local giving through the network of community foundations.

Community foundations are charities located throughout the UK dedicated to strengthening local communities, creating opportunities and tackling issues of disadvantage and exclusion. Community foundations target grants that make a genuine difference to the lives of local people. They manage funds donated by individuals and organisations, building endowment and acting as the vital link between donors and local needs, connecting people with causes, and enabling clients to achieve far more than they could ever by themselves.

There are three categories of community foundations: Members are established community foundations; Associates are aspiring foundations; and Affiliates are foundations outside the UK, partner organisations in the UK or other grant-makers that are committed to improving local communities.

Further information can be obtained from UK Community Foundations, 12 Angel Gate, 320-326 City Road, London EC1V 2PT Tel: 020 7713 9326 E-mail: network@ukcommunityfoundations.org Web: www.communityfoundations.org.uk

ENGLAND

Bedfordshire

BEDFORDSHIRE AND LUTON COMMUNITY FOUNDATION
The Old School, Southill Road, Cardington, Bedfordshire MK44 3SX
Tel: 01234 834930

Bournemouth

DORSET COMMUNITY FOUNDATION
Abchurch Chambers, 24 St Peters Road, Bournemouth BH1 2LN
Tel: 01202 292255
Email: .... philanthropy@dorsetcf.org

Bristol

QUARTET COMMUNITY FOUNDATION
Royal Oak House, Royal Oak Avenue, Bristol BS1 4GB
Tel: 0117 989 7700
Fax: 0117 989 7701
Email: .... info@quartetcf.org.uk

Buckinghamshire

BUCKINGHAMSHIRE COMMUNITY FOUNDATION (A)
Foundation House, 119a Bicester Road, Aylesbury, Buckinghamshire HP19 9BA
Tel: 01296 330134
Email: .... info@buckscf.org.uk

MILTON KEYNES COMMUNITY FOUNDATION
Acorn House, 381 Midsummer Boulevard, Milton Keynes, Buckinghamshire MK9 3HP
Tel: 01908 690276
Email: ..... info@mkcommunityfoundation.co.uk

Cambridgeshire

CAMBRIDGESHIRE COMMUNITY FOUNDATION
The Quorum, Barnwell Road, Cambridge, Cambridgeshire CB5 8RE
Tel: 01223 410535
Email: .... info@cambscf.org.uk

Cheshire

CHESHIRE COMMUNITY FOUNDATION
Warren House, Rudheath Way, Northwich, Cheshire CW9 7LT
Tel: 01606 330607
Email: office@cheshirecommunityfoundation.org.uk

Co. Durham

COUNTY DURHAM COMMUNITY FOUNDATION
Whitfield Court, St John's Road, Durham, Co. Durham DH7 8XL
Tel: 0191 378 6340
Email: .... info@cdcf.org.uk

Cornwall

CORNWALL COMMUNITY FOUNDATION
Suite 1, Sheers Barton, Lawhitton, Launceston, Cornwall PL15 9NJ
Tel: 01566 779333
Email: .... office@cornwallfoundation.com

Cumbria

CUMBRIA COMMUNITY FOUNDATION (A)
Dovenby Hall, Dovenby, Cockermouth, Cumbria CA13 0PN
Tel: 01900 825760
Email: .... enquiries@cumbriafoundation.org

Derbyshire

DERBYSHIRE COMMUNITY FOUNDATION
Foundation House, Unicorn Business Park,
Wellington Street, Ripley, Derbyshire DE5 3EH
Tel: 01773 514850
Fax: 01773 741410
Email: . info@derbyshirecommunityfoundation.co.
uk

Devon

DEVON COMMUNITY FOUNDATION (A)
The Factory, Leat Street, Tiverton, Devon
EX16 5LL
Tel: 01884 235887
Email: . . . . admin@devoncf.com

East Sussex

SUSSEX COMMUNITY FOUNDATION
Suite B, Falcon Wharf, Railway Lane, Lewes, East
Sussex BN7 2AQ
Tel: 01273 409440
Email: . . . . info@sussexgiving.org.uk

Essex

**EAST LONDON COMMUNITY
FOUNDATION (A)**
Office 7, Chadwell Heath Industrial Park, Kemp
Road , Dagenham, Essex RM8 1SL
Tel: 0300 303 1203
Email: . . . . enquiries@elcf.org.uk

ESSEX COMMUNITY FOUNDATION
121 New London Road, Chelmsford, Essex
CM2 0QT
Tel: 01245 355947
Fax: 01245 346391
Email: . . . . general@essexcf.org.uk

Gloucestershire

**GLOUCESTERSHIRE COMMUNITY
FOUNDATION**
Barnett Way, Barnwood, Gloucester,
Gloucestershire GL4 3RS
Tel: 01452 656385

Greater Manchester

**COMMUNITY FOUNDATION FOR
GREATER MANCHESTER**
Speakers House, 39 Deansgate, Manchester,
Greater Manchester M3 2BA
Tel: 0161 214 0940
Fax: 0161 214 0941
Email: . . . . info@forevermanchester.com

Hampshire

**HAMPSHIRE AND THE ISLE OF WIGHT
COMMUNITY FOUNDATION**
Sun Alliance House, Wote Street, Basingstoke,
Hampshire RG21 1LU
Tel: 01256 776101
Email: . . . . info@hantscf.org.uk

Herefordshire

**HEREFORDSHIRE COMMUNITY
FOUNDATION**
The Fred Bulmer Centre, Wall Street, Hereford,
Herefordshire HR4 9HP
Tel: 01432 272550

Hertfordshire

**HERTFORDSHIRE COMMUNITY
FOUNDATION**
Foundation House, 2-4 Forum Place, Hatfield,
Hertfordshire AL10 0RN
Tel: 01707 251351
Fax: 01707 251133
Email: . . . . office@hertscf.org.uk

Kent

KENT COMMUNITY FOUNDATION
Office 23, Evegate Park Barn, Evegate, Smeeth,
Ashford, Kent TN25 6SX
Tel: 01303 814500
Fax: 01303 815150
Email: . . . . admin@kentcf.org.uk

Lancashire

**COMMUNITY FOUNDATION FOR
LANCASHIRE**
Chorley House, Centurion Way, Leyland,
Lancashire PR26 6TT
Tel: 01772 642387
Email: . . . . info@lancsfoundation.org.uk

Leicestershire

**LEICESTERSHIRE, LEICESTER AND
RUTLAND COMMUNITY FOUNDATION**
20a Millstone Lane, Leicester, Leicestershire
LE1 5JN
Tel: 0116 251 0675
Email: . . . admin@llrcommunityfoundation.org.uk

Lincolnshire

**LINCOLNSHIRE COMMUNITY
FOUNDATION**
4 Mill House, Moneys Yard, Sleaford, Lincolnshire
NG34 7TW
Tel: 01529 305825

London

LONDON COMMUNITY FOUNDATION
357 Kennington Lane, Lambeth, London
SE11 5QY
Tel: 020 7582 5117
Fax: 020 7582 4020
Email: . . . . info@londoncf.org.uk

ST KATHARINE & SHADWELL TRUST
One Bishops Square, London E1 6AD

Merseyside

**COMMUNITY FOUNDATION FOR
MERSEYSIDE (A)**
3rd Floor, Stanley Buildings, 43 Hanover Street,
Liverpool, Merseyside L1 3DN
Tel: 0151 232 2444
Fax: 0151 232 2445
Email: . . . . info@cfmerseyside.org.uk

Milton Keynes

**MILTON KEYNES COMMUNITY
FOUNDATION**
Acorn House, 381 Midsummer Boulevard, Central
Milton Keynes, Milton Keynes MK9 3HP
Tel: 01908 690276
Fax: 01908 233635
Email: . . . . . info@mkcommunityfoundation.co.uk

Norfolk

NORFOLK COMMUNITY FOUNDATION
St James Mill, Whitefriars, Norwich, Norfolk
NR3 1SH
Tel: 01603 623958
Email: . . . . grahamtuttle@norfolkfoundation.com

North Yorkshire

TWO RIDINGS COMMUNITY FOUNDATION
Buttercrambe Road, Stamford Bridge, York, North
Yorkshire YO41 1AW
Tel: 01759 377400
Email: . . . . office@ynycf.org.uk

Northamptonshire

**NORTHAMPTONSHIRE COMMUNITY
FOUNDATION**
19 Guildhall Road, Northampton,
Northamptonshire NN1 1DP
Tel: 01604 230033
Email: . . . . enquiries@ncf.uk.com

Nottinghamshire

**NOTTINGHAMSHIRE COMMUNITY
FOUNDATION**
Cedar House, Ransom Wood Business Park,
Southwell Road West, Mansfield, Nottinghamshire
NG21 0HJ
Tel: 01623 636365
Email: . . . . enquiries@nottscf.org.uk

Oxfordshire

**OXFORDSHIRE COMMUNITY
FOUNDATION**
3 Woodins Way, Oxford, Oxfordshire OX1 1HD
Tel: 01865 798666
Email: . . . . ocf@oxfordshire.org

Reading

BERKSHIRE COMMUNITY FOUNDATION
Arlington Business Park, Theale, Reading
RG7 4SA
Tel: 0118 930 3021
Fax: 0118 929 8001

Shropshire

**COMMUNITY FOUNDATION FOR
SHROPSHIRE AND TELFORD (A)**
Meeting Point House, Southwater Square, Telford,
Shropshire TF3 4HS
Tel: 01952 201858
Fax: 01952 210500
Email: . . . contact@cfshropshireandtelford.org.uk

Somerset

SOMERSET COMMUNITY FOUNDATION
Yeoman House, Royal Bath and West
Showground, Shepton Mallet, Somerset BA4 6QN
Tel: 01749 344949
Email: . . . . info@somersetcf.org.uk

South Yorkshire

**SOUTH YORKSHIRE COMMUNITY
FOUNDATION**
G1 Building, Unit 3, 6 Leeds Road, Sheffield,
South Yorkshire SN 3TY
Tel: 0114 242 4857
Fax: 0114 242 4605
Email: . . . . admin@sycf.org.uk

Staffordshire

**STAFFORDSHIRE COMMUNITY
FOUNDATION**
The Dudson Centre, Hope Street, Stoke-on-Trent,
Staffordshire ST1 5DD

Stockton-on-Tees

TEES VALLEY COMMUNITY FOUNDATION
Wallace House, Falcon Court, Stockton-on-Tees
TS18 3TXB
Tel: 01642 260860
Email: . . . . info@teesvalleyfoundation.org

Suffolk

SUFFOLK FOUNDATION
The Old Barns, Peninsula Business Centre,
Ipswich, Suffolk IP9 2BB
Tel: 01473 602602
Email: . . . . info@suffolkfoundation.org.uk

Surrey

COMMUNITY FOUNDATION FOR SURREY
1 Bishops Wharf, Walnut Tree Close, Guildford,
Surrey GU1 4RA
Tel: 01483 409230
Email: . . info@communityfoundationsurrey.org.uk

Tyne & Wear

**COMMUNITY FOUNDATION TYNE &
WEAR AND NORTHUMBERLAND**
Cale Cross, 156 Pilgrim Street, Newcastle upon
Tyne, Tyne & Wear NE1 6SU
Tel: 0191 222 0945
Fax: 0191 230 0689
Email: . . . general@communityfoundation.org.uk

West Midlands

**BIRMINGHAM AND BLACK COUNTRY
COMMUNITY FOUNDATION**
Nechells Baths, Nechells Park Road, Nechells,
Birmingham, West Midlands B7 5PD
Tel: 0121 322 5560
Fax: 0121 322 5579
Email: . . . . team@bbccf.org.uk

**HEART OF ENGLAND COMMUNITY
FOUNDATION (ALSO COVERS
COVENTRY AND WARWICKSHIRE) (A)**
Pinley House, HOECF, 2 Sunbeam Way,
Coventry, West Midlands CV3 1ND
Tel: 024 7688 4386
Email: . . . . info@heartofenglandcf.co.uk

West Yorkshire

COMMUNITY FOUNDATION FOR CALDERDALE
1855 Building, 1st Floor, Discovery Road, Halifax, West Yorkshire HX1 2NG
Tel: 01422 349700
Fax: 01422 350017
Email: .... enquiries@cffc.co.uk

LEEDS COMMUNITY FOUNDATION
Ground Floor, 51a St Paul Street, Leeds, West Yorkshire LS1 2TE
Tel: 0113 242 2426
Email: .. info@leedscommunityfoundation.org.uk

ONE COMMUNITY FOUNDATION
c/o Chadwick Lawrence Solicitors, 13 Railway Street, Huddersfield, West Yorkshire HD1 1JS
Tel: 01484 468397

WAKEFIELD DISTRICT COMMUNITY FOUNDATION
Vincent House, 136 Westgate, Wakefield, West Yorkshire WF2 9SR
Tel: 01924 239181

Wiltshire

THE COMMUNITY FOUNDATION FOR WILTSHIRE & SWINDON
Sandcliffe House, 21 Northgate Street, Devizes, Wiltshire SN10 1JX
Tel: 01380 729284
Email: .... info@wscf.org.uk

Worcestershire

WORCESTERSHIRE COMMUNITY FOUNDATION
Community House, Stourport Road, Kidderminster, Worcestershire DY11 7QE
Tel: 01562 733133
Email: .... vikki@worcscf.org.uk

NORTHERN IRELAND

Belfast

COMMUNITY FOUNDATION FOR NORTHERN IRELAND
Community House, Citylink Business Park, Albert Street, Belfast BT12 4HQ
Tel: 028 9024 5927
Fax: 028 9032 9839
Email: .... info@communityfoundationni.org

Co. Fermanagh

FERMANAGH TRUST
Fermanagh House, Broadmeadow Place, Enniskillen, Co. Fermanagh BT74 7HR
Tel: 028 6632 0210
Fax: 028 6632 0230
Email: .... info@fermanaghtrust.org

SCOTLAND

Edinburgh

SCOTTISH COMMUNITY FOUNDATION
2nd Floor, Calton House, 22 Calton Road, Edinburgh EH8 8DP
Tel: 0131 524 0300
Fax: 0131 524 0329
Email: .... info@scottishcf.org

WALES

Cardiff

COMMUNITY FOUNDATION IN WALES
9 Coopers Yard, Curran Road, Cardiff CF10 5NB
Tel: 029 2053 6590
Fax: 029 2034 2118
Email: .... info@cfiw.org.uk

COUNCILS FOR VOLUNTARY SERVICE, RURAL COMMUNITY COUNCILS AND FEDERATIONS OF COMMUNITY ORGANISATIONS

Organisations marked "A" are members of the National Association for Voluntary and Community Action (NAVCA), those marked "B" are members of Community Matters and those marked "C" are members of Action with Communities in Rural England (ACRE).

For more information go to: www.navca.org.uk, www.communitymatters.org.uk, www.acre.org.uk

ENGLAND

Bracknell Forest

BRACKNELL COUNCIL FOR VOLUNTARY SERVICE (A)
5th Floor, Fitzwilliam House, Skimped Hill Lane, Bracknell, Bracknell Forest RG12 1BQ
Tel: 01344 304404
Fax: 01344 411878
Email: .... info@bfva.org

Buckinghamshire

BUCKINGHAMSHIRE COMMUNITY ACTION (A, C)
Unit B, The Firs, Aylesbury Road, Bierton, Aylesbury, Buckinghamshire HP22 5DX
Tel: 01296 421036
Fax: 01296 331464
Email: .... bca@bucks-comm-action.org.uk

Cambridgeshire

CAMBRIDGE COUNCIL FOR VOLUNTARY SERVICE (A)
Llandaff Chambers, 2 Regent Street, Cambridge, Cambridgeshire CB2 1AX
Tel: 01223 464696
Fax: 01223 500486
Email: .... enquiries@cambridgecvs.org.uk

PETERBOROUGH COUNCIL FOR VOLUNTARY SERVICE (A)
3 Lincoln Court, Lincoln Road, Peterborough, Cambridgeshire PE1 2RP
Tel: 01733 342683
Fax: 01733 559057
Email: .... pcvs@pcvs.co.uk

Cheshire

CHESTER VOLUNTARY ACTION (A)
Folliott House, 53 Northgate Street, Chester, Cheshire CH1 2HQ
Tel: 01244 323527
Fax: 01244 311680
Email: .... enquiries@chesterva.org.uk

CREWE & NANTWICH COUNCIL FOR VOLUNTARY SERVICE AND VOLUNTEER BUREAU (A)
Ashton House, 1A Gatefield Street, Crewe, Cheshire CW1 2JP
Tel: 01270 211545
Fax: 01270 211545
Email: .... wendy.gjerstad@bnva.co.uk

HALTON & ST HELEN'S VCA (A)
Sefton House, Public Hall Street, Runcorn, Cheshire WA7 1NG
Tel: 01928 592405
Email: .... haltonva@haltonva.org.uk

Co. Durham

DERWENTSIDE COUNCIL FOR VOLUNTARY SERVICE
The Tommy Armstrong Centre, Clifford Road, Stanley, Co. Durham DH9 0XG
Tel: 01207 218055
Fax: 01207 218849
Email: .... dcvs@derwentside.org.uk

EVOLUTION DARLINGTON (A)
Church Row, Darlington, Co. Durham DL1 5QD
Tel: 01325 266888
Fax: 01325 266899
Email: ...... enquiries@evolutiondarlington.com

HARTLEPOOL VOLUNTARY DEVELOPMENT AGENCY (A)
Rockhaven, 36 Victoria Road, Hartlepool, Co. Durham TS26 8DD
Tel: 01429 262641
Fax: 01429 265056
Email: .... info@hvda.co.uk

Derbyshire

AMBER VALLEY COUNCIL FOR VOLUNTARY SERVICE (A)
Market Place, Ripley, Derbyshire DE5 3HA
Tel: 01773 512078
Fax: 01733 748688
Email: .... admin@avcvs.org

CHESTERFIELD AND NE DERBYSHIRE COUNCIL FOR VOLUNTARY SERVICE AND ACTION (LINKS CVS) (A)
Ground Floor, Bleneim Court, 17 Newbold Road, Chesterfield, Derbyshire S41 7PG
Tel: 01246 274844
Fax: 01246 274844
Email: .... linkscvs@btconnect.com

East Sussex

EASTBOURNE ASSOCIATION OF VOLUNTARY SERVICES (A)
8 Saffrons Road, Eastbourne, East Sussex
BN21 1DG
Tel: 01323 639373
Fax: 01323 410977
Email: .... eastbourneinfo@3va.org.uk

HASTINGS VOLUNTARY ACTION (A)
Jackson Hall, Portland Place, Hastings, East
Sussex TN34 1QN
Tel: 01424 446060
Email: .. infoworker@hastingsvoluntaryaction.org

Essex

BASILDON, BILLERICAY AND WICKFORD COUNCIL FOR VOLUNTARY SERVICE (A)
The George Hurd Centre, Audley Way, Basildon,
Essex SS14 2FL
Tel: 01268 294124
Fax: 01268 534845
Email: .... admin@bbwcvs.org.uk

COLCHESTER COMMUNITY VOLUNTARY SERVICES (A)
Winsley's House, High Street, Colchester, Essex
CO1 1UG
Tel: 01206 505250
Fax: 01206 500367
Email: .... information@ccvs.org

RURAL COMMUNITY COUNCIL OF ESSEX
Threshelfords Business Park, Inworth Road,
Feering, Essex CO5 9SE
Tel: 0844 477 3938
Fax: 01376 573524
Email: ...... nick.shuttleworth@essexrcc.org.uk

SOUTHEND ASSOCIATION OF VOLUNTARY SERVICES (A)
SAVS Centre, 29-31 Alexandra Street, Southend-
on-Sea, Essex SS1 1BW
Tel: 01702 356000
Fax: 01702 356011

THURROCK COUNCIL FOR VOLUNTARY SERVICE (A)
The Beehive, (Voluntary and Community
Resource Centre), West Street, Grays, Essex
RM17 6XP
Tel: 01375 389881
Fax: 01375 389886
Email: .... tcvs@thurrockvols.demon.co.uk

Gloucestershire

CHELTENHAM VOLUNTARY AND COMMUNITY ACTION
Neighbourhood Resource Centre, 340 High
Street, Cheltenham, Gloucestershire GL50 3JF
Tel: 01242 227737
Fax: 01242 693589
Email: .... cheltadmin@gavca.org.uk

Hampshire

BASINGSTOKE VOLUNTARY SERVICES (A)
The Orchard, White Hart Lane, Basingstoke,
Hampshire RG21 4AF
Tel: 01256 423816
Fax: 01256 423825
Email: .... bvs@voluntaryservices.com

Herefordshire

HEREFORDSHIRE VOLUNTARY ACTION
Berrows Business Centre, Bath Street, Hereford,
Herefordshire HR1 2HE
Tel: 01432 343932
Fax: 01432 343932
Email: .... info@herefordshireva.org

Hertfordshire

ST ALBANS DISTRICT COUNCIL FOR VOLUNTARY SERVICES (A)
31 Catherine Street, St Albans, Hertfordshire
AL3 5BJ
Tel: 01727 852657
Fax: 01727 852656
Email: .... enquiries@cvsstalbans.org.uk

Lancashire

WEST LANCASHIRE COUNCIL FOR VOLUNTARY SERVICE (A)
Ecumenical Centre, Northway, Skelmersdale,
Lancashire WN8 6LU
Tel: 01695 733737
Fax: 01695 558073
Email: .... enquiries@wlcvs.org

Leicestershire

NORTH WEST LEICESTERSHIRE COUNCIL FOR VOLUNTARY SERVICE (A)
The Marlene Reid Centre, 85 Belvoir Road,
Coalville, Leicestershire LE67 3PH
Tel: 01530 510515
Fax: 01530 814632
Email: .... mail@nwlcvs.org.uk

VOLUNTARY ACTION LEICESTER (A)
9 Newark Street, Leicester, Leicestershire
LE1 5SN
Tel: 0116 258 0666
Fax: 0116 257 5059
Email: .... info@valonline.org.uk

London

ENFIELD VOLUNTARY ACTION (A)
Community House, 311 Fore Street, London
N9 0PZ
Tel: 020 8373 6268
Fax: 020 8373 6267
Email: .... admin@enfieldva.org.uk

Merseyside

WIRRAL COUNCIL FOR VOLUNTARY SERVICE (A)
46 Hamilton Square, Birkenhead, Merseyside
CH41 5AR
Tel: 0151 647 5432
Fax: 0151 647 5432
Email: .... admin@wirralcvs.org.uk

Norfolk

WEST NORFOLK VOLUNTARY & COMMUNITY ACTION
16 Tuesday Market Place, King's Lynn, Norfolk PE30 1JN
Tel: 01553 760568
Fax: 01553 774399
Email: .... info@westnorfolkvca.org

North Yorkshire

HARROGATE AND AREA COUNCIL FOR VOLUNTARY SERVICE (A)
Community House, 46-50 East Parade, Harrogate, North Yorkshire HG1 5RR
Tel: 01423 504074
Fax: 01423 502126
Email: .... cvs@harrogate.org

RIPON COUNCIL FOR VOLUNTARY SERVICE (A)
Community House, Allhallowgate, Ripon, North Yorkshire HG4 1LE
Tel: 01765 603631
Fax: 01765 645923
Email: .... info@riponcvs.co.uk

THIRSK, SOWERBY AND DISTRICT COMMUNITY CARE ASSOCIATION (A)
14a Market Place, Thirsk, North Yorkshire YO7 1LB
Tel: 01845 523115
Fax: 01845 525605
Email: .... robert.webb@tscca.org.uk

Northumberland

WANSBECK COUNCIL FOR VOLUNTARY SERVICE (A)
107-109 Station Road, Ashington, Northumberland NE63 8RS
Tel: 01670 858 688
Fax: 01670 813179
Email: .... enquire@wansbeckcvs.org.uk

Nottinghamshire

MANSFIELD COMMUNITY & VOLUNTARY SERVICE (A)
Community House, 36 Wood Street, Mansfield, Nottinghamshire NG18 1QA
Tel: 01623 651177
Fax: 0114 227 4105
Email: .... info@mansfieldcvs.org

Slough

SLOUGH COUNCIL FOR VOLUNTARY SERVICE (A)
27 Church Street, Slough SL1 1PL
Tel: 01753 524176
Fax: 01753 578243
Email: .... enquiries@sloughcvs.org.uk

Somerset

TAUNTON DEANE COUNCIL FOR VOLUNTARY SERVICE (A)
Flook House, Belvedere Road, Taunton, Somerset TA1 1BT
Tel: 01823 284470
Email: .... enquiries@tauntoncvs.org.uk

South Yorkshire

DONCASTER CVS (A)
Units 5 & 6 Trafford Court, Doncaster, South Yorkshire DN1 1PN
Tel: 01302 343300
Fax: 01302 321121
Email: .... enquiries@doncastercvs.org.uk

Staffordshire

LICHFIELD & DISTRICT COMMUNITY AND VOLUNTARY SECTOR SUPPORT (A)
Mansell House, 22 Bore Street, Lichfield, Staffordshire WS13 6LL
Tel: 01543 303030
Fax: 01543 303034
Email: .... rosevakis@ldcvs.org.uk

STAFFORD DISTRICT VOLUNTARY SERVICES (A)
131-141 North Walls, Stafford, Staffordshire ST16 3AD
Tel: 01785 606670
Fax: 01785 606669
Email: .... admin@sdvs.org.uk

Surrey

RUNNYMEDE ASSOCIATION OF VOLUNTARY SERVICES
12-13 The Sainsbury Centre, Chertsey, Surrey KT16 9AG
Tel: 01932 571122
Fax: 01932 566077
Email: .... ravs@ravs.info

WOKING ASSOCIATION OF VOLUNTARY SERVICE (A)
Provincial House, 26 Commercial Way, Woking, Surrey GU21 6EN
Tel: 01483 751456
Fax: 01483 740929
Email: .... info@wavs.org.uk

Tyne & Wear

GATESHEAD VOLUNTARY ORGANISATIONS COUNCIL (A)
John Haswell House, 8-9 Gladstone Terrace, Gateshead, Tyne & Wear NE8 4DY
Tel: .... 0191 478 4103; 0191 478 6318 Minicom
Fax: 0191 477 1260
Email: .... enquiries@gvoc.org.uk

Warwickshire

STRATFORD-UPON-AVON DISTRICT COUNCIL FOR VOLUNTARY SERVICE (A)
3 Arden Court, Arden Street, Stratford-upon-Avon, Warwickshire CV37 6NT
Tel: 01789 298115
Fax: 01789 262886
Email: .... info@stratfordcvs.org.uk

West Midlands

BIRMINGHAM VOLUNTARY SERVICE COUNCIL (A)
138 Digbeth, Birmingham, West Midlands B5 6DR
Tel: 0121 643 4343
Fax: 0121 643 4541
Email: .... administration@bvsc.org

SOLIHULL CVS
The Priory, Church Hill Road, Solihull, West
Midlands B91 3LF
Tel: 0121 788 1264

**WOLVERHAMPTON VOLUNTARY
SECTOR COUNCIL (A)**
16 Temple Street, Wolverhampton, West Midlands
WV2 4AN
Tel: 01902 773761
Fax: 01902 310270
Email: .... info@wolverhamptonvsc.org.uk

West Sussex

**ADUR COUNCIL FOR VOLUNTARY
SERVICE (A)**
Chesham House, 124 South Street, Lancing, West
Sussex BN15 8AJ
Tel: 01903 854980
Email: .... info@adurcvs.org

**CHICHESTER & DISTRICT COUNCIL FOR
VOLUNTARY SERVICE (A)**
60a North Street, Chichester, West Sussex
PO19 1NB
Tel: 01243 528615
Email: .... admin@chichester-cvs.org.uk

West Yorkshire

KEIGHLEY VOLUNTARY SERVICES (A)
135 Skipton Road, Keighley, West Yorkshire
BD21 3AU
Tel: 01535 665258
Fax: 01535 691436
Email: .... info@keighleyvs.org

VOLUNTARY ACTION KIRKLEES (A)
15 Lord Street, Kirklees, Huddersfield, West
Yorkshire HD1 1QB
Tel: 01484 518457
Fax: 01484 518457
Email: ...... info@voluntaryactionkirklees.co.uk

SCOTLAND

Clackmannanshire

CVS CLACKMANNANSHIRE
Support Group, 12-14 Primrose Street, Alloa,
Clackmannanshire FK10 1JG
Tel: 01259 217852
Fax: 01259 213525

South Lanarkshire

CVS HAMILTON & EAST KILBRIDE
155 Montrose Crescent, Hamilton, South
Lanarkshire ML3 6LQ
Tel: 01698 300390
Fax: 01698 300 394

WALES

Denbighshire

**DENBIGHSHIRE VOLUNTARY SERVICES
COUNCIL**
Naylor Leyland Centre, Well Street, Ruthin,
Denbighshire LL15 1AF
Tel: 01824 702441; 01824 703805
Fax: 01824 705412
Email: .... office@dvsc.co.uk

HOSPICE SERVICES

This section comprises hospices/palliative care in-patient services in the UK. Hospice or palliative care may also be provided at home (with support from specially trained staff), in a hospital or at a hospice day centre. A full list, together with other useful information, is published in the Hospice and Palliative Care Directory available from Help the Hospices, who can be reached at:

Help the Hospices, Hospice House, 34 – 44 Britannia Street, London WC1X 9JG
Tel: 020 7520 8200
Fax: 020 7278 1021
Email: info@helpthehospices.org.uk
Web: www.helpthehospices.org.uk

ENGLAND

Blackpool

TRINITY - THE HOSPICE IN THE FYLDE
Low Moor Road, Bispham, Blackpool FY2 0BG
Tel: 01253 358881
Email. . . . . . trinity.enquiries@trinityhospice.co.uk

Bristol

BRISTOL HAEMATOLOGY & ONCOLOGY CENTRE
Horfield Road, Bristol BS2 8ED
Tel: 0117 342 2416

Co. Durham

WILLOW BURN HOSPICE
Maidenlaw Hospital, Lanchester, Co. Durham DH7 0QS
Tel: 01207 529224
Fax: 01207 529303
Email: . . . . enquiries@willowburn.co.uk

Cumbria

HOSPICE AT HOME WEST CUMBRIA
Workington Community Hospital, Park Lane, Workington, Cumbria CA14 2RW
Tel: 01900 873173
Fax: 01900 873173
Email: . info@hospiceathomewestcumbria.org.uk

Dorset

JOSEPH WELD HOSPICE
Herrington Road, Dorchester, Dorset DT1 2SL
Tel: 01305 215300
Fax: 01305 267099

Essex

HAVENS HOSPICES, INCORPORATING FAIR HAVENS HOSPICE AND LITTLE HAVENS HOSPICE
47 Second Avenue, Westcliff-on-Sea, Essex SS0 8HX
Tel: 01702 220350
Fax: 01702 220351
Email: . . . . sseiffert@havenshospices.org.uk

Greater Manchester

BEECHWOOD CANCER CARE CENTRE
Chelford Grove, Stockport, Greater Manchester SK3 8LS
Tel: 0161 476 0384
Fax: 0161 477 5306
Email: . enquiries@beechwoodcancercarecentre.co.uk

BURY HOSPICE
Dumers Lane, Radcliffe, Manchester, Greater Manchester M26 2QD
Tel: 0161 725 9800
Fax: 0161 723 0662

FRANCIS HOUSE CHILDREN'S HOSPICE
390 Parrswood Road, East Didsbury, Manchester, Greater Manchester M20 5NA
Tel: 0161 434 4118
Fax: 0161 445 1927

Hampshire

THE ROWANS HOSPICE
Purbrook Heath Road, Purbrook, Waterlooville,
Hampshire PO7 5RU
Tel: 023 9225 0001
Fax: 023 9226 8567
Email: .... info@rowanshospice.co.uk

Kent

ELLENORLIONS HOSPICES, NORTHFLEET
Coldharbour Road, Northfleet, Gravesend, Kent
DA11 7HQ
Tel: 01474 320007
Fax: 01474 564018

PILGRIMS HOSPICE IN CANTERBURY
56 London Road, Canterbury, Kent CT2 8JA
Tel: 01227 812612
Fax: 01227 812606

PILGRIMS HOSPICE IN THANET
Ramsgate Road, Margate, Kent CT9 4AD
Tel: 01843 233920
Fax: 01843 233931

Lancashire

ST CATHERINE'S HOSPICE (PRESTON)
Lostock Hall, Lostock Lane, Preston, Lancashire
PR5 5XU
Tel: 01772 629171
Fax: 01772 696399
Email: .... admin@stcatherines.co.uk

Leicestershire

RAINBOWS CHILDREN'S HOSPICE
Lark Rise, Loughborough, Leicestershire
LE11 2HS
Tel: 01509 638000
Fax: 01509 216472
Email: .... administration@rainbows.co.uk

Lincolnshire

ST BARNABAS HOSPICE
36 Nettleham Road, Lincoln, Lincolnshire
LN2 1RE
Tel: 01522 511566

London

GREENWICH & BEXLEY COMMUNITY HOSPICE
185 Bostall Hill, Abbey Wood, London SE2 0GB
Tel: 020 8312 2244
Fax: 020 8312 0202
Email: .... kateheaps@gbch.org.uk

LONDON LIGHTHOUSE
111-117 Lancaster Road, Ladbroke Grove,
London W11 1QT
Tel: 020 7313 2900
Fax: 020 7229 1258
Email: .... info.ladbrokegrove@tht.org.uk

RICHARD HOUSE CHILDREN'S HOSPICE
Richard House Drive, Beckton, London E16 3RG
Tel: 020 7540 0200
Fax: 020 7511 0220
Email: .... info@richardhouse.org.uk

ST JOHN'S HOSPICE
Hospital of St John & St Elizabeth, 60 Grove End
Road, St John's Wood, London NW8 9NH
Tel: 020 7806 4040
Fax: 020 7806 4041

ST JOSEPH'S HOSPICE
Mare Street, Hackney, London E8 4SA
Tel: 020 8525 6000
Fax: 020 8533 0513
Email: .... info@stjh.org.uk

TRINITY HOSPICE
30 Clapham Common North Side, Clapham,
London SW4 0RN
Tel: 020 7787 1000
Fax: 020 7498 9726
Email: .... enquiries@trinityhospice.org.uk

Merseyside

MARIE CURIE HOSPICE, LIVERPOOL
Speke Road, Woolton, Liverpool, Merseyside
L25 8QA
Tel: 0151 801 1400
Fax: 0151 801 1458
Email: .... info@mariecurie.org.uk

**ST JOSEPH'S HOSPICE ASSOCIATION
(JOSPICE INTERNATIONAL)**
Ince Road, Thornton, Liverpool, Merseyside
L23 4UE
Tel: 0151 924 3812
Fax: 0151 924 6134
Email: .... jospice@3tc4u.net

North Yorkshire

ST LEONARD'S HOSPICE
185 Tadcaster Road, York, North Yorkshire
YO24 1GL
Tel: 01904 708553
Fax: 01904 704337
Email: ..... enquiries@stleonardshospice.org.uk

TEESSIDE HOSPICE CARE FOUNDATION
1a Northgate Road, Linthorpe, Middlesbrough,
North Yorkshire TS5 5NW
Tel: 01642 816777
Fax: 01642 823034

Oxfordshire

HELEN & DOUGLAS HOUSE

Helen & Douglas House
HOSPICE CARE FOR CHILDREN AND YOUNG ADULTS

**14a Magdalen Road, Oxford, Oxfordshire
OX4 1RW**
Tel: **01865 799150**
Fax: **01865 202702**
Email: ... admin@helenanddouglas.org.uk
Web: ...... www.helenanddouglas.org.uk
Helen & Douglas House has the time and
expertise to care for children and young adults
with life-shortening conditions. The two hospice
houses offer specialist symptom and pain
management, medically supported short breaks
and end-of life care, as well as counselling and
practical support for the whole family. Our aim is
to help every young person, aged from birth to
35, to live life to the full, even when that life is
short.

South Yorkshire

ST JOHN'S HOSPICE
Weston Road, Balby, Doncaster, South Yorkshire
DN4 8JS
Tel: 01302 796666

Stockton-on-Tees

BUTTERWICK HOSPICE CARE
Middlefield Road, Stockton-on-Tees TS19 8XN
Tel: 01642 628930

Suffolk

ST NICHOLAS HOSPICE CARE
Hardwick Lane, Bury St Edmunds, Suffolk
IP33 2QY
Tel: 01284 766133
Fax: 01284 715599
Email: .... enquiries@stnh.org.uk

Surrey

ST RAPHAEL'S HOSPICE
London Road, North Cheam, Surrey SM3 9DX
Tel: 020 8335 4575
Fax: 020 8335 4574
Email: .... enquiries@straphaels.org.uk

Tyne & Wear

MARIE CURIE HOSPICE, NEWCASTLE
Marie Curie Drive, Newcastle upon Tyne, Tyne &
Wear NE4 6SS
Tel: 0191 219 1000
Fax: 0191 219 1099
Email: .... info@mariecurie.org

Warwickshire

THE MYTON HOSPICES
Myton Lane, Myton Road, Warwick, Warwickshire
CV34 6PX
Tel: 01926 492518
Email: .... enquiry@mytonhospice.org

West Midlands

ACORNS CHILDREN'S HOSPICE TRUST
103 Oak Tree Lane, Selly Oak, Birmingham, West
Midlands B29 6HZ
Tel: 0121 248 4850

JOHN TAYLOR HOSPICE
76 Grange Road, Erdington, Birmingham, West
Midlands B24 0DF
Tel: 0121 465 2000
Fax: 0121 255 2410

West Sussex

CHESTNUT TREE HOUSE CHILDREN'S HOSPICE
Dover Lane, Arundel, West Sussex BN18 9PX
Tel: 01903 871800
Fax: 01903 871828
Email: ...... admin@chestnut-tree-house.org.uk
Web: .... www.chestnut-tree-house.org.uk
Beds: 10 + HC/DC/BS/MND/V/HSN

ST BARNABAS HOUSE
Columbia Drive, Worthing, West Sussex
BN13 2QF
Tel: . 01903 534030 Admin; 01903 264222 Care;
01903 265824 Fundraising
Fax: 01903 524138

West Yorkshire

MARIE CURIE HOSPICE, BRADFORD
Maudsley Street, Bradford, West Yorkshire
BD3 9LE
Tel: 01274 337000
Fax: 01274 337094
Email: .... info@mariecurie.org.uk

MARTIN HOUSE. A HOSPICE FOR CHILDREN & YOUNG PEOPLE

Martin House
children's hospice

**Grove Road, Clifford, Wetherby, West
Yorkshire LS23 6TX**
Tel: **01937 844569**
Fax: **01937 849058**
Web: .... www.martinhouse.org.uk

Windsor & Maidenhead

THAMES HOSPICECARE
Pine Lodge, Hatch Lane, Windsor, Windsor &
Maidenhead SL4 3RW
Tel: 0845 612 8812
Fax: 0845 612 8712
Email: .... contact@thameshospice.org.uk

NORTHERN IRELAND

Belfast

MARIE CURIE HOSPICE, BELFAST
Kensington Road, Belfast BT5 6NF
Tel: 028 9088 2000
Fax: 028 9088 2022
Email: .... legacies@mariecurie.org.uk

Co. Londonderry

FOYLE HOSPICE
61 Culmore Road, Londonderry, Co. Londonderry
BT48 8JE
Tel: 028 7135 1010
Fax: 028 7135 1010
Email: .... care@foylehospice.com

SCOTLAND

Fife

HOSPICE WARD (WARD 16)
Queen Margaret Hospital, Whitefield Road,
Dunfermline, Fife KY12 0SU
Tel: 01383 627016
Fax: 01383 674044

Glasgow

MARIE CURIE HOSPICE, HUNTERS HILL
1 Belmont Road, Hunters Hill, Glasgow G21 3AY
Tel: 0141 531 1300
Fax: 0141 531 1301
Email: .... info@mariecurie.org.uk

**PRINCE & PRINCESS OF WALES
HOSPICE**

The Prince & Princess
of Wales Hospice

71 Carlton Place, Glasgow G5 9TD
Tel: 0141 429 5599
Web: .... http://www.ppwh.org.uk
Beds: 14+HC/DC/BS/MND/AID/OTI/V/HST

Orkney Islands

ORKNEY MACMILLAN HOUSE
Balfour Hospital, New Scapa Road, Kirkwall,
Orkney Islands KW15 1BH
Tel: 01856 888000

Perth & Kinross

**CHILDREN'S HOSPICE ASSOCIATION
SCOTLAND - RACHEL HOUSE**
Avenue Road, Kinross, Perth & Kinross KY13 8FX
Tel: 01577 865777
Fax: 01577 865888

WALES

Denbighshire

MACMILLAN UNIT
Denbigh Infirmary, Ruthin Road, Denbigh,
Denbighshire LL16 3ES
Tel: 01745 818100

Rhondda Cynon Taff

Y BWTHYN
Pontypridd and District Hospital, The Common,
Pontypridd, Rhondda Cynon Taff CF37 4AL
Tel: 01443 486144

Swansea

TY OLWEN PALLIATIVE CARE SERVICE
Morriston Hospital, ABM University NHS Trust,
Swansea SA6 6NL
Tel: 01792 703412
Fax: 01792 703695

Vale of Glamorgan

MARIE CURIE HOSPICE, HOLME TOWER
Bridgeman Road, Penarth, Vale of Glamorgan
CF64 3YR
Tel: 029 2042 6000
Fax: 029 2042 6036
Email: .... info@mariecurie.org.uk

FREE LEGAL ADVICE

If in doubt as to how to find legal advice services, consult the Citizens Advice Bureau (CAB) in the area concerned (see directory listing for the local office). The following organisations provide specialist services or information.

ENGLAND

Essex

CHILDREN'S LEGAL CENTRE
c/o University of Essex, Wivenhoe Park,
Colchester, Essex CO4 3SQ
Tel: 01206 877910
Email: .... clc@essex.ac.uk

Greater Manchester

EQUALITY AND HUMAN RIGHTS COMMISSION
Arndale House, Arndale Centre, Manchester,
Greater Manchester M4 3AQ
Tel: 0845 604 6610
Email: .... info@equalityhumanrights.com

London

ADVISORY SERVICE FOR SQUATTERS
Angel Alley, 84b Whitechapel High Street, London
E1 7QX
Tel: 020 3216 0099
Email: .... advice@squatter.org.uk

AT EASE ADVICE, INFORMATION AND COUNSELLING SERVICE
Bunhill Fields Meeting House, Quaker Court,
Banner Street, London EC1Y 8QQ
Tel: 020 7490 5223

EQUALITY AND HUMAN RIGHTS COMMISSION
3 More London, Riverside Tooley Street, London
SE1 2RG
Tel: 020 3117 0235
Email: .... info@equalityhumanrights.com

FAMILY RIGHTS GROUP
The Print House, 18 Ashwin Street, London
E8 3DL
Tel: 0808 801 0366 Freephone Advice; 020 7923
2628 Admin
Fax: 020 7923 2683
Email: .... office@frg.org.uk

FREE REPRESENTATION UNIT
6th Floor, Falcon House, 289 - 293 High Holborn,
London WC1V 7HZ
Tel: .... 020 7611 9555 Open 10am-6pm
Fax: 020 7611 9551
Email: .... admin@freerepresentationunit.org.uk

IMMIGRATION ADVICE SERVICE
County House, 190 Great Dover Street, London
SE1 4YB
Tel: 0844 974 4000
Fax: 020 7378 0665

JOINT COUNCIL FOR THE WELFARE OF IMMIGRANTS
115 Old Street, London EC1V 9RT
Tel: 020 7251 8708
Fax: 020 7251 8707

MARY WARD LEGAL CENTRE
10 Great Turnstile, London WC1V 7JU
Tel: 020 7831 7079
Email: .... enquiries@marywardlegal.org.uk

MIND
Granta House, 15-19 Broadway, Stratford, London
E15 4BQ
Tel: 020 8519 2122
Fax: 020 8522 1725
Email: .... willsandtrust@mind.org.uk

ONE PARENT FAMILIES - GINGERBREAD
255 Kentish Town Road, London NW5 2LX
Tel: 020 7428 5400
Fax: 020 7482 4851

RELEASE
124-128 City Road, London EC1V 2NJ
Tel: 020 7324 2989
Email: .... ask@release.org.uk

UK COUNCIL FOR INTERNATIONAL STUDENT AFFAIRS (UKCISA)
9-17 St Albans Place, Islington, London N1 0NX
Tel: 020 7288 4330
Fax: 020 7288 4360

VICTIM SUPPORT
National Office, Hallam House, 56-60 Hallam
Street, London W1W 6JL
Tel: 020 7268 0200
Fax: 020 7268 0210
Email: .... legacies@victimsupport.org

SCOTLAND

Glasgow

EQUALITY AND HUMAN RIGHTS COMMISSION
The Optima Building, 58 Robertson Street,
Glasgow G2 8DU
Tel: 0141 228 5910

WALES

Cardiff

EQUALITY AND HUMAN RIGHTS COMMISSION
3rd Floor, 3 Callaghan Square, Cardiff CF10 5BT
Tel: 029 2044 7710
Fax: 029 2044 7712
Email: .... wales@equalityhumanrights.com

LAW CENTRES

The following Law Centres provide free legal advice and representation in areas of social welfare law only. They are listed according to alphabetical order of county / unitary authority / region in England, Scotland, Wales and Northern Ireland and by numbered postal districts in Greater London. For further information contact the Law Centres Network: 64 Great Eastern Street, London EC2A 3QR
E-mail: info@lawcentres.org.uk Web: www.lawcentres.org.uk

ENGLAND

Bedfordshire

LUTON LAW CENTRE
6th Floor, Cresta House, Alma Street, Luton, Bedfordshire LU1 2PL
Tel: 01582 481000; 01582 482000
Fax: 01582 482581
Email: . . . . admin@lutonlawcentre.co.uk

Bristol

AVON & BRISTOL LAW CENTRE
2 Moon Street, Bristol BS2 8QF
Tel: 0117 924 8662
Fax: 0117 924 8020
Email: . . . . mail@ablc.org.uk

Cumbria

CUMBRIA LAW CENTRE
8 Spencer Street, Carlisle, Cumbria CA1 1BG
Tel: 01228 515129
Fax: 01228 515819
Email: . . . . reception@comlaw.co.uk

Derbyshire

CHESTERFIELD LAW CENTRE
44 Park Road, Chesterfield, Derbyshire S40 1XZ
Tel: 01246 550674
Fax: 01246 551069
Email: . . . . clc@chesterfieldlawcentre.org.uk

DERBY CITIZENS ADVICE AND LAW CENTRE
Stuart House, Green Lane, Derby, Derbyshire DE1 1RS
Tel: 01332 295711
Email: . . advice@citizensadviceandlawcentre.org

Gloucestershire

GLOUCESTER LAW CENTRE
3rd Floor, 75-81 Eastgate Street, Gloucester, Gloucestershire GL1 1PN
Tel: 01452 423492
Fax: 01452 387594
Email: . . . . . . admin@gloucesterlawcentre.co.uk

Greater Manchester

BURY LAW CENTRE
8 Bank Street, Bury, Greater Manchester BL9 0DL
Tel: 0161 272 0666
Fax: 0161 272 0031
Email: . . . . info@burylawcentre.co.uk

ROCHDALE LAW CENTRE
15 Drake Street, Rochdale, Greater Manchester OL16 1RE
Tel: 01706 657766
Fax: 01706 346558
Email: . . . . info@rochdalelawcentre.org.uk

SOUTH MANCHESTER LAW CENTRE
584 Stockport Road, Longsight, Manchester, Greater Manchester M13 0RQ
Tel: 0161 225 5111
Fax: 0161 225 0210
Email: . . . . admin@smlc.org.uk

TRAFFORD LAW CENTRE
2nd Floor, John Darby House, 88-92 Talbot Road, Old Trafford, Manchester, Greater Manchester M16 0GS
Tel: 0161 872 3669
Fax: 0161 872 2208
Email: . . . . admin@traffordlawcentre.org.uk

Isle of Wight

ISLE OF WIGHT LAW CENTRE
Exchange House, St Cross Lane, Newport, Isle of Wight PO30 5BZ
Tel: 01983 524715
Fax: 01983 522606
Email: . . . . iowlc@iowlc.org.uk

Kent

STREETWISE COMMUNITY LAW CENTRE
28a Beckenham Road, Beckenham, Kent BR3 4LS
Tel: 020 8663 4747
Fax: 020 8658 9257

London

BARNET LAW SERVICE (LAW CENTRE)
9 Bell Lane, London NW4 2BP
Tel: 020 8203 4141
Fax: 020 8203 8042
Email: . . . . info@barnetlaw.org.uk

BATTERSEA LAW CENTRE (SWLLC)
125 Bolingbroke Grove, London SW11 1DA
Tel: 020 7585 0716
Fax: 020 7585 0718
Email: . solicitors@battersealawcentre.fsnet.co.uk

BRENT COMMUNITY LAW CENTRE
389 Willesden High Road, London NW10 2JR
Tel: 020 8451 1122
Fax: 020 8208 5734
Email: . . . . brentlaw@brentlaw.org.uk

CAMBRIDGE HOUSE LAW CENTRE
137 Camberwell Road, Camberwell, London
SE5 0HF
Tel: 020 7358 7025
Fax: 020 7277 0401
Email: . . . . info@ch1889.org

CAMDEN COMMUNITY LAW CENTRE
2 Prince of Wales Road, London NW5 3LQ
Tel: 020 7284 6510
Fax: 020 7267 6218
Email: . . . . admin@cclc.org.uk

CENTRAL LONDON LAW CENTRE
14 Irving Street, London WC2H 7AF
Tel: 020 7839 2998
Fax: 020 7839 6158
Email: . . . . renata@londonlawcentre.org.uk

GREENWICH COMMUNITY LAW CENTRE
187 Trafalgar Road, Greenwich, London
SE10 9EQ
Tel: 020 8305 3350
Fax: 020 8858 5253
Email: . . . . info@gclc.co.uk

HACKNEY COMMUNITY LAW CENTRE
8 Lower Clapton Road, London E5 0PD
Tel: . 020 8985 8364; 020 8985 5236 Emergency
Fax: 020 8533 2018
Email: . . . . info@hclc.org.uk

HAMMERSMITH & FULHAM LAW CENTRE
1st Floor, 142-144 King Street, London W6 0QU
Tel: 020 8741 4021
Fax: 020 8741 1450; 020 8741 5521
Email: . . . . hflaw@hflaw.org.uk

HARINGEY LAW CENTRE
Ground Floor Offices, 7 Holcombe Road, London
N17 9AA
Tel: 020 8808 5354
Fax: 020 8801 1516
Email: . . . . tottenhamlawcentre@tiscali.co.uk

ISLINGTON LAW CENTRE
161 Hornsey Road, London N7 6DU
Tel: 020 7607 2461
Fax: 020 7700 0072
Email: . . . . info@islingtonlaw.org.uk

LAMBETH LAW CENTRE
Unit 4, The Co-op Centre, 11 Mowll Street,
London SW9 6BG
Tel: 020 7840 2000
Email: . . . . admin@lambethlawcentre.org

NORTH KENSINGTON LAW CENTRE
74 Golborne Road, London W10 5PS
Tel: 020 8969 7473
Fax: 020 8968 0934
Email: . . . . info@nklc.co.uk

PADDINGTON LAW CENTRE
439 Harrow Road, London W10 4RE
Tel: 020 8960 3155
Fax: 020 8968 0417
Email: . . . . paddingtonlaw@btconnect.com

PLUMSTEAD COMMUNITY LAW CENTRE
105 Plumstead High Street, London SE18 1SB
Tel: 020 8855 9817
Fax: 020 8316 7903

SOUTHWARK LAW CENTRE
Hanover Park House, 14-16 Hanover Park,
London SE15 5HG
Tel: 020 7732 2008
Fax: 020 7732 2034

SPRINGFIELD LAW CENTRE
Admissions Buildings, Springfield University
Hospital, 61 Glenburnie Road, London SW17 7DJ
Tel: 020 8767 6884
Fax: 020 8767 6996
Email: . . . . info@springfieldlawcentre.org.uk

TOWER HAMLETS LAW CENTRE
214 Whitechapel Road, Whitechapel, London
E1 1BJ
Tel: 020 7247 8998
Fax: 020 7247 9424
Email: . . . . info@thlc.co.uk

Merseyside

VAUXHALL LAW & INFORMATION CENTRE
Silvester Street, Liverpool, Merseyside L5 8SE
Tel: 0151 482 2001
Fax: 0151 207 4948
Email: . . . . advice@lawcentre.vnc.org.uk

Middlesex

HILLINGDON LAW CENTRE
12 Harold Avenue, Hayes, Middlesex UB3 4QW
Tel: 020 8561 9400
Fax: 020 8756 0837
Email: . . . . info@hillingdonlawcentre.co.uk

South Yorkshire

SHEFFIELD LAW CENTRE
1st Floor, Waverley House, 10 Joiner Street,
Sheffield, South Yorkshire S3 8GW
Tel: . . . . 0114 273 1888 (Advice Line)
Email: . . . . post@slc.org.uk

Surrey

KINGSTON & RICHMOND LAW CENTRE (SWLLC)
Siddeley House, 50 Canbury Park Road, Kingston
on Thames, Surrey KT2 6LX
Tel: 020 8547 2882
Fax: 020 8547 2350

SURREY LAW CENTRE
34-36 Chertsey Street, Guildford, Surrey
GU1 4HD
Tel: 01483 215000
Fax: 01483 750770
Email: . . . . info@surreylawcentre.org

WANDSWORTH & MERTON LAW CENTRE (SWLLC)
112 London Road, Morden, Surrey SM4 5AX
Tel: 020 8543 4069
Fax: 020 8542 3814

Tyne & Wear

NEWCASTLE LAW CENTRE
Ist Floor, 1 Charlotte Square, Newcastle upon Tyne, Tyne & Wear NE1 4XF
Tel: 0191 230 4777
Fax: 0191 233 0295
Email: .... info@newcastlelawcentre.co.uk

West Midlands

BIRMINGHAM LAW CENTRE
Dolphin House, 54 Coventry Road, Small Heath, Birmingham, West Midlands B10 0RX
Tel: 0121 766 7466
Fax: 0121 766 8860
Email: ..... admin@birminghamlawcentre.org.uk

COVENTRY LAW CENTRE
Oakwood House, St Patricks Road Entrance, Coventry, West Midlands CV1 2HL
Tel: 024 7622 3053
Fax: 024 7622 8551
Email: .... enquiries@covlaw.org.uk

West Yorkshire

BRADFORD LAW CENTRE
31 Manor Row, Bradford, West Yorkshire BD1 4PS
Tel: 01274 306617
Fax: 01274 390939
Email: info@bradfordlawcentre.co.uk

HAREHILLS & CHAPELTOWN LAW CENTRE
263 Roundhay Road, Leeds, West Yorkshire LS8 4HS
Tel: 0113 249 1100
Fax: 0113 235 1185
Email: .... skhan@leedslawcentre.org.uk

KIRKLEES LAW CENTRE
Units 11/12, Empire House, Wakefield Old Road, Dewsbury, West Yorkshire WF12 8DJ
Tel: 01924 439829
Fax: 01924 868140
Email: .... manager@kirkleeslc.org.uk

Wiltshire

WILTSHIRE LAW CENTRE
Temple House, 115-118 Commercial Road, Swindon, Wiltshire SN1 5PL
Tel: 01793 486926
Fax: 01793 432193
Email: .... info@wiltslawcentre.co.uk

NORTHERN IRELAND

Belfast

LAW CENTRE (NORTHERN IRELAND)
124 Donegall Street, Belfast BT1 2GY
Tel: 028 9024 4401
Fax: 028 9023 6340
Email: .... admin.belfast@lawcentreni.org

Co. Londonderry

LAW CENTRE (NORTHERN IRELAND) WESTERN AREA OFFICE
Western Area Office, 9 Clarendon Street, Londonderry, Co. Londonderry BT48 7EP
Tel: 028 7126 2433
Fax: 028 7126 2343
Email: .... admin.derry@lawcentreniwest.org

SCOTLAND

Glasgow

CASTLEMILK LAW AND MONEY ADVICE CENTRE
155 Castlemilk Drive, Castlemilk, Glasgow G45 9UG
Tel: 0141 634 0313
Fax: 0141 634 1944
Email: mail@castlemilklawcentre.co.uk

ETHNIC MINORITIES LAW CENTRE
41 St Vincent Place, Glasgow G1 2ER
Tel: 0141 204 2888
Email: .... admin@emlc.org.uk

WALES

Cardiff

CARDIFF LAW CENTRE
41-42 Clifton Street, Cardiff CF24 1LS
Tel: 029 2049 8117
Fax: 029 2049 7118
Email: .... cardiff.lawcentre@dial.pipex.com

VOLUNTARY ORGANISATIONS FOR BLIND & PARTIALLY SIGHTED PEOPLE

Nearly half of the UK's local societies for blind and partially sighted people have resource centres holding classes in braille, typing and cooking. All provide advice and information. Local societies have their own organisations, Visionary - linking local sight loss charities (Tel: 020 8417 0942), and the RNIB supports local activities through centres for blind and partially sighted people in the UK.

Registration and welfare of blind people is undertaken by local authorities. See also organisations listed in the object index under Blind people.

ENGLAND

Bath & North East Somerset

VISION BATH
7 Green Park Station, Bath, Bath & North East
Somerset BA1 1JB
Tel: 01225 446555
Fax: 01225 446555
Email: .... resource@bwsbps.org.uk

Bedfordshire

SIGHT CONCERN (BEDFORDSHIRE)
Kings House, 245 Ampthill Road, Bedford,
Bedfordshire MK42 9AZ
Tel: 01234 311555
Email: .... office@sightconcern.org.uk

Blackpool

BLACKPOOL, FYLDE & WYRE SOCIETY FOR THE BLIND
Resource Centre, Bosworth Place, Blackpool
FY4 1SH
Tel: 01253 362692
Fax: 01253 407010
Email: .... info@vision-nw.co.uk

Bournemouth

BOURNEMOUTH SOCIETY FOR THE VISUALLY IMPAIRED
5 Victoria Park Road, Bournemouth BH9 2RB
Tel: 01202 546644
Fax: 01202 519006
Email: .... enquiries@bsvi.org.uk

Brighton & Hove

SUSSEX LANTERN (FORMERLY BRIGHTON SOCIETY FOR THE BLIND)
William Moon Lodge, The Linkway, Brighton,
Brighton & Hove BN1 7EJ
Tel: 01273 507251
Fax: 01273 507249
Email: .... info@bsblind.co.uk

Bristol

ACTION FOR BLIND PEOPLE SOUTHWEST
10 Stillhouse Lane, Bedminster, Bristol BS3 4EB
Tel: 0117 953 7750
Fax: 0117 953 7751
Email: ...... bristol@actionforblindpeople.org.uk

Buckinghamshire

BUCKSVISION
Resource and Training Centre, 143 Meadowcroft,
Aylesbury, Buckinghamshire HP19 9HH
Tel: 01296 487556
Fax: 01296 436290
Email: .... reception@bucksvision.co.uk

Cambridgeshire

CAMSIGHT
167 Green End Road, Cambridge,
Cambridgeshire CB4 1RW
Tel: 01223 420033
Fax: 01223 501829
Email: .... info@camsight.org.uk

HUNTINGDONSHIRE SOCIETY FOR THE BLIND
8 St Mary's Street, Huntingdon, Cambridgeshire
PE29 3PE
Tel: 01480 453438
Fax: 01480 453556
Email: .... huntsblind@btconnect.com

PETERBOROUGH ASSOCIATION FOR THE BLIND
The Former Pharmacy, c/o The Medical Centre,
Saltersgate, Peterborough, Cambridgeshire
PE1 4YL
Tel: 01733 703570

RNIB PETERBOROUGH
Bakewell Road, Orton Southgate, Peterborough,
Cambridgeshire PE2 6XU
Tel: 01733 375000

RNIB TALKING BOOK SERVICE
PO Box 173, Peterborough, Cambridgeshire
PE2 6WS
Tel: 0845 762 6843
Fax: 01733 375001

Cheshire

IRIS VISION RESOURCE CENTRE
14 Chapel Street, Crewe, Cheshire CW2 7DQ
Tel: 01270 250316
Fax: 01270 214262
Email: .... info@iriscentre.org.uk

MACCLESFIELD EYE SOCIETY
15 Queen Victoria Street, Macclesfield, Cheshire
SK11 6LP
Tel: 01625 422602

WARRINGTON, WIDNES AND DISTRICT SOCIETY FOR THE BLIND
Rex Furness Centre, 4 Museum Street,
Warrington, Cheshire WA1 1HU
Tel: 01925 632700
Email: .... info@wwblindsociety.org.uk

Co. Durham

COUNTY DURHAM SOCIETY FOR THE BLIND & PARTIALLY SIGHTED
4 Red Hill Villas, Durham, Co. Durham DH1 4BA
Tel: 0191 386 8175
Email: .... info@cdslops.co.uk

Cornwall

CORNWALL BLIND ASSOCIATION
The Sight Centre, Newham Road, Truro, Cornwall
TR1 2DP
Tel: 01872 261110
Fax: 01872 222349
Email. .... info@cornwallblind.org.uk

CORNWALL COMMUNITY VOLUNTEER SERVICE
Community Centre, South Terrace, Camborne,
Cornwall TR14 8SU
Tel: 01209 718844
Fax: 01209 712620

Cumbria

BARROW AND DISTRICTS SOCIETY FOR THE BLIND
67-69 Cavendish Street, Barrow-in-Furness,
Cumbria LA14 1QD
Tel: 01229 820698
Fax: 01229 826064
Email: .... info@barrowblindsociety.org.uk

CARLISLE SOCIETY FOR THE BLIND
9 Brunswick Street, Carlisle, Cumbria CA1 1PB
Tel: 01228 593104

EDEN VOLUNTARY SOCIETY FOR THE BLIND & PARTIALLY SIGHTED
1 Mostyn Hall, Friargate, Penrith, Cumbria
CA11 7XR
Tel: ...... 01768 891724 (answerphone service)

SOUTH LAKES SOCIETY FOR THE BLIND
Stricklandgate House, 92 Stricklandgate, Kendal,
Cumbria LA9 4PU
Tel: 01539 742633

WEST CUMBRIA SOCIETY FOR THE BLIND
22 Lowther Street, Whitehaven, Cumbria
CA28 7DG
Tel: 01946 592474

Derbyshire

DERBYSHIRE ASSOCIATION FOR THE BLIND
65-69 Nottingham Road, Derby, Derbyshire
DE1 3QS
Tel: 01332 292262
Fax: 01332 287017

Devon

DEVON INSIGHT
Station House, Holman Way, Topsham, Exeter,
Devon EX3 0EN
Tel: 01392 876666
Fax: 01392 874442
Email: .... devon-blind@btconnect.com

HEARING & SIGHT CENTRE
Ernest English House, Buckwell Street, Plymouth,
Devon PL1 2DA
Tel: .. 01752 201766; 01752 241087 (Textphone)
Fax: 01752 202214
Email: .... has@hascentre.org.uk

NEWTON ABBOT CARE OF THE BLIND SOCIETY
37B Knowles Hill Road, Newton Abbot, Devon
TQ12 2PP
Tel: 01626 366001

East Sussex

EAST SUSSEX ASSOCIATION OF BLIND AND PARTIALLY SIGHTED PEOPLE (ESAB)
Prospect House, 7-9 George Street, Hailsham,
East Sussex BN27 1AD
Tel: 01323 832252
Fax: 01323 833054
Email: .... info@eastsussexblind.org

EASTBOURNE BLIND SOCIETY
124-142 Longstone Road, Eastbourne, East
Sussex BN22 8DA
Tel: 01323 729511
Fax: 01323 649135

HASTINGS & ROTHER VOLUNTARY ASSOCIATION FOR THE BLIND
3 Upper Maze Hill, St Leonards-on-Sea, East
Sussex TN38 0LQ
Tel: 01424 436359
Email: .... hrvab@freeuk.com

Essex

COLCHESTER SOCIETY FOR THE BLIND
29 Lucy Lane South, Stanway, Colchester, Essex
CO3 0HE
Tel: 01206 533711

ESSEX BLIND CHARITY
Read House, 23 The Esplanade, Frinton-on-Sea,
Essex CO13 9AU
Tel: 01255 673654
Fax: 01255 673177
Email: .... info@essexblind.co.uk

Gloucestershire

GLOUCESTERSHIRE COUNTY ASSOCIATION FOR THE BLIND
81 Albion Street, Cheltenham, Gloucestershire
GL52 2RZ
Tel: 01242 221170
Fax: 01242 701152
Email: .... enquiries@glos-blind.co.uk

Greater Manchester

BURY SOCIETY FOR THE BLIND & PARTIALLY SIGHTED PEOPLE
36 Bolton Street, Bury, Greater Manchester
BL9 0LL
Tel: 0161 763 7014
Fax: 0161 763 3395

HEYWOOD BLIND WELFARE SOCIETY
Social Centre for the Blind, 1 Starkey Street,
Heywood, Greater Manchester OL10 4JS
Tel: 01706 369382

OLDHAM METROPOLITAN SOCIETY FOR THE BLIND
8 Montgomery House, Hawthorn Road,
Hollinwood, Oldham, Greater Manchester
OL8 3QG
Tel: 0161 682 8019

WHITEFIELD BLIND AID SOCIETY
23 Frankton Road, Whitefield, Manchester,
Greater Manchester M45 7FB
Tel: 0161 766 7915

WIGAN, LEIGH AND DISTRICT SOCIETY FOR THE BLIND
Room 8, 28 Upper Dicconson Street, Wigan,
Greater Manchester WN1 2AG
Tel: 01942 242891
Email: .... wiganleighblind@btinternet.com

Hampshire

PORTSMOUTH ASSOCIATION FOR THE BLIND
48 Stubbington Avenue, North End, Portsmouth,
Hampshire PO2 0HY
Tel: 023 9266 1717
Fax: 023 9262 6019
Email: .... portsmouthblind@btconnect.com

SOUTHAMPTON SOCIETY FOR THE BLIND
3 Bassett Avenue, Bassett, Southampton,
Hampshire SO16 7DP
Tel: 023 8076 9882

Hertfordshire

HERTFORDSHIRE SOCIETY FOR THE BLIND
The Woodside Centre, The Commons, Welwyn
Garden City, Hertfordshire AL7 4SE
Tel: 01707 324680
Email: .... office@hertsblind.com

Isle of Man

MANX BLIND WELFARE SOCIETY
Corrin Court, Heywood Avenue, Onchan, Douglas,
Isle of Man IM3 3AP
Tel: 01624 674727
Fax: 01624 675912
Email: .... enquiries@mbws.org.im

Isle of Wight

ISLE OF WIGHT SOCIETY FOR THE BLIND
137 Carisbrooke Road, Newport, Isle of Wight
PO30 1DD
Tel: 01983 522205
Fax: 01983 522792
Email: .... enquiries@iwsb.org.uk

Kent

KENT ASSOCIATION FOR THE BLIND
72 College Road, Maidstone, Kent ME15 6SJ
Tel: 01622 691357
Fax: 01622 663999
Email: .... supportus@kab.org.uk

ROYAL LONDON SOCIETY FOR THE BLIND
Dorton Campus, Wildernesse Avenue, Seal,
Sevenoaks, Kent TN15 0EB
Tel: 01732 592500
Fax: 01732 592506
Email: .... web-master@rlsb.org.uk

Kingston upon Hull

HULL AND EAST RIDING INSTITUTE FOR THE BLIND
Beech Holme, Beverley Road, Hull, Kingston upon
Hull HU5 1NF
Tel: 01482 342297
Fax: 01482 443111

Lancashire

ACCRINGTON AND DISTRICT BLIND SOCIETY
32 Bank Street, Accrington, Lancashire BB5 1HP
Tel: 01254 233332

BLACKBURN AND DISTRICT BLIND SOCIETY
1-2 Thwaites House, Railway Road, Blackburn,
Lancashire BB1 5AX
Tel: 01254 54143; 01254 65535
Fax: 01254 694710

BURNLEY AND DISTRICT SOCIETY FOR THE BLIND
3 Bedford Avenue, Burnley, Lancashire BB12 6AE
Tel: 01282 438507

GALLOWAY'S SOCIETY FOR THE BLIND
Howick House, Howick Park Avenue,
Penwortham, Preston, Lancashire PR1 0LS
Tel: 01772 744148
Email: .... peter.taylor@galloways.org.uk

Leicestershire

VISTA
Margaret Road, Off Gwendolen Road, Leicester,
Leicestershire LE5 5FU
Tel: 0116 249 0909
Fax: 0116 249 8811
Email: .... info@vistablind.org.uk

Lincolnshire

LINCOLN & LINDSEY BLIND SOCIETY
Bradbury House, Ramsgate, Louth, Lincolnshire
LN11 0NB
Tel: 01507 605604
Fax: 01507 608802
Email: .... info@llbs.co.uk

London

ACTION FOR BLIND PEOPLE - PART OF RNIB GROUP
14-16 Verney Road, London SE16 3DZ
Tel: 020 7635 4919
Fax: 020 7635 4892
Email: . . . . supportercare@afbp.org.uk

BLINDAID

Lantern House, 102 Bermondsey Street,
London SE1 3UB
Tel: 020 7403 6184
Fax: 020 7234 0708
Email: . . . . enquiries@blindaid.org.uk
BlindAid has over 175 years of experience.
Working in the 12 Inner London Boroughs, we
provide vital home visits to over 600 isolated blind
and visually impaired people offering friendship,
company and conversation.

BRENT VISUALLY HANDICAPPED GROUP
Cameron House, 80 Pound Lane, Willesden,
London NW10 2HT
Tel: . . . . , 020 8451 4354 Answerphone

THE HARINGEY PHOENIX GROUP
Winkfield Resource Centre, 33 Winkfield Road,
Wood Green, London N22 5RP
Tel: 020 8889 7070
Email: . . . . . haringeyphoenixgroup@yahoo.co.uk

IN TOUCH ISLINGTON
99 Shepperton Road, London N1 3DF
Tel: 020 7359 6827

JEWISH CARE
Amelie House, Maurice & Vivienne Wohl Campus,
221 Golders Green Road, London NW11 9DQ
Tel: 020 8922 2000
Email: . . . . info@jcare.org

MERTONVISION
c/o The Guardian Centre, 67 Clarendon Road,
Colliers Wood, London SW19 2DX
Tel: 020 8540 5446
Fax: 020 8544 0059
Email: . . . . info@mertonvision.org.uk

NEWHAM VOLUNTARY ASSOCIATION FOR THE BLIND
Jordan Hall, Curwen Centre, 2 London Road,
Plaistow, London E13 0DE
Tel: 020 8548 1977

RNIB HEADQUARTERS
105 Judd Street, London WC1H 9NE
Tel: 020 7388 1266
Fax: 020 7388 2034
Email: . . . . helpline@rnib.org.uk

ROYAL NATIONAL INSTITUTE OF BLIND PEOPLE (RNIB)
105 Judd Street, London WC1H 9NE
Tel: 0845 600 0313
Fax: 020 7388 2034
Email: . . . . legacyservices@rnib.org.uk

Merseyside

BRADBURY FIELDS
The Bradbury Centre, Youens Way, Liverpool,
Merseyside L14 2EP
Tel: 0151 221 0888
Fax: 0151 221 0889
Email: . . . . info@bradburyfields.org.uk

CATHOLIC BLIND INSTITUTE
Christopher Grange, Youens Way, Liverpool,
Merseyside L14 2EW
Tel: 0151 220 2525
Fax: 0151 220 1972

GALLOWAY'S SOCIETY FOR THE BLIND
Paton House, 22 Wright Street, Southport,
Merseyside PR9 0TL
Tel: 01704 534555
Email: . . . . southeast@galloways.org.uk

WIRRAL SOCIETY OF THE BLIND AND PARTIALLY SIGHTED
Ashville Lodge, Ashville Road, Birkenhead,
Merseyside CH41 8AU
Tel: 0151 652 8877
Fax: 0151 651 0635

Middlesex

MIDDLESEX ASSOCIATION FOR THE BLIND
Suite 18 - Freetrade House, Lowther Road,
Stanmore, Middlesex HA7 1EP
Tel: 020 8423 5141; 0845 838 0480
Fax: 0520 8099 7003
Email: . . . . info@aftb.org.uk

Norfolk

NORFOLK AND NORWICH ASSOCIATION FOR THE BLIND
106 Magpie Road, Norwich, Norfolk NR3 1JH
Tel: 01603 629558
Fax: 01603 766682
Email: . . . . office@nnab.org.uk

North Somerset

VISION NORTH SOMERSET
3 Neva Road, Weston-super-Mare, North
Somerset BS23 1YD
Tel: 01934 419393
Fax: 01934 613950
Email: . . . . celia.henshall@visionns.org.uk

North Yorkshire

HARROGATE & DISTRICT SOCIETY FOR THE BLIND (INC. RIPON)
Russell Sergeant House, 23 East Parade,
Harrogate, North Yorkshire HG1 5LF
Tel: 01423 565915
Email: . . . . . . enquiries@harrogateblindsoc.co.uk

SCARBOROUGH BLIND AND PARTIALLY SIGHTED SOCIETY (INCLUDING WHITBY & RYEDALE)
183 Dean Road, Scarborough, North Yorkshire
YO12 7JH
Tel: 01723 354417
Fax: 01723 503304

SELBY DISTRICT VISION
Unit 12, The Prospect Centre, Prospect Way,
Selby, North Yorkshire YO8 8BD
Tel: 01757 709800
Email: .... info@selbydistrictvision.co.uk

TEESSIDE AND DISTRICT SOCIETY FOR THE BLIND
Stockton Road, Newport, Middlesbrough, North
Yorkshire TS5 4AH
Tel: 01642 247518

Northamptonshire

NORTHAMPTONSHIRE ASSOCIATION FOR THE BLIND
Wardington Court, Welford Road, Kingsthorpe,
Northampton, Northamptonshire NN2 8AG
Tel: 01604 719193
Fax: 01604 719193
Email: .... helpline@nab.org.uk

Northumberland

NORTHUMBERLAND COUNTY BLIND ASSOCIATION
Reiver House, Stathers Lane, Morpeth,
Northumberland NE61 1TD
Tel: 01670 574316
Email: .... enquiries@ncba.org.uk

Oxfordshire

BANBURY SOCIETY FOR THE VISUALLY IMPAIRED
7 Willoughby Road, Banbury, Oxfordshire
OX16 9DZ
Tel: 01865 725595

OXFORDSHIRE ASSOCIATION FOR THE BLIND
Bradbury Lodge, Gordon Woodward Way,
Abingdon Road, Oxford, Oxfordshire OX1 4XL
Tel: 01865 725595
Fax: 01865 725596
Email: .... director@oxeyes.org.uk

Poole

DORSET BLIND ASSOCIATION
17 Bournemouth Road, Lower Parkstone, Poole
BH14 0EF
Tel: 01202 712860
Email: .... info@dorsetblind.org.uk

Reading

BERKSHIRE COUNTY BLIND SOCIETY
Midleton House, 5 Erleigh Road, Reading
RG1 5LR
Tel: 0118 987 2803
Email: .... office@bcbs.org.uk

READING ASSOCIATION FOR THE BLIND
Walford Hall, Carey Street, Reading RG1 7JS
Tel: 0118 957 2960
Email: .... readingblind@yahoo.co.uk

Shropshire

SHROPSHIRE VOLUNTARY ASSOCIATION FOR THE BLIND
SVAB Office, The Lantern, Meadow Farm Drive,
Shrewsbury, Shropshire SY1 4NG
Tel: 01743 210508

South Yorkshire

BARNSLEY BLIND AND PARTIALLY SIGHTED ASSOCIATION
The Resource Centre, 22 Regent Street South,
Barnsley, South Yorkshire S70 2HT
Tel: 01226 200618
Fax: 01226 297675

SHEFFIELD ROYAL SOCIETY FOR THE BLIND (SRSB)
5 Mappin Street, Sheffield, South Yorkshire
S1 4DT
Tel: 0114 272 2757
Fax: 0870 706 5171
Email: .... info@srsb.org.uk
Web: .... http://www.srsb.org.uk
SRSB provides opportunity, support, friendship and
services to blind and partially sighted people in
Sheffield, helping them to achieve whatever they wish to
do and whatever they aspire to be.

SHEFFIELD VOLUNTARY TRUST FOR THE WELFARE OF THE BLIND AND PARTIALLY SIGHTED
Sheffield City Council, Sheffield, South Yorkshire
S1 2JQ
Tel: 0114 273 4973

Suffolk

EAST SUFFOLK ASSOCIATION FOR THE BLIND
Mallard House Business Centre, The Old Station,
Little Bealings, Woodbridge, Suffolk IP13 6LT
Tel: 01473 611011
Fax: 01473 614453

IPSWICH BLIND SOCIETY LTD
19 Tower Street, Ipswich, Suffolk IP1 3BE
Tel: .... 01473 219712 24hr Answerphone
Email: .... ipswichblindsociety@tiscali.co.uk

WEST SUFFOLK VOLUNTARY ASSOCIATION FOR THE BLIND
4 Bunting Road, Moreton Hall Estate, Bury St
Edmunds, Suffolk IP32 7BX
Tel: 01284 748800
Email: .... info@wsvab.org

Surrey

CROYDON VOLUNTARY ASSOCIATION FOR THE BLIND
Bedford Hall, 72-74 Wellesley Road, Croydon,
Surrey CR0 2AR
Tel: 020 8688 2486
Fax: 020 8681 7525

KINGSTON-UPON-THAMES ASSOCIATION FOR THE BLIND
Adams House, Vicarage Lane, New Malden,
Surrey KT3 3FF
Tel: 020 8605 0060

SUTTON ASSOCIATION FOR THE BLIND
1st Floor, 3 Robin Hood Lane, Sutton, Surrey SM1 2SW
Tel: 020 8409 7166/7

Tyne & Wear

BLIND SOCIETY FOR NORTH TYNESIDE
Parkside House, Elton Street, Wallsend, Tyne & Wear NE28 8QU
Tel: 0191 262 0869

COMMUNITY FOUNDATION (FORMERLY TYNE & WEAR FOUNDATION)
9th Floor, Cale Cross, 156 Pilgrim Street, Newcastle upon Tyne, Tyne & Wear NE1 6SU
Tel: 0191 222 0945
Fax: 0191 230 0689
Email: ... general@communityfoundation.org.uk

GATESHEAD & SOUTH TYNESIDE SIGHT SERVICE (FORMERLY NORTHUMBRIA SIGHT SERVICE)
Badbury Centre, Bensham Hospital, Saltwell Road, Gateshead, Tyne & Wear NE8 4YL
Tel: 0191 478 5959

LONGBENTON VOLUNTARY COMMITTEE FOR THE BLIND
Beech House, 12 The Spinney, Killingworth Village, Newcastle upon Tyne, Tyne & Wear NE12 6BG
Tel: 0191 268 1569

NEWCASTLE SOCIETY FOR BLIND PEOPLE
3rd Floor, MEA House, Ellison Place, Newcastle upon Tyne, Tyne & Wear NE1 8XS
Tel: 0191 232 7292
Email: enquiries@ncbp.co.uk

SUNDERLAND AND NORTH DURHAM ROYAL SOCIETY FOR THE BLIND
8 Foyle Street, Sunderland, Tyne & Wear SR1 1LB
Tel: 0191 567 3939
Email: .... office@sundrsb.org.uk

TYNEMOUTH BLIND WELFARE SOCIETY
Pearey House, Preston Park, North Shields, Tyne & Wear NE29 9JR
Tel: 0191 257 4388

West Midlands

BEACON CENTRE FOR THE BLIND
Wolverhampton Road East, Wolverhampton, West Midlands WV4 6AZ
Tel: 01902 880111
Fax: 01902 886795
Email: .... enquiries@beacon4blind.co.uk

COVENTRY RESOURCE CENTRE FOR THE BLIND
33 Earlsdon Avenue South, Coventry, West Midlands CV5 6TH
Tel: 024 7671 7522

FOCUS BIRMINGHAM
48-62 Woodville Road, Harborne, Birmingham, West Midlands B17 9AT
Tel: .... 0121 478 5200 (Switchboard); 0121 478 5222 (Helpline)

RNIB BIRMINGHAM
58-72 John Bright Street, Birmingham, West Midlands B1 1BN
Tel: 0121 665 4200

WALSALL SOCIETY FOR THE BLIND
Hawley House, 11 Hatherton Road, Walsall, West Midlands WS1 1XS
Tel: 01922 627683
Fax: 01922 637010

West Sussex

4SIGHT (FORMERLY WEST SUSSEX ASSOCIATION FOR THE BLIND)
Bradbury Centre, 36 Victoria Drive, Bognor Regis, West Sussex PO21 2TE
Tel: 01243 828555
Fax: 01243 838003
Email: .... enquiries@4sightsussex.co.uk

WORTHING SOCIETY FOR THE BLIND
75 Richmond Road, Worthing, West Sussex BN11 4AQ
Tel: 01903 235782
Fax: 01903 212924
Email: .... info@wsftb.org.uk

West Yorkshire

HALIFAX SOCIETY FOR THE BLIND
34 Clare Road, Halifax, West Yorkshire HX1 2HX
Tel: 01422 352383

KEIGHLEY AND DISTRICT ASSOCIATION FOR THE BLIND
1 Albert Street, Keighley, West Yorkshire BD21 2AT
Tel: 01535 602354
Email: .... enquiries@keighleyblind.org

LEEDS JEWISH BLIND SOCIETY
The Margery & Arnold Ziff Community Centre, 311 Stonegate Road, Leeds, West Yorkshire LS17 6AZ
Tel: 0113 268 4211
Fax: 0113 203 4915

THE LEEDS SOCIETY FOR DEAF & BLIND PEOPLE
Centenary House, North Street, Leeds, West Yorkshire LS2 8AY
Tel: 0113 243 8328
Fax: 0113 243 3553

PUDSEY VOLUNTARY COMMITTEE FOR THE WELFARE OF THE BLIND
8 Monson Avenue, Calverley, Pudsey, West Yorkshire LS28 5NP
Tel: 0113 229 5257

SHIPLEY AND BAILDON BLIND WELFARE ASSOCIATION
8 Hill End Grove, Bradford, West Yorkshire BD7 4RP
Tel: 01274 571074

SOCIETY FOR THE BLIND OF DEWSBURY, BATLEY AND DISTRICT
The Whitfield Centre, 180 Soothill Lane, Batley, West Yorkshire WF17 6HP
Tel: 01924 445222
Fax: 01924 420156

WAKEFIELD SOCIETY FOR THE BLIND
c/o Bardon, Runtlings, Ossett, West Yorkshire
WF5 8JJ
Tel: 01924 262643

WEST RIDING BLIND ASSOCIATION
Parkside Centre, Leeds Road, Outwood,
Wakefield, West Yorkshire WF1 2PN
Tel: 01924 215555

Worcestershire

SIGHT CONCERN WORCESTERSHIRE
The Bradbury Centre, 2 Sansome Walk,
Worcester, Worcestershire WR1 1LH
Tel: 01905 723245
Fax: 01905 332909
Email: .... info@sightconcern.co.uk

NORTHERN IRELAND

Co. Armagh

LURGAN BLIND WELFARE COMMITTEE
15 Market Street, Lurgan, Co. Armagh BT66 8AR

SCOTLAND

Dumfries & Galloway

DUMFRIES & GALLOWAY ASSOCIATION FOR THE BLIND
Mount St Michael, Craigs Road, Dumfries,
Dumfries & Galloway DG1 4UT
Tel: 01387 248784

Dundee

DUNDEE BLIND & PARTIALLY SIGHTED SOCIETY
Thomas Herd House, 10-12 Ward Road, Dundee
DD1 1LX
Tel: 01382 227101
Fax: 01382 203553
Email: .... sandra.gollan@dbpss.org.uk

Edinburgh

RNIB SCOTLAND
12-14 Hillside Crescent, Edinburgh EH7 5EA
Tel: 0131 652 3140
Email: .... rnibscotland@rnib.org.uk

Fife

FIFE SOCIETY FOR THE BLIND
Fife Sensory Impairment Centre, Wilson Avenue,
Kirkcaldy, Fife KY2 5EF
Tel: 01592 644979
Email: .... info@fsbinsight.co.uk

Glasgow

JEWISH BLIND SOCIETY (SCOTLAND)
Walton Community Centre, May Terrace, Giffnock,
Glasgow G46 6LD
Tel: 0141 620 1800

VISIBILITY (FORMERLY GLASGOW AND WEST OF SCOTLAND SOCIETY FOR THE BLIND)
2 Queens Crescent, Glasgow G4 9BW
Tel: 0141 332 4632
Email: .... info@visibility.org.uk

Highland

HIGHLAND SOCIETY FOR BLIND PEOPLE
38 Ardconnel Street, Inverness, Highland IV2 3EX
Tel: 01463 233663
Email: .... denise@highlandblindcraft.co.uk

WALES

Cardiff

CARDIFF INSTITUTE FOR THE BLIND
Shand House, 20 Newport Road, Cardiff
CF24 0YB
Tel: 029 2048 5414
Fax: 029 2046 5222
Email: .... postmaster@cibi.co.uk

Gwynedd

NORTH WALES SOCIETY FOR THE BLIND
325 High Street, Bangor, Gwynedd LL57 1YB
Tel: 01248 353604
Fax: 01248 371048

Merthyr Tydfil

MERTHYR TYDFIL INSTITUTE FOR THE BLIND
Unit 4, Triangle Business Park, Pentrebach,
Merthyr Tydfil CF48 4TQ
Tel: 01685 370072
Fax: 01685 370073
Email: .... info@mtib.co.uk

Swansea

SWANSEA AND DISTRICT FRIENDS OF THE BLIND
3 De La Beche Street, Swansea SA1 3EY
Tel: 01792 655424
Email: .... john_allen_10@hotmail.com

VISION IMPAIRED WEST GLAMORGAN
2 Gonhill, West Cross, Swansea SA3 5PL
Tel: 01792 776360
Email: .... judith@cibi.co.uk

Torfaen

GWENT ASSOCIATION FOR THE BLIND
Badbury House, Park Buildings, Park Road,
Pontypool, Torfaen NP4 6JH
Tel: 01495 764650
Fax: 01495 763650

VOLUNTARY ORGANISATIONS & RESIDENTIAL HOMES FOR DEAF PEOPLE

This information was originally supplied by the Royal National Institute for Deaf People (RNID) who are now known as Action on Hearing Loss. The charity has detailed lists of local organisations and clubs for deaf people. Telephone numbers below are for voice only unless otherwise specified. Action on Hearing Loss should be contacted at the following address:

19-23 Featherstone Street, London EC1Y 8SL Tel: 020 7296 8000 Web: www.actiononhearingloss.org.uk

ENGLAND

Bath & North East Somerset

ACTION ON HEARING LOSS BATH SUPPORTED HOUSING
112 Freeview Road, Twerton, Bath, Bath & North East Somerset BA2 1DZ
Tel: 01225 342930
Fax: 01225 426774

ACTION ON HEARING LOSS NEWBRIDGE HILL
51 Newbridge Hill, Lower Weston, Bath, Bath & North East Somerset BA1 3PR
Tel: ... 01225 443019; 01225 443019 Textphone
Fax: 01225 443019
Email: ...... ursula.forbush@hearingloss.org.uk

ACTION ON HEARING LOSS POOLEMEAD
Poolemead House, Watery Lane, Twerton-on-Avon, Bath, Bath & North East Somerset BA2 1RN
Tel: ... 01225 332818 Voice/Textphone; 01225 332818
Fax: 01225 480825

Blackpool

BLACKPOOL, FYLDE AND WYRE SOCIETY FOR THE DEAF
64 Cornwall Avenue, Blackpool FY2 9QW
Tel: 01253 351369
Fax: 01253 355894

Brighton & Hove

ACTION ON HEARING LOSS WILBURY GARDENS
13 Wilbury Gardens, Hove, Brighton & Hove BN3 6HQ
Tel: .... 01273 205044 Voice/Minicom
Fax: 01273 771891
Email: .... scrinne.maer@hearingloss.org.uk

Cambridgeshire

CAMSIGHT
167 Green End Road, Cambridge, Cambridgeshire CB4 1RW
Tel: 01223 246237 Voice; 01223 411801 Minicom
Email: .... office@cambsdeaf.org

Cheshire

DEAFNESS SUPPORT NETWORK
144 London Road, Northwich, Cheshire CW9 5HH
Tel: 01606 47831
Fax: 01606 49456
Email: .... dsn@dsnonline.co.uk

Cornwall

ACTION ON HEARING LOSS PENDEAN COURT
16 Pendean Court, Barras Cross, Liskeard, Cornwall PL14 6DZ
Tel: ... 01579 340201; 01579 340450 Textphone

Devon

ACTION ON HEARING LOSS PIPPIN HOUSE
8 Keyberry Park, Newton Abbot, Devon TQ12 1BZ
Tel: ... 01626 354521; 01626 337251 Textphone
Fax: 01626 337251

East Sussex

HEARING CONCERN LINK
27-28 The Waterfront, Eastbourne, East Sussex BN23 5UZ

Essex

FOLEY HOUSE
115 High Garrett, Braintree, Essex CM7 5NU
Tel: .... 01376 326652 Voice
Fax: 01376 553350
Email: .... enquiries@foleyhouse.org.uk

ROYAL ASSOCIATION FOR DEAF PEOPLE
Century House South, Riverside Office Centre, North Station Road, Colchester, Essex CO1 1RE
Tel: .. 0845 688 2525; 0845 688 2527 (Minicom)
Email: .... info@royaldeaf.org.uk

Greater Manchester

MANCHESTER DEAF CENTRE
Crawford House, Booth Street East, Manchester, Greater Manchester M13 9GH
Tel: ...... 0161 273 3415 Voice; 0161 273 3415 Minicom
Fax: 0161 273 6698

Hampshire

SONUS
Spitfire House, 28-29 High Street, Southampton,
Hampshire SO14 2DF
Tel: 023 8051 6516
Email: . . . . enquiries@sonus.org.uk

Isle of Wight

EASTHILL HOME FOR DEAF PEOPLE
7 Pitt Street, Ryde, Isle of Wight PO33 3EB
Tel: . . . . 01983 564068 Voice/Minicom
Fax: 01983 811857

Kent

ACTION ON HEARING LOSS CLIFFE AVENUE
15 Cliffe Avenue, Westbrook, Margate, Kent
CT9 5DU
Tel: . . . . . 01843 232122; 01843 232624 Minicom
Fax: 01843 230455

ACTION ON HEARING LOSS ROPER HOUSE
St Dunstans Street, Canterbury, Kent CT2 8BZ
Tel: . . . . . . 01227 462155; 01227 781915 Voice/
Textphone
Fax: 01227 452351

Lancashire

EAST LANCASHIRE DEAF SOCIETY
8 Heaton Street, Blackburn, Lancashire BB2 2EF
Tel: . . . 01254 844550; 01254 262460 (Minicom)
Fax: 01254 844551
Email: . . . . burnley@elds.org.uk

Leicestershire

ACTION DEAFNESS
Orchardson Avenue, Leicester, Leicestershire
LE4 6DP
Tel: . . 0116 257 4800 Voice; 0116 257 4850 Text
Email: . . . . enquiries@actiondeafness.org.uk

London

ACTION ON HEARING LOSS BRONDESBURY ROAD
113 Brondesbury Road, Queens Park, London
NW6 6RY
Tel: . . . . . . 020 7328 8540 Voice; 020 7328 8544
Minicom
Fax: 020 7372 8965

JEWISH DEAF ASSOCIATION
Julius Newman House, Woodside Park Road, Off
High Road, North Finchley, London N12 8RP
Tel: . . . . . 020 8446 0502 (Voice); 020 8446 4037
(Textphone)
Fax: 020 8445 7451
Email: . . . . mail@jda.dircon.co.uk

Merseyside

MERSEYSIDE SOCIETY FOR DEAF PEOPLE
Queens Drive, West Derby, Liverpool, Merseyside
L13 0DJ
Tel: . . . . 0151 228 0888 Voice/Minicom
Fax: 0151 228 4872

SOUTHPORT CENTRE FOR THE DEAF
19A Stanley Street, Southport, Merseyside
PR9 0BY
Tel: . . . . 01704 537001 Voice/Minicom

North Yorkshire

DEAF SOCIETY YORK & DISTRICT
Centre for the Deaf, Bootham House, 61
Bootham, York, North Yorkshire YO3 7BT
Tel: . . . . 01904 623459 Voice/Minicom

Nottinghamshire

NOTTINGHAMSHIRE DEAF SOCIETY
22 Forest Road West, Nottingham,
Nottinghamshire NG7 4EQ
Tel: . . . . 0115 970 0516 Voice/Minicom
Fax: 0115 942 3096
Email: . . . . nds@nottsdeaf.org.uk

Reading

READING DEAF CENTRE
131 Cardiff Road, Reading RG1 8JF
Tel: . . . . 0118 959 4969 Voice/Minicom

South Yorkshire

SHEFFIELD CENTRAL DEAF CLUB
Victoria Hall Methodist Church, Norfolk Street,
Chapel Walk, Sheffield, South Yorkshire S1 2PD
Tel: . . . . . . 0114 275 5307 Voice; 0114 275 5307
Minicom
Email: . . . . andrew.brown26@btconnect.com

Surrey

ACTION ON HEARING LOSS GIBRALTAR CRESCENT
36a Gibraltar Crescent, Epsom, Surrey KT19 9BT
Tel: . . . . . . 020 8393 0865 Voice; 020 8393 7623
Minicom
Fax: 020 8393 8649

West Midlands

ACTION ON HEARING LOSS MULBERRY HOUSE
70 Lichfield Street, Walsall, West Midlands
WS4 2BY
Tel: . . 01922 615218 Voice; 01922 722658 Mincom
Fax: 01922 615218

ACTION ON HEARING LOSS OLIVE LANE
60 Olive Lane, Halesowen, West Midlands
B62 8LZ
Tel: . 0121 559 0031; 0121 559 0280 (Textphone)
Fax: 0121 561 1288
Email: . . . . rosie.foster@rnid.org.uk

BID SERVICES
Ladywood Road, Birmingham, West Midlands
B16 8SZ
Tel: 0121 246 6100
Fax: 0121 246 6125
Email: . . . . info@bid.org.uk

COVENTRY DEAF SOCIAL CLUB
Henry Fry Centre, Hertford Place, Coventry, West
Midlands CV1 3JZ
Tel: . . . . 024 7622 2321 Voice/Minicom
Fax: 024 7622 2321
Email: . . . . henryfry@dsl.pipex.com

NORTHERN IRELAND

Co. Londonderry

ACTION ON HEARING LOSS HARKNESS GARDENS
1-2 Harkness Gardens, Brigade Road,
Londonderry, Co. Londonderry BT47 6GG
Tel: ...... 028 7134 1005 Voice; 028 7134 2262
Minicom
Fax: 028 7134 2262

SCOTLAND

Aberdeen

ABERDEEN AND NE SOCIETY FOR THE DEAF
13 Smithfield Road, Aberdeen AB24 4NR
Tel: ... 01224 494566; 01224 495675 (Minicom)
Fax: 01224 483894
Email: .... info@aneds.org.uk

Dundee

DEAF ACTION
36 Roseangle, Dundee DD1 4LY
Tel: ...... 01382 221124; 01382 224052; 01382 227052 Voice/Minicom
Fax: 01382 200025
Email: .... tynesideadmin@deafaction.org

Edinburgh

DEAF ACTION
49 Albany Street, Edinburgh EH1 3QY
Tel: ...... 0131 556 3128; 0131 557 0419 (Text)
Fax: 0131 557 8283
Email: .... admin@deafaction.org

Glasgow

DEAF CONNECTIONS
Glasgow Centre for the Deaf, 100 Norfolk Street,
Glasgow G5 9EJ
Tel: .... 0141 420 1759 Voice/Text
Fax: 0141 429 6860
Email: .... enquiries@deafconnections.co.uk

LOCAL ASSOCIATIONS OF AND FOR DISABLED PEOPLE

Information on local associations of and for disabled people was originally supplied by the Royal Association for Disability and Rehabilitation (RADAR). RADAR has since merged with Disability Alliance and the National Centre for Independent Living to form Disability Rights UK. Disability Rights UK can be contacted at: 12 City Forum, 250 City Road, London EC1V 8AF Tel: 020 7250 3222.

Information from DIAL UK is also listed. DIAL UK is now managed by Scope. For more information, please visit www.scope.org.uk/dial or call 01302 310123.

ENGLAND

Bournemouth

CMT UNITED KINGDOM
98 Broadway, Southbourne, Bournemouth
BH6 4EH
Tel: 0800 652 6316

Cambridgeshire

FRIENDS WITH DISABILITIES
5 Grieve Court, Cambridge, Cambridgeshire
CB4 1FR
Tel: 01223 425595

Cornwall

DISABILITY CORNWALL
Units 1G & H Guildford Road Industrial Estate,
Guildford Road, Hayle, Cornwall TR27 4QZ
Tel: . . . . . . 01736 756655; 01736 759500 (DIAL)
Email: . . . . info@disabilitycornwall.org.uk

North Yorkshire

INDEPENDENT LIVING CENTRE
Lansdowne Centre, Holyrood Lane,
Middlesbrough, North Yorkshire TS4 2QT
Tel: 01642 250749

Somerset

SOUTH WEST ACTION FOR LEARNING AND LIVING OUR WAY
The Old Engine House, Old Pit Road, Midsomer
Norton, Somerset BA3 4BQ
Tel: 01761 414034
Email: . . . . info@swallowcharity.org
Web: . . . . http://www.swallowcharity.org
SWALLOW supports people with learning disabilities to lead fulfilling, independent lives. The services that we provide include supported housing, training in independent living skills and creative courses such as art, pottery and drama. We also offer training for employment and social activities. Our centre provides a warm and welcoming environment for our members to meet and make friends.

Wiltshire

INDEPENDENT LIVING CENTRE (WILTSHIRE & BATH)
St George's Road, Semington, Trowbridge,
Wiltshire BA14 6JQ
Tel: 01380 871007
Fax: 01380 871 113
Email: . welcome.ilc.semington@googlemail.com

ENGLAND - NON RADAR MEMBERS

Buckinghamshire

CENTRE FOR INTEGRATED LIVING
330 Saxon Gate West, Milton Keynes,
Buckinghamshire MK9 2ES
Tel: 01908 231344
Fax: 01908 231335
Email: . . . . info@mkcil.org.uk

DISABILITY INFORMATION NETWORK
6 The Courtyard, Gatehouse Close, Aylesbury,
Buckinghamshire HP19 8DP
Tel: 01298 487924
Email: . . . . bucksdin@hotmail.com

Cheshire

HALTON DISABILITY INFORMATION SERVICES
Collier Street, Runcorn, Cheshire WA7 1HB
Tel: . . . 01928 717445; 01928 718999 (Minicom)

Isle of Wight

DIAL ISLE OF WIGHT
The Riverside Centre, The Quay, Newport, Isle of
Wight PO30 2QR
Tel: 01983 522823
Email: . . . . dial.iw@hotmail.co.uk

Lancashire

WEST LANCS DISABILITY HELPLINE
Whelmar House, 2nd Floor, Southway,
Skelmersdale, Lancashire WN8 6NN
Tel: . . . 01695 51819; 0800 220676 (Advice line)
Fax: 01695 722844
Email: . . . . enquiries@wldh.org.uk

Leicestershire

MOSAIC : SHAPING DISABILITY SERVICES
2 Oak Spinney Park, Ratby Lane, Leicester, Leicestershire LE3 3AW
Tel: 0116 231 8720
Email: . . . . enquiries@mosaic1898.co.uk

London

DISABILITY ACTION IN ISLINGTON
90-92 Upper Street, London N1 0NP
Tel: . . . . 020 7226 0137; 020 7359 1891 Minicom
Fax: 020 7359 1855

DISABILITY COALITION - TOWER HAMLETS
40-50 Southern Grove, Mile End, London E3 4PX
Tel: 020 8980 2200
Fax: 020 8981 8007

North Lincolnshire

CARERS' SUPPORT CENTRE
11 Redcombe Lane, Brigg, North Lincolnshire DN20 8AU
Tel: 01652 650585
Fax: 01652 653637
Email: . . . . info@carerssupportcentre.com

North Somerset

DIAL
Room 5, Roselawn, 28 Walliscote Road, Weston-super-Mare, North Somerset BS23 1LL
Tel: 01934 419426
Fax: 01934 419426
Email: . . . . mail@westondial.co.uk

North Yorkshire

SELBY AND DISTRICT DIAL
12 Park Street, Selby, North Yorkshire YO8 4PW
Tel: 01757 210495
Fax: 01757 290427
Email: . . . . selbydial@tiscali.co.uk

Northamptonshire

ADVICE DAVENTRY
The Abbey, off Market Square, Daventry, Northamptonshire NN11 4XG
Tel: 01327 701646

DIAL
Resource Centre, Patrick Road, Corby, Northamptonshire NN18 9NT
Tel: 01536 204742
Email: . . . . dial.corby@btconnect.com

South Yorkshire

DISABILITY INFORMATION SERVICE
c/o Central Library, Walker Place, Rotherham, South Yorkshire S65 1JH
Tel: 01709 373658

West Yorkshire

CALDERDALE DART
Harrison House, 10 Harrison Road, Halifax, West Yorkshire HX1 2AF
Tel: 01422 346040

DISABILITY ADVICE BRADFORD
103 Dockfield Road, Shipley, West Yorkshire BD17 7AR
Tel: 01274 594173
Fax: 01274 530432
Email: . . . . enquiry@disabilityadvice.org.uk

ONE VOICE - FEDERATION OF DISABLED PEOPLE
17-18 Queensgate Market Arcade, Huddersfield, West Yorkshire HD1 2RA

ENGLAND - RADAR MEMBERS

Bracknell Forest

BERKSHIRE DISABILITY INFORMATION NETWORK
Brakenhale School, Rectory Lane, Bracknell, Bracknell Forest RG12 7BA
Tel: . . . 01344 301572; 01344 427757 (Minicom)
Fax: 01344 302293

Brighton & Hove

BLUEBIRD SOCIETY FOR THE DISABLED
176 Portland Road, Hove, Brighton & Hove BN3 5QN
Tel: 01273 207664
Fax: 01273 207664
Email: . . . . bluebirdsociety@waitrose.com

BRIGHTON & HOVE FEDERATION OF DISABLED PEOPLE
Montague House, Somerset Street Entrance, Montague Place, Brighton, Brighton & Hove BN2 1JE
Tel: 01273 203016
Email: . . . . disabilityadvice@bhfederation.org.uk

Bristol

DISABILITY ADVICE CENTRE
Disability Information & Advice Service, West of England Centre for Inclusive Living (WECI), Leinster Avenue, Knowle West, Bristol BS4 1AR
Tel: 0117 983 2828

Cambridgeshire

DIAL PETERBOROUGH
The Kingfisher Centre, The Cresset, Bretton, Peterborough, Cambridgeshire PE3 8DX
Tel: 01733 265551
Fax: 01733 260977
Email: . . . . dialpeterborough@btconnect.com

Cheshire

DIAL HOUSE CHESTER
DIAL House, Hamilton Place, Chester, Cheshire CH1 2BH
Tel: 01244 345655
Fax: 01244 315025
Email: . . . . . contactus@dialhousechester.org.uk

DISABILITY INFORMATION BUREAU
Pierce Street, Macclesfield, Cheshire SK11 6ER
Tel: 01625 501759
Fax: 01625 869685
Email: . . . . info@dibservices.org.uk

VALE ROYAL DISABILITY SERVICES
VRDS Head Office, 4 Hartford Business Centre,
Chester Road, Hartford, Northwich, Cheshire
CW8 2AB
Tel: 01606 888400
Fax: 01606 888244
Email: .... office@vrds.org.uk

Co. Durham

EVOLUTION (DARLINGTON CVS)
Church Row, Darlington, Co. Durham DL1 5QD
Tel: 01325 266888
Fax: 01325 266899
Email: ...... enquiries@evolutiondarlington.com

Cornwall

CORNWALL DISABLED ASSOCIATION
1 Riverside House, Heron Way, Newham, Truro,
Cornwall TR1 2XN
Tel: 01872 273518
Email: .... info@cornwalldisabled.co.uk

Cumbria

ALLERDALE DISABILITY ASSOCIATION
Curwen Centre, Curwen Park, Workington,
Cumbria CA14 4YB
Tel: 0845 129 9954
Fax: 0845 123 2729
Email: .... access@adanet.org.uk

**BARROW AND DISTRICT DISABILITY
ASSOCIATION**
71-77 School Street, Barrow-in-Furness, Cumbria
LA14 1EJ
Tel: 01229 432599
Fax: 01229 834884
Email: .... info@bdda.org.uk

Derbyshire

DISABILITY DIRECT
227 Normanton Road, Normanton, Derby,
Derbyshire DE23 6UT
Tel: ... 01332 299449; 01332 368585 (Minicom)
Fax: 01332 365055
Email: .... info@disabilitydirectderby.co.uk

Devon

**PLYMOUTH AND DISTRICT DISABLED
FELLOWSHIP**
Astor Hall, 157 Devonport Road, Stoke, Plymouth,
Devon PL1 5RB
Tel: 01752 562729

ST LOYE'S FOUNDATION
Brittany House, New North Road, Exeter, Devon
EX4 4EP
Tel: 01392 286286
Fax: 01392 420889
Email: .... info@stloyes.ac.uk

Dorset

DISABILITY ACTION
Christchurch Hospital, Fairmile Road,
Christchurch, Dorset BH23 2JX
Tel: 01202 705496
Fax: 01202 477914

Essex

DIAL BASILDON & SOUTH ESSEX
The Basildon Centre, St Martin's Square,
Basildon, Essex SS14 1DL
Tel: 01268 294400
Fax: 01268 294495
Email: .... enquiries@dialbasildon.co.uk

Gloucestershire

**NEWENT ASSOCIATION FOR THE
DISABLED**
Sheppard House, Onslow Road, Newent,
Gloucestershire GL18 1TL
Tel: 01531 821227
Fax: 01531 820078

Greater Manchester

**BURY & DISTRICT DISABLED ADVISORY
COUNCIL**
Seedfield Resource Centre, Parkinson Street,
Bury, Greater Manchester BL9 6NY
Tel: 0161 253 6888
Email: .... info@baddac.org.uk

DISABILITY STOCKPORT
16 Meyer Street, Cale Green, Stockport, Greater
Manchester SK3 8JE
Tel: .. 0161 480 7248; 0161 480 7248 (Minicom)
Fax: 0161 480 7248
Email: .... email@disabilitystockport.org.uk

Hertfordshire

**DISABILITY INFORMATION SERVICE FOR
HERTFORDSHIRE (D.I.S.H.)**
PO Box 979, St Albans, Hertfordshire AL1 9JF
Tel: .... 0800 181 067 (Helpline)
Email: .... info@dish.uk.net

**HERTFORDSHIRE ACTION ON
DISABILITY**
The Woodside Centre, The Commons, Welwyn
Garden City, Hertfordshire AL7 4DD
Tel: 01707 324581
Fax: 01707 371297
Email: .... info@hadnet.org.uk

Isle of Man

**MANX FOUNDATION FOR THE
PHYSICALLY DISABLED**
Masham Court, Victoria Avenue, Douglas, Isle of
Man IM2 4AW
Tel: 01624 628926
Fax: 01624 670821

Kent

DIAL
9a Gorrell Road, Whitstable, Kent CT5 1RN
Tel: 01227 771155; 01227 771645
Fax: 01227 772631

DIAL NORTH WEST KENT
7 The Hives, Northfleet, Kent DA11 9DE
Tel: 01474 356962
Email: .... info@dialnwk.org.uk

Kingston upon Hull

COUNCIL OF DISABLED PEOPLE
35 Ferensway, Hull, Kingston upon Hull HU2 8NA
Tel: 01482 326140
Fax: 01482 588482

Lancashire

DIAL WEST LANCASHIRE
49 Westgate, Sandy Lane, Skelmersdale,
Lancashire WN8 8LP
Tel: 0800 220 676

Lincolnshire

CLUB 87 FOR THE YOUNGER DISABLED
The Old Orchard, Davy's Lane, Bracebridge
Heath, Lincoln, Lincolnshire LN4 2NB
Tel: 01522 527583

DISABILITY LINCS
Ancaster Day Centre, Boundary Street, Lincoln,
Lincolnshire LN5 8NJ
Tel: 01522 870602
Email: .... enquiries@disabilitylincs.org.uk

London

ACTION DISABILITY KENSINGTON & CHELSEA
ADKC Centre, Whitstable House, Silchester Road,
London W10 6SB
Tel: .... 020 8960 8888; 020 8964 8066 Minicom
Fax: 020 8960 8282
Email: .... adkc@adkc.org.uk

ADVOCACY CONCERNS
Willesden Centre for Healthcare, Robson Avenue,
London NW10 3SG
Tel: 020 8459 1493

DISABILITY IN CAMDEN (DISC)
58 Phoenix Road, London NW1 1EU
Tel: 020 7387 1466; 020 7383 4775
Email: .... info@discnwl.org.uk

FITZGIBBON ASSOCIATES
Omnibus Business Centre, 39-41 North Road,
London N7 9DP
Tel: 0845 111 6543

HAMMERSMITH & FULHAM ACTION ON DISABILITY (HAFAD)
Greswell Centre, Greswell Street, London
SW6 6PX
Tel: 020 7471 8510
Fax: 020 7610 9786
Email: .... info@hafad.org.uk

HARINGEY CONSORTIUM OF DISABLED PEOPLE AND CARERS
551B High Road Tottenham, London N17 6SB
Tel: 020 8801 5757; 020 8801 9576
Email: .... director.hcdc@btconnect.com

SOUTHWARK DISABLEMENT ASSOCIATION
Aylesbury Day Centre, Room 48, 2 Bradenham
Close, London SE17 2QB
Tel: 020 7701 1391
Fax: 020 7277 0481
Email: .... sda@dircon.co.uk

Merseyside

WIRED - WIRRAL INFORMATION RESOURCE FOR EQUALITY & DISABILITY
Wirral Business Centre, Arrowbrook Road, Wirral,
Merseyside SH 49 1SX
Tel: .. 0151 670 1500; 0151 670 0777 (Helpline);
0151 653 3230 Minicom
Email: .... contact@wired.me.uk

Middlesex

LONDON BOROUGH OF HARROW SOCIAL SERVICES DEPARTMENT
Civic Centre, Station Road, Harrow, Middlesex
HA1 2XF
Tel: 020 8863 5611

Norfolk

CENTRE 81
Tarworks Road, Great Yarmouth, Norfolk
NR30 1QR
Tel: 01493 852573
Email: .... admin@centre81.com

HAND
38a Bull Close, Magdalen Street, Norwich, Norfolk
NR3 1SX

North Yorkshire

DIAC YORK
Room 2, Nursery Block, Priory Street Centre, 17
Priory Street, York, North Yorkshire Y01 6ET
Tel: 01904 638467
Fax: 01904 010200

DISABILITY ACTION YORKSHIRE
Unit i4A, Hornbeam Park Oval, Harrogate, North
Yorkshire HG2 8RB
Tel: 01423 855410
Email: .... fundraising@da-y.org.uk

SCARBOROUGH AND DISTRICT DISABLEMENT ACTION GROUP
Allatt House, 5 West Parade Road, Scarborough,
North Yorkshire YO12 5ED
Tel: ... 01723 379397; 01723 379397 (Minicom)
Fax: 01723 379397
Email: .... scardag@onyxnet.co.uk

Northumberland

BERWICK BOROUGH DISABILITY FORUM
Voluntary Centre, 5 Tweed Street, Berwick-upon-
Tweed, Northumberland TD15 1NG
Tel: 01289 308888
Fax: 01289 308366

BLYTH VALLEY DISABLED FORUM
20 Stanley Street, Blyth, Northumberland
NE24 2BU
Tel: 01670 360927
Fax: 01670 361900

DISABILITY ASSOCIATION
Austin House, 11 Sandersons Arcade, Morpeth,
Northumberland NE61 1NS
Tel: 01670 504488

NORTHUMBRIAN CALVERT TRUST
Kielder Water, Hexham, Northumberland
NE48 1BS
Tel: 01434 250232
Fax: 01434 250015

Nottinghamshire

DISABILITY NOTTINGHAMSHIRE
1 Byron Street, Mansfield, Nottinghamshire
NG18 5NX
Tel: ... 01623 625891; 01623 656556 (Minicom)
Fax: 01623 427753
Email: .. advice@disabilitynottinghamshire.org.uk

**DISABLED PEOPLE'S ADVOCACY:
NOTTINGHAMSHIRE**
Voluntary Action Centre, 7 Mansfield Road,
Nottingham, Nottinghamshire NG1 3FB
Tel: 0115 934 9504

South Gloucestershire

COUNCIL FOR THE DISABLED
c/o Kingswood Borough Council, Civic Centre,
High Street, Kingswood, Thornbury, South
Gloucestershire BS15 2TR

South Yorkshire

DIAL
9 Doncaster Road, Barnsley, South Yorkshire
S70 1TH
Tel: 01226 240273
Fax: 01226 287269
Email: .... dialbarnsley2@hotmail.com

DIAL (DONCASTER)
Shaw Wood Business Park, Shaw Wood Way,
Doncaster, South Yorkshire DN2 5TB
Tel: ... 01302 327800; 01302 768297 (Minicom)
Fax: 01302 327205
Email: .... advice@dialdoncaster.co.uk

**FEDERATION FOR THE DISABLED SELF-
HELP GROUPS**
Five Arches Community Centre, Penrith Road,
Shirecliffe, Sheffield, South Yorkshire S5 8UA

Suffolk

DIAL
Waveney Centre for Independent Living, 161
Rotterdam Road, Lowestoft, Suffolk NR32 2EZ
Tel: 01502 511333
Email: .... info@dialnet.f2s.com

DISABLED ADVICE BUREAU
Room 11, 19 Tower Street, Ipswich, Suffolk
IP1 3BE
Tel: 01473 217313
Fax: 01473 288123
Email: .... dab.ipswich@btopenworld.com

OPTUA
Optua House, Hill View Business Park, Claydon,
Ipswich, Suffolk IP6 0AJ
Tel: .. 01473 836777; 01473 836779 (Textphone)
Fax: 01473 836778
Email: .... enquiries@optua.org.uk

Surrey

**ACCESS GROUP GUILDFORD
(FORMERLY GUILDFORD ACCESS FOR
THE DISABLED)**
c/o Guildford Borough Council, Millmead House,
Millmead, Guildford, Surrey GU2 4BB
Tel: 01483 444056
Fax: 01483 444109

DISABILITY INITIATIVE SERVICES LTD
Resource Centre, Knoll Road, Camberley, Surrey
GU15 3SY
Tel: 01276 676302
Fax: 01276 673200
Email: .... info@disabilityinitiative.org.uk

DISABILITYCROYDON
Room 2.07, Strand House, Zion Road, Thornton
Heath, Surrey CR7 8RG
Tel: 020 8684 5538
Fax: 020 8689 3414
Email: .... info@disabilitycroydon.org.uk

Tyne & Wear

**CITY OF SUNDERLAND COUNCIL FOR
THE DISABLED**
100 Norfolk Street, Sunderland, Tyne & Wear
SR1 1EA
Tel: 0191 514 3346

**NORTH TYNESIDE DISTRICT DISABILITY
FORUM**
The Shiremoor Centre, Earsdon Road, Shiremoor,
North Shields, Tyne & Wear NE27 9HJ
Tel: 0191 200 8570
Fax: 0191 200 8570
Email: .... info@ntdf.co.uk

Warwickshire

DIAL
New Ramsden Centre, School Walk,
Attleborough, Nuneaton, Warwickshire CV11 4PJ
Tel: 024 7634 9954
Fax: 024 7632 8867
Email: .... enquiries@nbdial.com

West Midlands

CARES
The Carers Centre, 2 Bearwood Road,
Smethwick, West Midlands B66 4HH
Tel: 0121 558 7003
Fax: 0121 558 7229

**COUNCIL OF DISABLED PEOPLE
(WARWICKSHIRE & COVENTRY)**
Room 6, Koco Building, Unit 15, The Arches
Industrial Estate, Spon End, Coventry, West
Midlands CV1 3JQ
Tel: 01926 889349; 01926 889349
Email: .... info@cdp.org.uk

DISABLED ASSOCIATION
7 Albion Street, Brierley Hill, West Midlands
DY5 3EE

FELLOWSHIP OF THE DISABLED
9 Wingate Road, Bentley, Walsall, West Midlands
WS2 0AS

**FELLOWSHIP OF THE PHYSICALLY
HANDICAPPED**
3 Avon House, Peak Drive, Gornal, Dudley, West
Midlands DY3 2BY

**VOLUNTARY ASSOCIATION FOR THE
PHYSICALLY HANDICAPPED**
1 Barns Lane, Rushall, West Midlands WS4 1HQ

WEST MIDLANDS FAMILY PLACEMENT SERVICES
Trinity House, Trinity Road, Dudley, West
Midlands DY1 1JB
Tel: 01384 458585
Email: .... wmfp@barnardos.org.uk

West Sussex

VOICE FOR DISABILITY
7 St. John's Parade, Allinora Crescent, Goring,
West Sussex BN12 4HJ
Tel: 01903 2444457
Email: .... info@wsad.org.uk

West Yorkshire

DIAL (LEEDS)
The Mary Thornton Suite, Armley Grange Drive,
Leeds, West Yorkshire LS12 3QH
Tel: . 0113 214 3630; 0113 214 3627 (Textphone)
Fax: 0113 214 3628
Email: .... dial.leeds@btconnect.com

DIAL (WAKEFIELD)
Highfield House Resource Centre, Love Lane,
Castleford, Wakefield, West Yorkshire WF10 5RT
Tel: 01977 723933/4; 01977 724 081 (Textphone)
Fax: 01977 724 081
Email: .... advice@dialwakefield.co.uk

KEIGALEY DISABLED PEOPLE'S CENTRE
Temple Row Centre, 23 Temple Row, Keighley,
West Yorkshire BD21 2AH
Tel: 01535 606700

Wiltshire

WESSEX REHABILITATION ASSOCIATION
Glanville Centre, Salisbury District Hospital,
Salisbury, Wiltshire SP2 8BJ
Tel: .... 01722 336262 ext. 4057
Fax: 01722 325904

NORTHERN IRELAND

Belfast

PHABLINE
24-26 North Street Arcade, Belfast BT1 1PB

NORTHERN IRELAND - RADAR MEMBERS

ROYAL NATIONAL INSTITUTE FOR DEAF PEOPLE
Portside Business Park, 189 Airport Road West,
Belfast BT3 9ED
Tel: . 028 9029 7880; 028 9029 7882 (Textphone)
Fax: 028 9029 7881
Email: .... hq@disabilityaction.org

SCOTLAND - NON RADAR MEMBERS

East Dunbartonshire

CONTACT POINT IN EAST DUNBARTONSHIRE
The Park Centre, 45 Kerr Street, Kirkintilloch, East
Dunbartonshire G66 1LF
Tel: . . 0141 578 0183; 0141 578 0183 (Minicom)
Fax: 0141 578 0183
Email: .... contactp@yahoo.com

Edinburgh

GRAPEVINE LOTHIAN DISABILITY INFORMATION SERVICE
Norton Park Centre, 57 Albion Road, Edinburgh
EH7 5QY
Tel: . . 0131 475 2370; 0131 475 2370 (Minicom)
Fax: 0131 475 2392
Email: .... lcil@lothiancil.org.uk

Falkirk

DUNDAS DISABILITY INFORMATION SERVICE
Falkirk Council, Oxgangs Road, Grangemouth,
Falkirk FK3 9EF

Glasgow

CAREPARTNERS
154-156 Raeberry Street, Maryhill, Glasgow
G20 6EA

Renfrewshire

DISABILITY RESOURCE CENTRE (PAISLEY)
74 Love Street, Paisley, Renfrewshire PA3 2EA
Tel: 0141 848 1123
Fax: 0141 842 1075

Scottish Borders

THE BRIDGE
6a Roxburgh Street, Galashiels, Scottish Borders
TD1 1PF
Tel: 01896 755370

WALES - NON RADAR MEMBERS

Rhondda Cynon Taff

LLANTRISANT AND DISTRICT DIAL
Ambulance Hall, Pontyclun, Llan Harry, Rhondda
Cynon Taff CF7 8HY
Tel: 01443 237937

RACIAL EQUALITY COUNCILS

Racial Equality Councils (RECs), formerly known as Community Relations Councils, are autonomous, voluntary organisations. RECs work to eliminate racial discrimination and to promote equality of opportunity between different racial and ethnic groups.

Members of RECs are drawn from statutory and voluntary bodies, ethnic minority organisations and individuals who support their aims. RECs can advise individual complainants of their rights under the Race Relations Act 1976 and provide information and assistance to organisations on developing and implementing equal opportunity policies.

For more information go to www.bforec.co.uk

ENGLAND

Bournemouth

DORSET RACE EQUALITY COUNCIL
Suite 3, 4th Floor Richmond House, 33 Richmond Hill, Bournemouth BH2 6EZ
Tel: 01202 553003
Email: .... enquiries@dorsetrec.org.uk

Buckinghamshire

AYLESBURY VALE EQUALITY & HUMAN RIGHTS COUNCIL
c/o Bucks County Council, Old County Hall, Aylesbury, Buckinghamshire HP20 1UA
Tel: 01296 425334
Fax: 01296 425334
Email: .... avrec@ukonline.co.uk

Cambridgeshire

CAMBRIDGE ETHNIC COMMUNITY FORUM (CECF)
62-64 Victoria Road, Cambridge, Cambridgeshire CB4 3DU
Tel: 01223 315877
Fax: 01223 315877
Email: .... cecf.enquiries@cecf.co.uk

Cheshire

CHESHIRE HALTON & WARRINGTON REC
92 Watergate Street, Chester, Cheshire CH1 2LF
Tel: 01244 400730
Fax: 01244 400722
Email: .... office@chawrec.org.uk

Essex

BARKING & DAGENHAM REC
Unit 2, 30 Thames Road, Barking, Essex IG11 0HZ
Tel: 020 8594 2773
Email: .... bardag-rec@yahoo.co.uk

Greater Manchester

BOLTON EQUALITIES CENTRE
Office Unit 4, Bolton Market, Ashburner Street, Bolton, Greater Manchester BL1 1TQ
Tel: 01204 331002
Fax: 01204 331046
Email: .... boltonrec@boltonrec.org.uk

Kent

MEDWAY HUMAN RIGHTS & EQUALITY COUNCIL
Gun Wharf, 3rd Floor, Dock Road, Chatham, Kent ME4 4TR
Tel: 01634 333880
Email: .... mrec@hotmail.co.uk

Lancashire

PRESTON & WESTERN LANCASHIRE REC
Town Hall Annexe, Birley Street, Preston, Lancashire PR1 2RL
Tel: 01772 906422
Fax: 01772 906685
Email: .... admin@prestonrec.org.uk

Leicestershire

HUMAN RIGHTS & EQUALITIES CHARNWOOD
66 Nottingham Road, Loughborough, Leicestershire LE11 1EU
Tel: 01509 261651
Fax: 01509 267826
Email: .... info@ humanrightsandequalitiescharnwood.org

THE RACE EQUALITY CENTRE IN LEICESTER AND LEICESTERSHIRE
3rd Floor, Epic House, Lower Hill Street, (off Charles Street), Leicester, Leicestershire LE1 3SH
Tel: 0116 299 9800
Fax: 0116 299 9801
Email: . administrator@theraceequalitycentre.org.uk

London

EALING REC
The Lido Centre, 63 Mattock Lane, Ealing, London
W13 9LA
Tel: 020 8579 3861
Fax: 020 8280 2257
Email: .... info@ealingrec.org.uk

ENFIELD REC
Community House, 311 Fore Street, Edmonton,
London N9 0PZ
Tel: 020 8373 6271
Fax: 020 8373 6281
Email: .... info@enfieldrec.org.uk

HARINGEY REC
14 Turnpike Lane, London N8 0PT
Tel: 020 8889 6871
Fax: 020 8889 6455
Email: .... info@haringeyrec.org.uk

WALTHAM FOREST REC
Community Place, 806 High Road, Leyton,
London E10 6AE
Tel: 020 8279 2425
Fax: 020 8279 2496
Email: .... info@wfrec.org.uk

Middlesex

HOUNSLOW REC
45 Treaty Centre, Hounslow, Middlesex TW3 1ES
Tel: 020 8572 5532
Fax: 020 8583 5603
Email: .... info@hounslowrec.co.uk

Northamptonshire

NORTHAMPTONSHIRE REC
Victoria Centre, Palk Road, Wellingborough,
Northamptonshire NN8 1HT
Tel: 01933 278000
Fax: 01933 272409
Email: .... info@northamptonshirerec.org.uk

Oxfordshire

OXFORDSHIRE REC
The Old Court House, Floyds Row, St Aldates,
Oxford, Oxfordshire OX1 1SS
Tel: 01865 791891
Fax: 01865 726150
Email: .... patrick@oxrec.org

Reading

**READING COUNCIL FOR RACIAL
EQUALITY**
1 St Giles Court, off Southampton Street, Reading
RG1 2QL
Tel: 0118 951 0279
Email: .... rajinder@rcre.co.uk

Somerset

SOMERSET REC
PO Box 75, Somerton, Somerset TA11 9AR
Tel: 01458 274200
Email: .... info@srec.org.uk

Suffolk

**IPSWICH & SUFFOLK COUNCIL FOR
RACIAL EQUALITY**
46A St Matthew's Street, Ipswich, Suffolk IP1 3EP
Tel: 01473 408111; 01473 400082
Fax: 0879 900 4218
Email: .... office@iscre.org.uk

Surrey

**KINGSTON RACE & EQUALITIES
COUNCIL (KREC)**
Neville House, 55 Eden Street, Kingston upon
Thames, Surrey KT1 1BW
Tel: 020 8547 2332
Email: .... enquiries@kingstonrec.org

SUTTON REC
2 Grove Cottage, Grove Park High Street, Grove
Park, Carshalton, Surrey SM5 3BB
Tel: 020 8770 6199
Fax: 020 8770 6198
Email: .... admin@suttonrec.org.uk

Warwickshire

**WARWICKSHIRE RACE EQUALITY
PARTNERSHIP**
10 Hamilton Terrace, Leamington Spa,
Warwickshire CV32 4LY
Tel: 0844 800 9900
Email: .... info@wrep.org.uk

West Midlands

CENTRE FOR EQUALITY & DIVERSITY
10A Stone Street, Dudley, West Midlands
DY1 1NS
Tel: 01384 456166
Fax: 01384 861010
Email: .... admin@cfed.org.uk
Web: .... http://www.cfed.org.uk

Wiltshire

WILTSHIRE REC
Bridge House, Stallard Street, Trowbridge,
Wiltshire BA14 9AE
Tel: 01225 766439
Email: .... wiltsrec@gmail.com

Worcestershire

WORCESTERSHIRE REC
Queen Elizabeth House, The Trinity, Worcester,
Worcestershire WR1 2PW
Tel: 01905 29283
Fax: 01905 29317
Email: .... wrec@hotmail.co.uk

SCOTLAND

Edinburgh

EDINBURGH & LOTHIANS REC
14 Forth Street, Edinburgh EH1 3LH
Tel: 0131 556 0441
Fax: 0131 556 8577
Email: .... admin@lrec.org.uk

Glasgow

WEST OF SCOTLAND RACIAL REC
Napiershall Street Centre, 39 Napiershall Street,
Glasgow G20 6EZ
Tel: 0141 337 6626
Email: . . . . admin@wsrec.co.uk

WALES

Newport

SOUTH EAST WALES REC
137 Commercial Street, Newport NP20 1LN
Tel: 01633 250006
Fax: 01633 264075
Email: . . . . info@sewrec.org.uk

Swansea

SWANSEA BAY REC
Third Floor, Grove House, Grove Place, Swansea
SA1 5DF
Tel: 01792 457035
Fax: 01792 459374
Email: . . . . beverley@sbrec.org.uk

VOLUNTEER CENTRES

Volunteer Centres are local agencies whose main purpose is to match up would-be volunteers with suitable opportunities and promote good practice in volunteering. They provide training and support as required and help develop new opportunities for volunteering in their communities. Volunteer Centres are unique in that their primary concern is with the well-being of volunteers, rather than the organisations they assist.

Volunteer Centres keep information on the entire range of local volunteer opportunities, from those with well-known national organisations (e.g. Samaritans) to small local agencies and individuals. The trained staff at the bureau will spend time discussing your interests and experience, to help pinpoint the opportunities which would be best for you.

To take the first step, phone or drop in at your local Volunteer Centre. If possible, you will be seen immediately, otherwise you will be asked to make an appointment to call back. Either way, the staff will spend as much time as needed trying to ensure that your experience of voluntary work is a positive one, both for you and the organisation that you assist.

For further information contact:
Volunteering England, Regent's Wharf, 8 All Saints Street, London N1 9RL Tel: 020 7713 6161
Email: ncvo@ncvo-vol.org.uk Web: www.volunteering.org.uk;
Volunteer Development Scotland, Jubilee House, Forthside Way, Stirling FK8 1QZ
Tel: 01786 479593 Fax: 01786 849767 Web: www.vds.org.uk; or
Volunteer Development Agency - Northern Ireland, 129 Ormeau Road, Belfast BT7 1SH Tel: 028 9023 2020
Email: ormeau@volunteernow.co.uk Web: www.volunteernow.co.uk

ENGLAND

Bedfordshire

VOLUNTEER CENTRE BEDFORD
43 Bromham Road, Bedford, Bedfordshire
MK40 2AA
Tel: 01234 213100
Fax: 01234 347503

Bracknell Forest

BRACKNELL FOREST VOLUNTARY ACTION
BFVA, Ground Floor, Amber House, Market Street, Bracknell, Bracknell Forest RG12 1JB
Tel: 01344 304404

Brighton & Hove

IMPETUS
Intergen House, 65-67 Western Road, Hove, Brighton & Hove BN3 2JQ
Tel: 01273 737888
Fax: 01273 711537

Bristol

VOLUNTEER BRISTOL
Royal Oak House, Royal Oak Avenue, Bristol
BS1 4GB
Tel: 0117 989 7733
Fax: 0117 922 1749

Buckinghamshire

COMMUNITY IMPACT BUCKINGHAMSHIRE
Unit B The Firs, Bierton, Aylesbury, Buckinghamshire HP22 5DX
Tel: 0845 3890389

VOLUNTEER CENTRE WYCOMBE DISTRICT
11 Priory Road, High Wycombe, Buckinghamshire HP13 6SL
Tel: 01494 451700
Fax: 01494 523247
Email: . . . . . wycombevb@volunteerfocus.org.uk

Cambridgeshire

CAMBRIDGE VOLUNTEER CENTRE
Llandaff Chambers, 2 Regent Street, Cambridge, Cambridgeshire CB2 1AX
Tel: 01223 356549

FENLAND VOLUNTEER BUREAU
Queen Mary Centre, Queens Road, Wisbech, Cambridgeshire PE13 2PE
Tel: 01945 582192

PETERBOROUGH COUNCIL FOR VOLUNTARY SERVICE
3 Lincoln Court, Lincoln Road, Peterborough, Cambridgeshire PE1 2RP
Tel: 01733 311016; 01733 342683
Fax: 01733 559057

Cheshire

CHESTER VOLUNTARY ACTION
Folliott House, 53 Northgate Street, Chester,
Cheshire CH1 2HQ
Tel: 01244 316587

CONGLETON VOLUNTEER BUREAU
54 Lawton Street, Congleton, Cheshire
CW12 1RS
Tel: 01260 299022
Fax: 01260 299022

(CREWE & NANTWICH VB) NANTWICH BRANCH
Nantwich Office, Beam Street, Nantwich, Cheshire
CW5 5DE
Tel: . . . . All Enquiries to the Main Office

CREWE & NANTWICH VOLUNTARY ACTION
Ashton House, 1a Gatefield Street, Crewe,
Cheshire CW1 2JP
Tel: 01270 211545
Fax: 01270 211545
Email: . . . . enquiries@cvce.org.uk

CVS CHESHIRE EAST
81 Park Lane, Macclesfield, Cheshire SK11 6TX
Fax: 01625 619101

HALTON & ST HELEN'S VOLUNTARY & COMMUNITY ACTION
Sefton House, Public Hall Street, Runcorn,
Cheshire WA7 1NG
Tel: 01928 592405
Fax: 01928 568713
Email: . . . . info@haltonsthelensvca.org.uk

HALTON YOUNG VOLUNTEERS BUREAU
Information Shop for Young People, 2 Frederick
Street, Widnes, Cheshire WA8 6PG
Tel: 0151 420 7888
Fax: 0151 429 7555

(MACCLESFIELD CVS VB) KNUTSFORD BRANCH
St John's Wood Millenium Community Centre,
Longridge, Knutsford, Cheshire WA16 8PA
Tel: 01565 652538
Fax: 01565 652538

VOLUNTEER CENTRE WARRINGTON
9 Suez Street, Warrington, Cheshire WA1 1EF
Tel: 01925 637609
Fax: 01925 232070

Co. Durham

2D (SUPPORT FOR THE VOLUNTARY AND COMMUNITY SECTOR OF TEESDALE & WEAR VALLEY)
Unit 9, Crook Business Centre, New Road, Crook,
Co. Durham DL15 8QX
Tel: 01388 762220
Fax: 01388 762225

DERWENTSIDE CVS & VOLUNTEER BUREAU
The Tommy Amstrong Centre, Clifford Road,
Stanley, Co. Durham DH9 0XG
Tel: 01207 218855
Fax: 01207 218849

DURHAM ASSOCIATION OF YOUTH AND COMMUNITY ORGANISATIONS (D.A.Y.C.O.)
Thornley Community Association, Hartlepool
Street North, Hartlepool, Co. Durham DH6 3AB
Tel: 01429 821311

EASINGTON & DISTRICT VOLUNTEER BUREAU
13 Upper Yoden Way, Peterlee, Co. Durham
SR8 1AX
Tel: 0191 586 5427

EVOLUTION DARLINGTON
Church Row, Darlington, Co. Durham DL1 5QD
Tel: 01325 266888
Fax: 01325 266899

HARTLEPOOL VOLUNTARY DEVELOPMENT AGENCY
Rockhaven, 36 Victoria Road, Hartlepool, Co.
Durham TS26 8DD
Tel: 01429 262641
Fax: 01429 265056
Email: . . . . info@hvda.co.uk

Cornwall

(CORNWALL CFV) BUDE BRANCH
Neetside, The Crescent, Bude, Cornwall
EX23 8LB
Tel: 01288 352700
Fax: 01288 352700

(CORNWALL CFV) NORTH CORNWALL BRANCH
1 Hamley Court, Dennison Road, Bodmin,
Cornwall PL31 2LL
Tel: 01208 79565

(CORNWALL CFV) VOLUNTEER CENTRE CARADON
Shop B, 6 Church Street, Liskeard, Cornwall
PL14 3AG
Tel: 01579 344818
Fax: 01579 344818

(PENWITH VB) HAYLE BRANCH
Unit 4 Foundry House, Foundry Square, Hayle,
Cornwall TR27 4HH
Tel: 01736 757364
Fax: 01736 757086

PENWITH VOLUNTEER BUREAU
Parade Street, Penzance, Cornwall TR18 4BU
Tel: 01736 330988
Fax: 01763 334688

RESTORMEL VOLUNTEER CENTRE CORNWALL REST FOR VOLUNTEERS
17 Duke Street, St Austell, Cornwall PL25 5PQ
Tel: 01726 71087

VOLUNTEER CORNWALL
Acorn House, Heron Way, Newham, Truro,
Cornwall TR1 2XN
Tel: 01872 265305

Cumbria

WEST CUMBRIA VOLUNTEER CENTRE
12a Selby Terrace, Maryport, Cumbria CA15 6NF
Tel: 01900 819191

Derbyshire

AMBER VALLEY CVS VOLUNTEER BUREAU
Market Place, Ripley, Derbyshire DE5 3HA
Tel: 01773 512076
Fax: 01773 748688

CHESTERFIELD & NE DERBYSHIRE VOLUNTEER CENTRE
35 Rose Hill, Chesterfield, Derbyshire S40 1TT
Tel: 01246 276777
Fax: 01246 276777
Email: .... info@chesterfieldvc.org.uk

EREWASH CVS VOLUNTEER CENTRE
Springfield House, 4/5 Granby Street, Ilkeston, Derbyshire DE7 8HN
Tel: 0115 850 8860
Fax: 0115 930 9191
Email: .... enquiries@erewashcvs.org.uk

GLOSSOP & DISTRICT VOLUNTEER BUREAU
Howard Town House, High Street East, Glossop, Derbyshire SK13 8DA
Tel: 01457 865722
Fax: 01457 891425
Email: .... info@gvb.org.uk

NEW MILLS AND DISTRICT VOLUNTEER CENTRE
33-35 Union Road, High Peak, New Mills, Derbyshire SK22 3EL
Tel: 01663 744196

VOLUNTEER CENTRE BUXTON & DISTRICT
16 Eagle Parade, Buxton, Derbyshire SK17 6EQ
Tel: 01298 23970
Fax: 01298 70713

VOLUNTEER CENTRE DERBYSHIRE DALES
Ashbourne Business Centre, Dig Street, Ashbourne, Derbyshire DE6 1GF
Tel: 01335 348602

Devon

CREDITON & DISTRICT VOLUNTEER CENTRE
The Old Surgery, 55 The High Street, Crediton, Devon EX17 3JX
Tel: 01363 777711

DAWLISH & EAST TEIGNBRIDGE VOLUNTEER BUREAU
The Manor, Old Town Street, Dawlish, Devon EX7 9AW
Tel: 01626 888321
Fax: 01626 888321

INVOLVE - VOLUNTARY ACTION IN MID DEVON
Raymond Penny House, Phoenix Lane, Tiverton, Devon EX16 6LU
Tel: 01884 255734
Fax: 01884 232198

NORTH DEVON VOLUNTEERING DEVELOPMENT AGENCY
149 High Street, Ilfracombe, Devon EX34 9EZ
Tel: 01271 866300

TEIGNBRIDGE VOLUNTEER CENTRE
Forde House, Brunel Road, Newton Abbot, Devon TQ12 4XX
Tel: 01626 215902
Email: .... funding@teigncvs.org.uk

(TORRIDGE VB) HOLSWORTHY BRANCH
Holsworth Volunteer Centre, Unit 1, Manor Court, Victoria Square, Holsworthy, Devon EX22 6AA
Tel: 01409 254484
Fax: 01409 254484

(TORRIDGE VB) TORRINGTON BRANCH
1st Floor, Castle Hill, South Street, Torrington, Devon EX38 8AA
Tel: 01805 626123

WEST DEVON COMMUNITY AND VOLUNTARY SERVICES
The Carlton Centre, St James Street, Okehampton, Devon EX20 1DW
Tel: 01837 53392
Fax: 01837 55047

WEST DEVON CVS & VOLUNTEER CENTRE
5 King Street, Tavistock, Devon PL19 0DS
Tel: 01822 618230

Dorset

DORCHESTER VOLUNTEER BUREAU
1 Colliton Walk, Dorchester, Dorset DT1 1TZ
Tel: 01305 269214

ISLAND VOLUNTEERS FOR YOU (IVY)
19 Easton Street, Portland, Dorset DT5 1BS
Tel: 01305 823789
Email: .... island.volunteers@virgin.net

VOLUNTEER CENTRE DORSET
1 Colliton Walk, Dorchester, Dorset DT1 1TZ
Tel: 01305 269214

East Riding of Yorkshire

EAST RIDING (CENTRAL) CVS VOLUNTEER BUREAU
Morley's House, Morley's Yard, Walkergate, Beverley, East Riding of Yorkshire HU17 9BY
Tel: 01482 871077
Email: .... office@ervas.org.uk

East Sussex

EASTBOURNE ASSOCIATION OF VOLUNTARY SERVICES (EAVS)
8 Saffrons Road, Eastbourne, East Sussex BN21 1DG
Tel: 01323 639373
Fax: 01323 410977
Email: .... eastbourneinfo@3va.org.uk

HASTINGS VOLUNTARY ACTION
Jackson Hall, Portland Place, Hastings, East Sussex TN34 1QN
Tel: 01424 446060
Email: .. infoworker@hastingsvoluntaryaction.org

PEACEHAVEN & TELSCOMBE VOLUNTEER BUREAU
43 Longridge Avenue, Saltdean, East Sussex BN2 8LG
Tel: 01273 390408
Fax: 01273 390408

SUSSEX DOWNS CVS VOLUNTEER CENTRE
66 High Street, Lewes, East Sussex BN7 1XG
Tel: 01273 470108
Email: .... lewesinfo@3va.org.uk

UCKFIELD VOLUNTEER & INFORMATION CENTRE
Unit 3, 79 High Street, Uckfield, East Sussex TN22 1AS
Tel: 01825 760019
Email: .... uvic@btconnect.com

Essex

BARKING & DAGENHAM VOLUNTEER BUREAU
Unit 6, St George's Day Centre, St George's Road, Dagenham, Essex RM9 5JB
Tel: 020 8227 5464
Fax: 020 8227 5448
Email: .... bardagvb@hotmail.co.uk

BASILDON, BILLERICAY AND WICKFORD CVS VOLUNTEER BUREAU
The George Hurd Centre, Audley Way, Basildon, Essex SS14 2FL
Tel: 01268 294124
Fax: 01268 534845
Email: .... admin@bbwcvs.org.uk

CASTLE POINT VOLUNTEERS BUREAU
The Tyrells Centre, 39 Seamore Avenue, Thundersley, Benfleet, Essex SS7 4EX
Tel: 01268 638416
Fax: 01268 638415

CHELMSFORD AGENCY FOR VOLUNTEERING
2nd Floor, 59 New Street, Chelmsford, Essex CM1 1NE
Tel: 01245 283606
Fax: 01245 283607

CLACTON & DISTRICT VOLUNTEER BUREAU
Imperial House, 22 Rosemary Road, Clacton-on-Sea, Essex CO15 1NZ
Tel: 01255 427888

COLCHESTER VOLUNTEER CENTRE
15 Church Walk, Colchester, Essex CO1 1NS
Tel: 01206 768930

HANDS AND GILLINGHAM VOLUNTEER BUREAU
Cranford House, 24a Longley Road, Rainham, Essex ME8 7RY
Tel: 01634 830371
Fax: 01634 264464

MALDON CVS VOLUNTEER BUREAU
The Square, Holloway Road, Heybridge, Maldon, Essex CM9 4ER
Tel: 01621 851891
Fax: 01625 851896

SOUTHEND VOLUNTEER BUREAU
SAVS Centre, 29-31 Alexandra Street, Southend-on-Sea, Essex SS1 1BW
Tel: 01702 356060
Fax: 01702 356011

VOLUNTARY ACTION EPPING FOREST
Homefield House, Civic Offices Site, High Street, Epping, Essex CM16 4BZ
Tel: 01992 564256
Fax: 01992 564254
Email: .... admin@vaef.org.uk

VOLUNTEER CENTRE UTTLESFORD
Saffron Walden Community Hospital, Radwinter Road, Saffron Walden, Essex CB11 3HY
Tel: 01799 513626
Fax: 01799 522788

Gloucestershire

CHELTENHAM VOLUNTEER CENTRE
Sandford Park Offices, College Road, Cheltenham, Gloucestershire GL53 7HX
Tel: 01242 257727
Fax: 01242 700076
Email: enquiries@volunteeringcheltenham.org.uk

COTSWOLD COUNCIL FOR VOLUNTARY SERVICE
The Volunteer Centre, 23 Sheep Street, Cirencester, Gloucestershire GL7 1QW
Tel: 01285 658802

COTSWOLD COUNCIL FOR VOLUNTARY SERVICE (FAIRFORD CENTRE)
3 London Street, Fairford, Gloucestershire GL7 4AH
Tel: 01285 713852

FOREST VOLUNTARY ACTION FORUM
Rheola House, Belle Vue Centre, Cinderford, Gloucestershire GL14 2AB
Tel: 01594 822073
Fax: 01594 822073
Email: .... info@svas.org.uk

GLOUCESTER ASSOCIATION FOR VOLUNTARY AND COMMUNITY ACTION
75-81 Eastgate Street, Gloucester, Gloucestershire GL1 1PN
Tel: 01452 332424
Fax: 01452 332131
Email: .... volunteering@gavca.org.uk

(VCA) DURSLEY VOLUNTEER CENTRE
Community Shop, 24 Parsonage Street, Dursley, Gloucestershire GL11 4AA
Tel: 01453 548801
Fax: 01453 548801

VOLUNTEER & COMMUNITY ACTION
The Old Town Hall, The Shambles, High Street, Stroud, Gloucestershire GL5 1AP
Tel: 01453 759005
Fax: 01453 765147

Greater Manchester

BOLTON VOLUNTEER BUREAU
64 St Georges Road, Bolton, Greater Manchester BL1 2DD
Tel: 01204 380692
Fax: 01204 362141

BURY CVS
6 Tenterden Street, Bury, Greater Manchester BL9 0EG
Tel: 0161 4478454
Fax: 0161 761 5881

CVSR
Sparrow Hill, Rochdale, Greater Manchester
OL16 1QT
Tel: 01706 631291
Fax: 01706 710769

VOLUNTEER CENTRE SALFORD
The Old Town Hall, off Irwell Place, Eccles,
Salford, Greater Manchester M30 0EJ
Tel: 0161 707 7067
Fax: 0161 789 0818

VOLUNTEER CENTRE TAMESIDE
95-97 Penny Meadow, Ashton-under-Lyne,
Greater Manchester OL6 6EP
Tel: 0161 339 2345
Fax: 0161 343 7527

WIGAN & LEIGH CVS
93 Church Street, Leigh, Greater Manchester
WN7 1AZ
Tel: 01942 514234
Fax: 01942 514352
Email: .... info@cvswl.org

Hampshire

BASINGSTOKE CCS VOLUNTEER BUREAU
The Orchard, White Hart Lane, Basingstoke,
Hampshire RG21 4AF
Tel: 01256 423850
Fax: 01256 423825
Email: .. sarah.robinson@voluntaryservices.com

COMMUNITY FIRST NEW FOREST (FORMERLY NEW FOREST VOLUNTARY SERVICE COUNCIL)
Public Offices, 65 Christchurch Road, Ringwood,
Hampshire BH24 1DH
Tel: 01425 482773
Fax: 01425 482666
Email: .... admin@cfnf.org.uk

EAST HAMPSHIRE VOLUNTEER BUREAU (BORDON BRANCH)
St. Mark's Church, Forest Centre, Bordon,
Hampshire GU35 0TN
Tel: 01420 475 536

GOSPORT VOLUNTEER CENTRE
Martin Snape House, 96 Pavilion Way, Gosport,
Hampshire PO12 1FG
Tel: 023 9258 8347
Fax: 023 9260 4684

HART VOLUNTEER BUREAU
Civic Offices, Harlington Way, Fleet, Hampshire
GU51 4AE
Tel: 01252 815652
Email: ... voluntarybureau@hartvolaction.org.uk

HAVANT VOLUNTEER CENTRE
Havant Council or Community Service, 47 Market
Parade, Havant, Hampshire PO9 1PY
Tel: 023 9248 1845
Fax: 023 9278 2300
Email: .... volunteering@havantccs.org.uk

VOLUNTEER CENTRE EASTLEIGH
One Community, 16 Romsey Road, Eastleigh,
Hampshire SO50 9AL
Tel: 023 8090 2457
Fax: 023 8090 2413
Email: .... volunteer@1community.org.uk

VOLUNTEER CENTRE TEST VALLEY (ANDOVER BRANCH)
2nd Floor, East Wing, Wessex Chambers, South
Street, Andover, Hampshire SP10 2BN
Tel: 01264 362600
Fax: 01264 353010
Email: .... volunteers@tvcs.org.uk

VOLUNTEER CENTRE WINCHESTER
The Winchester Centre, 68 St Georges's Street,
Winchester, Hampshire SO23 8AH
Tel: 01962 848030
Fax: 01962 848029

Herefordshire

HAY & DISTRICT COMMUNITY SUPPORT
Oxford Road, Hay on Wye, Hereford,
Herefordshire HR3 5AL
Tel: 01497 821031
Fax: 01497 821094

HEREFORDSHIRE VOLUNTARY ACTION
Berrows Business Centre, Bath Street, Hereford,
Herefordshire HR1 2HE
Tel: 01432 343932
Fax: 01432 343932

LEDBURY & DISTRICT VOLUNTEER BUREAU
Salters Yard, Bye Street, Ledbury, Herefordshire
HR8 2AA
Tel: 01531 635339
Fax: 01531 636333

Hertfordshire

(DACORUM VB) BERKHAMSTED BRANCH
Berkhamsted Civic Centre, 161-166 High Street,
Berkhamsted, Hertfordshire HP4 3HB
Tel: 01442 228933

ROYSTON & DISTRICT VOLUNTEER CENTRE
Royston Hospital, London Road, Royston,
Hertfordshire SG8 9EN
Tel: 01763 243020
Email: .... info@roystonvolunteer.org.uk

ST ALBANS VOLUNTEER CENTRE
31 Catherine Street, St Albans, Hertfordshire
AL3 5BJ
Tel: 01727 852657; 01727 852656
Fax: 01727 852656
Email: .... enquiries@cvsstalbans.org.uk

VOLUNTEER CENTRE BROXBOURNE & EAST HERTS
Silverline House, 1-3 Albury Grove Road,
Cheshunt, Hertfordshire EN8 8NS
Tel: 01992 638633
Fax: 01992 638644

VOLUNTEER CENTRE DACORUM
The Roundhouse, Marlowes, Hemel Hempstead,
Hertfordshire HP1 1BT
Tel: 01442 247209; 01442 214734

THE VOLUNTEER CENTRE HERTSMERE
Allum Lane Community Centre, Allum Lane,
Elstree, Hertfordshire WD6 3PJ
Tel: 020 8207 4504
Fax: 020 8207 1467

VOLUNTEER CENTRE THREE RIVERS
Basing House, 46 High Street, Rickmansworth, Hertfordshire WD3 1HP
Tel: 01923 711174

VOLUNTEER CENTRE WATFORD
149 The Parade, Watford, Hertfordshire WD17 1RH
Tel: 01923 248304
Fax: 01923 213377
Email: .... volunteering@watfordcvs.net

WELWYN HATFIELD CVS VOLUNTEER BUREAU
40 Town Centre, Hatfield, Hertfordshire AL10 0JJ
Tel: 01707 274861

Isle of Wight

ISLAND VOLUNTEERS
39 Quay Street, Newport, Isle of Wight PO30 5BA
Fax: 01983 527333

Kent

CANTERBURY & HERNE BAY VOLUNTEER CENTRE
Tower Works, Simmonds Road, Canterbury, Kent CT1 3RA
Tel: 01227 452278
Fax: 01227 768546

COMMUNITY LINKS BROMLEY
Community House, South Street, Bromley, Kent BR1 1RH
Tel: 020 8315 1900
Fax: 020 8315 1924
Email: ... admin@communitylinksbromley.org.uk

DOVER DISTRICT VOLUNTEERING CENTRE
26 Victoria Road, Deal, Kent CT14 7BJ
Tel: 01304 367898

DOVER DISTRICT VOLUNTEERING CENTRE
26 Victoria Road, Deal, Kent CT14 7BJ
Tel: 01304 367898
Fax: 01304 367898

HANDS ROCHESTER VOLUNTEER CENTRE
5a New Road Avenue, Chatham, Kent ME4 6BB
Tel: 01634 830371
Email: .... rochestervb@pcihosting.co.uk

MALLING AREA VOLUNTEER CENTRE
18 Twisden Road, East Malling, Maidstone, Kent ME19 6SA
Tel: 01732 843346
Fax: 01732 845647

NEW ASH GREEN VOLUNTEER CENTRE
Youth Centre, Ash Road, New Ash Green, Kent DA3 8JY
Tel: 01474 879168

SHEPWAY VOLUNTEER CENTRE
URC Community Centre, Castle Hill Avenue, Folkestone, Kent CT20 2QL
Tel: 01303 253339

SWALE CVS
Central House, Central Avenue, Sittingbourne, Kent ME10 4NU
Tel: 01795 473828
Fax: 01795 599220

THANET VOLUNTEER BUREAU
Forresters Hall, Meeting Street, Ramsgate, Kent CT11 9RT
Tel: 01843 590935; 01843 597115

TONBRIDGE VOLUNTEER BUREAU
3 St Mary's Road, Tonbridge, Kent TN9 2LD
Tel: 01732 357978
Fax: 01732 363050

TUNBRIDGE WELLS & DISTRICT VOLUNTEER BUREAU
Wood House, Wood Street, Tunbridge Wells, Kent TN1 2QS
Tel: 01892 540131
Fax: 01892 511627

VOLUNTARY ACTION MAIDSTONE
39-48 Marsham Street, Maidstone, Kent ME14 1HH
Tel: 01622 677337
Fax: 01622 757134

NORTH WEST VOLUNTARY CENTRE
33 Essex Road, Dartford, Kent DA1 2AU
Tel: 01322 272476
Fax: 01322 291102

NORTH WEST VOLUNTARY CENTRE
45 Windmill Street, Gravesham, Gravesend, Kent DA12 1BA
Tel: 01474 322729
Fax: 01474 333001

VOLUNTEER CENTRE BEXLEY
8 Brampton Road, Bexleyheath, Kent DA7 4EY
Tel: 020 8304 0911
Fax: 020 8298 9583
Email: .... bexleyvc@bvsc.co.uk

VOLUNTEER CENTRE SEVENOAKS
34 Buckhurst Avenue, Sevenoaks, Kent TN13 1LZ
Tel: 01732 454785
Fax: 01732 465878
Email: .... volunteering@vawk.org.uk

VOLUNTEER CENTRE SWANLEY & DISTRICT
Library and Information Centre, London Road, Swanley, Kent BR8 7AE
Tel: 01322 669292; 0845 2412180

WHISTABLE VOLUNTEER CENTRE
St Mary's Hall, Oxford Street, Whitstable, Kent CT5 1DD
Tel: 01227 772248
Fax: 01227 771095
Email: .... manager@whitstablevc.org.uk

Kingston upon Hull

HULL CVS: VOLUNTEER CENTRE HULL
29 Anlaby Road, Hull, Kingston upon Hull HU1 2PG
Tel: 01482 324474
Fax: 01482 580565

Lancashire

BLACKPOOL VOLUNTEERING CENTRE
57 Cookson Street, Blackpool, Lancashire
FY1 3DR
Tel: 01253 627173
Email: . . . . blackpoolvc3@yahoo.co.uk

HYNDEBURN & RIBBLE VALLEY CVS
1 Swan Mews, Off Castle Street, Clitheroe,
Lancashire BB7 2BX
Tel: 01200 422721
Fax: 01200 423656
Email: . . . . dorothyshears@
hyndeburnandribblevalleycvs.org

WEST LANCASHIRE CVS VOLUNTEER BUREAU
Ecumenical Centre, Northway, Skelmersdale,
Lancashire WN8 6LU
Tel: 01695 733737
Fax: 01695 558073

Leicestershire

(COALVILLE & DISTRICT CVS VB) ASHBY BRANCH
Ivanhoe Community College, North Street, Ashby,
Leicestershire LE65 1HX

(COALVILLE AND DISTRICT CVS VB) ASHBY, MEASHAM, AND MOIRA BRANCHES
17 Ashby Road, Moira, Leicestershire DE12 6DJ
Tel: 01283 551261
Fax: 01283 552251

(COSBY, BLABY & DISTRICT) NARBOROUGH BRANCH
Narborough Parish Centre, Narborough,
Leicestershire LE9 5EL

LUTTERWORTH & BROUGHTON ASTLEY VC (BROUGHTON ASTLEY BRANCH)
The Community Cabin, 38a Main Street,
Broughton Astley, Leicestershire LE9 6RD

NORTH WEST LEICESTERSHIRE VOLUNTEER CENTRE
The Marlene Reid Centre, 85 Belvoir Road,
Coalville, Leicestershire LE67 3PH
Tel: 01530 510515
Fax: 01530 814632

VOLUNTARY ACTION FOR OADBY & WIGSTON
132a Station Road, Wigston, Leicestershire
LE18 2DL
Tel: 0116 281 0026

VOLUNTARY ACTION HINCKLEY & BOSWORTH
12 Waterloo Road, Hinckley, Leicestershire
LE10 0QJ
Tel: 01455 615962
Fax: 01455 615962

VOLUNTARY ACTION LEICESTER
9 Newarke Street, Leicester, Leicestershire
LE1 5SN
Tel: 0116 258 0666
Fax: 0116 257 5059
Email: . . . . info@valonline.org.uk

VOLUNTARY ACTION SOUTH LEICESTERSHIRE
The Settling Rooms, St Mary's Place, Springfield
Street, Market Harborough, Leicestershire
LE16 7DR
Tel: 01858 432014
Fax: 01858 410047

VOLUNTEER CENTRE - BLABY DISTRICT
Parker House, 254 Braunstone Lane, Braunstone,
Leicestershire LE3 3AS
Tel: 0116 223 8338
Fax: 0116 223 8339
Email: . . . . info@volunteerblabydistrict.org.uk

VOLUNTEER CENTRE LUTTERWORTH
One Stop Shop, Wycliffe House, Gilmorton Road,
Lutterworth, Leicestershire LE17 4DY
Tel: 01455 555570
Email: . . . . info.luttvc@onestopshop.org.uk

VOLUNTEER CENTRE SHEPSHED
9a Charnwood Road, Shepshed, Leicestershire
LE12 9QE
Tel: 01509 508040
Fax: 01509 508040

Lincolnshire

BOSTON & DISTRICT VOLUNTEER CENTRE
The Len Medlock Voluntary Centre, St George's
Road, Boston, Lincolnshire PE21 8YB
Tel: 01205 365588
Fax: 01205 315903

KESTEVEN VOLUNTARY ACTION
26-27 St Catherine's Road, Grantham,
Lincolnshire NG31 6TT

LOUTH AREA VOLUNTARY CENTRE (MABLETHORPE)
The Interagency Building, Stanley Avenue,
Mablethorpe, Lincolnshire LN12 2AP
Tel: 01507 479632

NORTH KESTEVEN CVS LTD
Annex B, Eslaforde Centre, 1 Kesteven Street,
Sleaford, Lincolnshire NG34 7DT
Tel: 01529 415417
Fax: 01529 415438

SOUTH LINK CVS
The Len Medlock Voluntary Centre, St Georges
Road, Boston, Lincolnshire PE21 8YB
Tel: 01205 365580
Fax: 01205 315903

VOLUNTARY CENTRE SERVICES WEST LINDSEY
Unit 9, The Lindsey Centre, Gainsborough,
Lincolnshire DN21 2BT
Tel: 01427 613470
Fax: 01427 613470
Email: . . info@voluntarysupportwestlindsey.org.uk

VOLUNTEER CENTRE LINCOLN
The Voluntary Sector Hub, Beaumont Fee,
Lincoln, Lincolnshire LN1 1UW
Tel: 01522 551683
Fax: 01522 551684
Email: . . . . info@info@vcslincoln.org.uk

VOLUNTEER CENTRE NORTH KESTEVEN
26 Carre Street, Sleaford, Lincolnshire NG34 7TR
Tel: 01529 308450
Fax: 01529 419084
Email: . . . . info@volunteercentrenk.org.uk

London

ENFIELD VOLUNTARY ACTION
Community House, 311 Fore Street, London
N9 0PZ
Tel: 020 8373 6348
Fax: 020 8373 6267
Email: . . . . admin@enfieldva.org.uk

HACKNEY VOLUNTARY ACTION
92 Dalston Lane, Hackney, London E8 1NG
Tel: 020 7241 4443
Fax: 020 7241 0043

**HAMMERSMITH & FULHAM VOLUNTEER
CENTRE**
148 King Street, Hammersmith, London W6 0QU
Tel: 020 8741 9876
Fax: 020 8741 3344

ISLINGTON VOLUNTEER CENTRE
6-9 Manor Gardens, Islington, London N7 6LA
Tel: 020 7686 6800; 020 7833 9691
Fax: 020 7686 6805

VOLUNTEER CENTRE CAMDEN
293-299 Kentish Town Road, Camden, London
NW5 2TJ
Tel: 020 7424 9990
Fax: 020 7284 0049
Email: volunteercentrecamden@camdenvb.org.uk

VOLUNTEER CENTRE GREENWICH
The Forum at Greenwich, Trafalgar Road,
Greenwich, London SE10 9EQ
Tel: 020 8853 1331

**VOLUNTEER CENTRE KENSINGTON &
CHELSEA**
Canalside House, 383 Ladbroke Grove, London
W10 5AA
Tel: 020 8960 3722
Fax: 020 8960 3750

VOLUNTEER CENTRE TOWER HAMLETS
Norvin House, 1st Floor, 45-55 Commercial Street,
Tower Hamlets, London E1 6BD
Tel: 020 7377 0956
Fax: 020 7426 9979
Email: . . . . info@towerhamlets.org.uk

VOLUNTEER CENTRE WANDSWORTH
170 Garratt Lane, Wandsworth, London
SW18 4DA
Tel: 020 8870 4319
Fax: 020 8871 3502

VOLUNTEER CENTRE WESTMINSTER
53-55 Praed Street, London W2 1NR
Tel: 020 7402 8076
Fax: 020 7402 3124
Email: . . . info@volunteercentrewestminster.org.uk

THE VOLUNTEER NETWORK CENTRE
Emmanuel Parish Church, Romford Road, London
E7 8BD
Tel: 020 8221 4514
Email: . . . . . . gurdialbharma@vncnewham.co.uk

Merseyside

VOLUNTEER CENTRE LIVERPOOL
7th Floor, Gosdins Building, 32-36 Hanover Street,
Liverpool, Merseyside L1 4LN
Tel: 0151 707 1113
Fax: 0151 709 5006

VOLUNTEER CENTRE SEFTON
3rd Floor, Merseyside 3TC Centre, 16 Crosby
Road North, Waterloo, Liverpool, Merseyside
L22 0NY
Tel: 0151 920 0726
Fax: 0151 920 1036

VOLUNTEER CENTRE SEFTON
Top Floor, Shakespeare Centre, Shakespeare
Street, Southport, Merseyside PR8 5AB
Tel: 01704 501024
Fax: 01704 531192

WIRRAL CVS VOLUNTEER CENTRE
46 Hamilton Square, Birkenhead, Merseyside
L41 5AR
Tel: 0151 647 5432
Fax: 0151 647 5432

Middlesex

**BINGHAM VB (WEST BRIDGEFORD &
DISTRICT VB BRANCH)**
Harlequin House, 7 High Street, Teddington,
Middlesex TW11 8EL

HOUNSLOW VOLUNTEER BUREAU
45 Treaty Centre, High Street, Hounslow,
Middlesex TW3 1ES
Tel: 020 8570 5083
Fax: 020 8570 5083

Milton Keynes

VOLUNTEER CENTRE MILTON KEYNES
Acorn House, 383 Midsummer Boulevard, Central
Milton Keynes, Milton Keynes MK9 3HP
Tel: 01908 662744
Fax: 01908 395757

Norfolk

FAKENHAM COMMUNITY SERVICES
Community Health Services, Fakenham Medical
Practice, Greenaway Lane, Fakenham, Norfolk
NR21 8ET
Tel: 01328 862751
Fax: 01328 864225

VOLUNTARY NORFOLK
83-87 Pottergate, Norwich, Norfolk NR2 1DZ
Tel: 01603 614474
Fax: 01603 764109
Email: . . . . admin@voluntarynorfolk.org.uk

VOLUNTARY NORFOLK
The Market Surgery, 26 Norwich Road, Aylsham,
Norfolk NR11 6BW
Tel: 01263 731478
Email: . . . . aylshamvsc@voluntarynorfolk.org.uk

**VOLUNTARY NORFOLK
(ATTLEBOROUGH BRANCH)**
Attleborough Health Centre, Station Road,
Attleborough, Norfolk NR17 2AS
Tel: 01953 456643
Fax: 01953 456644

VOLUNTARY NORFOLK (BOWTHORPE BRANCH)
Bowthorpe Health Centre, Wendene, Norwich, Norfolk NR5 9HA
Fax: 01603 741615

VOLUNTARY NORFOLK (BRUNDALL BRANCH)
Brundall Health Centre, The Dales, The Street, Brundall, Norwich, Norfolk NR13 5RP
Tel: 01603 712255

VOLUNTARY NORFOLK (CROMER BRANCH)
Benjamin Court, Intensive Service Centre, Roughton Road, Cromer, Norfolk NR27 0EU
Tel: 01263 517989
Fax: 01263 517984
Email: ...... cromervsc@voluntarynorfolk.org.uk

VOLUNTARY NORFOLK (DISS BRANCH)
The Health Centre, Mount Street, Diss, Norfolk IP22 4WG
Tel: 01379 644513
Fax: 01379 640324
Email: .... dissvsc@voluntarynorfolk.org.uk

VOLUNTARY NORFOLK (EAST DEREHAM BRANCH)
Dereham Hospital, Northgate, Dereham, Norfolk NR19 2EX
Tel: 01362 692391
Fax: 01362 695457
Email: . eastderehamvsc@voluntarynorfolk.org.uk

VOLUNTARY NORFOLK (LAWSON ROAD BRANCH)
Lawsom Road Health Centre, Lawson Road, Norwich, Norfolk NR3 4LE
Tel: 01603 428104
Fax: 01603 483395

VOLUNTARY NORFOLK LONG STRATTON BRANCH
Long Stratton Health Centre, Flowerpot Lane, Long Stratton, Norfolk NR15 2TS
Tel: 01508 531175
Email: .. longstrattonvsc@voluntarynorfolk.org.uk

VOLUNTARY NORFOLK (NORTH WALSHAM BRANCH)
North Walsham Hospital, Yarmouth Road, North Walsham, Norfolk NR28 9AP
Tel: 01692 408314
Fax: 01692 407688

VOLUNTARY NORFOLK (THETFORD BRANCH)
Riversdale, Tanner Street, Thetford, Norfolk IP24 2BQ
Tel: 01842 761377

VOLUNTARY NORFOLK (THORPE ST ANDREW)
The Health Centre, Williams Loke, St Williams Way, Norwich, Norfolk NR7 0AJ
Tel: 01603 430205
Fax: 01603 701855

VOLUNTARY NORFOLK (WYMONDHAM BRANCH)
Wymondham Health Centre, 18 Bridewell Street, Wymondham, Norfolk NR18 0AR
Tel: 01953 606201
Fax: 01953 609428
Email: . wymondhamvsc@voluntarynorfolk.org.uk

WEST NORFOLK VOLUNTARY & COMMUNITY ACTION
16 Tuesday Market Place, King's Lynn, Norfolk PE30 1JN
Tel: 01553 760568
Fax: 01553 774399
Email: .... info@westnorfolkvca.org

North East Lincolnshire

NORTH EAST LINCOLNSHIRE VOLUNTEER CENTRE
14 Town Hall Street, Grimsby, North East Lincolnshire DN31 1HN
Tel: 01472 231123
Fax: 01472 231122
Email: .... volunteer@vanel.org.uk

North Somerset

VOLUNTARY ACTION NORTH SOMERSET
The Badger Centre, 3-6 Wadham Street, Weston-super-Mare, North Somerset BS23 1JY
Tel: 01934 410192
Fax: 01934 410199
Email: .... enquiries@vansweb.org.uk

North Yorkshire

BEDALE VOLUNTARY CENTRE
Bedale Hall, Bedale, North Yorkshire DL8 1AA
Tel: 01677 425329

HARROGATE & AREA VOLUNTEER CENTRE
Community House, 46-50 East Parade, Harrogate, North Yorkshire HG1 5RR
Tel: 01423 509004
Fax: 01423 502126
Email: .... volunteer@harrogate.org

MIDDLESBOROUGH COUNCIL FOR VOLUNTARY DEVELOPMENT
New Exchange Building, Middlesbrough, North Yorkshire TS1 2AA
Tel: 01642 225158
Fax: 01642 247409

RICHMONDSHIRE VOLUNTEER CENTRE
6 Flints Terrace, Richmond, North Yorkshire DL10 7AH
Tel: 01748 822335
Fax: 01748 822335

RIPON CVS VOLUNTEER CENTRE
Sharow View, Allhallowgate, Ripon, North Yorkshire HG4 1LE
Tel: 01765 603631
Fax: 01765 645923

RYEDALE CVA VOLUNTEER ACTION
Ryedale Community House, Wentworth Street, Malton, North Yorkshire YO17 7BN
Tel: 01653 600120
Fax: 01653 695377

**STOKESLEY AND DISTRICT CCA
VOLUNTEER CENTRE**
The Community Care Association, Town Close,
North Road, Stokesley, North Yorkshire TS9 5DH
Tel: 01642 710085

THIRSK VOLUNTEER CENTRE
14a Market Place, Thirsk, North Yorkshire
YO7 1LB
Tel: 01845 523115
Fax: 01845 526332

VOLUNTEER BUREAU OF CRAVEN
1st Floor Office, 27 Newmarket Street, Skipton,
North Yorkshire BD23 2JE
Tel: 01756 701648
Fax: 01756 701611
Email: . . . . info@cravenva.org.uk

VOLUNTEERING HAMBLETON
Community House, 10 South Parade,
Northallerton, North Yorkshire DL7 8SE
Tel: 01609 780458
Fax: 01609 770570

YORK CVS VOLUNTEER CENTRE
15 Priory Street, York, North Yorkshire YO1 6ET
Tel: 01904 621133
Fax: 01904 630361

Northamptonshire

CORBY VOLUNTEER BUREAU
The TA Building, Elizabeth Street, Corby,
Northamptonshire NN17 1PN
Tel: 01536 267873
Fax: 01536 267884

DAVENTRY VOLUNTEER CENTRE
The Library, North Street, Daventry,
Northamptonshire NN11 4GH
Tel: 01327 300614
Email: . . . . info@daventryvolunteers.org.uk

NORTHAMPTON VOLUNTEER CENTRE
15 St Giles Street, Northampton,
Northamptonshire NN1 1JA
Tel: 01604 637522
Fax: 01604 601221

OUNDLE VOLUNTEER ACTION
The Old Market Hall, Market Place, Oundle,
Northamptonshire PE8 4BA
Tel: 01832 275433

**SOUTH NORTHANTS VOLUNTEER
BUREAU**
The Volunteer Centre, Moat Lane, Towcester,
Northamptonshire NN12 6AD
Tel: 01327 358264
Fax: 01327 358428

**VOLUNTEER CENTRE
WELLINGBOROUGH**
1-3 Orient Way, Wellingborough,
Northamptonshire NN8 1AF
Tel: 01933 276933
Fax: 01933 223660
Email: . . . info@wellingborough-volunteers.org.uk

Northumberland

**NORTH NORTHUMBERLAND
VOLUNTARY ACTION**
Bondgate Centre, 22 Bondgate, Alnwick,
Northumberland NE66 1PN

TYNEDALE VOLUNTARY ACTION
Hexham Community Centre, Gilesgate, Hexham,
Northumberland NE46 3NP
Tel: 01434 601201
Fax: 01434 606201

**WANSBECK CENTRE FOR VOLUNTARY
SERVICE**
107 & 109 Station Road, Ashington,
Northumberland NE63 8RS
Tel: 01670 858688
Fax: 01670 784160

Nottinghamshire

**(BASSETLAW BCVS INVOLVE PROJECT)
RETFORD BRANCH**
Community Shop, 18 West Street, Retford,
Nottinghamshire DN22 6ES
Tel: 01777 709650

**BASSETLAW COMMUNITY & VOLUNTEER
SERVICE**
BCVS Dukeries Centre, Park Street, Worksop,
Nottinghamshire S80 1HH
Tel: 01909 476118
Fax: 01909 480501

EASTWOOD VOLUNTEER BUREAU
Wellington Place, Eastwood, Nottingham,
Nottinghamshire NG16 3GB
Tel: 01773 535255
Fax: 01773 537890

MANSFIELD VOLUNTEER CENTRE
Community House, 36 Wood Street, Mansfield,
Nottinghamshire NG18 1QA
Tel: 01623 651177
Fax: 01623 635258
Email: . . . . volunteer@mansfieldcvs.org

**(NEWARK & SHERWOOD VB)
FARNSFIELD BRANCH**
Farnsfield Village Centre, Lower Hall, New Hill,
Newark, Nottinghamshire NG22 8JM

**(NEWARK & SHERWOOD VB) WESTERN
DISTRICT BRANCH**
Bedehouse Chapel, Bedehouse Lane,
Barnbygate, Newark, Nottinghamshire NG24 1PU
Tel: 01636 707418
Fax: 01636 707418

OUR CENTRE
6 Pond Street, Kirkby-in-Ashfield, Nottinghamshire
NG17 7AH
Tel: 01623 753192
Fax: 01623 750469

RUSHCLIFFE VOLUNTEER CENTRE
Park Lodge, Bridgford Road, West Bridgford,
Nottinghamshire NG2 6AT
Tel: 0115 969 9060

STAPLEFORD CARE CENTRE
Church Street, Stapleford, Nottinghamshire
NG9 8DB
Tel: 0115 949 1175
Email: . . . . margaretsb@hotmail.co.uk

**SUTTON IN ASHFIELD VOLUNTEER
BUREAU**
The Old Police Station, Brook Street, Sutton-in-
Ashfield, Nottinghamshire NG17 1AL
Tel: 01623 515614
Fax: 01623 558255

VOLUNTEER CENTRE BROXTOWE
8 Chilwell Road, Beeston, Nottinghamshire
NG9 1EJ
Tel: 0115 917 8080

**WEST BRIDGFORD & DISTRICT
VOLUNTEER BUREAU**
Park Lodge, Bridgford Road, West Bridgford,
Nottinghamshire NG2 6AT
Tel: 0115 969 9060
Fax: 0115 974 8097

Oxfordshire

WEST OXFORDSHIRE VOLUNTEER LINK-UP
Methodist Church, 10 Wesley Walk, Witney,
Oxfordshire OX28 6ZJ
Tel: 01993 776277

Redcar & Cleveland

**REDCAR & CLEVELAND VOLUNTARY
DEVELOPMENT AGENCY**
Second Floor, Craighton House, Central Terrace,
Redcar, Redcar & Cleveland TS10 1DJ
Tel: 01642 440571
Fax: 01642 289177

Rutland

VOLUNTEER ACTION RUTLAND
Land's End Way, Oakham, Rutland LE15 6RB
Tel: 01572 722622

Shropshire

**NORTH SHROPSHIRE VOLUNTARY
ACTION**
c/o 3BC The Manse, Dodington, Whitchurch,
Shropshire SY13 1QT
Tel: 01948 667650
Fax: 01948 667651

OSWESTRY COMMUNITY ACTION
QUBE, Oswald Road, Oswestry, Shropshire
SY11 1RB
Tel: 01691 656882
Fax: 01691 680862

SHREWSBURY VOLUNTARY ACTION
Abbots House Courtyard, 13 Butcher Row,
Shrewsbury, Shropshire SY1 1UP
Tel: 01743 341700
Fax: 01743 244594

**SOUTH SHROPSHIRE VOLUNTEER
EXCHANGE**
2a Palmers House, 7 Corve Street, Ludlow,
Shropshire SY8 1DB
Tel: 01584 877756
Fax: 01584 876177

TELFORD VOLUNTEER DESK
Telford and Wrekin CVS, Meeting Point House,
Southwater Square, Town Centre, Telford,
Shropshire TF3 4HS
Tel: 01952 291350
Fax: 01952 290384

Slough

SLOUGH VOLUNTEER BUREAU
1st Floor, Kingsway URC, Slough SL1 1SZ
Tel: 01753 528632

Somerset

BRIDGWATER VOLUNTEER BUREAU
The Lions, West Quay, Bridgwater, Somerset
TA6 3HW
Tel: 01278 457685

TAUNTON DEANE VOLUNTEER BUREAU
Flook House, Belvedere Road, Taunton, Somerset
TA1 1BT
Tel: 01823 284470
Email: . . . . enquiries@tauntoncvs.org.uk

South Gloucestershire

**THORNBURY & DISTRICT VOLUNTEER
CENTRE**
The Town Hall, 35 High Street, Thornbury, South
Gloucestershire BS35 2AR
Tel: 01454 413392

VOLUNTEER CENTRE YATE
Yate Library, 44 West Walk, Yate, South
Gloucestershire BS37 4AX
Tel: 01454 324102

South Yorkshire

**BARNSLEY VOLUNTARY ADVISORY
SERVICE**
33 Queens Road, Barnsley, South Yorkshire
S71 1AN
Tel: 01226 295905
Fax: 01226 206580

DONCASTER CVS VOLUNTEER BUREAU
Units 5 & 6 Trafford Court, Doncaster, South
Yorkshire DN1 1PN
Tel: 01302 343300
Fax: 01302 365081

**VOLUNTARY ACTION SHEFFIELD
(INCLUDING VOLUNTEER CENTRE
SHEFFIELD)**
The Circle, 33 Rockingham Lane, Sheffield, South
Yorkshire S1 4FW
Tel: 0114 253 6600

Staffordshire

ADSIS
Alan Dean Centre, 23 Carter Street, Uttoxeter,
Staffordshire ST14 8EY
Tel: 01889 560550

**LICHFIELD & DISTRICT COMMUNITY AND
VOLUNTARY SECTOR SUPPORT**
Mansell House, 22 Bore Street, Lichfield,
Staffordshire WS13 6LL
Tel: 01543 303030
Fax: 01543 303034
Email: . . . . rosevakis@ldcvs.org.uk

STAFFORD VOLUNTEER CENTRE
Stafford District Voluntary Services, 131-141 North
Walls, Stafford, Staffordshire ST16 3AD
Tel: 01785 279934
Fax: 01785 606669

**STAFFORDSHIRE MOORLANDS
VOLUNTEER BUREAU**
Bank House, 20 St Edward Street, Leek,
Staffordshire ST13 5DS
Tel: 01538 398240

Suffolk

ALDEBURGH, LEISTON & SAXMUNDHAM VOLUNTEER CENTRE
Council Offices, 13 Main Street, Leiston, Suffolk
IP16 4ER
Tel: 01728 832829

THE BECCLES VOLUNTEER CENTRE
4-4a The Score, Northgate, Beccles, Suffolk
N34 7AR
Tel: 01502 710777

BURY ST EDMUNDS VOLUNTEER CENTRE LTD
86 Whiting Street, Bury St Edmunds, Suffolk
IP33 1NX
Tel: 01284 766126
Fax: 01284 760669

EYE & DISTRICT VOLUNTEER CENTRE
20 Broad Street, Eye, Suffolk IP23 7AF
Tel: 01379 871200

FELIXSTOWE VOLUNTEER CENTRE
108 Queens Road, Felixstowe, Suffolk IP11 7PG
Tel: 01394 284770

FRAMLINGHAM & DISTRICT VOLUNTEER CENTRE
10a Riverside, Framlingham, Suffolk IP13 9AG
Tel: 01728 621210

HAVERHILL & DISTRICT VOLUNTEER CENTRE
Haverhill Centre for Voluntary Agencies, Lower
Downs Slade, Haverhill, Suffolk CB9 9HB
Tel: 01440 708444
Fax: 01440 710670
Email: . . . . info@hvc.org.uk

IPSWICH & DISTRICT VOLUNTEER BUREAU
Room 32, 19 Tower Street, Ipswich, Suffolk
IP1 3BE
Fax: 01473 233599

STOWMARKET & DISTRICT VOLUNTEER CENTRE
Ipswich Road, Stowmarket, Suffolk IP14 1BE
Tel: 01449 612486

SUDBURY & DISTRICT VOLUNTEER CENTRE
The Christopher Centre, 10 Gainsborough Street,
Sudbury, Suffolk CO10 2EU
Tel: 01787 880711

VOLUNTEER CENTRE LOWESTOFT
15 Milton Road East, Lowestoft, Suffolk
NR32 1NT
Tel: 01502 562299
Fax: 01502 562299

Surrey

CATERHAM VOLUNTEER CENTRE
Soper Hall, Harestone Valley Road, Caterham,
Surrey CR3 6YN
Tel: 01883 344444

CROYDON VOLUNTEER CENTRE
2a Garnet Road, Thornton Heath, Surrey
CR7 8RD
Tel: 020 8684 2727
Fax: 020 8684 0171

FARNHAM VOLUNTEER CENTRE
Vernon House, 28 West Street, Farnham, Surrey
GU9 7DR
Tel: 01252 725961

GUILDFORD VOLUNTEERS' BUREAU
39 Castle Street, Guildford, Surrey GU1 3UQ
Tel: 01483 565456
Fax: 01483 304229

KINGSTON ON THAMES VOLUNTEER BUREAU
Siddeley House, 50 Canbury Park Road, Kingston
on Thames, Surrey KT2 6LX
Tel: 020 8225 8685
Fax: 020 8255 8804

(LINGFIELD & DORMANSLAND VB) OXTED BRANCH
Community Hub, 1st Floor, Oxted Library, 14
Gresham Road, Oxted, Surrey RH8 0BQ
Tel: 01883 722593

LINGFIELD & DORMANSLAND VOLUNTEER CENTRE
Lingfield Community Centre, High Street, Lingfield,
Surrey RH7 6AB
Tel: 01342 836774
Fax: 01342 836774
Email: . . . . lingfieldvc@btinternet.com

REIGATE & BANSTEAD CVS VOLUNTEER BUREAU
76 Station Road, Redhill, Surrey RH1 1PL
Tel: 01737 763156

REIGATE AND BANSTEAD VOLUNTEER BUREAU
The Help Shop, Victoria Square, Consort Way,
Horley, Surrey RH6 7AF
Tel: 01293 822677

RUNNYMEDE VOLUNTEER CENTRE
Unit 12-13, Sainsbury's Centre, Chertsey, Surrey
KT16 9AG
Tel: 01932 571122
Fax: 01932 566077

VOLUNTEER CENTRE CROYDON
2A Garnet Road, Thornton Heath, Surrey
CR7 8RD
Tel: 020 8684 2727
Fax: 020 8684 0171

VOLUNTEER CENTRE MERTON
The Vestry Hall, London Road, Mitcham, Surrey
CR4 3UD
Tel: 020 8640 7355
Fax: 020 8646 7549
Email: . . . . . . info@volunteercentremerton.org.uk

WOKING VOLUNTEER BUREAU
Provincial House, 26 Commercial Way, Woking,
Surrey GU21 6EN
Tel: 01483 751456
Fax: 01483 740929

Tyne & Wear

GATESHEAD VOLUNTEER BUREAU
John Haswell House, 8-9 Gladstone Terrace,
Gateshead, Tyne & Wear NE8 4DY
Tel: 0191 478 4103
Fax: 0191 477 1260

NORTH TYNESIDE VOLUNTARY ORGANISATIONS DEVELOPMENT AGENCY
The Shiremoor Centre, Earsdon Road, Shiremoor, Newcastle upon Tyne, Tyne & Wear NE27 0HJ
Tel: 0191 200 8555
Fax: 0191 200 8556
Email: . . . . admin@voda.org.uk

SOUTH TYNESIDE VOLUNTARY CENTRE
John Hunt House, 27 Beach Road, South Shields, Tyne & Wear NE33 2QA
Tel: 0191 456 9551
Fax: 0191 456 0603

Warwickshire

(NORTH WARWICKSHIRE VB) KINGSBURY BRANCH
Kingsbury Library, Bromage Avenue, Kingsbury, Warwickshire B78 2HN
Tel: . . . .   All Enquiries to the Main Office

STRATFORD-ON-AVON VOLUNTEER CENTRE
Suite 3, Arden Court, Arden Street, Stratford-on-Avon, Warwickshire CV37 6NT
Tel: 01789 262886

STRATFORD-ON-AVON VOLUNTEER CENTRE, ALCESTER BRANCH
Globe House, Priory Road, Alcester, Warwickshire B49 5DZ
Tel: 01789 763117

STRATFORD-ON-AVON VOLUNTEER CENTRE, SHIPSTON BRANCH
Medical Centre, Badgers Crescent, Shipston-on-Stour, Warwickshire CV36 4BQ
Tel: 01608 663122

STRATFORD ON AVON VOLUNTEER CENTRE, SOUTHAM BRANCH
The Grange, Coventry Road, Southam, Warwickshire CV33 0LY
Tel: 01926 817525

VOLUNTEER CENTRE NORTH WARWICKSHIRE
White Hart House, Long Street, Atherstone, Warwickshire CV9 1AX
Tel: 01827 717073
Email: . . . . info@vcnw.org.uk

VOLUNTEER CENTRE NUNEATON & BEDWORTH
4 School Road, Bulkington, Bedworth, Warwickshire CV12 9JB
Tel: 024 7631 5151
Fax: 024 7631 6799

VOLUNTEER CENTRE RUGBY
60 Regent Street, Rugby, Warwickshire CV21 2PS
Tel: 01788 561293

WARWICKSHIRE COMMUNITY & VOLUNTARY ACTION - WARWICK DISTRICT
The Town Hall, The Parade, Leamington Spa, Warwickshire CV32 4AL
Tel: 0845 051 1170
Fax: 01926 315112

West Berkshire

WEST BERKSHIRE VOLUNTEER CENTRE
1 Bolton Place, Northbrook Street, Newbury, West Berkshire RG14 1AJ
Tel: 01635 49004
Fax: 01635 524179

West Midlands

BIRMINGHAM VOLUNTEER CENTRE
138 Digbeth, Birmingham, West Midlands B5 6DR
Tel: 0121 678 8839
Fax: 0121 643 4541

DUDLEY CVS VOLUNTEER CENTRE
7 Albion Street, Brierley Hill, West Midlands DY5 3EE
Tel: 01384 573381
Fax: 01384 484587

VOLUNTEER CENTRE COVENTRY
c/o CVSC, 6th Floor, Coventry Point, Market Way, Coventry, West Midlands CV1 1EA
Tel: 024 7622 0381
Fax: 024 7625 7720
Email: . . . . info@volunteering-cov.org.uk

VOLUNTEER CENTRE SANDWELL
Municipal Buildings, Freeth Street, Oldbury, Warley, West Midlands B69 2AB
Tel: 0121 544 8326
Fax: 0121 544 3959

West Sussex

ADUR VOLUNTEER CENTRE
Chesham House, 124 South Street, Lancing, West Sussex BN15 8AJ
Tel: 01903 854985
Email: . . . . info@adurva.org

CRAWLEY VOLUNTEER CENTRE
The Orchard, 1-2 Gleneagles Court, Brighton Road, Crawley, West Sussex RH10 6AD
Tel: 01293 657145
Email: . . . . volbur@crawleycvs.org

EAST ARUN CVS VOLUNTEER BUREAU
The Dairy, 3-5 Church Street, Littlehampton, West Sussex BN17 5EL
Tel: 01903 731223
Fax: 01903 726229

EAST GRINSTEAD CVS
Old Court House, College Land, East Grinstead, West Sussex RH19 3LS
Tel: 01342 328080
Fax: 01342 324664

HORSHAM VOLUNTEER CENTRE
The Octagon, St Marks Court, Chart Way, Horsham, West Sussex RH12 1XL
Tel: 01403 232100

VOLUNTEER INFORMATION POINT, BURGESS HILL
38 Church Road, Burgess Hill, West Sussex RH15 9AE
Tel: 01444 870711

WORTHING VOLUNTEER CENTRE
Colonnade House, Warwick Street, Worthing, West Sussex BN11 3DH
Tel: 01903 528622
Email: . . . . worthingcvs@btconnect.com

West Yorkshire

KEIGHLEY VOLUNTEER CENTRE
8-10 North Street, Keighley, West Yorkshire
BD21 3SE
Tel: 01535 609506
Fax: 01535 609695

SHIPLEY & BINGLEY VOLUNTARY SERVICES
Cardigan House, Ferncliffe Road, Bingley, West Yorkshire BD16 2TA
Tel: 01274 781222
Fax: 01274 400050
Email: . . . . admin@sbvs.org.uk

VOLUNTARY ACTION KIRKLEES
15 Lord Street, Huddersfield, West Yorkshire
HD1 1QB
Tel: 01484 226608
Fax: 01484 518457

VOLUNTARY ACTION LEEDS
Stringer House, 34 Lupton Street, Hunslet, Leeds, West Yorkshire LS10 2QW
Tel: 0113 297 7931
Fax: 0113 297 7921

VOLUNTEERING BRADFORD
19-25 Sunbridge Road, Bradford, West Yorkshire
BD1 2AY
Tel: 01274 725434
Email: . . . . info@volunteeringbradford.org

Wiltshire

VOLUNTEER CENTRE SALISBURY
Greencroft House, 42-46 Salt Lane, Salisbury, Wiltshire SP1 1EG
Tel: 01722 421747
Email: . . . . info@wessexcommunityaction.org.uk

VOLUNTEER CENTRE SWINDON
1 John Street, Swindon, Wiltshire SN1 1RT
Tel: 01793 420557
Fax: 01793 420529

Windsor & Maidenhead

MAIDENHEAD VOLUNTEER BUREAU
Highview, 6 North Road, Maidenhead, Windsor & Maidenhead SL6 1PL
Tel: 01628 673937

WINDSOR & MAIDENHEAD VOLUNTEER CENTRE
67 St Leonards Road, Windsor, Windsor & Maidenhead SL4 3BX
Tel: 01753 622433

Wokingham

WOKINGHAM VOLUNTEER CENTRE
c/o The Old Social Club, Elms Road, Wokingham
RG40 2AA
Tel: 0118 977 0749

Worcestershire

BROMSGROVE & DISTRICT VOLUNTEER BUREAU
Britannic House, 13-15 Church Street, Bromsgrove, Worcestershire B61 8DD
Tel: 01527 577857
Fax: 01527 577857

DROITWICH SPA VOLUNTEER BUREAU
The Old Library Centre, 65 Ombersley Street East, Droitwich, Worcestershire WR9 8RA
Tel: 01905 795613

MALVERN VOLUNTEER CENTRE
The Volunteer Centre, Community Action, 29-30 Belle Vue Terrace, Malvern, Worcestershire
WR14 4PZ
Tel: 01684 580638

PERSHORE & DISTRICT VOLUNTARY HELP CENTRE
16 Priest Lane, Pershore, Worcestershire
WR10 1EB
Tel: 01386 554299
Fax: 01386 561107

VALE OF EVESHAM VOLUNTEER CENTRE
Wallace House, Oat Street, Evesham, Worcestershire WR11 4PJ
Tel: 01386 45035
Fax: 01386 40165

VOLUNTEER CENTRE - COMMUNITY ACTION WYRE FOREST
Burgage Lodge, 184 Franche Road, Kidderminster, Worcestershire DY11 5AD
Tel: 01562 862757
Fax: 01562 67008
Email: . . . . cvs@communityactionwf.org.uk

WORCESTER VOLUNTEER CENTRE
33 The Tything, Worcester, Worcestershire
WR1 1JL
Tel: 01905 24741
Fax: 01905 723688

NORTHERN IRELAND

Co. Antrim

VOLUNTARY SERVICE LISBURN
52a Bachelor's Walk, Lisburn, Co. Antrim
BT28 1XN
Tel: 028 9260 2479
Fax: 028 9260 5412

Co. Down

COALVILLE VOLUNTEER LINKS (MOIRA BRANCH)
17 Ashby Road, Moira, Co. Down DE12 6DJ
Tel: 01283 551261
Fax: 01283 552251

NEWRY CONFEDERATION OF COMMUNITY GROUPS
Ballybot House, 22 Cornmarket, Newry, Co. Down
BT35 8BG

Co. Londonderry

LONDONDERRY CHURCHES VOLUNTARY WORK BUREAU
22 Bishop Street, Londonderry, Co. Londonderry
BT48 6PP
Tel: 028 7127 1017
Fax: 028 7137 0859

SCOTLAND

Aberdeen

VOLUNTARY SERVICE ABERDEEN (VSA)
15a High Street, Inverurie, Aberdeen AB51 3QA
Tel: 01467 626060
Email: .... fundraising@vsa.org.uk

Aberdeenshire

VOLUNTEER CENTRE ABERDEENSHIRE
Head Office, 72a High Street, Banchory,
Aberdeenshire AB31 5SS
Tel: 01330 825794
Email: .... south@vcaberdeenshire.org.uk

Angus

VOLUNTEER CENTRE ANGUS
32-34 Guthrie Port, Arbroath, Angus DD11 1RN
Tel: 01241 875525

Dumfries & Galloway

VOLUNTEER ACTION DUMFRIES & GALLOWAY
24-26 Friars Vennel, Dumfries, Dumfries &
Galloway DG1 2RL
Tel: 01387 267311
Email: .... office@vb-dumfries.fsnet.co.uk

VOLUNTEER ACTION DUMFRIES & GALLOWAY
DAGAS, 23 Lewis Street, Stranraer, Dumfries &
Galloway DG9 7AB
Tel: 01776 707220
Email: ..... wigtownshire@volunteeraction.co.uk

VOLUNTEER ACTION DUMFRIES & GALLOWAY (ANNANDALE & ESKDALE BRANCH)
16 High Street, Annan, Lochmaben, Dumfries &
Galloway DG11 1NH
Tel: 01387 811571

Dundee

VOLUNTEER CENTRE DUNDEE
Number 10, 10 Constitution Road, Dundee
DD1 1LL
Tel: 01382 305705
Email: .... info@volunteerdundee.org.uk

East Ayrshire

VOLUNTEER CENTRE EAST AYRSHIRE
28 Grange Street, Kilmarnock, East Ayrshire
KA1 2DD
Tel: 01563 544765

East Dunbartonshire

VOLUNTEER CENTRE - EAST DUNBARTONSHIRE
Office 5, 10 Rochdale Place, Kirkintilloch, East
Dunbartonshire G66 1HZ
Tel: 0141 578 6680
Fax: 0141 578 6681
Email: .... admin@vced.org.uk

Edinburgh

VOLUNTEER CENTRE EDINBURGH
45 Queensferry Street Lane, Edinburgh EH2 4PF
Tel: 0131 225 0630
Email: ...... admin@volunteeredinburgh.org.uk

VOLUNTEER DEVELOPMENT EAST LOTHIAN
98 North High Street, Musselburgh, Edinburgh
EH21 6AS
Tel: 0131 665 3300
Email: .... info@vdel.co.uk

Falkirk

CVS FALKIRK & DISTRICT
Unit 6, The Courtyard, Callendar Business Park,
Callendar Road, Falkirk FK1 1XR
Tel: 01324 692000
Fax: 01324 692001
Email: .... info@cvsfalkirk.org.uk

Fife

VOLUNTEER CENTRE FIFE
29a Canmore Street, Dunfermline, Fife KY12 7NU
Tel: 01383 732136
Email: .... dunfermline@volunteeringfife.org

VOLUNTEER CENTRE FIFE
10 St Brycedale Avenue, Kirkcaldy, Fife KY1 1ET
Tel: 01592 645540
Fax: 01592 642713
Email: .... kirkcaldy@volunteeringfife.org

VOLUNTEER CENTRE FIFE
Volunteer House, 69-73 Crossgate, Cupar, Fife
KY15 5AS
Tel: 01334 659134
Fax: 01334 659134
Email: .... volunteeringfife@totalise.co.uk

VOLUNTEERING FIFE CENTRAL
232 High Street, Lower Methil, Leven, Fife
KY8 3EF
Tel: 01333 592225
Fax: 01333 592557

VOLUNTEERING FIFE DEVELOPMENT AGENCY
228 High Street
228 High Street, Kirkcaldy, Fife KY1 1LB
Email: .... volunteeringfifedev@supanet.com

Glasgow

THE VOLUNTEER CENTRE
84 Miller Street, 4th Floor, Glasgow G1 1DT
Tel: 0141 226 3431
Fax: 0141 221 0716
Email: .... info@volunteerglasgow.org

Highland

ROSS & CROMARTY VOLUNTEER CENTRE
The Gateway, 1A Millburn Road, Inverness,
Highland IV2 3PX
Tel: 01463 711393
Email: .. rossandcromarty@volunteeringhighland.org

VOLUNTEERING HIGHLAND
The Gateway, 1a Milburn Road, Inverness,
Highland IV2 3PX
Tel: 01463 711393
Fax: 01463 225001
Email: ..... enquiries@volunteeringhighland.org

Midlothian

VOLUNTEER CENTRE MIDLOTHIAN
The Computer House, Dalkeith Country Park,
Dalkeith, Midlothian EH22 2NA
Tel: 0131 660 1216
Email: .... info@volunteermidlothian.org.uk

Orkney Islands

VOLUNTARY ACTION ORKNEY/ VOLUNTEER CENTRE ORKNEY
Anchor Buildings, 6 Bridge Street, Kirkwall,
Orkney Islands KW15 1HR
Tel: 01856 872897
Fax: 01865 873167
Email: .... vc@vaorkney.org.uk

Perth & Kinross

VOLUNTEER CENTRE PERTH & KINROSS
The Gateway, North Methven Street, Perth, Perth
& Kinross PH1 5PP
Tel: 01738 567076

Renfrewshire

ENGAGE RENFREWSHIRE
c/o RCVS, The Wynd Centre, 6 School Wynd,
Paisley, Renfrewshire PA1 2DB
Tel: 0141 587 2487

VOLUNTEER CENTRE INVERCLYDE
175 Dalrymple Street, Greenock, Renfrewshire
PA15 1JZ
Tel: 01475 787414
Fax: 01475 784002
Email: . diane.mcallister@volunteerinverclyde.org.
uk

Scottish Borders

BERWICKSHIRE ASSOCIATION FOR VOLUNTARY SERVICE
Platform 1, Station Road, Duns, Scottish Borders
TD11 3HS
Tel: 01361 883137

THE BRIDGE - ROXBURGH
1 Veitch's Close, Jedburgh, Scottish Borders
TD8 6AY
Tel: 01835 863554
Fax: 01835 864456

THE BRIDGE - TWEEDALE
Volunteer Resource Centre, School Brae, High
Street, Brae, Peebles, Scottish Borders EH45 8AL
Tel: 01721 723123
Fax: 01721 723123

ROXBURGH ASSOCIATION OF VOLUNTARY SERVICE
1 Veitch's Close, Jedburgh, Scottish Borders
TD8 6AY
Tel: 01835 863554
Email: .... cbavs@scvo.org.uk

South Ayrshire

VOLUNTARY ACTION SOUTH AYRSHIRE
60 Kyle Street, Ayr, South Ayrshire KA7 1RZ
Tel: 01292 263626
Fax: 01292 267677

South Lanarkshire

SOLVE - VOLUNTEER CENTRE
14 Townhead Street, Hamilton, South Lanarkshire
ML3 7BE
Tel: 01698 286902
Fax: 01698 286026
Email: .... info@solve.uk.com

Stirling

VOLUNTEER CENTRE STIRLING
15 Friars Street, Stirling FK8 1HA
Tel: 01786 446071
Fax: 01786 470449
Email: .... info@volunteeringstirling.org.uk

West Lothian

VOLUNTEER CENTRE WEST LOTHIAN
36 - 40 North Bridge Street, Bathgate, West
Lothian EH48 4PP
Tel: 01506 650111
Fax: 01506 650222
Email: .... volunteer@vcwl.co.uk

Western Isles

VOLUNTEER CENTRE WESTERN ISLES
95 Cromwell Street, Stornoway, Western Isles
H51 2DG
Tel: 01851 700366
Email: . stornoway@volunteeringwesternisles.co.
uk

VOLUNTEER CENTRE WESTERN ISLES
Dell Hall, North Dell, Ness, Isle of Lewis, Western
Isles HS2 0TSW
Tel: 01851 810353

VOLUNTEER CENTRE WESTERN ISLES
c/o Room 5, Old Hostel, Tarbert, Western Isles
HS3 3DL
Tel: 01859 502575

WALES

Cardiff

CARDIFF VOLUNTARY COMMUNITY SERVICE
Brunel House, 2 Fitzalan Road, Cardiff CF24 0HA
Tel: 029 2022 7625

Denbighshire

DENBIGHSHIRE VOLUNTARY SERVICES COUNCIL
Naylor Leyland Centre, Well Street, Ruthin,
Denbighshire LL15 1AF
Tel: 01824 702441

Gwynedd

CAERNARFON VOLUNTEER BUREAU
Santes Helen Road, Caernarfon, Gwynedd
LL55 2YD
Tel: 01286 677337

Powys

LLANDRIDNOD WELLS VOLUNTEER BUREAU
c/o PAVO, Marlow, South Crescent, Llandrindod
Wells, Powys LD1 5DH
Tel: 0845 0093288

RHAYADER AND DISTRICT COMMUNITY SUPPORT
The Arches, West Street, Rhayader, Powys
LD6 5AB
Tel: 01597 810921
Fax: 01597 810921
Email: .... carolyn@rdcs.org.uk

YSTRADGYNLAIS VOLUNTEER CENTRE
16 Station Road, Ystradgynlais, Powys SA9 1NT
Tel: 01639 849192
Fax: 01639 849192

Wrexham

WREXHAM VOLUNTEER CENTRE
21 Egerton Street, Wrexham LL11 1ND
Tel: 01978 312556
Email: .... vb@avow.org

OBJECT INDEX

The following Object Index is based on the Object Codes listed at the start of the Digest (on page xli). Here we have further split these codes to reflect a charity's main areas of expertise (see below) and who the charity benefits.

The Charities' Main Areas of Expertise

GRANTS TO INDIVIDUALS
Barristers' Benevolent Association 16
Entertainment Artistes' Benevolent Fund 59
Frederick Andrew Convalescent Trust 65
Psychiatry Research Trust 120

GRANTS TO ORGANISATIONS
1989 Wilan Charitable Trust, The 1
Actors' Benevolent Fund 4
All Saints Educational Trust 9
Cancer Prevention Research Trust 30
Children Nationwide Medical Research Fund 38
Frederick Andrew Convalescent Trust 65
National Police Fund 105
WellChild 156

SERVICES PROVIDER
Book Aid International 23
Chai Cancer Care 36
National Society for the Prevention of Cruelty To Children
(NSPCC) 106
Wythall Animal Sanctuary 162

GRANTS TO ORGANISATIONS/CHARITIES
Almond Trust, The 9
Art Fund, The 13
Artists' General Benevolent Institution 13
Barristers' Benevolent Association 16
Barry Green Memorial Fund 16
Bedfordshire and Hertfordshire Historic Churches Trust 18
BEN - The Automotive Industry Charity 18
Birchington Convalescent Benefit Fund 18
Bluebell Railway Trust 22
British & International Sailors' Society 25
British Kidney Patient Association (BKPA) 27
BT Benevolent Fund 28
Catholic Fund for Homeless & Destitute People 34
The Charity for Civil Servants (formerly The Civil Service
Benevolent Fund) 36
The Charity Service Ltd 36
Christian Education Movement 40
CLIC Sargent (Scotland) 43

Crohn's and Colitis UK 46
CRUSAID 47
The CTBI - The Salespeoples Charity 47
Easington District Council of Voluntary Service 57
ERMULI Trust 61
Family Action 62
Footwear Benevolent Society, The (Footwear Friends) . 64
Frederick Andrew Convalescent Trust 65
Gardening For Disabled Trust 67
Glasgow Educational & Marshall Trust 69
Grace Wyndham Goldie (BBC) Trust Fund 70
Grand Lodge of Mark Master Masons Fund of
Benevolence 70
Guild of Aid for Gentlepeople 72
Guild of Benevolence of the Institute of Marine
Engineering, Science & Technology 72
HACT – The Housing Action Charity 72
Hampshire & Isle of Wight Military Aid Fund (1903) . . 74
Hilda Martindale Educational Trust 77
Historic Churches Preservation Trust 78
Hospital Saturday Fund Charitable Trust 78
Institution of Structural Engineers Benevolent Fund . . 82
Invalids-at-Home Trust 85
Isle of Anglesey Charitable Trust, The 86
Jewish Child's Day 87
Joint Educational Trust 87
Kirstin Royle Trust 89
Leather and Hide Trades Benevolent Institution 89
Leukaemia & Cancer Children's Fund 90
Leukaemia & Lymphoma Research 90
Lloyd Foundation, The 92
London Catalyst 92
Malcolm Sargent Cancer Fund for Children 93
Martindale (Hilda) Educational Trust 95
Masonic Samaritan Fund 95
Metropolitan Hospital-Sunday Fund 99
Mind 100
Monoux (Sir George) Exhibition Foundation 100
Morden College 101
Music Libraries Trust, The 101
National and Local Government Officers Association
(NALGO) 102
National Art Collections Fund 102
National Police Fund 105
Norton Foundation, The 109
The Nuclear Industry Benevolent Fund 109

Orthopaedic Research UK 110
Overseas Bishoprics' Fund 111
Pembroke House, Home for Aged Ex-Naval Men, Their
    Wives and Widows and former Wrens 116
Pottery & Glass Trades' Benevolent Fund 118
Prisoners Abroad 119
Provision Trade Benevolent Institution 120
Reed's School 123
Roald Dahl's Marvellous Children's Charity 125
Royal Archaeological Institute 126
Royal Artillery Charitable Fund 126
Royal Gardeners' Orphan Fund 127
Royal Marines Charitable Trust Fund 127
Royal Naval Benevolent Trust (Grand Fleet & Kindred
    Funds) 129
The Royal Scottish Corporation 130
RSABI 132
Sailors' Society 133
ScotsCare 135
Seafarers UK 136
Shipwrecked Mariners' Society 137
Sir George Monoux Exhibition Foundation 138
Sir Richard Stapley Educational Trust 138
Society for the Relief of Distressed Widows 139
Society of Friends of Foreigners in Distress 139
South Yorkshire Community Foundation 140
SPARKS - Sport Aiding medical Research for KidS . . 140
St Katharine & Shadwell Trust 143
St Luke's Healthcare for the Clergy 143
Telephones for the Blind Fund 147
TENOVUS Scotland 147
Thomas Howell's Trust 148
Timber Trades' Benevolent Society 149
Toy Trust, The 150
Tree Council, The 150
UNISON Welfare 151
Voluntary Action Cardiff 153

PENSIONS, BENEFITS OR SCHOLARSHIPS

Caravan, the Charity for Grocery People 32
CARAVAN, the trading name of The National Grocers
    Benevolent Fund 32
Chartered Institute of Logistics and Transport (UK), The 37
Licensed Trade Charity 91
Pottery & Glass Trades' Benevolent Fund 118
Provision Trade Benevolent Institution 120
Royal Alexandra and Albert School, The 125
Royal Artillery Charitable Fund 126
Schoolmistresses & Governesses Benevolent Institution
    133
Society of Licensed Victuallers 139
St Andrew's (Ecumenical) Trust 141
Swiss Benevolent Society 146
Timber Trades' Benevolent Society 149

SHELTERED ACCOMMODATION & HOSTELS

Autism London 15

Bromley & Sheppard's Colleges 28
Catholic Fund for Homeless & Destitute People 34
Central & Cecil Housing Trust 34
Centrepoint 36
Christina Noble Children's Foundation 40
Church of England Soldiers', Sailors' & Airmen's Clubs. 41
Church of England Soldiers', Sailors' and Airmen's
    Housing Association Limited 41
City of Exeter Y M C A 42
Crossways Community 46
Dorus Trust 54
Feilding (Mary) Guild 62
The Fircroft Trust (previously known as Mental Aid
    Projects) 63
Forest YMCA 64
Harrison Housing 75
Housing 21 79
Housing for Women 79
IDS (Industrial Dwellings Society 1885) 79
Jesse Mary Chambers Almshouses 87
Jewish Blind Society 87
Jewish Care 87
Jewish Welfare Board 87
Leo Trust, The 90
Mary Feilding Guild 95
Mental Aid Projects 97
Merchant Seamen's War Memorial Society 98
Morden College 101
Mrs Smith and Mount Trust, The 101
N.N.A.B. 101
Nacro - the crime reduction charity 102
Newham Asian Women's Project 107
Norfolk and Norwich Association for the Blind 107
Over Forty Association for Women Workers 111
The Royal Scottish Corporation 130
ScotsCare 135
Sense (The National Deafblind & Rubella Association) 136
Sheppard's College 137
Simon Community, The 138
Sunset Home Almshouses 145
Watford New Hope Trust 154
William Sutton Housing Association Ltd 158
William Sutton Trust 158
YMCA - Slough 162

HOUSING

Ann Watson's Trust 11
The Architectural Heritage Fund 12
Blackwood 20
Brendoncare Foundation 24
Bromley & Sheppard's Colleges 28
Bromley Autistic Trust 28
Central & Cecil Housing Trust 34
Centrepoint 36
The Church of England Pensions Board – Retirement
    Housing for Clergy Pensioners 41

Church of Scotland Housing & Loan Fund for Retired
   Ministers & Widows and Widowers of Ministers 41
City of Exeter Y M C A 42
The Disabilities Trust 51
Enable Care & Home Support Limited 59
Forest YMCA 64
Foundation Housing 64
HACT – The Housing Action Charity 72
Housing 21 79
Housing for Women 79
Huggens' College 79
IDS (Industrial Dwellings Society 1885) 79
Jesse Mary Chambers Almshouses 87
Merchant Seamen's War Memorial Society 98
Methodist Ministers' Housing Society 99
National Communities Resource Centre Ltd 103
Newham Asian Women's Project 107
Orpheus Centre 110
Over Forty Association for Women Workers 111
Providence Row Charity 120
Rainer 121
The Royal Scottish Corporation 130
ScotsCare 135
Shelter - National Campaign for Homeless People . . 137
Sheppard's College 137
Simon Community, The 138
South West Action for Learning and Living Our Way . 140
Sunset Home Almshouses 145
Thomas More Project, The 148
Watson's (Ann) Trust 154
The Westminster Society for people with learning
   disabilities 156
William Sutton Trust 158
Wytham Hall Limited 162
YMCA - Slough 162

DAY CENTRES

Age UK Calderdale & Kirklees 5
Age UK Enfield 6
Alcohol And Drug Service 7
Arthur Rank Hospice Charity 13
Asian People's Disability Alliance 13
Brambley Hedge Childrens Centre Charity Limited . . . 24
Bromley Autistic Trust 28
Cerebral Palsy Midlands 36
Connection at St Martin's, The 44
Enable Care & Home Support Limited 59
Fern Street Settlement 63
The Fircroft Trust (previously known as Mental Aid
   Projects) 63
Gateshead Crossroads - Caring for Carers 67
Harrogate District Hospice Care 75
HEADWAY - The Brain Injury Association 75
Hospice at Home West Cumbria 78
Isabel Hospice (Eastern Hertfordshire) 86
Jewish Blind Society 87
Jewish Care 87

Jewish Welfare Board 87
The Little Sisters of the Poor 91
London Catalyst 92
Martha Trust 95
The Meath Epilepsy Trust 97
Mental Aid Projects 97
Metropolitan Hospital-Sunday Fund 99
Mill Grove Christian Charitable Trust 100
Mrs Smith and Mount Trust, The 101
MSA For Midland People With Cerebral Palsy 101
Our Lady of Fidelity Charitable Trust 111
The Peace Hospice (South West Hertfordshire Hospice
   Charitable Trust) 114
Pelican Trust Limited 114
Pontefract Family Centre 118
Providence Row Charity 120
Redcar & Cleveland Mind 122
Saint Michael's Hospice (Harrogate) 133
St Barnabas House 142
St Christopher's Hospice 142
St Cuthbert's Centre 142
Watford New Hope Trust 154

ADVICE, COUNSELLING, INFORMATION

42nd Street - working with young people under stress . . 1
AbilityNet Advice and Information - UK's leading authority
   on disability and computing 2
ACRE (Action with Communities in Rural England) . . . 2
Action for Sick Children (National Association for the
   Welfare of Children in Hospital) 3
Action with Communities in Rural England 3
Actors' Benevolent Fund 4
Age Concern Manchester 5
Age UK Calderdale & Kirklees 5
Age UK Gateshead 6
Age UK Haringey 6
Age UK Newham 6
Age UK North Staffordshire 6
AHIMSA 7
AIDS Education & Research Trust (AVERT) 7
Air League Educational Trust - for Britain's Youth . . . 7
Alcohol And Drug Service 7
Animals In Distress Field of Dreams (Animal Retirement
   Home) 11
Animals in Distress Sanctuary 11
ASH - Action on Smoking & Health 13
Asthma UK 14
Asylum Aid 15
Autism Anglia 15
Autism London 15
AVERT 15
BACUP 15
Battersea Dogs & Cats Home 17
BCPC 17
Bliss 22
Bowel Cancer UK 23
Bradford Community for Voluntary Service 24

British & International Sailors' Society 25
British Deaf Association 26
British Dyslexia Association 26
British Migraine Association 27
British Sports Association for the Disabled 27
Bromley Autistic Trust 28
Brook Advisory Centre (Avon) 28
Cabrini Children's Society 28
Cancerbackup 30
Cancerwise 30
Canterbury District C.A.B 30
Catholic Fund for Homeless & Destitute People 34
Centre for Accessible Environments 36
Cerebra, The Foundation for Brain Injured Infants and
  Young People 36
CGD Society 36
Chai Cancer Care 36
Changing Faces - Supporting People with Disfigurements
  36
The Charity for Civil Servants (formerly The Civil Service
  Benevolent Fund) 36
The Charity for Civil Servants (formerly The Civil Service
  Benevolent Fund) 36
Charity Search - Free Advice for Older People 36
The Charity Service Ltd 36
Chartered Institute of Library and Information
  Professionals (CILIP) 37
Child Accident Prevention Trust 38
Childhood First 38
Children's Heart Federation 39
Chronic Granulomatous Disorder Research Trust . . . 40
Circulation Foundation 42
Claire House Children's Hospice 42
Coeliac UK 43
Colchester Community Voluntary Services 43
Connection at St Martin's, The 44
Contact a Family 44
Corona Worldwide 44
Counsel and Care 46
Crohn's and Colitis UK 46
Cystic Fibrosis Trust 47
Depression UK 49
Diabetes UK 51
Disabled Drivers' Association, The 52
Disabled Motoring UK 52
Dorus Trust 54
Dyslexia Association, British 57
Easington District Council of Voluntary Service 57
The Edinburgh Dog and Cat Home 57
ENABLE Scotland 59
Endometriosis UK 59
Environ Trust Ltd 59
Epigoni Trust 61
Epilepsy Society (The working name for the National
  Society for Epilepsy) 61
Equity Charitable Trust 61
Essex Autistic Society 61
Evangelical Library, The 61

Fairbridge 62
Family Action 62
Fegans Child & Family Care 62
The Fircroft Trust (previously known as Mental Aid
  Projects) 63
Foundation Housing 64
fpa - formerly The Family Planning Association 65
The Genetic Alliance UK Ltd 67
Groundwork Leicester & Leicestershire Ltd 71
Haemophilia Society 72
Harbour, The (formerly Red Admiral Project - Bristol) . . 74
HEADWAY - The Brain Injury Association 75
Health Care 75
Herpes Viruses Association 77
Hospice at Home West Cumbria 78
Hospice Information Service 78
IA (Ileostomy and Internal Pouch Support Group) . . . 79
In-volve 80
Independent Age 80
Independent Healthcare Association 81
Independent Healthcare Forum 81
Infertility Network UK 81
Institute of Credit Management 81
Intercountry Adoption Centre 82
Jerry Green Dog Rescue 86
Jewish Blind Society 87
Jewish Care 87
Jewish Marriage Council 87
Jewish Welfare Board 87
The Labrador Rescue Trust 89
Lady Hoare Trust for Physically Disabled Children . . . 89
Lambeth Elfrida Rathbone Society (Rathbone) 89
Learning Through Landscapes Trust 89
Legislation Monitoring Service for Charities 90
Leo Trust, The 90
Licensed Trade Charity 91
London Council for the Welfare of Women and Girls
  (LCWWG) 92
Lyttelton Well Limited 93
Medical Council on Alcohol, The 97
Mental Aid Projects 97
Merseyside Brook Advisory Centre 98
Migraine Action Association 100
Mind 100
Mr Fegan's Homes 101
National and Local Government Officers Association
  (NALGO) 102
National Association for Family Based Respite Care, The
  102
National Association for Voluntary and Community Action
  (NAVCA) 102
National Endometriosis Society 104
National Federation of Spiritual Healers (The NFSH
  Charitable Trust Ltd) 104
National Society for the Prevention of Cruelty To Children
  (NSPCC) 106
New Covenant Church 106
Newham Asian Women's Project 107

NFSH Charitable Trust LTD (The Healing Trust) . . . 107
The Nuclear Industry Benevolent Fund 109
Overseas Adoption Helpline 111
Oxfordshire Rural Community Council 112
Parkinson's UK 114
The Peace Hospice (South West Hertfordshire Hospice
    Charitable Trust) 114
Peper Harow Foundation 116
Perennial - Gardeners' Royal Benevolent Society . . . 116
Pharmacist Support 117
Positive East 118
Preston and Western Lancashire REC 119
Primary Immunodeficiency Association (PiA) 119
Prison Reform Trust 119
Prisoners Abroad 119
Prostate Action 119
Providence Row Charity 120
Quit 121
The Rathbone Centre 121
Raynaud's & Scleroderma Association 121
Redcar & Cleveland Mind 122
Refugee Legal Centre 123
Relationship Counselling for London 123
Release - the National Drugs & Legal Helpline 124
Royal Artillery Charitable Fund 126
Royal Gardeners' Orphan Fund 127
Royal Marines Association 127
Royal Masonic Benevolent Institution 128
Royal Naval Benevolent Trust (Grand Fleet & Kindred
    Funds) 129
The Royal Scottish Corporation 130
Royal United Kingdom Beneficent Association 131
RP Fighting Blindness 132
Rukba 132
Sailors' Society 133
ScotsCare 135
Scottish Society for the Mentally Handicapped 135
Sesame Institute UK 136
Sevenoaks Area Mind 136
Shared Care Network 137
Shelter - National Campaign for Homeless People . . 137
Shingles Support Society 137
Society of Licensed Victuallers 139
Southwark Diocesan Welcare 140
Spina bifida • Hydrocephalus • Information • Networking •
    Equality - SHINE 140
St Cuthbert's Centre 142
St Peter's Convent 144
St Peter's Home and Sisterhood 144
St Richard's Hospice, Worcester 144
Stock Exchange Benevolent Fund 145
Stoke on Trent Citizens Advice Bureau 145
Sussex Diocesan Association For the Deaf 145
Swale Citizens Advice Bureau 146
Swindon Counselling Service 146
Swiss Benevolent Society 146
Telecommunications Action Group (TAG) 147
Terrence Higgins Trust 147

Tourism For All UK 149
Turners Court Youth Trust 151
UNISON Welfare 151
Vegetarian Society of the UK Ltd, The 152
Victim Support 153
Voluntary Action Cardiff 153
Voluntary Action North East Lincolnshire 153
Volunteer Centre Wolverhampton 153
Watford New Hope Trust 154
WelCare Service for Parents & Children (Southwark
    Diocese) 156
Autism Wessex 156
Wessex Cancer Help Centre 156
Wheelpower - British Wheelchair Sport 157
Women in Prison 159
Women's Corona Society 159
Women's Environmental Network 159
Wytham Hall Limited 162
Yeldall Christian Centres 162
YWCA (Accommodation and Advisory Service) 163

EDUCATION, TRAINING

Action for Kids Charitable Trust 3
Afasic - Helping Children and Young People with Speech,
    Language & Communication Impairments 4
AHIMSA 7
Air League Educational Trust - for Britain's Youth 7
All Nations Christian College 8
All Saints Educational Trust 9
Amnesty International (UK Section) Charitable Trust
    (AIUKSCT) 9
Animal Care Trust 10
Ann Watson's Trust 11
Association for Language Learning, The 13
Association of Taxation Technicians 14
Autism Anglia 15
Bacon's City Technology College 15
BASPCAN (British Association for the Study and
    Prevention of Child Abuse and Neglect) 16
Bat Conservation Trust 16
Battle of Britain Memorial Trust 17
BCPC 17
Beaumont Animals' Hospital 17
Bell Memorial Home (Inc) 18
Birmingham Bible Institute Ministries, The 18
Birmingham Christian College 20
Birmingham Contemporary Music Group 20
Blackburn Groundwork Trust 20
Blandford Museum of Fashion 20
Bluebell Railway Trust 22
Book Aid International 23
British American Security Information Council (BASIC) . . 25
British and Foreign School Society 25
British Association for Immediate Care - BASICS 25
British Divers Marine Life Rescue 26
British Dyslexia Association 26
British Horse Society 26

British Migraine Association 27

British Plumbing Employers Council (Training) Limited . 27

British Record Industry Trust 27

Canbury School Limited 30

Cancerwise 30

Cat Survival Trust 33

Catholic Institute for International Relations (CIIR) . . . 34

Cavalcade of Costume Museum 34

Centre for Local Economic Strategies 36

Cerebral Palsy Midlands 36

Chai Cancer Care 36

Changing Faces - Supporting People with Disfigurements

. . . . 36

Chartered Institute of Library and Information

Professionals (CILIP) 37

Chartered Institute of Logistics and Transport (UK), The 37

Chartered Institution of Civil Engineering Surveyors . . 37

Chatham Historic Dockyard Trust 37

Child Accident Prevention Trust 38

Children & Youth Committee for Great Britain and Eire . 38

Cholmondeleys, The 40

Christ's Hospital 40

Christian Aid 40

Christian Witness to Israel 40

Christina Noble Children's Foundation 40

Church Action on Poverty 40

Church Lads' & Church Girls' Brigade 41

Circus Space, The 42

Cirdan Sailing Trust 42

Cliff College 43

Clubs for Young People (CYP) 43

Compton Hospice 44

Connection at St Martin's, The 44

Construction Industry Trust for Youth 44

Construction Youth Trust 44

Corona Worldwide 44

Dain Fund, The 47

The Dame Vera Lynn Trust for Children With Cerebral

Palsy 47

Danenberg Oberlin-in-London Program 47

Disability Essex (Essex Disabled Peoples Association Ltd)

. . . . 52

Dyslexia Action 57

Dyslexia Association, British 57

ECL Door of Hope 57

Emergency Exit Arts 58

EMFEC 58

Emmanuel Christian School Association 58

Environ Trust Ltd 59

Environmental Protection UK 59

ERMULI Trust 61

Essex Autistic Society 61

Essex Disabled People's Association Limited 61

European Sidhaland Association 61

Evangelical Library, The 61

Fairbridge 62

Feltham Community School Association 63

FIELD - (Foundation for International Environmental Law

and Development) 63

Finchale Training College for Disabled People 63

Free Churches Group, The 65

Galton Institute 66

The Game and Wildlife Conservation Trust 67

Godinton House Preservation Trust, The 69

Grace Wyndham Goldie (BBC) Trust Fund 70

Groundwork Leicester & Leicestershire Ltd 71

GuildHE Limited 72

Hawk Conservancy Trust 75

Higher Education Information Services Trust 77

HighScope GB 77

Hilda Martindale Educational Trust 77

Honourable Society of Gray's Inn Trust Fund 78

Hope UK (Drug Education) (formerly the Band of Hope) 78

In-volve 80

Institute of Credit Management 81

Institute of Direct Marketing, The 81

International Association For Religious Freedom (IARF) 82

International Glaucoma Association 85

International League for the Protection of Horses (ILPH) 85

International Records Management Trust, The 85

International Wheelchair & Amputee Sports Federation 85

Jerusalem and the Middle East Church Association . . 86

Jewish Marriage Council 87

Kent County Agricultural Society 88

Kent Wildlife Trust 88

Kidasha 88

The Labrador Rescue Trust 89

Lambeth Elfrida Rathbone Society (Rathbone) 89

Learning Through Action Trust 89

Learning Through Landscapes Trust 89

Life Academy 91

The Lifetrain Trust 91

Lloyd Foundation, The 92

London Jewish Cultural Centre 92

London Youth (formerly the Federation of London Youth

Clubs) 93

Manchester Development Education Project Ltd 94

The Manor Preparatory School Trust 94

Manor Training and Resource Centre Ltd 95

Martindale (Hilda) Educational Trust 95

The Mary Hare Foundation 95

Medical Council on Alcohol, The 97

Medical Research Foundation 97

Migraine Action Association 100

Motionhouse 101

MSA For Midland People With Cerebral Palsy 101

Museum of East Asian Art, The 101

Music Libraries Trust, The 101

National Association for Voluntary and Community Action

(NAVCA) 102

National Association of Boys' Clubs 102

National Association of Clubs for Young People 102

National Association of Youth Clubs 102

National Communities Resource Centre Ltd 103

National Examination Board in Occupational Safety and
Health, The (NEBOSH) 104
National Federation of Spiritual Healers (The NFSH
Charitable Trust Ltd) 104
National Foundation for Educational Research in England
and Wales - (NFER) 105
National Institute of Adult Continuing Education 105
National Youth Theatre of Great Britain 106
Nautical Institute 106
NEA (National Energy Action) 106
Newham Asian Women's Project 107
NFSH Charitable Trust LTD (The Healing Trust) . . . 107
ORBIS UK 110
Orpheus Centre 110
Orthopaedic Research UK 110
Osteopathic Centre for Children, London 111
Our Lady of Fidelity Charitable Trust 111
Parkinson's UK 114
Pontefract Family Centre 118
The Pre-Retirement Association 119
Princess Alice Hospice 119
Progressio 119
Prospect Education (Technology) Trust Ltd 119
Quit 121
Rainer 121
Rainer Foundation, The 121
The Rathbone Centre 121
Reed's School 120
Release the National Drugs & Legal Helpline 124
Riding For the Disabled Association (Northern Ireland)
Incorporating Carriage Driving 125
The Right to Life Charitable Trust 125
River & Rowing Museum Foundation 125
Royal Alexandra and Albert School, The 125
Royal Artillery Charitable Fund 126
Royal Gardeners' Orphan Fund 127
Royal Liverpool Philharmonic Society, The 127
Royal National Institute of Blind People (RNIB) 128
Royal National Institute of Blind People (RNIB) 128
Royal School for Deaf Children Margate 129
The Royal Scottish Corporation 130
The Royal Society for the Promotion of Health 130
The Royal Veterinary College 131
Save the Children 133
ScotsCare 135
Second Chance: A Charity for Children Who Need Special
Help 136
Sesame Institute UK 136
Sevenoaks Area Mind 138
SEVENOAKS DAY NURSERY TRUST 136
Shumei Eiko Limited 137
Siobhan Davies Dance/ Siobhan Davies Studios . . . 138
Sir Alister Hardy Foundation for Ocean Science . . . 138
Sir Richard Stapley Educational Trust 138
The Sisters of the Sacred Hearts of Jesus and Mary . 138
SOFA (Furniture Reuse Charity) 139
South Asian Concern Charitable Trust 139
South West Action for Learning and Living Our Way . 140

South West Action for Learning and Living Our Way . 140
Southern Convalescent Homes Inc 140
Spadework Limited 140
St Andrew's (Ecumenical) Trust 141
St Austell China Clay Museum Limited 141
St Brigid's School Limited 142
St Cuthbert's Centre 142
St Katharine & Shadwell Trust 143
St Luke's College Foundation 143
St Peter's Convent 144
St Peter's Home and Sisterhood 144
St Richard's Hospice, Worcester 144
St Ursula's High School Trust 144
Standing Conference of Principals Ltd 144
Thanet Early Years Project & Pals 148
Town & Country Planning Association 150
Trebah Garden Trust 150
The Trust for Education 150
TTE Management & Technical Training 151
Turners Court Youth Trust 151
UK Skills 151
Universities UK 151
University of Cape Town Trust 151
Urban Theology Unit 152
Voluntary Action Cardiff 153
Voluntary Action North East Lincolnshire 153
Waste Management Industry Training and Advisory Board,
The 154
Watson's (Ann) Trust 154
WDC, Whale and Dolphin Conservation 154
Wellbeing Of Women 156
Welshpool and Llanfair Light Railway Preservation Co
Limited 156
Wessex Cancer Help Centre 156
Wessex Foundation, The 156
West Kent YMCA - Helping Young People Build Their
Future 156
Whitehall and Industry Group, The 157
The Wildlife Aid Foundation 158
Women's Corona Society 159
Women's Technology / Blackburne House 159
Workers' Educational Association 159
World Horse Welfare 161
Yeldall Christian Centres 162
YMCA - Slough 162
Youth Aliyah - Child Rescue 163

PUBLICATIONS AND/OR FREE LITERATURE

ACRE (Action with Communities in Rural England) . . . 2
Action for Sick Children (National Association for the
Welfare of Children in Hospital) 3
Action with Communities in Rural England 3
Age UK Enfield 6
AIDS Education & Research Trust (AVERT) 7
Alzheimer's Research UK 9
ASH - Action on Smoking & Health 13
Association for Language Learning, The 13

AVERT 15
Bradford Community for Voluntary Service 24
British Deaf Association 26
British Plumbing Employers Council (Training) Limited . 27
Butterfly Conservation 28
Cancerwise 30
Catholic Institute for International Relations (CIIR) . . . 34
Centre for Local Economic Strategies 36
Chai Cancer Care 36
Chartered Institute of Library and Information
  Professionals (CILIP) 37
Chartered Institution of Civil Engineering Surveyors . . 37
Child Accident Prevention Trust 38
Children's Cancer and Leukaemia Group (CCLG) . . . 38
Children's Heart Federation 39
Children's Rights Alliance for England 39
China Inland Mission 40
Christian Education Movement 40
Christian Witness to Israel 40
Church Action on Poverty 40
Churches Community Work Alliance 42
Circulation Foundation 42
CLIC Sargent (Scotland) 43
Cystic Fibrosis Trust 47
Depression UK 49
Diabetes UK 51
EMFEC 58
Endometriosis UK 59
Environmental Protection UK 59
Folkestone & District MIND Resource Centre 64
Free Churches Group, The 65
Friends of Canterbury Cathedral 65
Gardening For Disabled Trust 67
Greenpeace Environmental Trust 70
Haemophilia Society 72
HEADWAY - The Brain Injury Association 75
Herpes Viruses Association 77
HighScope GB 77
Hope UK (Drug Education) (formerly the Band of Hope) 78
IA (Ileostomy and Internal Pouch Support Group) . . . 79
Infertility Network UK 81
Institute for European Environmental Policy, London . . 81
Institute of Direct Marketing, The 81
Intercountry Adoption Centre 82
International Glaucoma Association 85
Legislation Monitoring Service for Charities 90
Leukaemia & Cancer Children's Fund 90
Malcolm Sargent Cancer Fund for Children 93
Manchester Development Education Project Ltd 94
The Methodist Church 99
Mind 100
National Association of Youth Clubs 102
The National Deaf Children's Society 104
National Endometriosis Society 104
NEA (National Energy Action) 106
OMF International (UK) 110
Overseas Adoption Helpline 111
Overseas Missionary Fellowship 112

Oxfordshire Rural Community Council 112
Parkinson's UK 114
Partially Sighted Society 114
Prison Reform Trust 119
Progressio 119
Prostate Action 119
Redcar & Cleveland Mind 122
Release - the National Drugs & Legal Helpline 124
The Royal Society for the Promotion of Health 130
Scripture Union England and Wales 135
Sgript Cymru 137
Shingles Support Society 137
St Katharine & Shadwell Trust 143
Telecommunications Action Group (TAG) 147
Terrence Higgins Trust 147
Town & Country Planning Association 150
Trinitarian Bible Society 150
UCCF: The Christian Unions 151
Universities and Colleges Christian Fellowship 151
Universities UK 151
Urban Theology Unit 152
Volunteer Centre Wolverhampton 153
Wessex Cancer Help Centre 156
Wheelpower - British Wheelchair Sport 157

CO-ORDINATION, LIAISON

Attend 15
Blackburn Groundwork Trust 20
Bradford Community for Voluntary Service 24
British & International Sailors' Society 25
British Association for Immediate Care - BASICS 25
British Dyslexia Association 26
British Sports Association for the Disabled 27
Chai Cancer Care 36
The Charity for Civil Servants (formerly The Civil Service
  Benevolent Fund) 36
Churches Community Work Alliance 42
Colchester Community Voluntary Services 43
Corona Worldwide 44
Dyslexia Association, British 57
Free Churches Group, The 65
The Genetic Alliance UK Ltd 67
National Association for Voluntary and Community Action
  (NAVCA) 102
National Association of Hospital and Community Friends
  102
National Council for Voluntary Youth Services 103
Order of St John 110
Oxfordshire Rural Community Council 112
Parkinson's UK 114
Sailors' Society 133
UK Skills 151
Voluntary Action North East Lincolnshire 153
Volunteer Centre Wolverhampton 153
Whitehall and Industry Group, The 157
Women's Corona Society 159

www.alzheimers.org.uk

WORKSHOPS & OTHER EMPLOYMENT

Artlink West Yorkshire 13
Nacro - the crime reduction charity 102
Pelican Trust Limited 114
Sgript Cymru 137

CARE EQUIPMENT, PRACTICAL SERVICES

The British Heart Foundation (BHF) 26
Carers Relief Service 32
A Cause for Concern 34
Chai Cancer Care 36
Christian Concern for the Mentally Handicapped 40
Crossroads Greenwich & Lewisham Ltd 46
Dorus Trust 54
Gateshead Crossroads - Caring for Carers 67
Greensleeves Homes Trust 71
Harrogate District Hospice Care 75
Hayward House Cancer Care Trust 75
Herefordshire Lifestyles 77
Housing 21 79
Isabel Hospice (Eastern Hertfordshire) 86
James Hopkins Trust 86
Lifeline 4 Kids / Handicapped Children's Aid Committee 91
Mobility Trust 100
Parkinson's UK 114
Prospects for People with Learning Disabilities 119
Redbridge, Epping & Harrow Crossroads - Caring for
    Carers 122
Royal National Institute of Blind People (RNIB) 128
Saint Michael's Hospice (Harrogate) 133
OOFA (Furniture Reuse Charity) 139
Southern Area Hospice Services 140
Terrence Higgins Trust 147
Vision Support 153
WRVS Trustees Ltd 162

MEDICAL TREATMENT, NURSING

Alder Hey Children's Charity 7
Arthur Rank Hospice Charity 13
Association for People with Lower Limb Abnormalities -
    steps 13
Attend 15
BACUP 15
Bliss 22
Bowel Cancer UK 23
Brendoncare Foundation 24
British Association for Immediate Care - BASICS 25
The British Heart Foundation (BHF) 26
Brook Advisory Centre (Avon) 28
Cancerbackup 30
Central Manchester University Hospitals NHS Foundation
    Trust Charity 34
CGD Society 36
Children in Distress 38
Children's Cancer and Leukaemia Group (CCLG) . . . 38
Children's Hospice South West 39
Chronic Granulomatous Disorder Research Trust . . . 40

The Church of England Pensions Board – Retirement
    Housing for Clergy Pensioners 41
Claire House Children's Hospice 42
Coeliac UK 43
Compton Hospice 44
Cumberland and Westmorland Convalescent Institution 47
Devon Air Ambulance Trust 51
Enable Care & Home Support Limited 59
Entertainment Artistes' Benevolent Fund 59
Epigoni Trust 61
Epilepsy Society (The working name for the National
    Society for Epilepsy) 61
Everyman - action against male cancer 62
Florence Nightingale Hospice - Florence Nightingale
    Hospice Charity 63
Friends of Cynthia Spencer Hospice 65
The Genetic Alliance UK Ltd 67
Great North Air Ambulance Service 70
Greensleeves Homes Trust 71
Harrogate District Hospice Care 75
Hayward House Cancer Care Trust 75
Herpes Viruses Association 77
Hope House Children's Hospices 78
Hospice at Home West Cumbria 78
Hospital Saturday Fund Charitable Trust 78
InDependent Diabetes Trust 81
Independent Healthcare Association 81
Independent Healthcare Forum 81
The Institute of Cancer Research: The Royal Cancer
    Hospital 81
Isabel Hospice (Eastern Hertfordshire) 86
James Hopkins Trust 86
Jerusalem and the Middle East Church Association . . 86
Kidasha 88
King Edward VII's Hospital Sister Agnes 88
Lambeth Elfrida Rathbone Society (Rathbone) 89
Leukaemia & Lymphoma Research 90
Leukaemia Busters 91
Macmillan Caring Locally 93
Masonic Samaritan Fund 95
The Meath Epilepsy Trust 97
Medical Council on Alcohol, The 97
Multiple Sclerosis Society 101
National Association of Hospital and Community Friends
    102
Osteopathic Centre for Children, London 111
Pain Relief Foundation 112
Parkinson's UK 114
The Peace Hospice (South West Hertfordshire Hospice
    Charitable Trust) 114
Pembroke House, Home for Aged Ex-Naval Men, Their
    Wives and Widows and former Wrens 116
Pied Piper Trust, The 117
Positive East 118
Princess Alice Hospice 119
Quit 121
The Rathbone Centre 121
Saint Michael's Hospice (Harrogate) 133

Service to the Aged 136
Shingles Support Society 137
Sister Agnes 138
Sobell House Hospice Charity Limited 138
Sound Seekers 139
Southern Area Hospice Services 140
St Anthony's Hospital, North Cheam 141
St Barnabas House 142
St Christopher's Hospice 142
St David's Foundation Hospice Care 143
St Luke's Healthcare for the Clergy 143
St Richard's Hospice, Worcester 144
STEPS Charity Worldwide 145
Stock Exchange Benevolent Fund 145
Vision Aid Overseas 153
Woking and Sam Beare Hospices 158
WRVS Trustees Ltd 162
Wytham Hall Limited 162

REHABILITATION, THERAPY

AHIMSA 7
Alcohol And Drug Service 7
Art in Healthcare 13
Chai Cancer Care 36
Children & Youth Committee for Great Britain and Eire . 38
Christopher Place 40
Compton Hospice 44
Crossways Community 46
Depression UK 49
The Disabilities Trust 51
Epigoni Trust 61
European Sidhaland Association 61
Finchale Training College for Disabled People 63
Mare and Foal Sanctuary 95
The Meath Epilepsy Trust 97
Moorcroft Racehorse Welfare Centre 100
Mrs Smith and Mount Trust, The 101
Nacro - the crime reduction charity 102
Pain Relief Foundation 112
Paintings in Hospitals Scotland 112
Parkinson's UK 114
Pelican Trust Limited 114
Pharmacist Support 117
Pod Charitable Trust 117
Princess Alice Hospice 119
REACH - the association for children with upper limb
    deficiency 121
Riding For the Disabled Association (Northern Ireland)
    Incorporating Carriage Driving 125
Sesame Institute UK 136
Speech, Language and Hearing Centre, The 140
St Barnabas House 142
St Francis Leprosy Guild 143
Sussex Horse Rescue Trust 145
Vision Support 153
Yeldall Christian Centres 162
Youth Aliyah - Child Rescue 163

SOCIAL ACTIVITIES & RELATIONSHIPS

42nd Street - working with young people under stress . . 1
Age UK Haringey 6
Age UK Newham 6
Age UK North Staffordshire 6
Attend 15
BASPCAN (British Association for the Study and
    Prevention of Child Abuse and Neglect) 16
Carers Relief Service 32
Chai Cancer Care 36
Christian Education Movement 40
Community Network 43
Dutch Home for the Elderly 56
Fairbridge 62
Folkestone & District MIND Resource Centre 64
Friends of Canterbury Cathedral 65
Galton Institute 66
Glasgow Children's Holiday Scheme 69
Independent Age 80
Jewish Marriage Council 87
Kirstin Royle Trust 89
The Labrador Rescue Trust 89
Learning Through Action Trust 89
Leo Trust, The 90
The Lifetrain Trust 91
The Little Sisters of the Poor 91
Maidstone & Northwest Crossroads 93
National Association of Hospital and Community Friends
    102
New Covenant Church 106
Parkinson's UK 114
Pod Charitable Trust 117
Relationship Counselling for London 123
Riverside Vineyard Church 125
Royal Artillery Charitable Fund 126
Royal Marines Association 127
Royal United Kingdom Beneficent Association 131
Rukba 132
Sevenoaks Area Mind 136
South Yorkshire Community Foundation 140
Sussex Diocesan Association For the Deaf 145

ADOPTION, FOSTERING

Battersea Dogs & Cats Home 17
Cabrini Children's Society 28
Care for the Wild International 32
Childhood First 38
Intercountry Adoption Centre 82
Jerry Green Dog Rescue 86
Manchester & Cheshire Dogs' Home 94
National Association for Family Based Respite Care, The
    102
NCH 106
Overseas Adoption Helpline 111
Peper Harow Foundation 116
RSPCA Bristol Branch and Bristol Dogs and Cats Home
    132
Shared Care Network 137

MISSIONARY & OUTREACH WORK AT HOME OR ABROAD

All Nations Christian College 9
Almond Trust, The 9
Birmingham Bible Institute Ministries, The 18
Birmingham Christian College. 20
A Cause for Concern 34
China Inland Mission 40
Christian Concern for the Mentally Handicapped 40
Christian Witness to Israel 40
Clarendon Trust Ltd 42
Cliff College 43
Emmanuel International UK 58
Focus on Israel 64
Frontiers 66
The Garden Tomb (Jerusalem) Association. 67
International Connections Trust 85
Jerusalem and the Middle East Church Association . . 86
Lyttelton Well Limited 93
The Methodist Church. 99
Military Ministries International 100
New Covenant Church 106
New Frontiers International 107
OMF International (UK) 110
Overseas Bishoprics' Fund 111
Overseas Missionary Fellowship. 112
Prayer Book Society 119
Prospects for People with Learning Disabilities 119
Riverside Vineyard Church. 125
Scripture Union England and Wales 135
Siloam Christian Ministries - Education, Healthcare &
   Relief as a Vehicle for the Gospel 138
The Sisters of the Sacred Hearts of Jesus and Mary . 138
Society of the Precious Blood 139
South Asian Concern Charitable Trust 139
Spring Project, The 141
St Andrew's (Ecumenical) Trust 141
St Augustine's Foundation 141
St Francis Leprosy Guild. 143
St Luke's Healthcare for the Clergy 143
Trinitarian Bible Society 150
UCCF: The Christian Unions 151
Universities and Colleges Christian Fellowship 151

CULTURAL PURSUITS

The Architectural Heritage Fund 12
Art Fund, The 13
Art in Healthcare 13
Artists' General Benevolent Institution 13
Birmingham Contemporary Music Group 20
Blandford Museum of Fashion 20
Bluebell Railway Trust. 22
Burton Constable Foundation, The 28
Cavalcade of Costume Museum 34
Cholmondeleys, The 40
Circus Space, The. 42
Clubs for Young People (CYP) 43
Dance North. 47

Emergency Exit Arts. 58
Friends of Canterbury Cathedral 65
International Association For Religious Freedom (IARF) 82
International Organ Festival Society Ltd, The 85
London Jewish Cultural Centre 92
Museum of East Asian Art, The 101
National Art Collections Fund 102
National Association of Boys' Clubs 102
National Association of Clubs for Young People . . . 102
The National Trust for Scotland 106
National Youth Theatre of Great Britain 106
Oily Cart Company, The 109
Orpheus Centre 110
Paintings in Hospitals Scotland 112
Prayer Book Society 119
Royal Archaeological Institute 126
Royal Liverpool Philharmonic Society, The 127
Sgript Cymru 137
Siobhan Davies Dance/ Siobhan Davies Studios . . 138
Tate Foundation 146
Welshpool and Llanfair Light Railway Preservation Co
   Limited 156
Workers' Educational Association 159

RECONCILIATION

Churches Together in England 42

OVERSEAS AID OR SERVICE

ActionAid 3
AHRTAG - Appropriate Health Resources & Technologies
   Action Group 7
Amnesty International (UK Section) Charitable Trust
   (AIUKSCT) 9
Book Aid International 23
CBM 34
Chernobyl Children Life Line 37
Children in Distress 38
Christian Aid 40
Cliff College 43
David Livingstone International Ltd 48
Emmanuel International UK 58
Father Marek Sujkowski, Children's Aid To Ukraine,
   Romania and Poland 62
Frontiers 66
Greyhounds in Need 71
HALO Trust, The 74
Healthlink Worldwide 75
International China Concern 82
International Connections Trust 85
International League for the Protection of Horses (ILPH) 85
International Records Management Trust, The 85
International Wheelchair & Amputee Sports Federation 85
The Methodist Church. 99
Methodist Relief and Development Fund 99
Opportunity International UK. 110
ORBIS UK 110
Overseas Bishoprics' Fund 111

Practical Action (formerly ITDG) 118
Save the Children 133
Siloam Christian Ministries - Education, Healthcare &
   Relief as a Vehicle for the Gospel 138
The Sisters of the Sacred Hearts of Jesus and Mary . 138
Sound Seekers. 139
Spring Project, The 141
Spurgeon's Child Care 141
University of Cape Town Trust 151
VEGFAM (Feeds the Hungry Without Exploiting Animals)
   152
Vision Aid Overseas 153
WaterAid 154
Womankind Worldwide 159
World Horse Welfare 161

HOLIDAYS

Birchington Convalescent Benefit Fund 18
BREAK: High Quality Support For Vulnerable Children And
   Families 24
Calvert Trust Exmoor 29
Chernobyl Children Life Line 37
Entertainment Artistes' Benevolent Fund 59
Evelyn Norris Trust 61
Fern Street Settlement 63
Glasgow Children's Holiday Scheme 69
Happy Days Children's Charity 74
Health Care 75
Look: National Federation of Families with Visually
   Impaired Children 93
National and Local Government Officers Association
   (NALGO) 102
RAINY DAY TRUST (Incorporating the Pottery & Glass
   Trades' Benevolent Fund) 121
Royal Artillery Charitable Fund 126
Royal Metal Trades Benevolent Society 128
The Royal Scottish Corporation 130
ScotsCare 135
Scripture Union England and Wales 135
Tourism For All UK 149
UNISON Welfare 151

The Charity Benefits

ANIMALS AND/OR BIRDS

Alderman Tom F Spence Charity, The 7
Animal Care Trust 10
Animal Concern Advice Line (ACAL) 10
Animal Rescue Cumbria (the Wainwright Shelter) . . . 11
Animals In Distress Field of Dreams (Animal Retirement
   Home) 11
Animals in Distress Sanctuary 11
Assisi Animal Charities Foundation 13
Barry Green Memorial Fund 16
Bat Conservation Trust 16
Battersea Dogs & Cats Home 17
Beaumont Animals' Hospital 17
Birmingham Dogs' Home, The 20

Blue Cross 22
British Divers Marine Life Rescue 26
British Horse Society 26
Campaign to Protect Rural England - CPRE 29
Care for the Wild International 32
Cat Survival Trust 33
Cat Welfare Trust 33
Catastrophes Cat Rescue 33
The Dick Vet Animal Health and Welfare Fund 51
Dog Care Association (and Cats) 52
Dogs Trust 54
The Edinburgh Dog and Cat Home 57
Feline Advisory Bureau 62
Gloucestershire Animal Welfare Association and
   Cheltenham Animal Shelter 69
The Gorilla Organization 69
Greyhounds in Need 71
Hawk Conservancy Trust 75
Hearing Dogs for Deaf People (Head Office) 77
International Animal Rescue 82
International Fund for Cat Welfare Feline Advisory Bureau
   85
International League for the Protection of Horses (ILPH) 85
Jerry Green Dog Rescue 86
Kent County Agricultural Society 88
Kent Wildlife Trust 88
The Labrador Rescue Trust 89
Manchester & Cheshire Dogs' Home 94
Mare and Foal Sanctuary 95
The Marine Connection 95
Moorcroft Racehorse Welfare Centre 100
The National Trust for Scotland 106
Pine Ridge Dog Sanctuary 117
Retraining of Racehorses (ROR) 124
Royal Society for the Prevention of Cruelty to Animals,
   Liverpool Branch 130
The Royal Veterinary College 131
RSPCA Bristol Branch and Bristol Dogs and Cats Home
   132
Scottish Society for the Prevention of Cruelty to Animals
   (Scottish SPCA) 135
Staffordshire Wildlife Trust 144
Sussex Horse Rescue Trust 145
Swan Lifeline 146
Tiggywinkles: The Wildlife Hospital Trust 149
Vegetarian Society of the UK Ltd, The 152
VEGFAM (Feeds the Hungry Without Exploiting Animals)
   152
WDC, Whale and Dolphin Conservation 154
Wildfowl & Wetlands Trust 157
The Wildlife Aid Foundation 158
The Woodland Trust 159
World Horse Welfare 161
World Wide Fund For Nature 161
World Wildlife Fund 161
WWF-UK 162
Wythall Animal Sanctuary 162
Yorkshire Wildlife Trust 162

HUMANITARIAN RELIEF

VEGFAM (Feeds the Hungry Without Exploiting Animals)
. . . . 152

MEDICAL RESEARCH

Brain Research Trust 24
Circulation Foundation 42
Pain Relief Foundation. 112

RELIEF OF POVERTY

NEA (National Energy Action) 106
Pharmacist Support 117

ETHNIC MINORITIES

Asian People's Disability Alliance 13
BACUP 15
Cancerbackup. 30
Construction Industry Trust for Youth 44
Construction Youth Trust 44
Field Lane Foundation 63
The Gorilla Organization 69
Greyhounds in Need 71
In-volve 80
Leeds REC 89
The Lifetrain Trust 91
Newham Asian Women's Project 107
NEWTEC 107
Ockenden International 109
Preston and Western Lancashire REC 119
Refugee Legal Centre 123
Shelter - National Campaign for Homeless People . . 137
Society of Friends of Foreigners in Distress 139
South Asian Concern Charitable Trust 139
Thanet Early Years Project & Pals 148
Toynbee Hall 150
Women's Technology / Blackburne House 159

EX PROFESSIONAL OR TRADE WORKERS

Actors' Benevolent Fund 4
Barristers' Benevolent Association 16
BEN - Motor & Allied Trades Benevolent Fund 18
BEN - The Automotive Industry Charity 18
British Dental Association Benevolent Fund 26
BT Benevolent Fund 28
Caravan, the Charity for Grocery People 32
CARAVAN, the trading name of The National Grocers
    Benevolent Fund. 32
Chartered Institute of Logistics and Transport (UK), The 37
Church of Scotland Housing & Loan Fund for Retired
    Ministers & Widows and Widowers of Ministers . . . 41
Cinema & Television Benevolent Fund (CTBF) 42
Corporation of the Sons of the Clergy 44
The CTBI - The Salespeoples Charity. 47
Dain Fund, The 47
Equity Charitable Trust 61
Evelyn Norris Trust 61
Footwear Benevolent Society, The (Footwear Friends) . 64

Glasgow Educational & Marshall Trust 69
Guild of Benevolence of the Institute of Marine
    Engineering, Science & Technology 72
Institution of Structural Engineers Benevolent Fund . . 82
Leather and Hide Trades Benevolent Institution 89
Licensed Trade Charity 91
Musicians Benevolent Fund 101
National Police Fund 105
Perennial - Gardeners' Royal Benevolent Society . . . 116
Pottery & Glass Trades' Benevolent Fund 118
Provision Trade Benevolent Institution 120
Rainy Day Trust (Incorporating the Pottery & Glass Trades'
    Benevolent Fund) 121
Royal General Theatrical Fund Association 127
Royal Metal Trades Benevolent Society 128
Royal Theatrical Fund 131
Schoolmistresses & Governesses Benevolent Institution
    133
Shelter - National Campaign for Homeless People . . 137
Shipwrecked Mariners' Society 137
Society of Licensed Victuallers 139
Timber Trades' Benevolent Society 149
Waste Management Industry Training and Advisory Board,
    The 154

MUSEUMS, MEMORIALS

Art Fund, The 13
Battle of Britain Memorial Trust 17
Bluebell Railway Trust 22
Burton Constable Foundation, The 28
Chatham Historic Dockyard Trust 37
Godinton House Preservation Trust, The 69
Horniman Museum and Gardens 78
National Art Collections Fund 102
River & Rowing Museum Foundation 125
St Austell China Clay Museum Limited 141
Tate Foundation 146

MERCHANT NAVY & FISHING FLEET

Seafarers UK. 136

CONSERVATION & ENVIRONMENT

Alderman Tom F Spence Charity, The 7
Ancient Monuments Society 9
The Architectural Heritage Fund 12
Bat Conservation Trust 16
Bedfordshire and Hertfordshire Historic Churches Trust 18
Bluebell Railway Trust. 22
British Divers Marine Life Rescue 26
British Horse Society 26
Burton Constable Foundation, The 28
Butterfly Conservation. 28
Campaign for National Parks 29
Campaign to Protect Rural England - CPRE 29
Care for the Wild International 32
Cat Survival Trust 33
Chatham Historic Dockyard Trust 37

Cotswold Archaeology Limited 46
Council for National Parks. 46
Environ Trust Ltd 59
Environmental Protection UK 59
FIELD - (Foundation for International Environmental Law
   and Development) 63
Forest of Cardiff 64
The Game and Wildlife Conservation Trust 67
Godinton House Preservation Trust, The 69
The Gorilla Organization 69
Greenpeace Environmental Trust 70
Groundwork Leicester & Leicestershire Ltd 71
Groundwork UK 71
Hawk Conservancy Trust 75
Historic Churches Preservation Trust 78
Institute for European Environmental Policy, London . . 81
International Animal Rescue 82
Kent County Agricultural Society 88
Kent Wildlife Trust 88
Living Streets 92
The Marine Connection 95
National Examination Board in Occupational Safety and
   Health, The (NEBOSH). 104
The National Gardens Scheme (NGS). 105
The National Trust for Scotland 106
Polden Puckham Charitable Foundation 117
Practical Action (formerly ITDG) 118
Ramblers' Association 121
Royal Archaeological Institute 126
Royal Society for the Prevention of Cruelty to Animals,
   Liverpool Branch 130
Shenley Park Trust. 137
Sir Alister Hardy Foundation for Ocean Science 138
SOFA (Furniture Reuse Charity) 139
St Austell China Clay Museum Limited 141
Staffordshire Wildlife Trust 144
Swan Lifeline. 146
Trebah Garden Trust. 150
Tree Council, The 150
Tuberous Sclerosis Association 151
Vegetarian Society of the UK Ltd, The 152
WDC, Whale and Dolphin Conservation 154
Welshpool and Llanfair Light Railway Preservation Co
   Limited 156
Wessex Foundation, The 156
Wildfowl & Wetlands Trust 157
Women's Environmental Network 159
The Woodland Trust 159
Woodroffe Benton Foundation 159
Works Trust, The 159
World Wide Fund For Nature 161
World Wildlife Fund 161
WWF-UK. 162
Yorkshire Wildlife Trust 162

FAMILIES

Pine Ridge Dog Sanctuary 117

CHILDREN, YOUNG PEOPLE

42nd Street - working with young people under stress . . 1
Action for Children 3
Action for Kids Charitable Trust 3
Action for Sick Children (National Association for the
   Welfare of Children in Hospital) 3
Afasic - Helping Children and Young People with Speech,
   Language & Communication Impairments 4
AHRTAG - Appropriate Health Resources & Technologies
   Action Group 7
AIDS Education & Research Trust (AVERT) 7
Air League Educational Trust - for Britain's Youth 7
Alder Hey Children's Charity 7
Artists' General Benevolent Institution 13
Association for People with Lower Limb Abnormalities -
   steps 13
Association for Real Change 13
Asthma UK 14
AVERT 15
Bakewell & Eyam Community Transport 16
BASPCAN (British Association for the Study and
   Prevention of Child Abuse and Neglect) 16
Birchington Convalescent Benefit Fund 18
Birmingham Children's Hospital Charities 20
Blackburn Groundwork Trust 20
Bliss 22
The Boys' Brigade (National Office) 24
Brambley Hedge Childrens Centre Charity Limited . . . 24
BREAK: High Quality Support For Vulnerable Children And
   Families 24
British and Foreign School Society 25
British Kidney Patient Association (BKPA) 27
Brook Advisory Centre (Avon) 28
Cabrini Children's Society 28
CALIBRE Audio Library 29
Calvert Trust Exmoor 29
Canbury School Limited 30
Cancer Prevention Research Trust 30
Central Manchester University Hospitals NHS Foundation
   Trust Charity 34
Centrepoint 36
Cerebra, The Foundation for Brain Injured Infants and
   Young People 36
Chai Cancer Care 36
Chernobyl Children Life Line 37
Childhood First 38
Children & Youth Committee for Great Britain and Eire . 38
Children Nationwide Medical Research Fund 38
Children's Cancer and Leukaemia Group (CCLG) . . . 38
Children's Heart Federation 39
Children's Hospice South West 39
Children's Rights Alliance for England 39
The Children's Society 40
Christ's Hospital 40
Christian Aid 40
Christina Noble Children's Foundation 40
Christopher Place 40
Church Lads' & Church Girls' Brigade 41

Circus Space, The. 42
Cirdan Sailing Trust 42
City of Exeter Y M C A 42
Claire House Children's Hospice 42
CLIC Sargent (Scotland) 43
Clubs for Young People (CYP) 43
Construction Industry Trust for Youth 44
Construction Youth Trust 44
Contact a Family 44
Dain Fund, The 47
The Dame Vera Lynn Trust for Children With Cerebral
    Palsy. 47
Dance North. 47
Danenberg Oberlin-in-London Program 47
David Livingstone International Ltd 48
Derian House Children's Hospice for the North West . . 49
Dyslexia Action 57
ECL Door of Hope. 57
Emergency Exit Arts. 58
Emmanuel Christian School Association 58
ENABLE Scotland. 59
Family Action 62
Father Marek Sujkowski, Children's Aid To Ukraine,
    Romania and Poland 62
Fegans Child & Family Care 62
Field Lane Foundation 63
Forest YMCA 64
fpa formerly The Family Planning Association 65
Glasgow Children's Holiday Scheme 69
Glasgow Educational & Marshall Trust 69
Groundwork UK 71
Happy Days Children's Charity 74
Harrow School of Gymnastics. 75
Healthlink Worldwide 75
Hearing Dogs for Deaf People (Head Office) 77
HighScope GB 77
Hope House Children's Hospices 78
Hope UK (Drug Education) (formerly the Band of Hope) 78
Hyde Park Appeal 79
InDependent Diabetes Trust 81
International China Concern 82
James Hopkins Trust 86
Jewish Child's Day 87
Joint Educational Trust 87
Kidasha 88
Kids Kidney Research. 88
Lady Hoare Trust for Physically Disabled Children . . . 89
Learning Through Action Trust 89
Learning Through Landscapes Trust 89
Leukaemia & Cancer Children's Fund. 90
Leukaemia Busters 91
Lifeline 4 Kids / Handicapped Children's Aid Committee 91
The Lifetrain Trust. 91
Listening Books 91
Listening Library. 91
Little Foundation. 91
Lloyd Foundation, The 92
London Jewish Cultural Centre 92

London Youth (formerly the Federation of London Youth
    Clubs) 93
Look: National Federation of Families with Visually
    Impaired Children 93
Maidstone & Northwest Crossroads. 93
Malcolm Sargent Cancer Fund for Children 93
The Manor Preparatory School Trust 94
The Marine Connection 95
Merseyside Brook Advisory Centre 98
Mill Grove Christian Charitable Trust 100
Mr Fegan's Homes. 101
National Association for Family Based Respite Care, The
    102
National Association of Boys' Clubs 102
National Association of Clubs for Young People. 102
National Association of Youth Clubs 102
National Communities Resource Centre Ltd 103
National Council for Voluntary Youth Services. 103
The National Deaf Children's Society 104
National Society for the Prevention of Cruelty To Children
    (NSPCC) 106
National Youth Theatre of Great Britain 106
NCH 106
Newham Asian Women's Project 107
Norton Foundation, The 109
Ockenden International 109
Oily Cart Company, The 109
Osteopathic Centre for Children, London 111
Our Lady of Fidelity Charitable Trust. 111
Peper Harow Foundation 116
Pied Piper Trust, The 117
Pod Charitable Trust 117
Prospect Education (Technology) Trust Ltd 119
Rainer 121
Rainer Foundation, The 121
REACH - the association for children with upper limb
    deficiency. 121
Reed's School 123
The Right to Life Charitable Trust 125
River & Rowing Museum Foundation 125
Riverside Vineyard Church. 125
Roald Dahl's Marvellous Children's Charity 125
Royal Alexandra and Albert School, The 125
Royal Gardeners' Orphan Fund 127
Royal School for Deaf Children Margate 129
Save the Children 133
Scottish Society for the Mentally Handicapped 135
Second Chance: A Charity for Children Who Need Special
    Help 136
Sevenoaks Day Nursery Trust 136
Shared Care Network 137
Shelter - National Campaign for Homeless People . . 137
Siloam Christian Ministries - Education, Healthcare &
    Relief as a Vehicle for the Gospel 138
South Yorkshire Community Foundation. 140
Southwark Diocesan Welcare 140
SPARKS - Sport Aiding medical Research for KidS . . 140
Speech, Language and Hearing Centre, The 140

Spurgeon's Child Care 141
St Brigid's School Limited 142
St Ursula's High School Trust 144
Staffordshire Wildlife Trust 144
STEPS Charity Worldwide 145
Stoke on Trent Citizens Advice Bureau 145
Thanet Early Years Project & Pals 148
Thomas Howell's Trust 148
Toy Trust, The 150
Toynbee Hall 150
TTE Management & Technical Training 151
Turners Court Youth Trust 151
UCCF: The Christian Unions 151
UK Skills 151
Universities and Colleges Christian Fellowship . . . 151
University of Cape Town Trust 151
WelCare Service for Parents & Children (Southwark
  Diocese) 156
WellChild 156
Wessex Foundation, The 156
West Kent YMCA - Helping Young People Build Their
  Future 156
The Westminster Society for people with learning
  disabilities 156
The Woodland Trust 159
Youth Aliyah - Child Rescue 163

OLDER PEOPLE

Abbeyfield - enhancing the quality of life for older people 1
AbilityNet Advice and Information - UK's leading authority
  on disability and computing 2
AFTAID - Aid for the Aged in Distress 4
Age Concern Manchester 5
Age UK Calderdale & Kirklees 5
Age UK Ealing 6
Age UK Enfield 6
Age UK Gateshead 6
Age UK Haringey 6
Age UK North Staffordshire 6
Alzheimer's Research UK 9
Alzheimer's Society 9
Ann Watson's Trust 11
Artists' General Benevolent Institution 13
Artlink West Yorkshire 13
Association for Real Change 13
Bakewell & Eyam Community Transport 16
Barristers' Benevolent Association 16
Bell Memorial Home (Inc) 18
Brendoncare Foundation 24
Bromley & Sheppard's Colleges 28
CALIBRE Audio Library 29
CALIBRE - Cassette Library for the Blind & Print Disabled
  29
CALIBRE Cassette Library of Recorded Books 29
Cam Sight (the Cambridgeshire Society for the Blind &
  Partially Sighted) 29
Cancer Prevention Research Trust 30

Caravan, the Charity for Grocery People 32
CARAVAN, the trading name of The National Grocers
  Benevolent Fund 32
Central & Cecil Housing Trust 34
Central Manchester University Hospitals NHS Foundation
  Trust Charity 34
Chai Cancer Care 36
Charity Search - Free Advice for Older People 36
The Church of England Pensions Board – Retirement
  Housing for Clergy Pensioners 41
Church of England Soldiers', Sailors' and Airmen's
  Housing Association Limited 41
Church of Scotland Housing & Loan Fund for Retired
  Ministers & Widows and Widowers of Ministers 41
Community Network 43
Counsel and Care 46
Crossroads Greenwich & Lewisham Ltd 46
Cumberland and Westmorland Convalescent Institution 47
Dance North 47
Dutch Home for the Elderly 56
Feilding (Mary) Guild 62
Fern Street Settlement 63
Florence Nightingale Hospice - Florence Nightingale
  Hospice Charity 63
Greensleeves Homes Trust 71
Guild of Aid for Gentlepeople 72
HACT – The Housing Action Charity 72
Harbour, The (formerly Red Admiral Project - Bristol) . . 74
Harrison Housing 75
Herefordshire Lifestyles 77
Hospice Information Service 78
Huggens' College 79
Hyde Park Appeal 79
IDS (Industrial Dwellings Society 1885) 79
Independent Age 80
InDependent Diabetes Trust 81
Independent Healthcare Association 81
Independent Healthcare Forum 81
International Glaucoma Association 85
Jesse Mary Chambers Almshouses 87
King Edward VII's Hospital Sister Agnes 88
Life Academy 91
Listening Books 91
Listening Library 91
Living Streets 92
London Catalyst 92
Mary Feilding Guild 95
Merchant Seamen's War Memorial Society 98
Metropolitan Hospital-Sunday Fund 99
Morden College 101
National Federation of Spiritual Healers (The NFSH
  Charitable Trust Ltd) 104
NFSH Charitable Trust LTD (The Healing Trust) . . . 107
Orthopaedic Research UK 110
Pine Ridge Dog Sanctuary 117
The Pre-Retirement Association 119
RAINY DAY TRUST (Incorporating the Pottery & Glass
  Trades' Benevolent Fund) 121

Redbridge, Epping & Harrow Crossroads - Caring for
Carers 122
Relationship Counselling for London. 123
Royal General Theatrical Fund Association 127
Royal Masonic Benevolent Institution 128
Royal Metal Trades Benevolent Society 128
Royal Theatrical Fund 131
Royal United Kingdom Beneficent Association 131
RSABI 132
Rukba 132
Service to the Aged 136
Shelter - National Campaign for Homeless People . . 137
Sheppard's College 137
Sister Agnes 138
Southern Convalescent Homes Inc 140
Stock Exchange Benevolent Fund 145
Sunset Home Almshouses 145
TTE Management & Technical Training 151
Watson's (Ann) Trust 154
Woodroffe Benton Foundation 159
WRVS Trustees Ltd 162

DISABLED PEOPLE

Action for Kids Charitable Trust 3
Afasic - Helping Children and Young People with Speech,
Language & Communication Impairments 4
AHRTAG - Appropriate Health Resources & Technologies
Action Group 7
Arthur Rank Hospice Charity 13
Artlink West Yorkshire 13
Asian People's Disability Alliance 13
Association for Real Change 13
Autism Anglia 15
Bakewell & Eyam Community Transport 16
Bell Memorial Home (Inc) 18
BLACKWOOD. 20
BLESMA - The Limbless Veterans 20
BREAK: High Quality Support For Vulnerable Children And
Families 24
British Kidney Patient Association (BKPA) 27
British Sports Association for the Disabled 27
Calvert Trust Exmoor 29
Cam Sight (the Cambridgeshire Society for the Blind &
Partially Sighted). 29
Carers Relief Service 32
A Cause for Concern 34
CBM 34
Centre for Accessible Environments 36
Cerebral Palsy Midlands 36
Changing Faces - Supporting People with Disfigurements
. . . . 36
Christian Concern for the Mentally Handicapped 40
Community Network 43
Contact a Family 44
Crohn's and Colitis UK 46
Crossroads Greenwich & Lewisham Ltd 46
Crossways Community 46

CRUSAID 47
The Dame Vera Lynn Trust for Children With Cerebral
Palsy 47
The Disabilities Trust 51
Disability Essex (Essex Disabled Peoples Association Ltd)
. . . . 52
Disabled Drivers' Association, The 52
Disabled Motoring UK 52
ENABLE Scotland 59
Essex Autistic Society 61
Essex Disabled People's Association Limited 61
Field Lane Foundation 63
Finchale Training College for Disabled People 63
Florence Nightingale Hospice - Florence Nightingale
Hospice Charity 63
Folkestone & District MIND Resource Centre 64
Gardening For Disabled Trust 67
Haemophilia Society 72
Happy Days Children's Charity 74
Harbour, The (formerly Red Admiral Project - Bristol) . . 74
Health Care 75
Healthlink Worldwide 75
Herefordshire Lifestyles 77
Hope House Children's Hospices 78
Hyde Park Appeal 79
International Wheelchair & Amputee Sports Federation . 85
Invalids-at-Home Trust 85
Lady Hoare Trust for Physically Disabled Children . . . 89
Lifeline 4 Kids / Handicapped Children's Aid Committee 91
The Lifetrain Trust 91
Listening Books 91
Listening Library 91
Living Streets 92
London Youth (formerly the Federation of London Youth
Clubs) 93
Maidstone & Northwest Crossroads 93
Manchester & Cheshire Dogs' Home 94
Martha Trust 95
Mobility Trust 100
MSA For Midland People With Cerebral Palsy 101
Multiple Sclerosis Society 101
N.N.A.B. 101
National Association of Swimming Clubs for the
Handicapped 102
NCH 106
Norfolk and Norwich Association for the Blind 107
Oily Cart Company, The 109
Pontefract Family Centre 118
Primary Immunodeficiency Association (PiA) 119
Prospects for People with Learning Disabilities 119
Raynaud's & Scleroderma Association 121
REACH - the association for children with upper limb
deficiency 121
Riding For the Disabled Association (Northern Ireland)
Incorporating Carriage Driving 125
RSABI 132
Scottish Society for the Mentally Handicapped 135
Shelter - National Campaign for Homeless People . . 137

South West Action for Learning and Living Our Way . 140
Southern Convalescent Homes Inc 140
Spadework Limited. 140
Spina bifida • Hydrocephalus • Information • Networking •
    Equality - SHINE 140
Spinal Research (International Spinal Research Trust) 141
St Francis Leprosy Guild. 143
Thomas More Project, The. 148
Tourism For All UK. 149
Tuberous Sclerosis Association 151
Autism Wessex 156
The Westminster Society for people with learning
    disabilities 156
Wheelpower - British Wheelchair Sport 157
White Horse Care Trust, The 157
Woodroffe Benton Foundation 159

BLIND PEOPLE

AbilityNet Advice and Information - UK's leading authority
    on disability and computing 2
CALIBRE Audio Library 29
CALIBRE - Cassette Library for the Blind & Print Disabled
    29
CALIBRE Cassette Library of Recorded Books 29
Cam Sight (the Cambridgeshire Society for the Blind &
    Partially Sighted). 29
CBM 34
Father Marek Sujkowski, Children's Aid To Ukraine,
    Romania and Poland 62
Galloway's Society for the Blind 66
Galloway's Society for the Blind 66
International Glaucoma Association 85
Look: National Federation of Families with Visually
    Impaired Children 93
N.N.A.B. 101
Norfolk and Norwich Association for the Blind 107
ORBIS UK 110
Partially Sighted Society 114
Royal National Institute of Blind People (RNIB) 128
RP Fighting Blindness 132
Sense (The National Deafblind & Rubella Association) 136
Shelter - National Campaign for Homeless People . . 137
Telephones for the Blind Fund 147
Vision Aid Overseas 153
Vision Support 153

DEAF PEOPLE

Artists' General Benevolent Institution 13
British Deaf Association 26
Hearing Dogs for Deaf People (Head Office) 77
The Mary Hare Foundation 95
The National Deaf Children's Society 104
Royal School for Deaf Children Margate 129
Sense (The National Deafblind & Rubella Association) 136
Shelter - National Campaign for Homeless People . . 137
Sound Seekers. 139
Sussex Diocesan Association For the Deaf 145

Telecommunications Action Group (TAG) 147

WOMEN

Arthur Townrow Pensions Fund 13
Asylum Aid 15
ATS & WRAC Association Benevolent Fund 15
Endometriosis UK 59
Feilding (Mary) Guild 62
fpa - formerly The Family Planning Association 65
Frederick Andrew Convalescent Trust 65
Hilda Martindale Educational Trust 77
Housing for Women 79
Infertility Network UK 81
The Little Sisters of the Poor 91
London Council for the Welfare of Women and Girls
    (LCWWG) 92
Martindale (Hilda) Educational Trust 95
Mary Feilding Guild 95
Merseyside Brook Advisory Centre 98
National Endometriosis Society 104
Newham Asian Women's Project 107
Ockenden International 109
Over Forty Association for Women Workers 111
Practical Action (formerly ITDG) 118
The Right to Life Charitable Trust 125
Schoolmistresses & Governesses Benevolent Institution
    133
Sevenoaks Day Nursery Trust 136
Shelter - National Campaign for Homeless People . . 137
Spurgeon's Child Care 141
Townrow (Arthur) Pensions Fund 150
Wellbeing Of Women 156
Womankind Worldwide 159
Women in Prison 159
Women's Environmental Network 159
Women's Technology / Blackburne House 159
YWCA (Accommodation and Advisory Service) 163

ARMED SERVICES & EX-SERVICES

ATS & WRAC Association Benevolent Fund 15
Battle of Britain Memorial Trust 17
BLESMA - The Limbless Veterans 20
Church of England Soldiers', Sailors' & Airmen's Clubs. 41
Fusiliers' Aid Society (Warwickshire) 66
Guild of Benevolence of the Institute of Marine
    Engineering, Science & Technology 72
Hampshire & Isle of Wight Military Aid Fund (1903) . . . 74
King Edward VII's Hospital Sister Agnes 88
Military Ministries International 100
Pembroke House, Home for Aged Ex-Naval Men, Their
    Wives and Widows and former Wrens 116
Poppyscotland (The Earl Haig Fund Scotland) 118
Queen Alexandra's Royal Army Nursing Corps Association
    (QARANC) 120
Royal Artillery Charitable Fund. 126
Royal Engineers Association. 127
Royal Marines Association 127

Royal Marines Charitable Trust Fund 127

Royal Naval Benevolent Trust (Grand Fleet & Kindred
Funds) 129

The Royal Scottish Corporation 130

ScotsCare 135

Seafarers UK 136

Shelter - National Campaign for Homeless People . . 137

Sister Agnes 138

ADVERTISER INDEX

Abbeyfield - enhancing the quality of life for older people 1

Action for Children xviii

Action for Kids Charitable Trust 2

Actors' Benevolent Fund xvii

Age Concern Manchester 5

Alzheimer's Society . . . .

. . . . .Front Cover, Logo on Spine, 8

Animal Health Trust 10

Artists' General Benevolent Institution 12

Athlone Trust, The 14

Barristers' Benevolent Association 17

Birmingham Children's Hospital Charities .xv, 19

BLESMA - The Limbless Veterans 21

Book Aid International 23

Britain Nepal Medical Trust 25

British Kidney Patient Association (BKPA) ii

Cancer Prevention Research Trust . . . . . . .ix, 31

Care for the Wild International 32

Cat Welfare Trust 33

Central Manchester University Hospitals NHS Foundation Trust Charity 35

Children in Distress 39

Circulation Foundation 41

Crohn's and Colitis UK 45

David Livingstone International Ltd 48

Dimbleby Cancer Care 50

Dog Aid Society of Scotland 52

Dogs Trust 53

Donkey Sanctuary, The . . . . .xi, 55

Donkey Sanctuary International, The . . . .xxi, 84

Dwarf Sport Association UK 56

Environmental Investigation Agency Trust . . . . . .

. . . . .viii, Outside Back Cover

Epilepsy Research UK 60

Foundation for Liver Research, The xix

Gambia Horse and Donkey Trust, The 67

Gorilla Organization, The 68

Great Ormond Street Hospital Children's Charity

. . . . , xix

Greenpeace Environmental Trust 71

HALO Trust, The 73

Help the Hospices 76

InDependent Diabetes Trust 80

International Animal Rescue . . . . .vii, 83

Lifeline 4 Kids / Handicapped Children's Aid Committee 90

Manchester & Cheshire Dogs' Home 94

Medical Research Foundation 96

Mercy Ships . . . . .Inside Front Cover

Methodist Church, The 98

Midlands Air Ambulance Charity viii

National Animal Welfare Trust 103

National Gardens Scheme (NGS), The 104

Northern Counties Kidney Research Fund . .108

Pact (Prison Advice & Care Trust) 111

Pain Relief Foundation . . . .

. . . . .xx, 113, Inside Back Cover

Partially Sighted Society xii

Passage, The . . . . .xiii, 115

People's Trust for Endangered Species 116

Prostate Cancer UK xii

Redwings Horse Sanctuary 122

Reed's School 123

Royal Air Force Benevolent Fund – RAFBF .124

Royal Alexandra and Albert School, The 126

Royal Naval Benevolent Trust (Grand Fleet & Kindred Funds) 128

Royal School for the Deaf Derby 129

Royal Society for the Prevention of Cruelty to Animals, Liverpool Branch 131

Samaritan's Purse 132

Scripture Union England and Wales 134

Sheppard Trust - Housing for Elderly Ladies, The

. v

St Elizabeth's - Positive Living & Learning for People with Epilepsy & Other Complex Needs .

. 142

Stroke Association, The v

Swan Lifeline 147

Thrombosis Research Institute 148

VEGFAM (Feeds the Hungry Without Exploiting Animals) . . . . .xiv, 152

WDC, Whale and Dolphin Conservation .xvi, 155

Wildlife Aid Foundation, The . . . . .xiv, 157

World Medical Fund .160

WSPA - World Society for the Protection of Animals x

Wythall Animal Sanctuary xvii